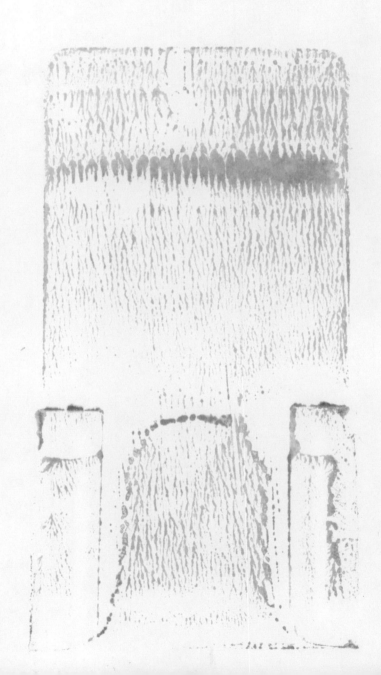

Fundamentals of

Food Processing Operations
Ingredients, Methods, and Packaging

other AVI books on food processing

Fundamentals of
Food Processing Operations
Ingredients, Methods,
and Packaging

by J. L. Heid, B.S., Chem. Eng.
Director, New Product Development,
Tri-Valley Growers,
San Jose, California

and Maynard A. Joslyn, M.S., Ph.D.
Professor of Food Technology,
University of California,
Berkeley, California

in collaboration with selected authorities
on the ingredients, methods, and packaging
used by the food industry

WESTPORT, CONNECTICUT

THE AVI PUBLISHING COMPANY, INC.

1967

Printed in the United States of America
BY MACK PRINTING COMPANY, EASTON, PENNSYLVANIA

Contributors to this Volume

DR. C. OLIN BALL, Consultant in Food Science, Technology and Engineering, New Brunswick, N. J.

MR. ZENAS BLOCK, Group Vice President, DCA Food Industries Inc., New York, N. Y.

MR. GEORGE E. BRISSEY, General Manager, Quality Assurance Department, Swift and Company, Chicago, Ill.

MR. R. F. ELLIS, Customer Service Group, Research and Development, American Can Company, Barrington, Ill.

DR. William B. ESSELEN, Head, Department of Food Science and Technology, University of Massachusetts, Amherst, Mass.

MR. BERNARD FEINBERG, U.S. Department of Agriculture, Western Regional Research Laboratory, Albany, Calif.

MR. PAUL A. GOESER, Head, Fresh Meats Division, Research Laboratories, Swift and Company, Chicago, Ill.

DR. S. A. GOLDBLITH, Professor of Food Science and Executive Officer, Department of Nutrition and Food Science, Massachusetts Institute of Technology, Cambridge, Mass.

DR. W. J. HOOVER, Director, Food and Feed Grain Institute, Kansas State University, Manhattan, Kans.

DR. MAYNARD A. JOSLYN, Professor of Food Technology, Department of Nutritional Sciences, University of California, Berkeley, Calif.

DR. M. KAREL, Associate Professor of Food Engineering, Department of Nutrition and Food Science, Massachusetts Institute of Technology, Cambridge, Mass.

MR. NEIL KELLY, President, The Sugar Association, Inc., New York, N. Y.

MR. JOHN H. KILBUCK, Manager, Western Division, Stange Co., Oakland, Calif.

MR. ROBERT L. LLOYD, Special Research and Development Consultant, Richmond, Calif.

DR. SAMUEL A. MATZ, Vice President, Research and Development, Robert A. Johnston Co., Milwaukee, Wis.

DR. JOHN T. R. NICKERSON, Professor, Department of Nutrition and Food Science, Massachusetts Institute of Technology. Cambridge, Mass.

MR. GEORGE K. PARMAN, Executive Secretary, Committee on Marine Resource Development, Food and Nutrition Board, National Academy of Sciences, National Research Council, Washington, D. C.

DR. CARL S. PEDERSON, Cornell University, New York State Agriculture Experiment Station, Geneva, N. Y.

DR. I. J. PFLUG, Professor, Department of Food Science, Michigan State University, East Lansing, Mich.

MR. G. J. SALINARD, Food Industry Manager, Hoffman-LaRoche Inc., Nutley, N. J.

MR. H. E. SWISHER, Assistant Manager, Research and Development Division, Sunkist Growers, Inc., Ontario, Calif.

Mrs. L. H. SWISHER, formely Research Librarian, Sunkist Growers, Inc., Ontario,
    Calif.
Mr. A. TIMMONS, Senior Process Engineer, Ralph M. Parsons Co., Los Angeles,
    Calif.
Mr. FRANK H. WRIGHT, West Coast Manager, Glass Container Manufacturers
    Institute, Inc., San Francisco, Calif.

Preface

The need for a reference text that could be used in introductory courses in food science and technology has long been recognized. Available texts are limited to a specific method of preservation (canning, freezing, dehydration) or to specific commodities (dairy products, fruit and vegetable products, cereal products).

Prescott and Proctor published a general survey of "Food Technology" in 1937 and von Loesecke's "Outline of Food Technology," published in 1942, was also a valuable review. However, food processing and preservation techniques have become so technical and complex that no single author is qualified to deal authoritatively in detail with the entire field. For this reason, the editors invited sixty specialists to collaborate in preparing a three volume reference series on "Food Processing Operations," directed toward supervisory personnel in the food industry. While this series has been widely used as a reference and text, several professors of food science and technology suggested collecting twenty-three (of some sixty) chapters relating to ingredients, methods of preservation and packaging to serve as an introductory text and reference on "Food Processing and Preservation."

The editors are indebted to the professors who aided in selecting material to be included in this volume, to the collaborators who share their skills and experience and to numerous other individuals and organizations without whose help and cooperation this volume could not have materialized. Suggestions as to how future editions of the text can be made more useful will be gratefully acknowledged.

J. L. HEID

MAYNARD A. JOSLYN

January 15, 1967

Contents

CHAPTER 1

M. A. Joslyn | # Water in Food Processing

INTRODUCTION

Availability of adequate water supplies of suitable quality is a primary consideration in selection of site and establishment of plant. The disposal of the large amounts of liquid wastes accumulated during processing is closely related to the consideration of water sources. Processors may install and operate their own water supply, usually from subsurface or ground waters such as wells, they may purchase water from a municipal water supply, or they may use a combination of these arrangements. After a plant is established, competition from expanding residential and industrial water users may reduce the supply critically. Consideration should be given to both immediate needs and those required for future expansion. Just as the ready availability of large quantities of potable water for present and future needs was not considered in the original establishment of communities, such as Los Angeles which rapidly outgrew the locally available water supply, so too often proper planning was not made either for an adequate water supply or for liquid waste disposal by many food industries.

Water supply has become one of our major national concerns both because of depletion of available supplies and pollution of surface and ground water supplies. The annual available water supply in the United States as a whole has been estimated to be 1,300 million acre-feet, or 424,000 billion gallons, of which 63,000 billion gallons or about 15 per cent are utilized annually. The greatest single use of fresh water in the United States is for irrigation. This amounted to about 90 billion gallons a day in 1950 or 50 per cent of total use. Industry and steam power plants are the next largest users of fresh water and withdraw about 70 billion gallons per day or 40 per cent of total. Domestic use amounted to about 20 billion gallons per day. The estimated requirements for 1975 are 215 billion gallons per day for industrial use (62 per cent of total), 110 billion gallons per day for irrigation (31 per cent of total), and 25 billion gallons for domestic use (7 per cent of total) (Huberty 1959).

M. A. Joslyn is Professor of Food Technology, Department of Nutritional Sciences, University of California, Berkeley, Calif.

While our potential national supply is more than six times as great as present usage, in the 17 Western states the total supply is only about four times present usage. In California, where supplies are limited and population and industry are expanding rapidly, where water is being flumed, pumped and piped hundreds of miles over and under mountains and deserts; Edmonton (1954) in Bulletin No. 2 of the California Division of Water Resources estimated that present use of water for all purposes exceeded safe yields of developed supplies by 15 per cent.

All processors are interested in the quality of water supplies. In many areas, packers are concerned with the quantitative aspects of their supply from the standpoint of adequacy and cost. In addition to its uses in crop production which will not be considered in this chapter, water is used by food processors for generating steam, for cleaning, peeling, grading and conveying products, as a heat exchange medium in heating and cooling operations, for cleaning plant and equipment, for condensing vapors, for fire protection and as an ingredient in finished products.

SOURCES

Processors may operate their own water supply, they may purchase water from a water company or they may use a combination of these arrangements.

In regard to origin, water supplies may be classified as surface waters (from lakes, streams, reservoirs) and subsurface waters (from shallow and deep wells). The characteristics of water from these sources vary with rainfall, the nature of materials with which the water comes in contact and the time of year. General trends are indicated in Table 1.

TABLE 1

CHARACTERISTICS OF WATER FROM VARIOUS SOURCES

Type	Organic Matter, Color—Odor	Microbial Content	Mineral Content
Surface	May be high	May be contaminated	Ordinarily low
Shallow well	Variable	Variable	Ordinarily low
Deep well	Usually low	Usually low	Usually high

The range of soluble impurities is indicated in Table 2 in which Bacon *et al.* (1953) summarize ranges encountered in California water supplies.

The suitability of water for any purpose depends upon (1) physical properties including color, odor, flavor and turbidity; (2) chemical

TABLE 2

RANGE IN ANALYSIS OF DEVELOPED CALIFORNIA WATER SUPPLIES

	Wells, p.p.m. Max.	Min.	Surface Water, p.p.m. Max.	Min.
Anions				
Bicarbonate	567	43	670	90
Sulfate	1,112	2	270	60
Chloride	1,960	106	106	35
Nitrate	18	0	...	..
Cations				
Sodium and Potassium	1,158	10	340	45
Magnesium	158	1	170	32
Calcium	649	10	168	30

properties including dissolved solids and gases, pH and hardness; and (3) microbiological contaminants including algae, pathogenic and nonpathogenic organisms. The presence of excessive amounts of hydrogen sulfide in ground and well waters and phenols and other organic substances from industrial wastes imparts undesirable off-flavors.

TABLE 3

REVISED STANDARDS FOR CHEMICAL CONTENT OF DRINKING WATER[1]

	Recommended Maximum Limits,[2] mg./liter	Concentrations Which Constitute Grounds for Rejection, mg./liter
Alkyl benzene sulfonate (detergent)	0.5	...
Arsenic	0.01	0.05
Barium	...	1.0
Cadmium	...	0.01
Carbon chloroform extract (exotic organic chemicals)	0.2	...
Chloride	250.0	...
Chromium	...	0.05
Copper	1.0	...
Cyanide	0.01	0.2
Fluoride	1.7	2.2
Iron	0.3	...
Lead	...	0.05
Manganese	0.05	...
Nitrate	45.0	...
Phenols	0.001	...
Selenium	...	0.01
Silver	...	0.05
Sulfate	250.0	...
Total Dissolved Solids	500.0	...
Zinc	5.0	...

[1] U. S. Public Health Service—1961.
[2] Concentration in water should not be in excess of these limits when more suitable supplies can be made available.

Water for use in a food processing plant should meet U. S. Public Health Standards for potable water. Table 3 indicates the maximum permissible content of a number of chemical constituents. The 1961 standards for potable water include for the first time limits on the concentrations of radio-active elements and total radio-activity. The maximum permissible levels of radio-activity are radium 226, 3 micromicro curies per liter; strontium 90, 10 micromicro curies per liter; gross beta activity, 1,000 micromicro curies per liter.

Chemical composition sometimes provides a clue to bacterial contamination. Nitrate in excess of 40 to 80 p.p.m. justifies careful testing to determine the possibility of sewage contamination. Water used in a food plant must be free from contamination with sewage, pathogenic organisms and nonpathogens of known intestinal origin. Pathogenic organisms may be spread in water, and the coliform group of bacteria is used as an index of their possible presence. Not over 1 coliform cell per 100 cc. is allowed. Nonpathogenic microorganisms may be of considerable importance in water for use in a food plant. They may influence flavor and odor and produce slime and bio-fouling of pipes. A high bacterial count in can cooling water may result in recontamination and spoilage.

Hardness is a factor which affects suitability of water for many uses in food processing operations. The words used for describing various conditions of hardness are defined in Table 4. Hardness is classified

TABLE 4

RANGE OF THE HARDNESS OF WATER[1]

| Degree of Hardness | Expressed as Calcium Carbonate | | Expressed as Calcium, p.p.m. |
	p.p.m.	Grains per Gal.	
Soft	Less than 50	Less than 2.9	Less than 20
Slightly Hard	50–100	2.9–5.9	20–40
Hard	100–200	5.9–11.8	40–80
Very Hard	Above 200	Above 11.8	Above 80

Note: One grain of calcium carbonate per U. S. gallon is equivalent to 17.1 p.p.m. 100 p.p.m of calcium carbonate is equivalent to 40 p.p.m. of calcium. In reference to magnesium carbonate, 100 p.p.m. of carbonate is equivalent to 24 p.p.m. of magnesium.
[1] From Bigelow and Stevenson (1923).

as permanent hardness due to chlorides and sulfates of calcium and magnesium cations or temporary hardness due to bicarbonates of these ions. Calcium and magnesium chlorides and sulfates will precipitate as a hard scale when waters containing these salts are evaporated. The bicarbonates precipitate on heating to form scale on pipes and equipment. Scale may harbor bacterial growth, may clog the water system and reduce rate and efficiency of heat transfer.

DEMAND IN CANNING

Most available information on the quantities of water used for processing are estimates. Only recently quantitative studies of water use in canning have been made: Murray and Peterson (1951), Mercer and Townsend (1954), Mercer *et al.* (1958). The results of metering exact quantities of water used for specific purposes would probably surprise most operators and might lead to steps which would effect economies without impairment of quality. Engineering has been one of the more neglected aspects of food technology, but larger operators are beginning to uncover profit possibilities in engineering studies of their operation, regardless of whether the process involves concentrating, drying, canning, glass packing, freezing or fermentation.

The wide range in water use is indicated by a tabulation by Murray and Peterson (1951) of estimates furnished by a large number of canners of the quantities of water used for all purposes in canning 23 food products (Table 5).

Mercer *et al.* (1958), in one phase of the long-range research undertaken by the National Canners Association on the possibilities and problems of water conservation in canning, reported an average use of 3,340 gal. of fresh water per ton of tomatoes (without recirculation or reuse). Of this volume, 1,320 gal. were used in washing, 1,200 gal. in can cooling and 820 gal. for other uses. In the preparation of tomato concentrate the volume of water discharged from the evaporators is often larger than that from any other single operation.

While large variations in quantities of water used for canning specific items must be attributed to the fact that quantities were estimated rather than measured, the fact remains that there is a large variation in quantities of water employed in different plants.

Normal factors contributing to this variation include: (1) the extent to which products are flumed rather than mechanically conveyed, (2) methods used in cooling and (3) the extent to which water is recovered and reused. Opportunities are apparent for advantageous application of engineering studies.

Opportunities for saving may be greater if water is purchased from an outside source than if pumped from wells of adequate capacity owned by the plant. In any event, savings in water beyond that required for best results also permits savings in the quantities of liquid waste to be disposed of. Table 6 indicates the gallonage of waste liquids, exclusive of cooling water, resulting from the canning of several vegetables.

Warrick *et al.* (1945) pointed out the interesting fact that, although there was considerable variation between different plants, the volume of waste in any one plant was usually constant when that plant was operated at uniform capacity.

TABLE 5

ESTIMATED WATER USE IN CANNING OPERATIONS

Product	Can Size	Per Case[1]	Gallons of Water Per Ton Farm Weight[2]
Fruit			
Apples	No. 10	75–150	1,475–4,425
Apricots	No. 2½	50–150	2,750–8,250
Cherries, sweet	No. 2½	90–180	5,540–11,080
Peaches	No. 2½	30–320	1,275–13,600
Pears	No. 2½	25–180	950–6,840
Plums	No. 2½	50–150	3,200–9,600
Misc. fruits	No. 2½	50–100	. . .
Tomatoes	No. 2½	50–66	1,855–2,450
Vegetables			
Asparagus	No. 2, 2 Tall, 300	65–190	3,445–10,070
Beans, green and wax	No. 2	45–55	4,310–5,260
Beans, lima	No. 2	40–55	1,800–5,230
Beets	No. 2	40–50	2,200–2,750
Corn, cream-style	No. 2	40–50	1,100–1,370
Corn, cream-style whole kernel	12 oz., 303, No. 2	25–82	. . .
Corn, whole kernel with peppers	12 oz.	50–82	1,270–2,080
Peas	303, No. 2, No. 2T	31–135	3,075–13,400
Pumpkin	No. 2½	60–165	1,500–4,130
Spinach and greens	No. 2, 2½	75–260	6,000–20,800
Others			
Misc. fruits and vegetables	. . .	60	. . .
Beans, baked	14 oz., 28 oz.	43–85	. . .
Beans, soaked dry	No. 2, 2½	30–123	. . .
Hominy	No. 2, 2½, 10	55–70	. . .

[1] Murray and Peterson (1951).
[2] Calculated from Murray and Peterson (1951) using U.S.D.A. Prod. and Marketing Admin., Conversion Factors and Weights and Measures for Agricultural Commodities and Their Products, May, 1952.

TABLE 6

CANNERY WASTE VOLUMES[1]

Product	Gallons[2] per No. 2 Can[3]		Gallons[2] per Case	(Warrick et al. 1945)
Bean, green or wax	1.09	. . .	26.2	26.
Beans, lima	. . .	. . .	. . .	50.
Beets	1.60	0.79	38.4	25.
Corn	1.01	0.83	24.2	25.
Peas[4]	1.19	0.81	28.6	25.
Tomatoes	. . .	3.30	79.2	. . .

[1] From Warrick et al. (1939).
[2] Average reported by packers for four years in Wisconsin, except for peas, which is for seven years.
[3] Measurements made at one cannery in 1938.
[4] The minimum waste was 0.58 and maximum 2.33 gal. per No. 2 can.

DEMAND IN FREEZING OPERATIONS

While even less exact information is available in water uses in freezing operations than on canning operations, there is fairly close correlation between the two. Lamb and Havighorst (1953) described a plant processing $7^1/_2$ tons of peas per hour, with the following quantities of water used as designated:

	g.p.m.
Washing and Fluming	150
Froth Cleaner	10
Reel Washer	120
Quality Grader	10
Elevators and Blanchers	20
Hydraulic Products Pump	120
Boiler Make up	10
Picking Belt	120

Without reuse, this amounted to 5,500 gal. of water per ton of peas. By reusing 50 per cent of the water through the washers, picking belts and product pump, the quantity was cut to 3,500 gal. per ton of peas.

For cooling the compressed refrigerant, 1,100 g.p.m. of water were used on the freezing operation and 110 g.p.m. for maintaining room temperatures. The defrosters required 20 g.p.m. As abundant water was available at an initial temperature of 63°F. it was used once with a temperature rise to 73°F. and not recirculated through a tower or otherwise recooled.

Frozen concentrates have become a leading item in the frozen food field. The quantity of water employed depends upon the type of evaporator used. Evaporators of the type engineered by Cross use water only for condensing vapors from steam ejectors, for clean up, and small quantities for balancing the heat pump cycle by removing superheat from the refrigerant.

The type of evaporator engineered by Kelly uses water as a heat exchange medium in evaporating and condensing water from the juice.

Double effect recompression type concentrators use the largest quantities of water to condense vapors from the juice plus steam used to compress these vapors. A cooling tower is generally employed with this type of concentrator so make-up water is required only to remove entrained solids.

Minimum water demand for the production of frozen concentrated orange juice has been estimated at 1,000 gal. of water per ton of fruit yielding 30 gal. of 42° Brix concentrate.

DEMAND IN DEHYDRATION

In the dehydration of fruits and vegetables, the quantities of water used in preparation and blanching compare closely with the quantities used in preparation for canning and freezing. Fruit prepared for sun-drying and dehydration, either as whole or cut, usually is not washed but some water is used in the hot water or lye-checking of grapes and prunes. The dried fruit during processing for marketing is washed and treated with hot water. The actual requirement for water in drying, dehydration and processing of dried fruits is not known. In the dehydration of vegetables considerably larger quantities of water are used. This varies from 10,000 to 20,000 gal. per hour for a plant processing 100 tons per day of potatoes and sweet potatoes to 8,000 to 16,000 gal. per hour for carrots, beets, rutabagas and onions, and to 2,400 to 4,000 gal. per hour for cabbage, according to estimates prepared during World War II by the Bureau of Agricultural and Industrial Chemistry (1944). This amounts to from a minimum of 600 gal. to a maximum of about 5,000 gal. per ton of raw material processed.

FERMENTATION AND BEVERAGES

In addition to alcoholic fermentations used in preparing wines and beer, lactic and acetic acid fermentations are extensively employed in preserving fruit and vegetable products. Juices are fermented to form vinegar. Cucumbers, cabbage and other vegetables are subjected to lactic acid fermentation for the production of pickles and kraut.

In the production of vinegars, water is used for cleaning fruit before pressing and for cleaning lines, pumps, filters, tanks and other equipment to maintain sanitary conditions essential to controlled fermentation; also for steam used for packing pasteurized vinegar.

In the production of distilled vinegar, the water used for diluting the vinegar stock should be of low solids, hardness and chloride content and particular care should be taken to avoid contamination with copper, iron, lead, zinc and tin salts which markedly reduce the efficiency of acetification in the generator process.

In the production of carbonated beverages assuredly sterile water, of low air content, free from odors or flavors and practically free of insoluble materials is needed. The production of such sparkling clear water, even from regular city drinking water, requires carefully controlled chemical coagulation, sand filtration, carbon purification, sterile filtration and deaeration. The laboratory control required in the production of such water is described in an article by Kratz and Lewis (1955).

WATER TREATMENT

Both private and municipal water supplies may require treatment before use depending on the impurities which they contain and the use to which this water is to be put. Municipal water supply, while usually above suspicion for drinking purposes, is not necessarily suitable for food processing. Occasionally municipal water supply may become infected with nonpathogenic microorganisms which may cause clogging of water distribution lines and objectionable tastes and odors.

Water used for processing (washing, blanching, in-product, etc.) must be substantially free from suspended insoluble matter, living microorganisms (both pathogenic and nonpathogenic), coloring matter, alkalinity and excessive mineral impurities (particularly calcium, magnesium, iron, manganese and copper salts).

Iron and manganese may occur as ferrous and manganous bicarbonates in ground waters, particularly from deep wells and springs. These salts, originally soluble and colorless, oxidize on contact with air and precipitate as yellow to red ferric hydroxides and gray to black manganese hydroxides. They are undesirable in boiler feed water and in processing water. Copper and other heavy metal salts are also undesirable. These salts are readily removed by natural and synthetic ion exchanger water softeners.

Suspended solids in water can be removed by coagulation, settling and filtration. When the suspended insoluble solids content is low, coagulation with aluminum sulfate and filtration is sufficient. But if the suspended solids content is high, then coagulation, settling and filtration are necessary. This clarification also reduces the microbial count but for sterilization of water, in-plant, break-point chlorination is necessary. This also aids in maintaining sanitary conditions in the plant.

Various treatments are used to reduce mineral content and remove dissolved gases (such as hydrogen sulfide, carbon dioxide, etc.). These include cold-lime precipitation to reduce hardness, hot lime-soda precipitation to soften boiler feed waters, softening with sodium-cation exchanger, hydrogen-cation exchanger or complete demineralization by ion exchange.

Water used for condensing vapors, for fire protection, for washing and conveying raw materials, for general plant clean up and for dilution of wastes requires less consideration than that used for blanching and for cooling blanched products, for heating and cooling tin or glass containers of hot packed foods, as an ingredient in products and for generating steam.

Boiler-Feed Water Treatment

Water containing appreciable quantities of soluble salts, particularly calcium and magnesium salts, is undesirable in boiler feed. The soluble salts are concentrated in the boiler as steam is evaporated. When objectionable carryover of solids in steam occurs (due largely to the use of boiler water of high solids contents, high alkalinity and the presence of substances that promote foaming), the steam generated will be strongly alkaline and corrosive to metals such as aluminum and tin. Etching and discoloration of the tin surface and subsequent rusting of cans will occur.

The maximum permissible boiler water solids content will vary with the operating pressure (decreasing from 3,500 p.p.m. at operating pressure of 0–330 p.s.i.g. to 1,000 p.p.m. at 1,000–1,500 p.s.i.g.). To reduce carryover Schafer (1954) suggests that when phosphates are used to reduce scale and adherent sludge formation, organic anti-foam agents be added to control boiler water foaming and consequent carryover.

Hard water will form scale or adherent sludge on boiler heat-transfer surfaces as a result of deposition of insoluble carbonates and sulphates of calcium and magnesium with or without silica. Scaling causes loss in efficiency, reduction in capacity and damage to the boiler. It is a major consideration in boiler water treatment.

Continuous or intermittent blowdown is used to remove concentrated and precipitated solids from boilers. Phosphates are useful compounds for treating water for processing operations. Acid phosphates are added to reduce alkalinity. Trisodium phosphate is added to reduce acidity. Other phosphates are used for other purposes, including control of scaling. However, the use of phosphates requires careful control to secure best results and to avoid difficulties.

Bicarbonates of calcium and magnesium, which cause temporary hardness in water, may be reduced by precipitating insoluble carbonates before boiler use. This may be accomplished by the cold lime process in which the bulk of the hardness is precipitated as calcium carbonate and magnesium hydroxide by addition of an accurately measured amount of hydrated lime, or hydrated lime and soda ash, in the presence of a small amount of aluminum sulfate as coagulant to assist in flocculation of finely divided precipitates. This treatment will reduce hardness to about 68 p.p.m. as calcium carbonate and also will reduce alkalinity due to bicarbonates.

The hot lime-soda process is used more widely in softening boiler feed waters because it is capable of reducing hardness to a greater extent (to 25 p.p.m.), and in addition deaerates the water. In this process, water is sprayed through an atmosphere of low pressure steam to heat and deaerate it, and then is mixed with lime-soda (dolomite lime or activated magnesia may be used to remove silica as well), and the precipitated sludge which forms drops into the bottom of the softener unit.

Permanent hardness, caused by the presence of sulfates and chlorides of calcium and magnesium, is not reduced by the lime-soda treatment. The calcium and magnesium ions (cations) may be removed by treatment with naturally occurring zeolites or with synthetic ion exchange resins. Softening with zeolites is widely used in the food industry.

In the sodium cation exchanger, hard water is passed over a bed of zeolite in the sodium form and the calcium and magnesium cations are completely removed from the water by the zeolite resin and replaced with sodium. Water of substantially zero hardness is obtained so long as the ion exchange capacity of the zeolite is not exceeded. At the end of the softening run, the zeolite is regenerated by treatment with a strong salt brine and rinsing to remove the calcium and magnesium chlorides and excess salt.

In the hydrogen zeolite softening, sodium and potassium as well as calcium and magnesium are removed and replaced by hydrogen, and the zeolite bed is regenerated with acid (usually sulfuric acid) instead of salt. If the raw waters contain sufficient bicarbonate to neutralize the hydrogen ions substituted for the cations present, complete demineralization is possible. Most waters, however, contain sulfates and chlorides as well as bicarbonates. Therefore, in treatment with hydrogen zeolite, an acid water containing sulfuric and hydrochloric acids in concentrations equivalent to cations present originally is obtained. This may necessitate neutralization with caustic soda or soda ash. Complete demineralization is possible by subsequent treatment with synthetic anion exchange resins, or simultaneously with mixed resins.

So many factors are involved in the quality of boiler feed water that generalities are of limited value. If a plant does not have a control laboratory equipped and staffed to determine and maintain proper treating procedures, the alternative should be to operate under the advice and periodic checking of a good consulting laboratory specializing in this field.

Boiler feed water should be sufficiently free from soluble solids to permit efficient generation of steam with a minimum of scaling and to produce steam sufficiently low in carryover to avoid deposits in steam lines, interfering with operation of valves and steam lines and contaminating product or container.   Particular care is necessary in generation of steam which comes in contact with the product or is introduced directly into the product, as in blanching or steam injection heating.   The generation and use of steam in food processing of suitable quality and adequate quantity is important.

Water Softening

The appearance and texture of many fruits and vegetable products is affected by the pH and the calcium, magnesium and sodium content of waters used for blanching, cooking and in brines and syrups.   Calcium and magnesium ions react with pectic compounds to firm or toughen such canned vegetables as tomatoes, peas, beans and lentils. The appearance of beets (white deposits) and of asparagus may be adversely affected.   These substances may reduce the efficiency of soaps and other detergents used in cleaning, or interfere with the effectiveness of lye peeling operations.   High alkalinity adversely affects the quality of carbonated beverages.

Sometimes advantage is taken from these effects.   Soft fruit and vegetables may be advantageously firmed by calcium within desirable limits.   This has been applied in canning ripe tomatoes and grapefruit sections.   Alkaline phosphates are intentionally used to tenderize the skins of fruits like prunes.

Iron, manganese or copper in syrups used for fruits can damage the color, flavor and food value.   Sodium salts, particularly in alkaline water, can rob pectic compounds of calcium, softening products and clouding syrups and brines.   Water used for diluting vinegar must be reasonably ion-free or clouding of the product will occur.

This serves to indicate the desirability of controlling the mineral content of water supplies used for specific purposes and specific products.   This is complicated when the water supply contains a variable proportion of water from two dissimilar sources—not uncommon a situation.   The laboratory in each plant gradually accumulates information on how best to deal with its own water supply in relation to each of the products which is packed.

Canning Vegetables.—Bigelow and Stevenson (1923) reported that with peas, the hardness of water used in preliminary washing and in spray rinsing after blanching had no appreciable effect on texture of canned peas, but the hardness of the water used in blanching and the calcium content of the brine in which the peas were canned (calcium and magnesium impurities in salt may contribute more to hardness of a brine than the water supply) had a large effect.

Blanching water having a hardness of 45 p.p.m. as calcium carbonate appreciably affected texture and water absorption of the peas during processing. The presence of 200 p.p.m. of hardness in the brine reduced the acceptability of peas. They recommended softening of hard water used for blanching peas and the use of soft water for making brines.

The hardening effect of calcium and magnesium salt in canning soaked dry beans and peas was found to be greater than in green peas. Beans were soaked in waters at three levels of hardness (0, 250 and 500 p.p.m.), and canned in brines prepared from water of the same hardness as that used for soaking and pure salt. With pinto, red kidney, black-eyed peas and lima beans, the beans soaked in and canned with hard water were definitely harder. With navy beans, hardening was detectable at 79 p.p.m. and became marked at 313 p.p.m. With wax beans and green refugee beans, water ranging from 0 to over 500 p.p.m. of hardness had little effect on texture. Calcium and magnesium were not found to exert a hardening influence on either cream-style or whole grain canned corn. With beets, water up to 350 p.p.m. of hardness exerted no detectable hardening effect but in hard waters precipitation of calcium and magnesium oxalates produced a white coating on the surface of the beets, especially apparent on cut beets.

More recent investigations, summarized by Murray and Peterson (1951), support the conclusions of Bigelow and Stevenson that hard water most severely affects texture when used for soaking, for blanching and for brine. Hardness has little effect in water used for cold washing of fluming, either before or after blanching. Excessively hard water may cause sufficient hardening of canned peas, lima beans and dry beans to result in down grading but zero-soft water may also cause down grading because of excessive softness and cloudy brine. The desirable range of hardness of water varies with operating conditions, but in general a total water hardness between 85 and 170 p.p.m. (5 to 10 grains per U. S. gallon) is optimal for peas, succulent lima beans, field peas and most dry beans. For dry lima beans, a hardness of 170 to 255 p.p.m. as calcium carbonate (10 to 15 grains per U. S. gallon) is preferable.

When water of the desired quality for canning leguminous seed vegetables is not available, water may be softened by zeolite base exchange treatment. Addition of 2 to 4 per cent of salt to hard blanching water markedly softens the skins of peas and beans. In recent years, however, sodium hexametaphosphate has been widely used for treatment of hard water for soaking and blanching of peas, lima beans, and dry beans.

Quantities of hexametaphosphate recommended by Murray and Peterson (1951) to soften water, by forming a soluble complex with calcium and magnesium ions and thus preventing their absorption by the vegetables, are shown in Table 7.

Fruit Canning.—Hardness in water tends to cause toughening and firming in fruits. While this may be desirable with tender fruits like ripe apples, pears, apricots and freestone peaches, it is undesirable in cling stone peaches—a major fruit pack. If the lye solution or rinsing solution used in cup-down peeling contains 50 p.p.m. of calcium as calcium carbonate, the quality of the product may be adversely affected. Comments made in regard to vegetables apply with minor modification to fruits.

Low-Sodium Foods.—In the production of low-sodium canned foods for special dietetic use, introduction of sodium from canning water and from lye-peeling, quality grading with salt brine and use of salt brine in inhibiting enzyme activity must be avoided. Clifcorn (1953) reported that any canning water containing over 10 mg. of sodium ion per 100 grams is unsuitable for use in canning low-sodium canned foods. Zeolite softened water cannot be used if the zeolite is in the sodium form unless sodium is subsequently removed. Completely demineralized water is preferable.

COOLING AND WASHING

An important use for water in processing foods is for cooling tin and glass containers of hot packed foods. Here water must be of low bacterial content to avoid the hazard of spoilage. It must not cause corrosion, spotting or detinning of metal containers or lids. With electrolytic tin plating, the problem requires special consideration to avoid difficulties. Final rinsing of cans with special water

TABLE 7

QUANTITIES OF SODIUM HEXAMETAPHOSPHATE REQUIRED TO SOFTEN WATER FOR SOAKING AND BLANCHING PEAS AND BEANS

Total Hardness as $CaCO_3$, p.p.m.	Sodium Hexametaphosphate	
	p.p.m.	oz./100 gal.
100	310	4.1
200	620	8.2
300	930	12.3
400	1,240	16.4
500	1,550	20.5

plus rapid drying is sometimes used. Water containing corrosive salts may be blown from cooled cans with blasts of steam. Sodium chromate, added to cooling water at the rate of one-half ounce per hundred gallons, is useful under some conditions for inhibiting corrosion. If sodium chromate is added, this water should be used for no other purpose. During recirculation through a water cooler, connections which might permit recirculated water to enter lines used for conducting fresh water supplies should be avoided.

Chemical and microbial contamination must also be avoided in water used in washing glass containers and cans before filling. This is particularly important in aseptic canning processes, where inside surfaces of containers and closures must be sterile.

A considerable proportion of the 1,000 to 6,000 gal. of water used per ton of product canned is required for cooling cans. This amounts to 30 per cent of total water usage in canning tomatoes and may be even higher for non-acid vegetables. Recirculation of can cooling water as cooling water is generally the most efficient way of conserving water in the cannery. To avoid post-process contamination, however, the cooling water must be chlorinated.

Smith (1946) discussed in some detail the relationship of spoilage to rough handling and contaminated cooling water. The bacterial content of water surrounding the can at the time of a critical dent damaging the double seam has a tremendous influence on the probability of spoilage resulting from leakage.

Can handling post-cooling also influences spoilage by post-process contamination. The effect of handling methods and equipment on this spoilage was investigated by Demsey (1958) and Bohrer and Yesair (1958). Their investigations indicated that bacterial contamination could develop on wet and dirty post-cooling can handling equipment even though the cooling waters were chlorinated or naturally of good sanitary quality. This bacterial contamination may be transferred to can double-seam areas and contributes to spoilage due to product recontamination.

IN-PLANT CHLORINATION

Chlorine and chlorine compounds have been used for many years as germicidal agents in hospitals and in domestic water sewage treating plants. The dairy industry very early began to employ hypochlorites to improve sanitation and prevent development of offensive odors. A. E. Griffin (1940, 1945) demonstrated the value of break-point chlorination in food processing operations. Hall and Blundell (1946) and Harris (1947) tested the process. Somers (1951) described observations in four canneries on the effect of break-point chlorination in canning a variety of fruits and vegetables.   Mercer and Somers (1957) critically reviewed and re-evaluated the available data on the use of chlorine in food plant sanitation.

For insuring the potability of water, for reducing spoilage hazards, for inhibiting the development of slimes and odors, for making clean-up easier, and for improving the quality of products, most food processing plants have turned or are turning to in-plant, break-point chlorination.   Automatic equipment is available to feed chlorine at rates varying between 4 and 400 lbs. in 24 hr., proportioned to the water flow.   Five to seven p.p.m. of residual chlorine is recom-mended for in-plant chlorine which may be increased to 15 to 25 p.p.m. during clean-up periods.

The active germicidal constituent present in solutions of hypo-chlorite is not definitely known, but believed to be the undissociated hypochlorous acid (Mercer and Somers 1957).   Charlton and Levine (1937) reported that the germicidal efficiency of chlorine compounds such as chloramine T is due to the presence of positively charged chlorine atoms.   The pH of solutions is an important factor in de-termining the effectiveness.   In solutions more alkaline than pH 8, the time required for killing microorganisms is greatly increased. Table 8 shows the relation between rate of kill and pH of calcium hypochlorite solution.

TABLE 8

RELATION OF PH AND TIME OF KILL IN 25 P.P.M. SOLUTION
OF AVAILABLE CHLORINE AT 68°F.

pH	Killing Time, (min.)
6.00	2.5
7.00	3.6
8.00	5.0
9.00	19.5
9.35	35.5
10.00	121.0
12.86	465.0

This relationship between pH and time required to kill test organ-isms is graphically portrayed in Fig. 1.

The relationship between concentration of chlorine and killing time at constant temperature and pH, as observed by Rudolph and Levine (1941), is shown in Fig. 2.

In these tests, spores of *B. metiens* were used because they are easily prepared and because their resistance to the killing action of chlorine remains constant over a considerable period of time.

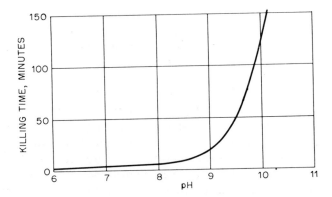

FIG. 1. EFFECT OF pH ON GERMICIDAL EFFICIENCY OF HYPOCHLORITE SOLUTION

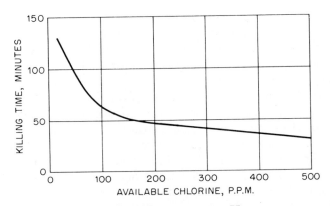

FIG. 2. EFFECT OF CONCENTRATION OF CALCIUM HYPOCHLORITE ON SURVIVAL
OF *B. metiens* SPORES AT 68°F. AND pH 10.0

Rudolph and Levine (1941) further observed that, with uniform
pH and chlorine concentration, the killing time decreased 40 to 60
per cent for each 18° rise in temperature in the range from 68° to 132°F.

Proper understanding of the value, limitations and hazards of
chlorination is essential for successful applications in the food industry.   The tendency of chlorine solutions to accelerate corrosion
of iron equipment must be considered but with proper control is less
than the corrosive effects of slimes which are eliminated.   Where the
available chlorine content of the water does not exceed six p.p.m. during operation and 25 p.p.m. during clean-up, accidental corrosion does
not occur.

Filice (1952) made commercial tests of the effect of chlorination in
fruit canning operations.   Four p.p.m. prevented sliming of belts dur-

ing cherry and apricot canning operations, but six p.p.m. were required during cling peach operations when loading of conveyors was heavier, and the carryover of lye from peeling operations raised the pH of water on the belts.

BREAK-POINT CHLORINATION

When organic compounds are present which react with chlorine more readily than the bacterial cells, the result is marginal chlorination unless residual chlorine persists after satisfaction of the organic demand.   If phenols are present even in small quantities, the reaction compound has a powerful and persistent medicinal odor which is highly objectionable in food products.   Break-point chlorination with free residual chlorine minimizes many objectionable features of marginal chlorination.

In Fig. 3, the lower curve shows the typical relationship between added and residual chlorine in water with a high chlorine demand due to the presence of organic substances which reach with chlorine, compared to water containing no such compounds in the upper curve.

The low point in the lower curve where it turns to parallel the curve of pure water is known as the break-point for that water.

For rinsing conveyor belts to maintain sanitary conditions, from 2 to 5 p.p.m. of residual chlorine are sufficient if the pH and temperatures are not outside the range usually encountered in normal water supplies.   This may require the addition of 4 to 7 p.p.m. of chlorine to maintain this residue.   It is usually necessary to spray both sides of inspection belts to maintain optimum sanitation.

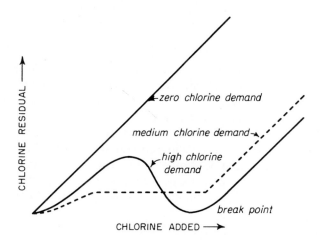

FIG. 3.   CHLORINE DEMAND CHARACTERISTICS OF WATER

Fruit and vegetable elevators may be maintained in satisfactory condition by spraying both sides either at the return cycle or just after fruit discharge. Canning table conveyors should be sprayed on both sides preferably at the discharge end and again at the other end before the conveyor is loaded.

For clean-up operation, residual chlorine should be increased to 20 to 25 p.p.m. With a good clean-up, this is sufficient to prevent fermentation during the usual shut-down period.

OFF-FLAVOR AVOIDANCE

Chlorinated water may be used safely in washing many fruits and vegetables before blanching, peeling and packing, without appreciably affecting flavor. To obtain the desired reduction in bacterial count of canned and frozen products, considerably more chlorine must be used than in continuous sanitizing of equipment, because of the higher chlorine demand. Particularly high levels of chlorine, for example, may be required in washing garlic and onions to reduce bacterial count in dehydrated products, and even at levels of over 50 p.p.m. detectable changes in flavor in the final dried product are not evident. In fruit and vegetable canning, care has to be taken not to use excessive chlorine in water used for blanching or in preparation of syrups and brines packed with the product. Some products are particularly sensitive to flavor changes as a result of chlorination. Of the 26 fruits and vegetables tested, Somers (1951) of the Western Branch Laboratory of N.C.A. reported apples, figs, peaches, pears, strawberries and yams to be most sensitive to flavor changes from excessive chlorination.

Where in-plant chlorination is used, a separate water line should be installed to supply unchlorinated water for syrup and brine preparation. This is particularly desirable for the preparation of spiced or herb flavored sauces such as tomato sauce for pork and beans.

At the levels indicated above, no increased corrosion of plant equipment has been observed. In the average cooling waters, addition of chlorine up to a residual of 10 p.p.m. and even higher has not been observed to increase rusting, unless the cans are cooled excessively or the cooling water contains corrosive compounds (high chloride and sulfate content).

Corrosive water should be chlorinated at the lowest level necessary and may also be treated with a corrosion inhibitor such as sodium chromate. In this case, special methods of controlling chlorine content are necessary since the usual colorimetric and volumetric methods are not applicable. The starch-iodine titration method, modified by controlled liberation of iodine from potassium iodine by chlorine at a pH where chromate will not oxidize iodine, may be used. Amperometric and other methods are also used for measuring the chlorine content of water containing chromates.

Ed Booker, frozen food processor of Knoxville, Tenn., reported a cleaner plant, with less odor and slime, safer, cleaner floors and a saving of $250 per month in clean-up costs. Merril Stanley reported that in the Puyallup plant of Washington Packers results were cleaner lug boxes and conveyor belts without slime, and concluded "In-plant chlorination added the ounce of prevention to keep our plant continuously sanitary." (See Joslyn 1955.)

Bruno Filice (1952) noted in the operation of Filice and Perrelli at Richmond, Calif., advantages of in-plant, break-point chlorination included: cleaner appearance, cleaner smell, lower spoilage losses and reduction in the cost of time and clean up.

For limited applications, hypochlorite solutions may be used as a source of chlorine, because no costly equipment is required for mixing and adding the solution to the water supply. However, the cost of chlorine in hypochlorite is relatively high and for most food processing operations, compressed chlorine gas is fed from cylinders manually, automatically or proportionally. Equipment for controlling this operation has been developed to a high degree. Sizes of interest to processors range in capacity from feeding 25 lbs. of chlorine in 24 hr. to feeding 400 lbs. in 24 hr.

Equipment for feeding 25 lbs. of chlorine in 24 hr. will chlorinate 250 g.p.m. of water, and equipment for feeding 400 lbs. in 24 hr. will chlorinate 4,000 g.p.m. of water. The equipment comprises a valve for reducing the pressure of chlorine in the cylinders and combining it with a measured volume of water to prepare a standard dosage solution, which is in turn fed into the main flow of water, at a manually, automatically or proportionately controlled rate. Residual chlorine is checked with a color comparator.

SAVING OF WATER

Economies in water usage in food processing are necessary to conserve water supplies, reduce operating costs and volume of liquid wastes. Unwise reduction in water can cause spoilage losses, poor sanitation, and lowering of quality.

While in food processing water of the highest quality is required, the use of water must be reduced to the lowest volume which will allow efficient and sanitary operation. The National Canners Association some 15 years ago undertook long-range research on the possibilities and limitations of water conservation in canning (Townsend and Somers 1949). Extensive investigations of water usage in product washing were made, first with peas (Mercer and Townsend 1954) and later with tomatoes (Mercer *et al.* 1958). These investigations were directed to reduction in water consumption through more efficient use of product wash water, prevention of spoilage or quality loss as a result of indiscriminate water saving practices, and development of design principles for product washing equipment. Reductions in water consumption must be accomplished by procedures which cause no undesirable effect on the physical appearance, nutritional qualities or sanitary conditions of the product. Water reclaimed for use in contact with food must be low in bacterial count, free of microorganisms having public health significance and free of materials which could constitute adulteration.

The first step in determining the possibility of advantageously reducing water consumption is to survey the operation and measure or estimate the quantity of water being used for each purpose in the plant. Tables 9, 10, and 11 provide data useful for estimating the flow of water to any outlet when metering is not available.

TABLE 9

WATER FLOW (GALLONS PER MINUTE) THROUGH 100 FEET CLEAN STEEL PIPE— STANDARD WEIGHT UNDER VARIOUS PRESSURE DIFFERENTIALS (POUNDS PER SQ. IN.)[1]

Pipe Size, in.	Pressure Difference, lbs./sq. in.								
	10	20	30	40	50	75	100	150	200
$1/8$	0.51	0.76	0.96	1.14	1.31	1.64	1.92	2.40	2.81
$1/4$	1.12	1.68	2.10	2.46	2.79	3.50	4.12	5.15	6.03
$3/8$	2.62	3.85	4.80	5.64	6.36	7.98	9.40	11.8	13.7
$1/2$	4.85	7.16	9.10	10.6	11.9	14.9	17.4	21.7	25.4
$3/4$	10.2	15.1	18.9	22.1	24.9	30.9	36.2	45.0	52.4
1	20.0	29.1	35.9	42.2	47.6	59.1	69.0	85.4	99.4
$1 1/4$	41.6	56.6	73.9	86.4	96.9	120.0	140.0	173.0	202.0
$1 1/2$	61.0	88.3	110.0	128.0	143.0	178.0	207.0	257.0	298.0
2	117.0	169.0	210.0	245.0	275.0	340.0	397.0	492.0	570.0
$2 1/2$	185.0	267.0	332.0	386.0	433.0	537.0	624.0	770.0	893.0
3	325.0	468.0	583.0	676.0	766.0	947.0	1088.0	1345.0	1555.0
$3 1/2$	475.0	687.0	846.0	981.0	1103.0	1363.0	1580.0	1955.0	2265.0
4	659.0	947.0	1175.0	1360.0	1530.0	1885.0	2190.0	2690.0	3120.0
5	1180.0	1695.0	2080.0	2420.0	2720.0	3365.0	3900.0	4790.0	5570.0

[1] From Baldwin Southwark, Hydraulic Tables and Other Data, Bulletin 150. Based on turbulent flow in clean steel pipes. The pressure differences indicated are true for flow between two points in a line of pipe and must be corrected for by adding velocity head in terms of initial pressure drop as given in Table 10.

The second step is to focus attention on the basic purposes for which water is used. Water used in washing operations not only prepares the raw material for processing by removing unsanitary extraneous material but may be used to transport the product and prevent damage by cushioning its transfer in successive line operations. The extraneous material to be removed includes microorganisms

better control of water volume to product load.   The effectiveness of the final spray wash is determined by construction of belt conveyor, location of sprays, volume, pressure and pattern of sprays and temperature of water.   For tomatoes, Mercer *et al.* (1958) report that a roller belt is preferable to other belts, that a minimum of four banks of sprays with 12 in. between spray headers and with nozzles spaced 12 in. apart are necessary, satisfactory results were obtained with nozzles 8 to 12 in. above the product, and best results with flat jet type of nozzle.   Warm water (100° to 130°F.) from can coolers or evaporators was 40 per cent more effective than an equal volume of cold water in washing.

(3)   Leafy vegetables, root vegetables, harder fruit and other raw materials can be partially cleaned by tumbling in reel cleaners or over shaker screens, reducing the load on washers and saving water required for cleaning.   Removal of spoiled material before washing reduces the load on the washer.   Dry cleaning is not desirable for soft-textured products such as ripe tomatoes which crush readily and become contaminated.   Soil and bacterial spores taken into the tissues of tomatoes broken by rough handling can not be adequately removed even with the most vigorous washing.

(4)   Substitution of mechanical conveyors for hydraulic conveying may be advantageous in some instances.   The gentle action of hydraulic fluming and pumping, combined with the added advantage of simultaneous cleaning and heating or cooling, makes hydraulic conveying advantageous for many purposes.   Pneumatic conveying is applicable only to dry products like sugar, flour, grains, etc.   Mechanical conveyors require maintenance.   They must be rinsed to maintain sanitary conditions and avoid build-up of microorganisms. Whether fluming or mechanical conveying will be most advantageous must be determined for individual applications.

(5)   The design of washers, coolers, blanchers and other equipment can affect the efficiency of water use.   The effect of design upon the efficiency of reel washers has been described.   In coolers the greatest efficiency in cooling and the greatest economy of water results if containers are agitated and raised under descending curtains of cooling water in complete counterflow, which would offer the additional advantage of rinsing the containers leaving the cooler with the fresh water, as it enters.

Other factors must be considered.   Many canned foods cannot be agitated at this stage of processing without physical damage.   The cost of building and maintaining a cooler of the described type would probably be higher than the advantages gained.

However, in rising-belt spinning juice can coolers, the cooling water is not uncommonly used in two to three stages counterflow, by re-pumping water used on coolest cans over cans entering the equipment.

(6)   Advantageous recirculation or reuse of water offers another possibility of reducing water use which is closely related to the problem of design, essential for the avoidance of difficulties.

In considering the extent to, and the manner in which water may be reused, the first consideration must be avoidance of hazards of contamination or spoilage of products.   To illustrate, when water is to be reused for can cooling, several precautions should be observed. First, cans should be rinsed before entering the cooler, to remove organic material and avoid build-up of solids in the cooling water. Second, the water should be continuously rechlorinated to avoid development of slime and spoilage organisms.   Third, the addition of make-up water should be under laboratory control to insure against costly headaches and the entire system must be periodically cleaned.

Principles involved in the reuse of water in pea canneries have been well defined by Mercer and Townsend (1954) in N.C.A. Bulletin 31L.   Simple recirculation of water for fluming should be avoided. Multistage counterflow reuse can be satisfactorily planned.   Final fluming of peas should be in fresh, break-point chlorinated water. Water should be rechlorinated to a five-second 0.5 p.p.m. residual chlorine between each use in collecting tanks equipped with auto-matically controlled make-up valves for fresh water addition as required, wasting water only at intended points.

Immediately after blanching, fresh water should be used to rinse and cool peas before entering the flumes.   This water should not again be used for fluming.   The operation should be supervised by a qualified, responsible employee to insure proper chlorination. In this bulletin, a diagram illustrates how the water may be recir-culated in the flumes so that contamination of product can be avoided. When these precautions are observed, substantial savings in water are possible.

The can-cooling water is most efficiently conserved by cooling after use and recirculation.   Where this is not possible, it and evapo-rator water can be used for product washing.   The temperature of the average reclaimed can-cooling water ranges from 90° to 100°F.;   that of evaporator water ranges from 120° to 130°F.   If these warm waters are used for washing tomatoes in soak tanks or flumes, Mercer et al. (1958) recommend that the volume added should not elevate the water temperature above 80°F., especially if recirculation is practiced. Warm water (100° to 130°F.) from can washers or evaporators, however, can be used in final spray wash and is most advantageous here.

When the operation of the tomato washer remains constant and the method of applying water to the product is the same, the degree of cleanliness of washed tomatoes increases with the volume of water used. Some washers, however, use less water per ton yet produce cleaner tomatoes. Mercer *et al.* (1958) reported data indicating that with some washer systems, 600 gal. of water per ton of tomatoes produced cleaner tomatoes than with others using 1,400 gal. of water per ton. They report that in tomato canning, recirculation of product wash water results in 16 per cent reduction of water usage, recirculation of can-cooling water results in 22 per cent reduction of water used, and recirculation of wash water and cooling water and reuse of evaporator water for product washing results in 45 per cent reduction of water used. The total water used per ton of tomatoes processed is reduced from 3,340 gal. to 2,825, 2,602 and 1,827 gal., respectively.

BIBLIOGRAPHY

Water Supply and Treatment

ANON. 1962. Coagulation of Water for Filtration. Univ. of Michigan School of Public Health, Ann Arbor, Mich.

ASSOC. FOOD IND. SANITARIANS. 1952. Sanitation for the Food Preservation Industries. McGraw-Hill Book Co., New York.

BABBITT, H. E., DOLAND, J. J., and CLEASBY, J. L. 1962. Water Supply Engineering. 6th Edition. McGraw-Hill Book Co., New York.

BUREAU AGR. IND. CHEM., AGR. RES. ADMN. 1944. Vegetable and fruit dehydration. A manual for plant operators. U. S. Dept. Agr. Misc. Pub. *540.*

CLIFCORN, L. E. 1953. Production and consumer aspects of low-sodium canned foods. Continental Can Co., Research Division Bull.; J. Am. Dietetic Assoc. *29,* No. 2, 116.

ECKENFELDER, W. W. JR., and O'CONNER, D. J. 1961. Biological Waste Treatment. Pergamon Press, New York.

EDMONTON, A. D. 1954. The water situation in California. Paper presented at the A.A.A.S. Meeting, Dec. 26–31, University of California, Berkeley. *See also* California State Water Resources Bull. *2,* 1955.

GAINEY, P. L., and LORD, T. H. 1952. Microbiology of Water and Sewage. Prentice-Hall Co., Inc., Englewood Cliffs, N. J.

HALVORSON, H. O. 1955. Municipal water. *In* Encyclopedia of Chemical Technology. Edited by R. E. Kirk and D. F. Othmer. Interscience Encyclopedia, Inc., New York.

HAMER, P., JACKSON, J. E., and THURSTON, E. F. 1961. Industrial Water Treatment Practice. Butterworth Publishers, London.

HEID, J. L., and KELLY, E. J. 1953. The concentration and dehydration of citrus juices. Canner *116,* No. 5, 9–13, 21–22, 24, 26–27, 30, 32; No. 6, 13–15, 18, 33.

HINICH, R. E. 1961. Efficiency checks for water softening systems. Food Eng. *33,* No. 11, 93–94.

HOCKENSMITH, R. D. (Editor). 1960. Water and Agriculture. A.A.A.S. Symposium, Dec. 1958. Amer. Assoc. Adv. Sci., Washington, D. C.

HOOVER, C. P. 1951. Water Supply and Treatment. 7th Edition. National Lime Assoc., Washington, D. C.

HUBERTY, M. R. 1959. Fresh-water resources. *In* Natural Resources. Edited by M. R. Huberty and W. L. Flock. McGraw-Hill Book Co., New York.

JOSLYN, M. A. 1955. Water in food products manufacture. Western Canner and Packer 47, No. 10, 14–18, 21, 24, 26–27, 30.

KRATZ, P. DEC., and LEWIS, J. I. 1955. Water quality control for a superior beverage. Food Processing 16, No. 7, 14–15.

LAMB, P., and HAVIGHORST, C. R. 1953. Top-rank quick-freeze operation. Food Eng. 25, No. 1, 68–73, 118–121.

MURRAY, R. V., and PETERSON, G. T. 1951. Water for canning. Continental Can Co., Research Division Bull. 22, 1–27.

NORDELL, E. 1955. Water treatment is a "must" in the modern food plant. Food Eng. 27, No. 4, 89–99.

NORDELL, E. 1961. Water Treatment for Industrial and Other Uses. Reinhold Publishing Corp., New York.

PARTRIDGE, E. P. 1955. Industrial water. *In* Encyclopedia of Chemical Technology. Edited by R. E. Kirk and D. F. Othmer. Interscience Encyclopedia, Inc., New York.

PAULSON, C. G. 1954. What to do about our growing demand for water. Paper presented at the A.A.A.S. Meeting, Dec. 26–31, University of California, Berkeley.

POWELL, S. T. 1954. Water Conditioning for Industry. McGraw-Hill Book Co., New York.

SCHAFER, C. J. 1954. How to curb boiler-water solids. Food Eng. 26, No. 7, 80–82.

U. S. DEPT. AGR. 1955. Water. Yearbook of Agriculture. Gov't Printing Office, Washington, D. C.

U. S. DEPT. HEALTH, EDUCATION AND WELFARE. 1961. Water Quality Measurement and Instrumentation. Proceedings of the 1960 seminar at Cincinnati, Ohio. Robert A. Taft Sanitary Engineering Center, Cincinnati, Ohio.

Water Softening

AM. CHEM. SOC. 1960. Saline Water Conversion. Advances in Chemistry Series No. 27, 1–246. Am. Chem. Soc., Washington, D. C.

BETZ, W. H., and BETZ, L. D. 1953. Betz Handbook of Water Conditioning. 4th Edition. Publ. by the author, Philadelphia, Pa.

BIGELOW, W. D., and STEVENSON, A. E. 1923. The effect of hard water in canning vegetables. Nat'l. Canners Assoc. Res. Lab. Bull. 20L.

CLIFCORN, L. E. 1953. Production and consumer aspects of low-sodium canned foods. J. Am. Dietetic Assoc. 29, 116–120. Reprinted as Bull. Res. Dept., Continental Can Co., Inc.

FELTON, G. E. 1949. Ion exchange application by the food industry. Advances in Food Research 2, 1–46.

PERMUTIT COMPANY. 1943. Water Conditioning Handbook. Permutit Company, New York.

SHAUB, F. J. 1940. New trends in boiler food water treatment. Univ. Illinois Eng. Expt. Sta. Bull. 38, No. 1.

Chlorination

BOHRER, C. W., and YESAIR, J. 1958. Bacteriological studies on post-cooling handling equipment on spoilage rates. Nat'l Canners Assoc. Inf. Letter 1666, 7–10.

CHARLTON, D., and LEVINE, M. 1937. Germicidal properties of chlorine compounds. Iowa Eng. Expt. Sta. Bull. 132.

DEMSEY, J. N.   1958.   The effect of post-cooling handling equipment on spoilage rates.   Nat'l Canners Assoc. Inf. Letter *1666*, 7–10.

FILICE, B. A.   1952.   Chlorination as applied to sanitation in a fruit cannery. Filice and Perrelli Co., Richmond, Calif.   Unpublished ms.

GRIFFIN, A. E.   1940.   Taste and odor control with break-point chlorination. Wallace and Tiernan Co., Tech. Pub., *207*, Newark, N. J.

GRIFFIN, A. E.   1945.   Break-point chlorination.   Wallace and Tiernan Co., Tech. Pub., *213*, Newark, N. J.

HALL, J. E., and BLUNDELL, C. C.   1946.   The use of break-point chlorination and sterilized water in canning and freezing plants.   Supplement to N.C.A. Information Letter *1073*, 81.   Reprinted by Wallace and Tiernan Co., Newark, N. J.

HARRIS, J. J.   1947.   Chlorination in the food plant.   Continental Can Co., Res. Dept. Bull. *13*.

KRAMER, A., and TWIGG, B. A.   1962.   Fundamentals of Quality Control for the Food Industry.   Avi Publishing Co., Westport, Conn.

MERCER, W. A., and SOMERS, I. I.   1957.   Chlorine in food plant sanitation. Advances in Food Research 7, 129–169.

RUDOLPH, A. S., and LEVINE, M.   1941.   Factors affecting the germicidal efficiency of hypochlorite solutions.   Iowa Eng. Expt. Sta. Bull. *150*.

SOMERS, I. I.   1951.   Studies on in-plant chlorination.   Food Technol. *5*, No. 2, 46–51.

SMITH, C. L.   1946.   The relationship of spoilage to rough handling and contaminated cooling water.   Continental Can Co., Res. Dept. Bull. *9*.

Water Saving

MERCER, W. A., and TOWNSEND, C. T.   1954.   Water reuse in canneries.   Section 1.   Pea Canneries.   Nat'l. Canners Assoc. Res. Lab. Bull. *31L*.

MERCER, W. A., ROSE, W. W., BUTLER, C. E., and APPLEMAN, M. M.   1958. More effective product washing with less water.   Nat'l Canners. Assoc. Inf. Letter *1666*, 2–7.

MERCER, W. A., and YORK, G. K.   1953.   Re-use of water in canning.   Nat'l Canners Assoc. Inf. Letter *1426*, 74–78.

N.C.A. TASK COMM. DEVELOPMENT SANITARY CONSTRUCTION BLANCHERS. 1955.   Recommendations for operation, modification and construction of drum type water blanchers.   Nat'l. Canners Assoc. Inf. Letter *1528*, 158–161.

N.C.A. TASK COMM. DEVELOPMENT SANITARY CONSTRUCTION CONVEYORS. 1955.   Recommendations of sanitary design for basic horizontal belt conveyors for in-process food products.   Nat'l. Canners Assoc. Inf. Letter *1528*, 158.

N.C.A. TASK COMM. DEVELOPMENT SANITARY CONSTRUCTION RAW FRUIT AND TOMATO WASHERS.   1959.   Tentative recommendations for operation, modification and construction of tomato washers.   Nat'l. Canners Assoc. Inf. Letter *1724*, 143–144.

TOWNSEND, C. T., and SOMERS, I. I.   1949.   How to save water in canneries. Food Inds., Western Ed. *21*, 11–12.

TRAVIS, H.   1950.   They cut their use of water 25%.   Food Inds. *22*, 1691–93.

Waste Disposal

[1] BACON, V. W., GLEASON, G. B., and WALLING, I. W.   1953.   Water quality as related to water pollution in California.   Ind. Eng. Chem. *45*, 2657–2665.

[1] HANNUM, W. T.   1953.   California water pollution control problem.   Ind. Eng. Chem. *45*, 2652–2655.

[1] SCHWAB, C. E.   1953.   Federal water pollution control act.   Ind. Eng. Chem. *45*, 2648–2652.

[1] SHAFER, R. A. 1953. Ground water and used water in basin recharge areas. Ind. Eng. Chem. *45*, 2666–2668.

[1] VAUGHN, R. V., and MARCH, G. L. 1953. Disposal of California winery wastes. Ind. Eng. Chem. *45*, 2686–2688.

WARRICK, L. F., McKEE, F. J., WIRTH, H. E., and SANBORN, N. H. 1939. Methods of treating cannery waste. Nat'l. Canners Assoc. Res. Lab. Bull. *28L*.

WARRICK, L. F., WISNIEWSKI, T. F., and SANBORN, N. H. 1945. Cannery waste disposal lagoons. Nat'l. Canners Assoc., Res. Lab. Bull. *29L*.

[1] WARRICK, L. F. 1953. Improving the quality of water resources. Ind. Eng. Chem. *45*, 2669–2688.

---

[1] Symposium on Industrial Process Water at Los Angeles in April 1953. Reprints of this symposium may be purchased from Reprint Dept., American Chemical Society, 1155 Sixteenth St., N.W., Washington, D. C.

CHAPTER 2

Neil Kelly | Sugar

INTRODUCTION

Stewart (1961) has listed the attributes of foods expected by consumers: (1) safety; (2) sensory properties; (a) appearance and color; (b) taste and odor (flavor); (c) texture; (d) sound and temperature; (3) convenience; (4) storage life; and (5) functional properties.

In processed foods, sugar (sucrose) makes a contribution to many of these attributes, but most significantly to the sensory properties. Its influence on appearance and color, taste and texture is evident in hundreds of familiar foods, ranging from baked goods to candy cotton. Yet, in many of these products, the quality most commonly associated with sugar —sweetness—is no more important than certain of its chemical and physical characteristics. To name some of them: the ease with which sugar hydrolyzes to form simple sugars, its high degree of solubility in water, its ready crystallization from supersaturated solutions, its reaction to heat (caramelization), its ability to disperse protein and its preservative action.

Sugar is pleasant to the taste, clean, uniform in quality, contains no waste and keeps indefinitely. These properties, and others, are well understood by food technologists, and are accepted as a matter of course in the day-to-day operations of the food processing industries. The refined granulated sugar of commerce is at least 99.9 per cent sucrose.

Deliveries of sugar in the United States during the early 1960's were more than 9,000,000 short tons annually, and about two-thirds of it were incorporated in commercially-prepared foods. Quantities of sugar delivered to various classes of buyers in 1960 are shown in Table 12. ·

THE MANUFACTURE OF SUGAR

The commercial sources of sucrose are the sugar cane (*Saccharum officinarum*) and the sugar beet (*Beta vulgaris*).

Sugar cane is a tall, grass-like plant which stores sugar in its stalk. The sugar beet, on the other hand, stores sugar in a long, whitish root. These dissimilarities in the form and structure of the plants are responsible for some of the obvious differences in the methods by which sugar is extracted from them. However, once the sugar-bearing juices are concentrated, the processes are basically parallel and the objectives are the

---

NEIL KELLY is President of The Sugar Association, Inc., New York, N. Y.

same. It is noteworthy that the cane sugar industry developed many of the methods that are now used not only in the manufacture of beet sugar but in other food and chemical processes as well. These include multiple-effect evaporation, vacuum pans, crystallization, centrifuging, chemical clarification of both raw juices and refined liquors, bone char filtration and atmospheric drying, as in granulators.

The technology of sugar production forms an extensive literature, and for present purposes a brief description of the major processes must

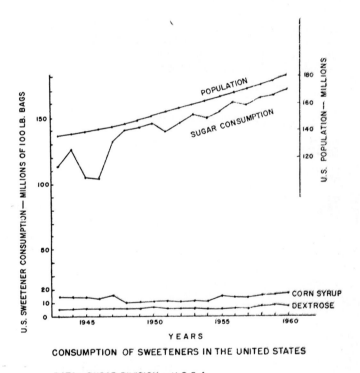

CONSUMPTION OF SWEETENERS IN THE UNITED STATES

DATA: SUGAR DIVISION — U.S.D.A.
Data from Sugar Division of U. S. Department of Agriculture

FIG. 4. CONSUMPTION OF SWEETENERS IN THE UNITED STATES

suffice. Those who seek greater detail may consult the references listed in the bibliography.

Raw Cane Sugar Production

Multiple mills are used in crushing the stalks of sugar cane and expressing their sugar-bearing juices. A train of mills may consist of a shredder, or crusher, and from 3 to 7 three-roller mills in tandem which extract the juice under heavy pressure, flexibly controlled by hydraulic cylinders. Dilute juice or hot water is usually applied to the *bagasse*—the woody residue of the cane—as it emerges from each of the three roller mills. By this means the residual juice is diluted, and the maximum percentage of

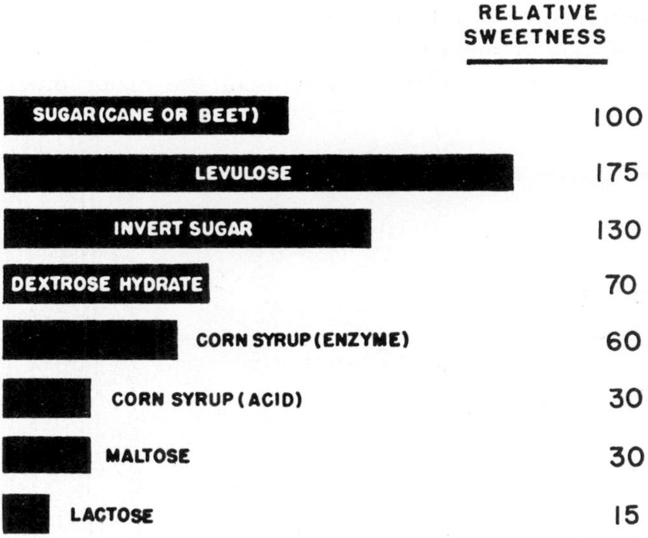

RELATIVE SWEETNESS

SUGAR (CANE OR BEET)	100
LEVULOSE	175
INVERT SUGAR	130
DEXTROSE HYDRATE	70
CORN SYRUP (ENZYME)	60
CORN SYRUP (ACID)	30
MALTOSE	30
LACTOSE	15

FIG. 5.   RELATIVE SWEETNESS RATING

TABLE 12

DISTRIBUTION OF REFINED SUGAR IN THE UNITED STATES[1,2] 1960

(In 100 lb. units)

Product of Business or Buyer	Beet	Cane	Off-Shore	Total	Liquid Sugar Included in Totals[3]
Bakery, cereal and allied products	6,600,615	13,504,510	847,958	20,953,083	1,750,158
Confectionery and related products	3,444,896	11,232,406	1,399,718	16,077,020	2,685,279
Ice cream and dairy products	2,424,756	4,641,584	246,051	7,312,391	3,956,873
Beverages	4,039,301	17,792,070	1,138,159	22,969,530	11,095,676
Canned, bottled, frozen foods, jams, jellies and preserves	6,736,235	6,715,210	2,357,087	15,808,532	5,524,668
Multiple and all other food uses	902,266	4,973,413	63,427	5,939,106	1,747,545
Nonfood products	43,519	796,619	451,794	1,291,932	236,597
Hotels, restaurants, institutions	89,627	1,151,521	65,426	1,306,574	51,549
Wholesale grocers, jobbers, sugar dealers	11,085,901	36,441,898	3,063,897	50,591,696	327,677
Retail grocers, chain stores, super markets	4,351,850	19,297,829	804,268	24,453,947	228,895
All other deliveries, including deliveries to Government agencies	539,723	1,170,380	45,336	1,755,439	2,302
Total Deliveries	40,258,689	117,717,440	10,483,121	168,459,250	27,607,219
Deliveries in consumer-size package (less than 50 lbs.)	8,812,981	47,754,781	758,954	57,326,716	...
Bulk deliveries	8,798,376	14,111,753[4]	0	22,910,129[3]	...

[1] Source: Sugar Division, Commodity Stabilization Service, U. S. Department of Agriculture.
[2] Represents approximately 96.9% of deliveries by primary distributors in continental U. S.
[3] Reported as produced or imported and delivered except liquid sugar which is on a sugar solid content.
[4] Reflects a 458,143 hundred weight plus adjustment in second quarter 1960 cane sugar bulk deliveries.

Fig. 6. Modern Sugar Beet Harvesters Lift and Top the Beets
Mechanically, and Dump Them into a Truck

Fig. 7. Mechanical Sugar Cane Harvesters Cut and Load the Cane

the sugar originally in the stalks is extracted. At this point, the sugar is dissolved in a thin juice, often called "mixed juice."

The thin juice is strained, limed to alkalinity, and heated. Impurities settle to the bottom and the clear, purified juice is decanted. The clear juice is concentrated in multiple-effect evaporators, then boiled under vacuum to a *massecuite*—that is, sugar crystals suspended in molasses. The *massecuite* is centrifuged to separate sugar crystals, which constitute the yellow-brown raw sugar of commerce destined for further processing into refined sugar.

FIG. 8. HARVESTED BEETS ARE STORED IN PILES UNTIL NEEDED IN THE MANUFACTURING PROCESS. IN THESE PILES ARE 190,000 TONS OF BEETS

Some raw sugar is refined in the areas of production, but in most instances it is shipped to refineries located nearer centers of consumption, usually at seaports. At one time, all raw sugar was packed in jute bags, but transportation in bulk cargo ships has superseded the older practice.

Cane Sugar Refining

Raw sugar, as it is delivered to refiners from the areas of production, is usually about 97 per cent sucrose, the remainder consisting of moisture, ash, invert sugar and organic nonsugars.

Typical composition of raw sugar is shown in the following table:

Polarization	97.70 to 97.80
	Per cent
Sucrose	97.80 to 98.20
Invert	0.03 to 0.06
Ash	0.03 to 0.06
Moisture	0.40 to 0.60
Organic nonsugars	0.20 to 1.00

The first operation in the refining process consists in mingling the raw sugar with hot saturated syrup, which softens the film of impurities that envelops each raw sugar crystal. The mixture is centrifuged, with the addition of a spray of water in the final stages to remove a part of the softened impurities.

The washed raws are dissolved in hot water, filtered and clarified, and then filtered through columns of bone char to remove color and most of the remaining impurities. The filtered liquor is evaporated, crystallized

FIG. 9. SUGAR CANE IS CRUSHED BETWEEN HEAVY, CORRU-
GATED METAL ROLLS TO EXTRACT THE SUGAR-BEARING JUICE

under vacuum, and once more centrifuged. The product is granulated sugar, which is dried, screened for crystal size, and packaged.

Typical composition of granulated sugar, based on product of Eastern refiners, is shown on the following table:

	Medium Granulated, %	Fine Granulated, %
Moisture	0.02	0.04
Total solids	99.98	99.96
Sucrose	99.95	99.90
Invert sugar	0.01	0.03
Ash	0.005	0.01
Relative solution color	Clear water white	Essentially water white

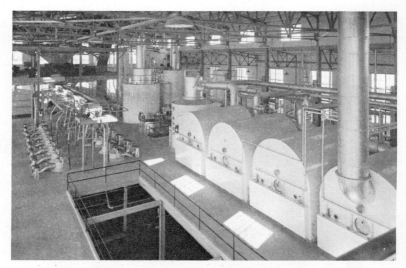

FIG. 10. INTERIOR VIEW OF A MODERN BEET SUGAR PLANT WITH EVAPORATOR IN THE FOREGROUND

Brown, or so-called "soft," sugars are prepared by crystallizing and centrifuging the sugar remaining in the syrup spun off during the processing of white granulated sugar.

Cube and tablet sugars may be produced by pressing moist granulated sugar into molds on a rotating cylinder. The individual pieces are ejected on metal plates and then placed in ovens for drying and hardening. In another process the moist sugar is formed into slabs which, after drying, are sawed and chipped into the proper sizes.

Beet Sugar Production

The manufacture of beet sugar in the United States and Canada is unique in that the entire process, from beets to crystals, is a single, integrated operation. The raw sugar phase is absent, even though in Europe and other areas raw beet sugars are produced for later refining.

Harvested beets are delivered by the grower at outlying stations or directly to the factory yard. The beets are brought into the factory as needed in the process, and are thoroughly washed to remove trash, stones and other material that might cause difficulty in the slicers.

After being weighed, the beets are cut into thin slices, called *cossettes,* whose form and size are often compared to "shoestring" potatoes. The slices are conveyed to the diffusion battery, where their sugar is extracted in hot water. The principle is that of dialysis, in which the cell walls of the beets act as membranes through which the sugar readily passes.

FIG. 11. THE CONTROL ROOM—THE "BRAIN CENTER" OF MODERN SUGAR REFINING OPERATIONS

Calcium hydroxide is added to the juice obtained from the diffusion battery, and carbon dioxide is introduced until virtually all the lime is precipitated in the form of calcium carbonate. The treatment effects both chemical and mechanical purification of the juice. Filtration follows, and the juice is treated again with carbon dioxide to complete the removal of the lime. After a second filtration, the juice is treated with sulfur dioxide, filtered a third time and then turned into the evaporators.

Evaporators consist of a number of large boiling vessels which are heated by exhaust steam. Each cell of the evaporator has a higher vacuum than one preceding, so that the juice boils at progressively lower temperatures. Here the juice is concentrated to a liquid containing 60 to 70 per cent solids.

After another filtration, the juice is boiled in vacuum pans until crystals form. In the vacuum pan the sugar boiler can regulate the size and uniformity of the crystals in the final sugar.

The material discharged from the vacuum pan consists of crystals of sugar suspended in a syrup. The syrup is removed by centrifuging, and the refined, granulated sugar is washed and dried, screened for size, and packed.

The syrup, thrown off in the centrifuge, is recycled for further recovery of sugar. The liquid product of the third centrifuging is usually subjected to the Steffens process, in which lime is added to precipitate a crop of sugar as calcium sucrate. This filtrate is also a source of monosodium glutamate. The sugar is liberated by carbon dioxide, and the juice returned to the process.

One manufacturer in the United States treats molasses from the Steffens process with barium hydroxide to recover additional sugar.

By-Products of the Sugar Industry

Commercially important by-products of the sugar industry are chiefly blackstrap molasses, bagasse, beet pulp and beet tops.

Blackstrap molasses, common to both branches of the industry, was once used extensively in the distillation of alcohol and solvents but it now finds primary outlets in cattle feeding. Limited quantities are also used in the production of yeast and citric acid.

Bagasse consists of the fiber and pith of the cane stalk which remain after the sugar-bearing juices have been expressed. Traditionally it has been used as fuel in raw sugar mills, and most of it is still disposed of in that way. However, in many parts of the world an increasing volume of bagasse is going into the production of paper and wallboard. Pentosans in bagasse may be converted into furfural, which has various uses in the chemical industry.

Beet pulp is a carbohydrate material used the world over to feed farm animals, principally cattle and sheep. Most pulp produced in the United States is treated with molasses and dried, although some "wet pulp" is fed in the areas of production. The pulp may be pressed into tablets or pellets, which are popular in range feeding during the winter months. Beet pulp is also a potential source of commercial pectin.

Beet tops consist of the leaves and crowns of the beets, which are removed during the harvest. Beet tops, like beet pulp, find their principal value in cattle feeding. Ensiling of beet tops is common practice in the Western States.

TYPES OF SUGARS AND THEIR USES

Sugar, by definition, is "a sweet crystallizable substance, colorless or white when pure, occurring in many fruit plant juices, and forming an important article of food. . . . The chief sources of sugar are sugar cane and sugar beets, the completely refined products of which are identical and form the granulated, loaf sugar, etc., of commerce."

By common usage as well as definition, sugar means sucrose (beet or cane sugar). The word "sugars," however, can refer in the chemical sense to the family of carbohydrates known as the saccharides, any member of which is properly called "a sugar" but not simply *sugar*. Chemists recognize dozens of sugars and the most familiar of them usually bear a prefix to identify their source, as *milk* sugar (lactose) *corn* sugar (dextrose) and *malt* sugar (maltose). Maple sugar is largely sucrose, but it is distinguished by a flavor that develops during processing of the sap.

Refined sugar and liquid sugar are manufactured in a number of types and grades, each having a particular use in the food processing industries. Their descriptive names ("fine," "standard," "berry," "sanding," etc.) are not uniformly applied by sugar companies but, for practical purposes, all refined sugars fall within the following broad categories:

Granulated Sugars

Ultra-Fine.—This grade is especially suited for cake work in the bakery and in dry mixes, such as dessert powders, and cake mixes, and for coating confectionery pan goods.

Very Fine.—This product is ideal for dry mixing with other finely divided materials in the production of cake mixes, pudding preparations, gelatin dessert powders and the like.

Fine.—This is "regular" granulated sugar, used for all-purpose, general food and beverage manufacture. It is the type of sugar usually served at the table.

Medium Coarse.—This grade is generally employed in the production of crystallizing syrups in confectionery and in fondant-making where an unusually white product is required. It is well adapted to the manufacture of cordials. Medium coarse is a "strong" sugar which resists color changes and inversion in high-temperature cooks.

Coarse.—This grade is sometimes preferred for the purposes to which a medium-coarse grain sugar is put.

Special Sugars.—These products are carefully tested to satisfy critical requirements.

Microbiological standards for sugar have been established by the National Canners Association and the American Bottlers of Carbonated

Beverages to meet the needs of those industries. The standards are summarized in Tables 13, 14, and 15.

Powdered Sugars

Ultra fine (Confectioners' 10X type) is recommended for smoothest-textured frostings and icings, and uncooked fondants.

TABLE 13

NATIONAL CANNERS ASSOCIATION'S BACTERIAL STANDARDS FOR SUGAR[1]

Total Thermophilic Spore Counts.—For the five samples examined, there shall be a maximum of not more than 150 spores and an average of not more than 125 spores per 10 gm. of sugar.
Flat Sour Spores.—For five samples examined, there shall be a maximum of not more than 75 spores and an average of not more than 50 spores per 10 gm. of sugar.
Thermophilic Anaerobic Spores.—These shall be present in not more than three (60%) of the five samples and in any one sample to the extent of not more than four (65%) of six tubes inoculated by the standard procedure.
Sulfide Spoilage Spores.—These shall be present in not more than two (40%) of the five samples and in any one sample to the extent of not more than five spores per 10 gm. This would be equivalent to two colonies in the six inoculated tubes.

[1] Source: National Canners Association Bulletin, November, 1958.

TABLE 14

BOTTLERS STANDARDS FOR DRY, GRANULATED SUGAR

The Tentative Standards which follow apply to dry granulated sugar only, and are not applicable to liquid sugars. Furthermore, these standards apply to sugar as produced, immediately prior to packing.
(1) **Containers.**—For protection of the products, "Bottlers'" sugar shall not be packed in cotton or fabric bags but shall be packed in multiwall paper bags or equivalent sanitary packages or bulk containers.
(2) **Container Identification.**—Each container shall be marked or coded to make it possible for the sugar producer to identify the place of production and date of packing.
(3) **Designation of Type.**—Each container shall be marked "Bottlers'."
(4) **Ash.**—The ash content of "Bottlers'" sugar shall not be more than 0.015%.
(5) **Color.**—The solution color of "Bottlers'" sugar shall not be more than 35 reference basis units.
(6) **Sediment.**—The sediment content of "Bottlers'" sugar shall not be more than shown on prepared sediment disk available upon request from American Bottlers of Carbonated Beverages, 1128 Sixteenth Street, Northwest, Washington, D. C.
(7) **Taste and Odor.**—"Bottlers'" sugar shall have no obviously objectionable taste or odor in either dry form or in a 10% sugar solution prepared with tasteless, odorless water.
(8) **Bacteriological.**—"Bottlers'" sugar shall not contain more than:

        200 Mesophilic bacteria   per 10 gm.
          10 yeast   per 10 gm.
          10 mold   per 10 gm.

(9) **Sampling.**—"Bottlers'" sugar shall be adequately sampled by the producer immediately prior to packing to assure compliance with these standards.
Turbidity and floc-producing substances are two other aspects of quality which are of extreme importance to the bottling industry.
Universally-accepted methods of testing for these factors have not yet been developed. For that reason the foregoing standards do not cover turbidity and floc-producing substances. However, as soon as accepted test methods and tolerances have been established they will be added to this standard. Meanwhile, it is imperative that "Bottlers" sugar be nearly free of turbidity and floc-producing substances.

TABLE 15

BOTTLERS STANDARDS FOR LIQUID SUGAR (SUGAR SYRUP)

(1) **Shipping Unit.**—The product shall be shipped in clean sanitary shipping units. The shipping unit shall be so constructed as to eliminate any possibility of adding any impurity to the liquid sugar.

(2) **Identification.**—The product shipped shall be identified on the bill of lading as "Bottlers Liquid Sugar," and shall specify whether it is sucrose type or 50% invert type.

(3) **Color.**—The color of Bottlers Liquid Sugar shall not be more than 35 reference basis units at the manufacturer's storage tank at the point of manufacture.

(4) **Sediment.**—The sediment content of Bottlers Liquid Sugar shall not be more than shown on a prepared sediment disk (approximately 2 p.p.m.) available upon request from American Bottlers of Carbonated Beverages.

(5) **Taste and Odor.**—Bottlers Liquid Sugar shall have no objectionable taste or odor in an undiluted form or in a 10% solution acidified to pH 2.5 with USP phosphoric acid.

(6) **Microbiological.**—

(a) **Yeast:** (1) Last 20 samples average 10 organisms or less per 10 gm. D.S.E.—dry sugar equivalent.

(2) Ninety-five per cent of last 20 counts show 18 organisms or less per 10 gm. D.S.E.

(3) Of the last 20 samples, only one sample showing a count of more than 18 yeast per 10 gm. D.S.E. may be excluded in calculating the running average, provided counts of other samples tested the same day are within the tolerances as stated 6, A-1 and 6, A-2.

(b) **Mesophilic bacteria:** (1) Last 20 samples average 100 organisms or less per 10 gm. D.S.E.

(2) Ninety-five per cent of last 20 counts show 200 organisms or less per 10 gm. D.S.E.

(3) Of the last 20 samples, only one sample showing a count of more than 200 bacteria per 10 gm., D.S.E., may be excluded in calculating the running average provided counts of other samples tested the same day are within the tolerances as stated in 6, B-1 and 6, B-2.

(c) **Mold:** (1) Last 20 samples average 10 organisms or less per 10 gm. D.S.E.—dry sugar equivalent.

(2) Ninety-five per cent of last 20 counts show 18 organisms or less per 10 gm D.S.E.

(3) Of the last 20 samples, only one sample showing a count of more than 18 mold per 10 gm D.S.E., may be excluded in calculating the running average, provided counts of other samples tested the same day are within the tolerances as stated in 6, C-1 and 6, C-2.

Microbiological Procedures.—All microbiological testing to be done according to the procedures of the Sugar-Bottling Industries Committee. Alternate procedures which have been shown to give equivalent reliability shall be permitted.

Microbiological Sampling.—Adequate tests on each day's shipments shall be made. Samples should be representative of the sugar as delivered to the bottler's plant or truck.

(7) **Floc Evaluation of Liquid Beet Sugars.**—Liquid beet sugar shall be floc tested by the manufacturer, whose responsibility it shall be to determine the suitability of such sugar for use in carbonated beverages. The "Spreckels Qualitative Floc Test" shall be used for determining the presence of these impurities.

Very fine (Confectioners' 6X type) is recommended for cream fillings in biscuit work, and for sprinkling on buns, pies and pastries. It is also suitable for uncooked fondants, frostings and icings. It mixes well with melted fats to make certain confectioners' coatings.

Fine (Confectioners' 4X type) is used in the manufacture of lozenges and chewing gum, and in packing such confections as marshmallows and

Turkish paste. Extensively employed in chocolate manufacture, it is also used for a finish coating of pan goods where a smooth surface is needed.

Medium and Coarse sugars are generally applicable to dusting mixtures where other powdered sugars are too fine, and the product is prone to accumulate surface moisture. It is used for dusting doughnuts and crullers.

Confectioners' sugars are usually packed with three per cent of corn starch to prevent caking.

Brown Sugars

Brown, or "soft," sugar is a mass of fine crystals covered with a film of highly refined, dark-colored, cane molasses flavored syrup. The syrup imparts to brown sugars the flavor and color for which they are primarily valued. Total sugar content ranges from 90 to 95 per cent, and moisture from about 2 to 4 per cent.

Light Yellow and Light Brown.—The lighter types of brown sugar are used in products in which mild flavor and light color are desirable. Examples are baked goods (including icings and glazes for doughnuts and buns) butterscotch and other candies, condiments, and glazes for ham.

Dark Brown.—The cane molasses flavor of these sugars makes them highly desirable for gingerbread, mince meat, plum pudding, baked beans and other dark-colored and full-flavored foods.

Invert Sugar

When a solution of sugar is heated in the presence of an acid (or treated with an enzyme, or passed over an acid ion exchange bed) the sugar combines chemically with 5.26 per cent of its own weight of water and breaks up into approximately equal weights of two sugars of simpler chemical structure. These two sugars are D-glucose, identical chemically with commercial dextrose, and D-fructose, a naturally occurring sugar sometimes called fruit sugar, or levulose. This mixture of dextrose and levulose is invert sugar, and the conversion of sugar to invert sugar is called inversion. In the process, there is a gain of 5.26 lbs. of solids for every 100 lbs. of sugar.

Process of Inversion

$$C_{12}H_{22}O_{11} + H_2O \rightarrow C_6H_{12}O_6 + C_6H_{12}O_6$$

$$\text{Sugar} + \text{Water} \rightarrow \text{Dextrose} + \text{Levulose}$$

$$\text{(100 lbs.)} \quad \text{(5.26 lbs.)} \quad \text{(52.63 lbs.)} \quad \text{(52.63 lbs.)}$$

Invert sugar is at least as sweet as sugar itself, inasmuch as the levulose fraction exceeds the sweetness of sugar to a greater degree than the dextrose fraction is less sweet. Mixtures of invert sugar and sugar have a greater solubility than sugar alone. The maximum is reached when the proportion of invert sugar and sugar is approximately one-to-one. Invert sugar has moisture-retention properties which make it useful for prolonging the shelf life of many foods in which it is an ingredient. In many food manufacturing operations, some invert sugar is formed spontaneously during processing.

Invert sugar syrup of commerce is substantially colorless or, as it is sometimes produced, a partially crystallized product of plastic consistency.

Liquid Sugars

Liquid sugars (sugar syrups) are clear, substantially colorless solutions (saturated at room temperatures) containing sugar in a highly purified form. The sugar may be partially or completely inverted. Liquid sugars are widely used in the food manufacturing industry since they permit mechanized handling when proper equipment is installed.

Water-White (Uninverted).—This is a brilliantly clear sugar syrup that is generally applicable, by proper balancing of formulas, wherever sugar and water are ingredients of a manufactured product. It is used in the following and many other products: canned foods, confectionery, dairy products, beverages, baked goods, flavored syrups, frozen fruits, pickles and ice cream.

Light Straw (Uninverted).—Another clear sugar syrup, available in some markets, which may be used in place of the water-white type wherever a small amount of color and slightly higher percentage of nonsugars do not affect the final product.

Invert.—The physical properties of liquid invert sugars make them desirable in many food products. Invert sugar is hygroscopic (that is, it attracts and retains water), a property which prolongs the freshness of baked goods and confections, and it retards the crystallization of sugar.

Invert sugar syrups are used in making beverages, preserves, baked goods, confectionery, glacé and conserved fruits, icings and syrups. They are also used in the manufacture of adhesives, and liquid pharmaceuticals. In the paper industry, invert sugar syrups are sometimes employed as plasticizers.

Brown.—Liquid brown sugars are ingredients of baked goods, table syrups, licorice, cough drops, confectionery and other items where their color and flavor impart desirable characteristics.

Refiners' Syrups and Edible Molasses

Refiners' Syrups.—Refiners' syrups are specially processed syrups having a characteristic cane-molasses flavor and ranging in color from light to very dark. They contain from 70 to 80 per cent solids and their total sugar content (sugar plus invert sugar) ranges from 50 to 75 per cent. The better grades of refiners' syrups are often used in the food processing industries, where their flavor and color are advantageous.

Edible Molasses.—In a broad sense, molasses means the concentrated juices extracted from sugar-bearing plants. It is thus a group of products which contain sugar as well as many of the substances that occur naturally in the plants. The oldest method of making molasses consists in boiling cane juice until a large part of the water is evaporated. This is open-kettle molasses, produced largely in the West Indies, and since sulfur dioxide is not used in its preparation it is sometimes called unsulfured molasses.

By other methods, part or most of the crystallizable sugar is recovered from the concentrated cane juice. Resulting products are known as centrifugal molasses, and the better grades are used in table syrups.

Molasses is used in gingerbread, spice and fruit cakes, rye and whole-wheat bread, cookies, baked beans and certain candies. It imparts cane-molasses flavor and color to these products, and provides nutritional values in the form of sugar and certain minerals, chiefly iron. Edible molasses is often used in blends of table syrups.

Fig. 12. Hopper-Type Trucks Used for Delivery of Bulk Granulated Sugar

Liquid and Bulk Granulated Sugars

Food processors whose operations use substantial quantities of sugar find distinct advantages in liquid sugars and in refined granulated dry sugar shipped in bulk. These advantages include, among others:

(1) **Lower Cost.**—Liquid sugars and granulated sugar in bulk are generally priced below bagged sugar. The lower prices reflect savings effected by cane refiners and beet processors through the elimination of conventional bags, and in lower handling costs in warehouses and at loading points.

(2) **Reduced Handling Costs.**—Labor charges involved in unloading and stacking bagged sugar are eliminated in food plants equipped to use bulk granulated or liquid sugars. Sugar is unloaded at the plant into storage bins or tanks and distributed to the point of use by a variety of mechanical means.

(3) **Elimination of Sugar Losses.**—Losses are almost inevitable when sugar is emptied from the conventional bag. Some is spilled, some clings to the bag itself. These losses are avoided in bulk handling.

Fig. 13. A Pneumatic-Lift System Delivers Bulk Dry Sugar to a Storage Bin Located at the Top of a Confectionery Plant

(4) **Improved Sanitation.**—Contamination hazards that are common in handling bagged sugar may be greatly reduced, or eliminated, in sealed systems for bulk granulated and liquid sugars.

(5) **Savings in Space.**—Storage tanks or bins can often be placed outside the plant, or in locations where bagged sugar cannot be stored.

Systems for handling bulk granulated or liquid sugars are usually justified if in-plant savings will pay for the cost of the necessary installation within five years. The decision whether liquid or bulk handling systems should be selected must be based on the circumstances peculiar to each food processing plant.

Liquid Sugar

Liquid sugar is basically a syrup—a saturated solution (at room temperature) of sugar in water. Because of trade preferences, densities of the syrups vary in different parts of the country but in the main they range from 66.5 to 77 per cent dissolved solids.

Approximate analyses are shown below:

	Uninverted Water-White, %	Uninverted Light-Straw Yellow, %	Partially Inverted, %	Completely Inverted, %
Total solids (wet basis)	66.5 to 68	66.5 to 68	73 to 77	70 to 76
Approximate ratios (dry basis)	...	...	...	...
Sugar	100	100	60	5
Invert Sugar	...	...	40	95

Many food processes in which sugar is dissolved are a potential market for liquid sugar. This includes specialty syrups, canned and frozen fruits, ice cream and dairy products, carbonated beverages, confectionery, baked goods, jams, jellies, and preserves. However, the operation should be large enough to warrant the expense of installing the necessary equipment. This means, ordinarily, that a food processor whose plant is some distance removed from the point at which liquid sugar is produced should have annual minimum requirements equivalent to 6,000 or 7,000 one-hundred-pound bags of granulated sugar. For those processors within tank-truck delivery range, the minimum is lower—about 3,000 bags a year.

Railroad tank cars for liquid sugar range in capacity from 6,000 to 10,000 gal., tank trucks from 1,500 to 4,000 gal. Tanks are meticulously cleaned before loading and are sealed after loading so that contamination during shipment is avoided.

Equipment and Handling.—Liquid sugar systems, like those for handling bulk granulated sugar, conform to well-established engineering principles, but variations in detail are almost without limit. Each system is designed to fit the particular processes and products involved, and is adapted to conditions imposed by the processing plant itself. Most systems are operated by using pumps, and a few by gravity.

Standard equipment required for proper handling of liquid sugar at the point of use includes storage tanks (usually not less than two), sterilizing lamps, ventilating system with filters, pumps, strainers, valves and meters, and receiving and distribution lines. The over-riding consideration in any installation is that the system be so designed and constructed that problems of sanitation are reduced to a minimum. Washing, flushing and draining must be made simple and effective.

Storage tanks are customarily fabricated of sheet steel with butt-welded joints, ground smooth on the inside and lined with a protective coating.

Tops and bottoms of vertical tanks are often dished. The protective lining may be painted on the interior surface, or baked on it. Painted linings, if properly applied, are serviceable for indefinite periods, and the baked linings can be expected to last for the life of the tank.

Usually two tanks are installed, each having a capacity greater than the normal unit of delivery. The advantage of this arrangement is that tanks may be used alternately. While one is being emptied of sugar, the other is available for refilling. Cleaning can be accomplished without shutting down the system. Moreover, reserve storage facilities are insurance against delayed delivery.

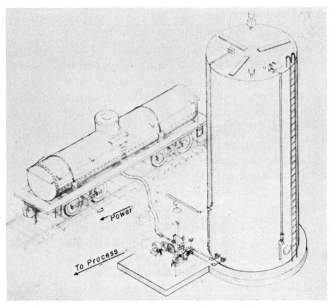

Fig 14. Typical Liquid Sugar Storage Installation

25,000 Gal. capacity liquid sugar storage tank.

Storage tanks may be installed at any location, either inside or outside the plant, but care must be taken to protect them against extreme heat or cold.

Even under favorable conditions, when liquid sugar is stored for any length of time, moisture from condensation is likely to collect on interior tank surfaces that are exposed to air. If condensation is excessive, it runs down the sides of the tank and dilutes the liquid sugar at its surface, thereby creating an environment favorable for the growth of yeasts and molds. To counteract such possibilities, a small fan may be installed to send filtered air into the tank and draw off moisture-laden atmosphere. Ultraviolet lamps placed in the top of the tank help to sterilize both the air and the surface of the liquid. Outlet and inlet connections, meters and other accessories should be so located and designed that they drain completely.

Pumps, valves, and delivery lines must be easy to clean and easy to drain when flushed. Pumps should preferably be constructed of stainless steel or bronze, or at least trimmed with it. Black iron is not recommended for pipe lines. A minimum requirement is hot-dipped galvanized iron of good quality.

Since cleanliness is essential, producers of liquid sugar have worked out detailed procedures of sanitation, which they supply to their customers. Nevertheless, some general observations apply.

In seasonal industries, such as canning, the sugar system should be thoroughly cleaned and sterilized before operations begin. Cleaning means, among other things, a careful inspection of the lining of the storage tanks to make certain that it is intact. The ultraviolet lamps need to be checked for effectiveness, and replaced if necessary. A solution containing not less than 100 p.p.m. of residual chlorine should be used to flush the system after it has been thoroughly washed with a detergent in hot water. Not less than a day before the arrival of the first shipment of liquid sugar the chlorine solution should be completely drained, and the ultraviolet lamps put into operation. At the end of the season, much the same practices are recommended: the storage tank and distribution lines are preferably washed with a detergent in hot water and flushed with a chlorine solution, then drained. Where circumstances permit, the tanks are dried with hot air and sealed.

In food processing plants in which operations are not seasonal, it is recommended that the system be cleaned and flushed at least once a year, and preferably twice, in line with practices already described. Ultraviolet lamps, too, should be inspected at least twice.

From what has been said, it is not to be assumed that liquid sugar is difficult to handle. A successful operation requires only a sensible approach to design and construction and attention to sanitary practices.

Bulk Granulated Sugar

The advantages of bulk dry sugar systems are most apparent in the preparation of dry food products which must be free-flowing, or in which addition of moisture must be restricted. Examples are powdered desserts, granular bases for beverages, prepared cake mixes, chocolate coatings, certain types of confectionery and baked goods, and sweetened fruit juices.

Each bulk dry sugar system must be tailored to the building in which it is installed, and to the character of the operation. For these reasons it is pointless to discuss, except in general terms, the methods by which dry bulk sugar may be handled in food processing plants.

Three types of equipment are currently in use to deliver bulk sugar from the manufacturer to the user's plant: (*a*) bin and hopper trucks; (*b*) hopper-type or air-slide railroad cars; and (*c*) portable-unit containers.

Bin and Hopper Trucks.—When the food processor's plant is not too distant from the refinery, sugar is ordinarily delivered in trailer-type bin or hopper trucks. The truck bodies are specially constructed of aluminum, or stainless or protective-coated steel, and capable of being sealed. Some are insulated. These trucks are usually discharged by elevating one end of the body with hydraulic lifts, or they may be emptied by gravity through discharge ports at the bottom of the hoppers. Pneumatic systems may also be used if the trucks are constructed with that purpose in view. Pressurized, closed-circuit systems of discharging, which are relatively recent developments, tend to minimize the degradation in the size of sugar crystals that takes place to some degree through attrition.

Hopper-Type Railroad Cars.—In instances in which the food processor's plant is too distant for economical truck service, sugar delivery may be made by hopper-type railroad cars of 80,000 to 140,000 lbs. capacity. The rail cars are specially designed for dry refined bulk sugar, and can be sealed to exclude dirt and dust and prevent leakage. Some are insulated. The cars may be lined with plywood or tempered particle-board. When not so lined, the inner surfaces of cars are treated with nontoxic protective coatings.

Cars of this type are equipped with sloping ends and may be divided to form two or three hoppers to facilitate unloading. Customarily the load is emptied by gravity through outlets at the bottom of the car, although pneumatically-aided systems may sometimes be used.

Portable-Container Units.—Food processing plants that cannot use bulk deliveries in hopper trucks or rail cars, may take sugar in sealed portable bins that are carried on conventional flat-bed trailer trucks or rail cars designed and built for the purpose. The bins are handled by fork-lift equipment.

In-Plant Handling.—The design of existing plant and equipment, and the food processor's preferences, are the determining factors in in-plant handling of bulk dry sugar. Methods used and proved in commercial practice include screw (scroll) conveyors, belt conveyors, belt or chain bucket elevators, vibrating or oscillating conveyors, drag-chain and drag-flight conveyors, mass-or-bulk flow conveyors and elevators, traveling lorries or portable bins, and pneumatic or vacuum systems. The most common methods are scroll and belt conveyors, and bucket elevators. Pneumatic systems are gaining in popularity.

Because so many types of equipment are available, in-plant handling systems take a variety of forms. All are satisfactory. However, when sugar must be conveyed some distance, or there is a multiplicity of use-points, mechanical handling tends to become more expensive than pneumatic systems.

Pneumatic systems may be either suction or pressure types, or a combination known as "push-pull." In some air systems, attrition will reduce the size of the sugar crystals in varying degrees and form small amounts of sugar dust which, if objectionable in the process, must be removed by separators and collectors. Formation of sugar dust, as well as the reduction in the size of crystals are consequences of the design of the equipment. Conveyor lines of the best air systems have wide-radius bends—and as few of them as possible.

Where there are many use-points, portable bins merit consideration. Bins are manufactured in a number of sizes, and capacities range from 2,400 to 5,400 lbs. of sugar. They are easily moved by fork-lift trucks. Some are discharged by tilting. In addition, the bins are compact storage units which reduce labor costs and prevent loss of sugar. On the other hand, since not all bins can be collapsed or nested, there is a practical limit to the distance they can be shipped. This is so because the expense of returning the bins to the shipper must be weighed against the saving in costs.

Permanent storage bins for bulk sugar should take into account the method of delivery (i.e., truck or rail car), the quantity needed at periods of peak usage, and optimum reserve supplies. Obviously, the shape and size of the bins are governed by the area in which they are constructed. Headroom may be a factor of importance. Where headroom is low, bins are usually rectangular, and equipped with bottoms of inverted pyramids. A distributing screw conveyor at the top of the bin and a discharge scroll at the opening of the pyramids fill and empty the bins satisfactorily. Where more headroom is available, the bins may be rectangular or circular, and fitted with eccentric or cone-shaped bottoms to facilitate the discharge of sugar. Bottoms should slope not less than 50° from the horizontal to insure complete emptying.

Whether bins are rectangular or circular, they are generally constructed of protectively coated sheet steel, aluminum or stainless steel. Satisfactory bins have also been constructed of steel or cement and lined with maple or tempered particle board. Whether the bins are insulated or housed depends on surrounding atmospheric conditions, or conditions within the plant. But regardless of the system used, bins should be designed for easy entry for inspection and cleaning. Tight-fitting sealed tops are essential to eliminate contamination by dust and dirt, and to prevent excessive exposure of the sugar to adverse atmospheric conditions.

Devices are available that convert granulated sugar into liquid sugar while a shipment is being unloaded from truck or railroad car. The basic element in one case is a light-weight metal converter that fastens to the outlet hopper of the delivery vehicle. Sugar flows by gravity into the converter, dissolves in a stream of water, and is pumped into the storage tank. Before unloading, water is drawn into the storage tank in the amount needed to produce the desired density of liquid sugar. (Example: if the load is 100,000 lbs. of granulated sugar, then 50,376 lbs. of water, or 6,050 gal. of water at room temperature, is measured into the tank to produce liquid sugar of 66.5° Brix.) Water is pumped from the storage tank to the converter, where it picks up sugar, and then back to the tank. The cycle is repeated until unloading is completed.

Storage.—Precautions necessary to the proper storage of sugar in permanent bins are few but important. The best method for preventing caking is to keep sugar in motion and, wherever possible, delivery schedules should be so arranged that the sugar is not stored without movement for more than one or two weeks. If longer storage periods are necessary, the sugar should be turned over at intervals. Insulation of storage bins and conveying equipment located outside a food plant is usually well worth while even though it is not always essential.

Ideal storage conditions for bulk granulated sugar are the same as those for bagged sugar. They include temperatures not in excess of 100°F., and a relative humidity of not more than 60 per cent. It is desirable to maintain temperature and humidity at uniform levels.

SUGAR IN STANDARDIZED FOOD PRODUCTS

It has already been mentioned that there are no generally applicable definitions and standards for the many types of sugar, except those for the canning and the carbonated beverage industries (Tables 13, 14 and 15, p. 40 and 41). The United States Food and Drug Administration has never attempted to establish standards for sugar, and in most cases the various forms of sugar are "defined" in terms of themselves. The Federal Standards for fruit butters, jellies and preserves (presented below) are typical.

For the purposes of this section: . . . (2) The term "sugar" means refined sugar (sucrose); (3) The term "invert sugar syrup" means a syrup made by inverting or partly inverting sugar or partly refined sugar; its ash content is not more than 0.3 per cent of its solids content, but if it is made from partly refined sugar, color and flavor other than sweetness are removed; (4) The term "invert brown sugar syrup" means a syrup made by inverting or partly inverting brown sugar.

The quantity of sugar that may be used in a food product for which a standard has been established by the Food and Drug Administration is often limited by the nonsugar ingredients that must be present. Thus, the fill-of-container provisions of the canned fruit standards clearly state how much fruit shall be placed in a can, which automatically restricts the amount of syrup that can be added. Moreover, the permitted ranges for the Brix reading of the syrups—slightly sweetened water, light syrup and heavy syrup—are stated specifically. Again, the total quantity of sugar in a product may be affected by the presence of sugar substitutes, as in canned fruits. There the permitted saccharine ingredient of the liquid packing media are stated as follows:

(1) Sugar.

(2) Any combination of sugar and dextrose in which the weight of the dextrose solids is not more than one-half the weight of the sugar solids.

(3) Any combination of sugar and corn syrup or glucose syrup in which the weight of the corn syrup or glucose syrup solids is not more than one-third of the weight of the sugar solids.

(4) Any combination of sugar, dextrose and corn syrup or glucose syrup in which twice the weight of the dextrose solids added to three times the weight of the corn syrup or glucose syrup solids is not more than the weight of the sugar solids.

Specifications (as distinguished from standards) for certain types of sugar have been issued by the Commissioner of the Federal Supply Service, General Services Administration, to be used by Federal agencies (chiefly the military) in their purchases of sugar. The pertinent portions of the specifications follow:

1   Classification

1.1   **Types.**—Beet or cane sugar covered by this specification shall be of the following types, as specified:

Type I. White, hard, refined   Type II. Brown, soft
    (a) Granulated   (a) Light
    (b) Powdered   (b) Medium
      (1) Coarse   (c) Dark
      (2) Confectioners
    (c) Tablet or cube

1.2   **Grade.**—Sugar shall be of the grade indicated herein.

3   Requirements

3.1   **Material.**—The product shall be pure and obtained only from sugar cane or sugar beets, except Type II, brown sugar, which shall be made from sugar cane. If Type II, brown sugar, is manufactured from Hawaiian raw sugar, it shall be so stated in the bid.

3.1.1 Type I (a), Granulated Sugar.—Type 1 (a) sugar shall be white and refined and shall contain not less than 99.5 per cent of sucrose, not more than 0.04 per cent of ash, and not more than 0.07 per cent of moisture. Not more than 4 per cent shall remain on a U.S. Standard No. 20 sieve and not more than 8 per cent shall pass through a U. S. Standard No. 100 sieve, when a 100-gm. sample is shaken for 5 min. in a mechanical shaker.

3.1.2 Type I (b) (1), Coarse Powdered Sugar.—Type I (b) (1) sugar shall be white and refined and shall contain not less than 99.5 per cent of sucrose, not more than 0.04 per cent of ash, and not more than 0.1 per cent of moisture. It shall pass through a U. S. Standard No. 40 sieve and not more than 20 per cent shall pass through a U. S. Standard No. 140 sieve when a 100-gm. sample is shaken for 5 min. in a mechanical shaker.

3.1.3 Type I (b) (2), Confectioner's Powdered Sugar.—Type I (b) (2) sugar shall be white and refined. The finished product shall contain not less than 96.5 per cent of sucrose, not more than 0.05 per cent of ash, not more than 0.8 per cent of moisture, and not less than 2.25 per cent nor more than 3.25 per cent of clean, edible starch, properly admixed, added to prevent caking. Not more than 2 per cent shall remain on a U. S. Standard No. 100 sieve and not less than 75 per cent shall pass through a U. S. Standard No. 200 sieve when brushed through with a soft brush.

3.1.4 Type I (c), Tablet or Cube Sugar.—Type I (c) sugar shall be white and refined and shall contain not less than 99.5 per cent of sucrose, not more than 0.04 per cent of ash, and not more than 0.3 per cent of moisture.

3.1.5 Type II (a), Light Brown Sugar.—Type II (a) sugar shall be of excellent flavor and uniform, light brown color. The product shall have a polarization of not less than 88° nor more than 94° sugar. It shall contain not more than 1.25 per cent of ash (except that light brown sugar made from Hawaiian raw sugar shall contain not more than 2.25 per cent ash) and shall contain not more than 4.25 per cent moisture. The color reflectance shall be not less than 50 nor more than 64 per cent.

3.1.6 Type II (b), Medium Brown Sugar.—Type II (b) sugar shall be of excellent flavor and medium brown color. The product shall have a polarization of not less than 84.5° nor more than 91° sugar, and shall contain not more than 2.0 per cent ash, except that medium brown sugar made from Hawaiian raw sugar shall contain not more than 3.25 ash. It shall contain not more than 4.50 per cent moisture. The color reflectance shall be not less than 38 nor more than 49 per cent.

3.1.7 Type II (c), Dark Brown Sugar.—Type II (c) sugar shall be of excellent flavor and dark brown color. The product shall have a polarization of not less than 82° nor more than 90° sugar. It shall contain not more than 2.5 per cent ash (except that dark brown sugar made from Hawaiian raw sugar shall contain not more than 3.5 per cent ash) and it shall contain not more than 4.50 per cent moisture. The color reflectance shall be not less than 18 nor more than 38 per cent.

3.2 Workmanship.—The product shall be manufactured under modern sanitary conditions and shall be free from any deleterious material or contamination from any source.

Table 16 shows solubility of sucrose in water at various temperatures, and solubility of various sugars in water at 68°F.

TABLE 16

SOLUBILITY OF SUCROSE IN WATER AT VARIOUS TEMPERATURES

Temperature, °F.	Parts Sugar per 100 Parts Solution	Sugar Dissolved by 100 Parts Water
32	64.18	179.2
50	65.58	190.5
68	67.09	203.9
86	68.70	219.5
104	70.42	238.1
122	72.25	260.4
194	80.61	415.7
212	82.97	487.2

SOLUBILITY OF VARIOUS SUGARS IN WATER AT 68 °F.

	Parts per 100 Parts Water
Sucrose	204
Levulose	375
Dextrose hydrate	107
Maltose hydrate	83
Lactose hydrate	20

CONSUMER PREFERENCE TESTS

In recent years, Sugar Research Foundation has conducted extensive studies of the influence of sugar on the quality and flavor of commercially prepared foods. Products subjected to analyses and consumer preference tests have included canned and frozen fruits and vegetables, ice cream, wine, pickles, olives and other nonsweet foods. In most instances consumers preferred foods containing higher levels of sugar than those found in average commercial packs, not because of added sweetness but because of an improvement in the characteristic flavor of the product.

Canned Fruits

Studies of the flavor of canned fruits were conducted over a period of six years in the Department of Food Science and Technology at the University of California (Davis). At the outset of the studies, experienced tasters sampled solutions of distilled water and varying amounts of sugar, food acids and imitation fruit flavors. The addition of more flavor or more acid was easily discernible. However, when more sugar was added, most judges believed that more flavor had been used as well as more sugar. Sweeter *samples* were judged more aromatic (Valdés *et al.* 1956).

The panel tasting of nectars was later extended to consumer tests of canned fruit. At Davis, Calif., 200 families tested five cans each of apricots packed in sugar syrups ranging from "very light" to "extra heavy." The fruit was eaten as a dessert at regular meal, and participants indicated their degree of "like" or "dislike" for each can separately. Low-acid apricots were preferred with in-going syrup of 40° Brix, whereas high-acid fruit had maximum flavor intensity at 50°. Most frequent reason given for liking the sweeter apricots was "good flavor" rather than sweetness (Valdés and Roessler 1956).

In still another fruit, red sour cherries, research has demonstrated that consumer acceptance as well as the color, flavor and firmness of the fruit, are all improved by relatively heavy sugar syrups. Moreover, the sugar-packed cherries have greater "versatility" than cherries packed in water because they can be used in more ways (Weckel *et al.* 1959).

As a part of the studies at the University of Wisconsin, Montmorency cherries were packed under commercial conditions with in-going syrups of 30°, 40°, 50°, 60° and 70° Brix, and their physical properties measured. One can packed at each sugar level was distributed to each of 200 families selected at random in Madison, Wis. Housewives were instructed to chill the fruit, and to serve it as a dessert at a regular meal. All members of the families six years of age and older were asked to indicate their preferences on separate cards.

Preferences varied among age groups, but the number of persons preferring sweetness levels of 50° and 60° and 70° Brix greatly exceeded those preferring the two lower levels. Color values, measured as redness, reached a peak at 50° Brix.

From the work, the experimenter reached the following conclusions, among others:

(*a*) the best level of sugar for red sour cherries to be processed for dessert lies between 50 and 60 per cent input syrup; (*b*) this level is equivalent to a soluble solids to acid ratio of 35.42; (*c*) at this level the redness of the cherries is at its maximum . . .; the relatively high degree of preference obtained for these cherries at all levels of sugar suggests that cherries packed in sugar syrup would meet considerable acceptance as dessert fruit."

The results of the work on canned fruits should have more than the passing interest of commercial packers. In the last decade (1950–1960) per capita consumption of canned fruits has remained at a fairly constant level, even though home canning decreased and personal income increased. At the same time, the consumption of other dessert foods, including ice cream and frozen fruits, has taken a greater dollar share of the market. Canned fruit that more nearly meets the consumers' preference in flavor can reasonably be expected to increase consumption.

Canned Vegetables

Canned vegetables, like canned fruits, are improved by the use of sugar in greater amounts than is customary in the canning trade. Here, again, the preference was ascribed to better flavor rather than to a higher level of sweetness.

Studies of the possibilities of improving the appearance and flavor of canned whole kernel corn were begun by Weckel at Wisconsin in 1957 (Weckel *et al.* 1960). Corn of the Sugar King variety was packed on a commercial line with five levels of sugar in the input brine: 3.06, 4.53, 5.95, 7.33 and 8.67 per cent. In all packs, salt remained constant at 22.5 lbs. to 150 gal. of brine. Paired samples of the corn (one pair for each of the possible combinations of the five sugar levels) were distributed to each of 260 families in Madison, Wis.

Increased preference for the flavor of corn was observed as the sugar content of the brine was increased. Distribution of the preference was:

Sugar content of brine, %	3.06	4.53	5.95	7.33	8.67
		Madison Panel			
No. of panelists preferring	708	1074	1200	1595	1498
% of panelists preferring	11.6	17.7	19.8	26.2	24.7
		Midwestern Panel			
No. of panelists preferring	697	813	1095	1203	1361
% of panelists preferring	13.5	15.7	21.2	23.3	26.3

From these tests Weckel concluded: "The results of this work demonstrate that the acceptability of canned whole kernel corn can be improved by packing with brine containing 7.30 to 8.7 per cent sugar, which is above the average range of 4.5 to 5.9 per cent used commercially."

From whole kernel corn, Weckel and his co-workers at Wisconsin turned to canned peas, in which canners of that state ordinarily use from 21 to 75 lbs. of sugar for every 150 gal. of brine (Weckel *et al.* 1961).

At Madison, Wis., a panel of 591 families passed judgment on the flavor and appearance of the products. The second panel, the Kroger Food Foundation Panel, consisted of 1,000 families in 22 states.

The taste preference for the high-level packs is shown in the following table:

Sample	Sugar, Lbs.	Salt, Lbs.	Kroger Panel	Madison Panel	Total
1	40	16	518	602	1,120
2	60	16	907	890	1,797
3	80	16	1,133	1,190	2,323
4	100	16	1,288	1,301	2,589
5	120	16	1,454	1,368	2,822

Consumer preference for *appearance* also came at sugar levels higher than in the average commercial pack.

Physical and chemical measurements of the peas gave these data: (1) soluble solids and total solids increased as the sugar was increased; (2) storage and variations in sugar levels did not affect alcohol insoluble solids; and (3) drained weight increased as the level of sugar was increased.

Canned tomatoes present a special problem. Most consumers like an acid "bite" in whole canned tomatoes, and a relatively high degree of acidity is essential in the product to discourage the growth of organisms that are responsible for spoilage. With the proper levels of acid, canners are able to heat and sterilize tomatoes in little more than half an hour. With low acid levels, the cooking period must be lengthened two or three times, and in the process the tomatoes lose in color, flavor, texture and shape, as well as in ascorbic acid content. The combination of low acidity and prolonged cooking adversely affects all major factors of quality.

Year by year the tomato crops of California, Colorado and some other states are becoming less acid. Loss of natural acidity affects flavor but, even more important, with low acidity there may be an increased incidence of spoilage and even the possibility of a public health problem.

Commercial canners, worried by the increasing dangers of spoilage, took their problem to the Department of Food Science and Technology at the University of California. There, small amounts of citric acid were put into experimental tomato packs to bring the total acidity to a desirable level. The products were safe, but too sour for the average palate. Then small amounts of sugar, as well as acid, were added to another pack and the results were entirely different.

"Additions of acid and sugar resulted in canned tomatoes that were liked as well as, and frequently better than, the control (pack which had no added sugar or acid). It is evident from these data that careful consideration must be given to the proper balance between saltiness, sourness and sweetness in this product in order to achieve reduced sterilization time and a palatable flavor blend" (Leonard *et al*. 1960).

Ice Cream

Three flavors of ice cream—vanilla, strawberry and chocolate—have been subjected to consumer preference tests. In strawberry and chocolate products, participants in the tests gave a clear preference for higher sugar levels. In vanilla, the preference was not so marked but a greater degree of sweetness was not objectionable.

Work on vanilla and strawberry ice cream was done by Nickerson of the Department of Food Science and Nutrition, University of California (Davis) and the consumer preference tests were conducted by the Department (Pangborn *et al*. 1957 and 1959).

In vanilla ice cream, the formula consisted of 12 per cent butterfat, 11 per cent nonfat milk solids, 0.3 per cent stabilizer. Sugar content varied by 2 per cent increments from 11 to 19 per cent. (Butterfat was held at

12 per cent because a panel was unable to distinguish between that level and 15 per cent, the standard for the industry.)

Participants in the taste tests liked samples containing 15, 17 and 19 per cent sugar equally well and had a significant preference for them over the 11 and 13 per cent levels. Males preferred a sweeter ice cream than females. Frequent users of ice cream preferred the sweeter samples.

In strawberry ice cream, the formula consisted of 12 per cent butterfat, 11 per cent nonfat milk solids, 0.3 per cent stabilizer. Sugar content varied by 2 per cent increments from 15 per cent to 21 per cent. Frozen berries, thawed and puréed, were added to give 15 per cent unsweetened berries in the flavored mix. The 19 per cent sugar level was most preferred, followed by 21 per cent. Younger people preferred sweeter ice cream than older people. Preferences for sweetness were similar for both male and females.

Answers indicated that consumers were willing to pay five cents a pint more for ice cream they prefer.

Work on chocolate ice cream was done at the University of Georgia by J. J. Sheuring, Professor of Dairying, and Eugene Finnegan, graduate assistant. Their consumer panel significantly preferred ice creams containing 17 and 19 per cent sugar to those containing 13 and 15 per cent. The preferences were ascribed not to increased sweetness but rather to a "richer," "creamier" and "more delectable chocolate flavor."

Four mixes were prepared. In all of them fat was held at 11 per cent, serum solids at 10 per cent, Dutch-natural blend cocoa at 4.5 per cent and emulsified stabilizer at 0.34 per cent. The sugar content was varied at 13, 15, 17 and 19 per cent.

Tabulation of the responses of homemakers showed that 32.8 per cent of the members of the panel preferred chocolate ice cream containing 19 per cent sugar, closely followed by the 29.7 per cent who liked the 17 per cent product best. Ice cream containing 15 per cent sugar got 20.4 per cent of the preferences, and the 13 per cent mix 17.1 per cent. Only 4.3 per cent of the 178 panelists thought the mix too sweet.

"This study indicated that a 17 to 19 per cent level of sugar in chocolate ice cream resulted in a more flavorful product that a majority of the panel members preferred."

Wine

Dry table wines (not including vermouth and sparkling wines) are consumed in the United States in only half the quantity of dessert wines, which are sweet in varying degrees. Recent work of the Sugar Foundation indicates, however, that some traditionally dry wines can be improved in flavor, and perhaps bouquet, by the addition of sugar and acid.

Preferences in wine were investigated by Professor H. W. Berg and his associates in the Department of Viticulture and Enology in the University of California (Davis) as a part of a broader study of the constituents of wine that affect hunger and appetite. The experiments used a white table wine of 12 per cent alcohol and 0.45 per cent total acidity, representing an average, undistinguished product. To test preferences, sugar was added to give concentrations ranging from 1 to 18 per cent at acid levels of 0.45, 0.70 and 0.90 per cent. The panel was composed of persons chosen for their superior ability to detect differences in flavors and for their familiarity with wines.

When wines were tested at 1, 3, 6, 9, 12, 15 and 18 per cent sugar content, the panel preferred those having 3 to 9 per cent sugar. The test was repeated over a narrower range of sugar content, and the wine containing 6 per cent sugar and 0.70 acid was clearly preferred. In all instances, the panel expressed preference for the wine having the two higher acidity levels.

The results strongly suggest that the flavor profile is closely related to sweetness and acidity, and that the proper balance of these two constituents will make wine taste and, possibly, even smell better.

Dill Pickles

Pickles brighten the plate and add a fillip to the diet. For that reason, flavor is extremely important. Yet flavor is far from uniform. It differs among brands produced by the 250 pickle packers of the United States, and it varies within brands. A Canadian study indicated that 56 per cent of all dill pickles tested were below "desirable quality"—a term that embraces color and texture as well as flavor. Five brands of commercially-packed dill pickles tested in the Department of Food Science and Technology at the University of California (Davis) were "not liked." Color and texture were acceptable, but all brands were judged defective in flavor because of sourness and unbalanced spicing.

In the University's study of quality and flavor, dill pickles were produced under standard commercial conditions and submitted to an expert taste panel. Sugar was added in amounts representing 3.0, 4.5 and 6.0 per cent of the weight of the pickles to give cut-out values of 1.0, 1.5 and 2.0 per cent of sugar by weight. A control sample with no added sugar was packed for each spicing group.

The research workers reported:

"The most outstanding finding made in this study was the improvement of flavor quality by the addition of sucrose. Average flavor scores for samples containing two per cent sucrose were significantly higher than those assigned to the controls. . . . Although it is not known whether more than two per cent sucrose would have been accompanied by higher flavor quality scores, it is felt that sugar levels much beyond two per cent would be perceived as sweetness, and would be undesirable in dill pickles. . . . The role of sugar appears to have been two-fold: (*a*) counteraction of the apparent over-acidity of the control samples, and (*b*) enhancement of the desirable spicing flavors (Pangborn *et al.* 1958B).

SUMMARY

Sugar is a pure carbohydrate whose physical and chemical properties make it an essential ingredient in a wide variety of manufactured food products. Basic processes of sugar manufacture are summarized, and the various type and grades of sugar are described. Tests indicate that consumers prefer foods packed with higher levels of sugar than is general commercial practice.

BIBLIOGRAPHY

ANON. 1949. Liquid sugar. Lamborn and Co., New York.

ANON. 1953. Marketing liquid sugar. U. S. Dept. Agr., Washington, D. C.

ANON. 1955. Dry sugar in bulk. Supplement, 1957. Lambert and Co., New York.

BERTUCCIO, J. F. 1954. Mechanical handling. Mfg. Confectioner *21*, No. 6, 24–25.

HEARD, R. R., JR. 1954. Pneumatic conveying. Mfg. Confectioner *21*, No. 6, 31, 34–37.

JUNK, W. R. 1956. Technical aspects of sugar production and distribution. Information Letter *1570*. Natl. Canners Assoc., Washington, D. C.

LEONARD, S., LUH, B. S., and PANGBORN, R. M. 1960. Effect of sodium chloride, citric acid, and sucrose on pH and palatability of canned tomatoes. Food Technol. *14*, 433–436.

LYLE, O. 1957. Technology for Sugar Refinery Workers. 3rd Edition, Chapman and Hall, London.

McGINNIS, R. A. 1951. Beet Sugar Technology. Reinhold Publishing Corp., New York.

MEADE, G. P. 1963. Spencer Meade Cane Sugar Handbook. A Manual for Cane Sugar Manufacturers and their Chemists. 9th Edition. John Wiley and Sons, New York.

MEEKER, E. W. 1954. The bulk sugar picture. A résumé. Mfg. Confectioner *21*, No. 6, 21–23.

PAGELS, E. A. 1954. Unit containers. Mfg. Confectioner *21*, No. 6, 26–30.

PANGBORN, R. M., and LEONARD, S. J. 1958. Factors influencing consumer opinion of canned Bartlett pears. Food Technol. *12*, 284–290.

PANGBORN, R. M., SIMONE, M., and NICKERSON, T. A. 1957. The influence of sugar on ice cream. Food Technol. *11*, 679–682.

PANGBORN, R. M., SIMONE, M. J., LEONARD, S. J., and GARNATZ, G. 1958A. Comparison of mass panel and household consumer responses to canned cling peaches. Food Technol. *12*, 693–698.

PANGBORN, R. M., SIMONE, M. J., and NICKERSON, T. A. 1959. The influence of sugar on ice cream. Food Technol. *13*, 107–109.

PANGBORN, R. M., VAUGHN, R. H., and YORK, G. K. 1958 B. Effect of sucrose and type of spicing on the quality of processed dill pickles. Food Technol. *12*, 144–147.

SIMONE, M. J., LEONARD, S. J., HINREINER, E., and VALDÉS, R. M. 1956. Consumer studies on sweetness of canned cling peaches. Food Technol. *10*, 279–282.

STEWART, G. F. 1961. Personal communication. Davis, Calif.

VALDÉS, R. M. HINREINER, E. H., and SIMONE, M. J. 1956. Effect of sucrose and organic acids on apparent flavor intensity. Food Technol. *10*, 282–285; 387–390.

VALDES, R. M., and ROESSLER, E. B. 1956. Consumer survey on the dessert quality of canned apricots. Food Technol. *10*, 481–486.

WECKEL, K. G., BUCK, P., BEYER, W., and BIRDSALL, J. 1959. Consumer preference of sweetness in syrup packed red sour pitted Montmorency cherries. Food Technol. *13*, 300–302.

WECKEL, K. G., MATHIAS, W. D., GARNATZ, G. F., and LYLE, M. 1961. Effect of added sugar on consumer acceptance of canned peas. Food Technol. *15*, 241–242.

WECKEL, K. G., STRONG, B., GARNATZ, G. F., and LYLE, M. 1960. The effect of added levels of sugar on consumer acceptance of whole kernel corn. Food Technol. *14*, 369–371.

CHAPTER 3

William J. Hoover | **Corn Sweeteners**

INTRODUCTION

The use of corn syrups and sugars during the past ten years has increased despite a decline in the over-all consumption of carbohydrates in foods (see Table 17). This is due to the greater production and consumption of processed foods and the consequent decline in home cooking. In addition, food processors have expanded their use of corn syrup and dextrose.

Confectioners, together with the chewing-gum manufacturers, consume more corn syrup than any other industry. Large quantities of corn syrup are utilized in mixed table syrups and in syrups for soda fountain use. The largest user of refined corn sugar or dextrose is the baking industry, which also consumes a significant amount of corn syrup. Corn sweeteners are also important ingredients of ice cream and other frozen desserts, canned and frozen fruits, jams, jellies, and preserves, beer and ale, soft drinks and numerous other food products.

The several types of corn sweeteners available differ in carbohydrate composition, and, as a result, possess different combinations of physical and chemical properties. Each of the several food industries mentioned in the previous paragraph utilize corn sweeteners for quality enhancement, but the particular combination of properties important and necessary differ for each food. For example, a baker is interested in a sweetener with high fermentability and the ability to promote a brown crust color, while a confectioner or a preserver is more interested in a combination of sweeteners which will prevent sugar crystallization and provide soluble solids without "cloying" sweetness. It is very important that the food manufacturer study his particular needs with the technical representative of his corn sweetener supplier to insure the selection of the types of sweeteners best suited for his product.

TYPES OF CORN SWEETENERS

Commercial corn syrups and sugars are of four general types:

Corn Syrups.—Clear, colorless, noncrystallizable, viscous liquids consisting of mixtures of dextrose, maltose, and higher saccharides.

WILLIAM J. HOOVER is Director, Food and Grain Institute, Kansas State University, Manhattan, Kansas.

TABLE 17

SHIPMENTS OF CORN SYRUP, CRUDE CORN SUGAR, AND DEXTROSE, 1950–1960[1]
(In 1000 lbs.)

Calendar Year	Corn Syrup	Crude Corn Sugar	Dextrose
1950	1,484,094	84,824	726,862
1951	1,496,181	68,394	685,425
1952	1,461,641	54,780	680,151
1953	1,505,410	60,927	702,858
1954	1,519,017	54,339	669,235
1955	1,580,334	46,926	657,643
1956	1,621,048	48,614	680,758
1957	1,633,113	46,402	666,225
1958	1,770,709	34,896	770,072
1959	1,874,638	22,580	818,261
1960	1,968,259	20,930	807,469

[1] Does not include shipments for export.

Corn Syrup Solids.—The solid substance obtained by dehydrating liquid corn syrup.

Crude Corn Sugar.—A solidified corn sugar "liquor," consisting essentially of dextrose.

Dextrose.—A pure, crystalline solid.

These products are all starch hydrolyzates and may be classified on the basis of the "dextrose equivalent (D.E.)" of the product. *Dextrose equivalent is a measure of the reducing-sugar content of a product calculated as dextrose and expressed as a percentage of the total dry substance.*

The classes of corn syrups and sugars commercially available are:

Low conversion corn syrup
    28 to, but not including 38 D.E.
Regular conversion corn syrup
    38 to, but not including 48 D.E.
Intermediate conversion corn syrup
    48 to, but not including 58 D.E.
High conversion corn syrup
    58 to, but not including 68 D.E.
"Extra" high conversion corn syrup
    greater than 68 D.E.
Crude corn sugar "70"
    80 to, but not including 90 D.E.
Crude corn sugar "80"
    90 to, but not including 95 D.E.
Dextrose
    100 D.E.

Corn syrups are produced by hydrolysis of corn starch, and are of two types, depending upon the method of manufacture: (1) acid-conversion; and (2) acid-enzyme or dual-conversion syrups. Historically, the corn sugars and dextrose have been products of acid hydrolysis, but recently an enzyme process has been introduced for dextrose production.

Advances in technology have resulted in the introduction of two new types of corn syrup in the last two years—acid-enzyme converted 42 D.E. syrup high in maltose content and an "extra" high acid-enzyme converted syrup in the 68 to 72 D.E. range. Each provides a combination of properties that will prove valuable in many food uses.

The carbohydrate composition of acid-enzyme (dual) conversion corn syrups differs from syrups of comparable D.E. produced by straight acid

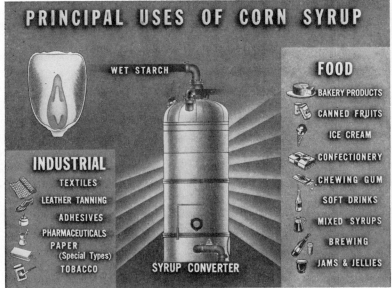

Courtesy of Corn Industries Research Foundation, Inc.

FIG. 15. GRAPHIC ILLUSTRATION OF MAJOR CORN SYRUP USES

conversion (see Table 18). In particular, the proportion of disaccharides is much higher in the dual-conversion syrups. The composition of these syrups can be varied by the type of enzyme used and by the extent of preliminary acid conversion.

Commercial corn syrups are sold on a Baumé basis, which is a measure of specific gravity indicating the dry substance content. Since these materials are quite viscous at room temperature, the Baumé determination is made at a temperature of 140°F. under controlled conditions and an arbitrary correction of 1.00° Baumé is added to the observed reading. This corrects the value approximately to that which would be obtained at 100°F. and is called commercial Baumé. Syrups are available commercially in the range of 41° to 46° Baumé, corresponding to a dry substance content of about 77 to 88 per cent. Most of the syrups used in the food industry, however, are in the 43° Baumé range.

TABLE 18

EXAMPLES OF CARBOHYDRATE COMPOSITION OF COMMERCIALLY AVAILABLE CORN SYRUPS

Type of Conversion	Dextrose Equivalent	Saccharides, %							
		Mono-	Di-	Tri-	Tetra-	Penta-	Hexa-	Hepta-	Higher
Acid	30	10.4	9.3	8.6	8.2	7.2	6.0	5.2	45.1
Acid	42	18.5	13.9	11.6	9.9	8.4	6.6	5.7	25.4
Acid-enzyme	43	5.5	46.2	12.3	3.2	1.8	1.5	...	29.5[1]
Acid	54	29.7	17.8	13.2	9.6	7.3	5.3	4.3	12.8
Acid	60	36.2	19.5	13.2	8.7	6.3	4.4	3.2	8.5
Acid-enzyme	63	38.8	28.1	13.7	4.1	4.5	2.6	...	8.2[1]
Acid-enzyme	71	43.7	36.7	3.7	3.2	0.8	4.3	...	7.6[1]

[1] Includes heptasaccharides.

Corn syrup solids are the solid substances obtained by dehydrating liquid corn syrup to a low moisture content. Commercial corn syrup solids are mostly of the regular and lower-conversion types and, except for moisture content, the composition is comparable with that of syrup from which obtained.

Dextrose, a commercially pure crystalline solid, is a monosaccharide or "simple" sugar. It is available in two forms: hydrous, containing 8.5 per cent water of crystallization; and anhydrous, containing essentially no moisture. Dextrose monohydrate, or hydrous dextrose, is the type generally used by canners and packers.

Many large canning plants now purchase liquid sweeteners exclusively, having installed permanent systems for the convenient and economical handling of products. Most of them use corn syrup. Other processors use dry sweeteners and find granular dextrose and dried corn syrup solids suited to their use. Some plants are equipped to handle both liquid and dry corn sweeteners, and use whichever is best suited for specific products.

MANUFACTURE OF CORN SWEETENERS

Corn sweeteners are produced in the United States by refiners who process enough corn to produce over six billion pounds of starch annually. Approximately two and one-half billion pounds of this total are converted into corn syrup (including corn syrup solids) and one billion pounds into sugar, which includes crude corn sugar and refined corn sugar or dextrose. By-products of the industry annually include over one-quarter billion pounds of corn oil and a million tons of livestock feed.

Eight companies of those comprising the U. S. corn refining industry produce sweeteners. All eight of these companies manufacture corn syrups, but not all produce corn syrup solids or dextrose (see Table 19).

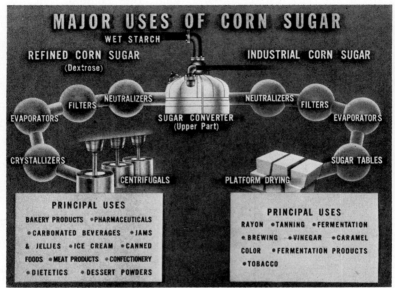

Courtesy of Corn Industries Research Foundation, Inc.

FIG. 16. GRAPHIC ILLUSTRATION OF THE MANUFACTURE AND MAJOR USES OF DEXTROSE

The manufacture of all corn sweeteners begins with the hydrolysis of corn starch. This is a process involving the splitting of the starch molecules by chemical reaction with water. It is carried out in converters ranging in size up to 24 ft. high and 6 ft. in diameter. A thoroughly agitated slurry of purified starch granules containing the required amount of dilute acid is brought to the desired temperature by the injection of live steam. A variety of acids will effect the conversion, but in the United States hydrochloric acid is used almost exclusively. Time and temperature are varied depending on the type of sweetener being manufactured.

TABLE 19

MANUFACTURERS OF CORN SWEETENERS IN THE UNITED STATES

| Company | Corn Syrup | | | | Corn Syrup Solids | Crude Corn Sugar | Dextrose |
	Low Conversion	Regular Conversion	Intermediate Conversion	High Conversion			
American Maize-Products Co.	x	x	x	x	x	x	
Anheuser-Busch, Inc.	x	x	x	x			
Clinton Corn Processing Co.	x	x	x	x	x	x	x
Corn Products Co.	x	x	x	x	x	x	x
The Hubinger Co.	x	x	x	x	x	x	
Penick & Ford, Ltd., Inc.	x	x	x	x		x	
A. E. Staley Mfg. Co.	x	x	x	x	x		
Union Starch and Refining Co.	x	x	x			x	

As the reaction progresses, the gelatinized starch is converted first to other polysaccharides and subsequently to sugars, mostly maltose and dextrose. The sugar content increases and viscosity decreases as conversion proceeds. Complete hydrolysis produces dextrose.

Corn Syrup

To produce corn syrup, the hydrolysis of the starch is halted when partially complete, the exact degree depending on the type of syrup being made. Partial hydrolysis of starch converts part of the starch completely to dextrose; the remainder, which is not completely hydrolyzed to dextrose, consists of maltose and higher saccharides. The proportions of saccharides vary depending on the extent and method of hydrolysis.

Two methods of hydrolysis are in commercial use for the production of corn syrup—the acid process and the acid-enzyme process. In the latter,

Courtesy of Corn Industries Research Foundation, Inc.

Fig. 17. Top of Starch Converter with Process Control Panel in Background

Starch is here converted to corn syrup and other hydrolyzate products.

acid hydrolysis is followed by conversion with an amylolytic enzyme resulting in a syrup with a higher proportion of maltose than can be obtained by acid hydrolysis alone. The dextrose–maltose ratio can be varied, within certain limits, depending on the type of enzyme employed and on the extent of the preliminary acid conversion.

In the acid-hydrolysis process, the hydrolysis is stopped when the reaction has reached the desired D.E. range by transferring the entire content of the converter into a neutralizing tank where the pH is raised to a level necessary to stop the reaction. The acid acts as a catalyst and does not combine chemically with the starch. It is partially neutralized by adding a calculated quantity of sodium carbonate (soda ash) to the solution.

Fatty substances which rise to the surface are skimmed, removed in centrifuges, or removed by precoated filters. Suspended solid matter is removed by filtering the "hydrolyzate" in vacuum filters. The filtrate then is evaporated to a density of about 60 per cent dry substance.

Courtesy of Corn Industries Research Foundation, Inc.

FIG. 18.　FILLING OPERATION DEPICTS CLARITY
OF CORN SYRUP

After this initial evaporation, the hydrolyzate is passed through either bone-char or other carbon filters which effect further clarification and decolorization so that the resulting syrup is clear and practically colorless. This process partially removes soluble mineral substances. The mineral substances can also be removed by an ion-exchange process.

After final filtration, evaporation is carried out in vacuum pans at relatively low temperature to avoid damage to the syrup. The syrup is cooled and may be stored or loaded directly in tank cars, tank trucks, steel drums or cans.

In the production of high-conversion acid-enzyme or dual-conversion syrups, acid hydrolysis is carried to a level of 48 to 55 D.E. The syrup then is neutralized, clarified and partially concentrated and the enzyme added. In other products the acid hydrolysis may be stopped as low as 15 D.E. When the enzyme hydrolysis has progressed to the desired degree the enzyme is inactivated. Adjustment of pH, further refining and final evaporation follow as in the production of acid-conversion syrup.

Corn Syrup Solids

To produce corn syrup solids, completely refined corn syrup is spray- or drum-dried to a moisture content of less than $3^1/_2$ per cent. The amorphous or glassy product may be ground in suitable mills to give finely divided material. Because corn syrup solids are hygroscopic, the material is packed in multiwall paper bags containing moisture barriers.

Crude Corn Sugar

The corn sugars are prepared by a more complete acid hydrolysis of starch than is used for the production of syrup. The resulting crude sugar "liquor" is then neutralized, filtered, clarified, and concentrated. The concentrated liquor is "seeded" with fine sugar from previous batches, "cast" in pans, partitioned troughs, or on casting floors, and the entire mass allowed to crystallize. These products are sold in slabs or billets, or are chipped and packed in 100-lb. bags, for various industrial and food-processing uses.

Dextrose

Maximum hydrolysis of the starch is required when dextrose is the end product. The conditions for hydrolysis, therefore, are so adjusted as to give a maximum dextrose content in the hydrolyzate. After purification and concentration, as in the manufacture of corn syrup, the highly refined dextrose liquor is "seeded" with dextrose crystals from a previous batch. Crystallization is then carried out under carefully controlled rates of cooling in large crystallizers equipped with agitators.

After approximately 100 hr. in the crystallizers the crystalline dextrose monohydrate which forms is removed from the magma (mixture of crystals and "mother liquor") in centrifuges, washed, dried and packed in 100-lb. paper bags. The mother liquor from the centrifuges is reconverted, clarified, concentrated and then passed through another crystallization cycle. As before, the dextrose crystals which form during this second cycle are removed from the magma by centrifuges. The dextrose obtained during this cycle is redissolved in water, added to new starch conversion liquor and recrystallized to give pure dextrose monohydrate. The mother liquor from the second crystallization is dark brown in color and has a bitter taste. This material is called "hydrol" or "corn sugar feeding molasses" and is used in animal feeding and industrial processes.

PROPERTIES OF CORN SWEETENERS

Corn syrups and dextrose are essentially tasteless except for sweetness. The sweetening power of various corn sweeteners, compared with sucrose, is primarily dependent not only upon the percentages of sweetener solids but also upon the *combination* of sweeteners.

Courtesy of Corn Industries Research Foundation, Inc.

Fig. 19.   Battery of Dextrose Centrifugals

Magma from large crystallizers above enters centrifugals where
liquid is removed.

The effect of increasing concentration is evident when dextrose solutions are compared with sucrose solutions. A two-per cent water solution of dextrose is about two-thirds as sweet as a sucrose solution of equivalent concentration. As the concentration is increased, the difference in sweetness is less apparent. In fact, at a level of 40 per cent solids, sucrose and dextrose solutions appear to be equally sweet.

Corn syrups also impart greater sweetness at higher concentrations. However, since syrups are less sweet than dextrose, the increase in their sweetening effect is less marked as the dextrose equivalent value decreases.

When corn syrup or dextrose is used in combination with sucrose, the resulting sweetness is usually greater than would be expected. For example, when tested at 45 per cent solids, a mixture of 25 per cent 42 D.E. corn syrup and 75 per cent sucrose is considered to be as sweet as a sucrose solution of 45 per cent solids. Hence, when corn sweeteners are

Courtesy of Corn Industries Research Foundation, Inc.

FIG. 20. INSIDE VIEW OF SPINNING CENTRIFUGAL

White substance on walls is crystalline dextrose monohydrate, end product of the starch-conversion process.

used with sucrose in products having a relatively high sweetener concentration, no loss of sweetness results. In less sweet products, or when only one sweetener is used, a decrease in sweetness may be expected by using corn sweeteners in place of sucrose.

Sweetness is also influenced by such factors as temperature of the product and the presence of acids, salts, flavoring materials and other nonsugar substances. It is impossible, therefore, to state accurately the relative sweetness of syrups and sugars for use in the food industries. Each product must be considered individually.

Corn syrup, corn syrup solids and dextrose are compatible with other sweeteners and with food flavors. They are widely used with other sweeteners, particularly sucrose.

Chemical Properties

Fermentability is an important chemical property of corn syrups and sugars in certain food applications. Dextrose and maltose are readily fermentable by many organisms. The fermentability of the corn syrups thus is roughly proportional to their content of dextrose and maltose. This property of fermentability does not affect the storage life of corn syrups or sugars because they do not ferment unless diluted with water.

Dextrose has also the ability to combine with nitrogenous compounds at elevated temperatures to produce brown coloration (the Maillard reaction). This property makes corn sweeteners useful in the manufacture of caramel color; promotes crust color in baking; and produces color and caramel flavor in other food products.

Dextrose, maltose and certain polysaccharides of corn sweeteners are technically termed "reducing sugars." This "reducing" property inhibits undesirable oxidative reactions in foods. It is useful in maintaining the natural color of canned fruits and preserves and in helping to retain desirable color in meat products.

All reducing sugars are subject to alkaline degradation. To prevent this, corn sweeteners are usually kept slightly on the acid side. They are available with a pH of from about 3.5 to 5.5.

Physical Properties

The physical properties of corn syrups and sugars are particularly important to food products in which these sweeteners are used.

Solubility is one of these properties. All corn sweeteners are readily soluble in water. For example, corn syrups are aqueous solutions containing around 80 per cent solids at room temperature. At a temperature of 82.4°F. a saturated dextrose solution contains 53 per cent anhydrous dextrose. Dextrose has a negative heat of solution; that is, it cools a mixture in which it is dissolved. This property is useful to bakers since · it has a cooling effect in the dough.

Anhydrous dextrose melts at 295°F., while dextrose hydrate with a melting point of 180°F. readily melts in a boiling water bath. Dried corn syrups or commercial corn syrup solids are noncrystalline amorphous powders which, when heated gradually, soften or dissolve in their own trace moisture.

Corn sweeteners are hygroscopic in varying degrees, and the degree of hygroscopicity increases as the D.E. increases. The higher conversion syrups, crude sugars and dextrose thus are employed as humectants (moisture conditioners and stabilizers).

The higher saccharides give corn syrup its cohesive and adhesive properties. They have some of the desirable attributes of certain vegetable gums; therefore, corn syrups are used in a number of products requiring these characteristics. The higher saccharides also contribute chewy texture to certain types of confections.

All of the corn sweeteners, particularly the corn syrups, control the crystallization of sucrose and other sugars. This property is especially advantageous in many types of confections, in ice cream and other frozen desserts, and in jams, jellies and preserves.

Corn syrups and sugars contribute substantially to the attractiveness of many foods. They are widely used in combination with sucrose by the fruit canning industry. The glossy appearance of fruits canned with cover syrups containing a corn sweetener is pleasing. These sweeteners also improve the gloss and clarity of hard candies, jams and jellies.

Dextrose, being a monosaccharide of molecular weight 180 (compared with 342 for sucrose), has a relatively high osmotic pressure which enhances its effectiveness in inhibiting microbial spoilage in preserves. Corn syrup of 55 D.E. has about the same *average* molecular weight as sucrose or lactose and hence has about the same osmotic properties as those sugars. Corn syrups of lower D.E. have higher molecular weights which mean lower osmotic pressures.

The effect of corn syrups and sugars on the freezing point of a solution is of practical significance in the manufacture of ice cream and frozen desserts. The lower- and regular-conversion syrups depress the freezing point somewhat less than does sucrose. Intermediate-conversion syrups have about the same effect as sucrose on the freezing point, while the high-conversion syrups lower the freezing point only slightly more than sucrose at the same concentrations. Dextrose lowers the freezing point slightly more than high-conversion syrups. Both corn syrup and dextrose, however, are used primarily by the ice-cream industry to control sweetness and improve body and texture.

Viscosity, one of the most important physical properties of corn syrups, is dependent on density, D.E. and temperature. It decreases as D.E. and temperature are raised, but increases with higher density. At 100°F., for example, a 43 Baumé syrup of 42 D.E. has a viscosity of about 12,500 centipoises (a common unit for expressing the viscosity of a liquid), while a 55 D.E. syrup of the same density has a viscosity of only 7,000 centipoises. Viscosity decreases markedly with increases in temperature.

TABLE 20

CORN SWEETENERS SPECIFIED IN FEDERALLY STANDARDIZED FOODS

Product	Proportion of Corn Sweetener Specified—% of Total Sweetener Content (Dry Solids Basis)		
	Corn Syrup	Corn Syrup Solids	Dextrose
Bakery products			
Bread and rolls or buns	No limitation	No limitation	No limitation
Dairy products			
Cheese foods, cheese spreads and related foods	As seasoning[1]	As seasoning[1]	As seasoning[1]
Ice cream and related products	No limitation	No limitation	No limitation
Milk, sweetened condensed	. . .	. . .	100[2]
Milk, corn syrup condensed	No limitation[3]	No limitation[3]	. . .
Dressings			
French dressing	As seasoning	As seasoning	As seasoning
Mayonnaise	As seasoning	As seasoning	As seasoning
Salad dressing	As seasoning	As seasoning	As seasoning
Fruits			
Apricots, canned	25	25	$33^1/_3$
Berries, canned	25	25	$33^1/_3$
Butters	25	25	100[4]
Cherries, canned	25	25	$33^1/_3$
Cocktail, canned	25	25	$33^1/_3$
Figs, canned	25	25	$33^1/_3$
Grapes, canned	25	25	$33^1/_3$
Jelly	25	25	100[4]
Lemonade, frozen concentrate	$33^1/_3$	$33^1/_3$	$33^1/_3$
Peaches, canned	25	25	$33^1/_3$
Pears, canned	25	25	$33^1/_3$
Pineapple, canned	25	25	$33^1/_3$
Plums, canned	25	25	$33^1/_3$
Preserves, jams	25	25	100[4]
Prunes, canned	25	25	$33^1/_3$
Meats			
Meat food products	2[5]	2[5]	No limitation
Chopped ham	2[5]	2[5]	No limitation
Corn beef hash	. . .	. . .	No limitation
Vegetables			
Beans, canned, green and waxed	. . .	. . .	No limitation
Catsup	$33^1/_3$	$33^1/_3$	100[2]
Peas, canned	. . .	. . .	No limitation
Sweet potatoes, canned	No limitation[6]	No limitation[6]	No limitation[6]
Other (35 listed in "Omnibus" Standard)	. . .	. . .	No limitation
Other			
Cacao products	. . .	25	$33^1/_3$

[1] Label declaration of seasoning ingredient is required.
[2] No restriction on amount except that dextrose must be combined with sucrose.
[3] Label declaration showing percentages of sweeteners by weight except when corn syrup is the only sweetener used.
[4] Any combination of dextrose and other sweetening ingredients.
[5] Not to exceed two per cent, calculated on a dry basis, of all the ingredients used.
[6] Sufficient to season.

For example, the same 42 D.E., 43 Baumé syrup which has a viscosity of about 12,500 centipoises at 100°F. shows only about 1,700 centipoises at 140°F.

SWEETENERS IN STANDARDIZED FOODS

Proportions of corn sweeteners specified as optional sweetening ingredients in foods for which Food and Drug Administration or Meat Inspection Division, United States Department of Agriculture, definitions and standards of identity have been established are listed in Table 20. Figures indicate maximum limits. No label declaration is required.

Mixed sweeteners containing more than·one corn sweetener are permitted in most standards. In those standards where limitations are placed on each type of corn sweetener, as in canned fruit, mixtures may consist of a combination of dextrose and sucrose solids in specified proportions with corn syrup solids (in either dried or liquid form). A practical formula for determining the proportions for such mixtures in canned fruits is as follows: Twice the dextrose solids plus three times the corn syrup solids equal the weight of sucrose solids used. For example, 12.5 lbs. of dextrose solids plus 25 lbs. of corn syrup solids (whether in liquid or dried form) would be mixed with 100 lbs. of sucrose solids [(2 x 12.5) + (3 x 25) = 100].

Proposed federal standards have been issued for frozen fruits and permit all of the corn sweeteners up to $33^{1}/_{3}$ per cent of the total sweetening ingredients.

SWEETENERS IN NONSTANDARDIZED FOODS

In nonstandardized foods requiring sweetening ingredients, there is no legal limitation on the quantity of corn sweeteners. The only applicable labeling requirements of the Federal Food, Drug and Cosmetic Act are that the labels of any such food include the names of any corn sweeteners as part of the statement which must list all ingredients in order of their predominance. Some of the more important foods in this category are candy and confectionery, cakes, cookies, dry bakery mixes, cranberry jelly and sauce, marmalade, fountain and table syrups and pickles.

A majority of states have also established regulations governing the preparation of processed foods, and these usually include canned and frozen fruits and vegetables. In general, they follow the pattern of the Federal standards, but in all cases processors should familiarize themselves with the specific regulations in their respective states.

HANDLING EQUIPMENT AND PROCEDURES

In general, the handling of corn sweeteners in users' plants will depend on the type of sweetener (liquid or dry) and on the rate of use. The required equipment and procedures are similar to those for handling other liquid or dry ingredients.

Corn syrups are usually shipped in steel cans, drums and tank trucks of various sizes, and in 8,000-gal. (or more) railroad tank cars. Liquid dextrose at approximately 72 per cent solids is available in bulk shipments. The dry sweeteners, dextrose and corn syrup solids, are shipped mostly in 100-lb. multiwall paper bags. Closed hopper cars sometimes are used for bulk shipment of dextrose.

Corn Syrup

Large users of corn syrup usually install stationary storage tanks of suitable size, depending on the quantities used, with permanent piping and pumps for conveying the syrup from the point of delivery to the storage tanks and from storage to the various points of use. Storage tanks are usually heated in some manner to keep the syrup at a temperature that will permit it to flow readily. Piping for syrup likewise is usually provided with a heating arrangement. In some plants special jacketed piping is used and in others the pipe is wound with a thermostatically controlled electric heating element.

To avoid heat damage which might result in off-flavor and discoloration, it is important that corn syrup not be held at elevated temperatures for any extended time. A temperature from 90° to 100°F. is best for normal storage periods.

As corn syrup is noncorrosive, both the storage tank and the permanent piping may be constructed of mild steel or other suitable materials. The tanks and their supporting structures must be of such design as to hold the maximum quantity of syrup with safety (it weighs about twelve pounds per gallon).

Because of their high solids content, commercially supplied corn syrups are not susceptible to biological spoilage except when diluted with water. Therefore, installations for storage and handling of the syrups should be designed to eliminate possible dilution from any source such as cleaning operations or condensation inside the tanks.

Storage tanks should be of all-welded construction with stiffeners or reinforcing members on the outside so as to keep the interior surfaces smooth. All interior corners should be rounded. Inner tank surfaces of mild steel which are not always submerged should be coated with a suitable nontoxic, nonabsorbent material. Manhole openings not smaller than 18 in. in diameter should be provided for all tank compartments. All vent openings should be screened and protected against the entry of insects and falling material.

Distribution piping continuously filled with corn syrup may be fabricated from mild steel or other suitable metals, but piping in intermittent use should be galvanized or stainless steel. Valves and stopcocks should be of iron or iron body with bronze trim. Many large users of corn syrup employ metering equipment which automatically shuts off after a predetermined amount of syrup has been pumped.

Smaller plants which purchase corn syrup in drums may find convenient any of the various handling devices on the market. Both hand and motor operated devices are available for raising and tipping the drums so that they may be easily emptied. A simple shutoff valve attached to a short length of pipe which is screwed into the outlet bung serves as a convenient means for drawing off required amounts.

Dry Corn Sweeteners

No special precautions are required in the handling of dextrose and corn syrup solids, except that they must be kept dry to avoid the absorption of moisture, and they should not be exposed to elevated temperatures. The 100-lb. paper bags in which these sweeteners are packed are usually handled on skids with ordinary hand or lift trucks. Bags should not be opened until needed.

BIBLIOGRAPHY

ALSTON, P. W. 1955. Sugars in the canning of fruits and vegetables. Advan. Chem. Ser. *12*, 75–77. American Chemical Society, Washington, D. C.

ANON. 1955. Down to points on high conversion corn syrup. Food Eng. *27*, 102, 105, 182.

ANON. 1958. Corn Syrups and Sugars. 2nd Edition, Corn Industries Research Foundation, Inc., Washington, D. C.

ANON. 1959. Recommendations for bulk corn syrup storage and distribution systems in food processing plants. 6th Printing. Corn Industries Research Foundation, Washington, D. C.

ANON. 1961. Products from corn specified in Federal food standards. 5th Edition. Corn Industries Research Foundation, Washington, D. C.

COHEE, R. F., JR. 1953. Corn sweeteners help processors in many ways. Food Eng. *25*, No. 6, 74–76, 108–112.

FABIAN, F. W., and PIONICK, H. 1953. Corn syrup wins place as pickle sweetener. Food Eng. *25*, No. 6, 97–98, 138, 140.

JONES, P. E., and THOMASON, F. G. 1951. Competitive relationships between sugar and corn sweeteners. U. S. Dept. Agr. Inform. Bull. *48*, U. S. Dept. Agr., Washington, D. C.

JOSLYN, M. A., and HOHL, L. A. 1948. The commercial freezing of fruit products. Calif. Univ. Agr. Expt. Sta. Bull. *703*, Univ. of Calif., Berkeley, Calif.

LEWIS, F. A. 1952. Quality preserves using corn syrup. Food Eng. *24*, No. 4, 78–79, 156, 158.

LEWIS, F. A. 1954. Batches without botches. Food Eng. *26*, No. 2, 67–68.

LEWIS, F. A.   1955.   Corn syrup is more than a sweetener.   Food Eng. *27*, No. 5, 75, 76, 195, 196.

LEWIS, F. A.   1956.   Corn sweeteners in food products manufacture.   Western Canner and Packer *48*, No. 10, 26–30.

LEWIS, F. A.   1957.   Quality and uses of corn sweeteners.   Natl. Provisioner *137*, No. 25, 19–20, 35.

MESCHTER, E. E.   1953.   Effects of carbohydrates and other factors on strawberry products.   J. Agr. Food Chem. *1*, 574–579.

NIEMAN, C.   1960.   Sweetness of glucose, dextrose, and sucrose.   Mfg. Confectioner *40*, No. 8, 19–24, 43–46.

OGLE, W. L., and KRAMER, A.   1954.   Puts brakes on browning of ketchup in bottle necks.   Food Eng. *26*, No. 9, 67–68.

OSER, B. L.   1955.   Sugars in standardized foods.   Advan. Chem. *12*, 125–132. American Chemical Society, Washington, D. C.

PECKHAM, G. T., JR.   1955.   Starch hydrolyzates in the food industry.   Advan. Chem. *12*, 43–48, American Chemical Society, Washington, D. C.

PRENTICE, H. A.   1952.   Types of corn syrup for manufacturing fruit spreads. Canner *114*, No. 16, 16, 18, 24.

SATHER, L., and WIEGAND, E. H.   1948.   The application of corn syrup in the freezing preservation of fruit.   Quick Frozen Foods *10*, No. 10, 81–83, 107–108.

STEIN, J. A., and WECKEL, K. G.   1954.   Factors affecting the color stability of frozen Montmorency cherries.   Food Technol. *8*, 445–447.

TALBURT, W. F.   1955.   Sugar in frozen foods.   Advan. Chem. *12*, 89–94, American Chemical Society, Washington, D. C.

WIEGAND, E. H.   1953.   Quality (frozen) fruits with corn syrup.   Food Eng. *25*, No. 5, 131, 133, 210.

CHAPTER 4

M. A. Joslyn and
A. Timmons

Salt—Use in Food Processing

INTRODUCTION

Salt was used in preservation of food, either alone or in combination with drying even before recorded history. In ancient Greece, salted fish formed a cheap article of diet for workers and slaves. Pickling and smoking of foods with added salt came later.

Herbiverous animals, both wild and domestic, crave salt but carniverous animals and Eskimos, who eat little vegetable matter, do not crave it and even abhor it. As Jensen (1953) pointed out, salt was probably introduced as a food supplement when man changed from a carniverous to a heavily vegetarian diet.

The human body, on the average, contains 100 gm. of salt (sodium chloride). The per capita consumption of salt for table use has been estimated as not over three pounds per year (Kaufmann 1960). The total per capita salt consumption has been estimated as equivalent to about ten grams per day, of which more than half is excreted as excess. The salt content of the food as purchased for dietary use averages 5 gm. per capita, but may vary from 0.5 to 10 gm. Salt is important not only as a dietary supplement but also in seasoning foods to promote food intake (Lepkovkky 1948). The long history of salt and its important role in politics and economy is described by Eskew (1948), in publications of salt manufacturers, and more recently by Kaufmann (1960).

The production and use of salt in the United States is reported annually in the U. S. Bureau of Mines Minerals Yearbook, published by the U. S. Government Printing Office, Washington, D. C., and is discussed in detail by Hester and Diamond (1955) and Kaufmann (1960). Of the approximately 22 million tons used in the United States during the past five years, over 70 per cent were used by the chemical industries, about five per cent used in commercial food processing and three per cent for domestic uses, including table salt, home canning and preserving, farm slaughtering, etc. The meat packing industry consumes most of the salt used in commercial food processing in the preparation of ground

M. A. JOSLYN is Professor of Food Technology, Department of Nutritional Sciences, University of California, Berkeley, and A. TIMMONS is a Senior Process Engineer, Ralph M. Parsons Co., Los Angeles, Calif.

meats, hams, bacon, corned beef. The canning and pickling industries are the second largest users, being followed by the dairy industry (butter and cheese), and the fish and marine products industries.

USES OF SALT

Applications of salt in commercial food processing may be classified on the basis of objective (flavor enhancement, preservative, conditioner), on the product in which it is used, or on the basis of particular operations (quality grading, blanching, etc.). The most important uses include the following:

(1) As a basic flavoring ingredient with universal appeal. Salt is the major or sole ingredient of the brines in which meat and meat products, poultry products, fish and sea foods, and vegetables are canned. The composition of the brines commonly used in canning vegetables are shown in Table 21; the salt content of such brines usually averages 1.5 to 2.0 per cent.

TABLE 21

COMPOSITION OF BRINES USED FOR CANNING VEGETABLES

Product	Brine, Lbs. per 100 Gal. Water
Asparagus	18–20 lbs. salt
Beans, green	16–23 lbs. salt
Beans, kidney	10–14 lbs. salt and 10–18 lbs. sugar
Beans and pork	20–24 lbs. salt, 60–80 lbs. sugar, and tomato pulp and seasoning
Bean sprouts	15–18 lbs. salt and 20 oz. citric acid
Beets	20 lbs. salt; 15–20 lbs. sugar may be added
Cabbage	13–21 lbs. salt
Corn (cream style)	15–25 lbs. salt and 0–150 lbs. sugar (varying with maturity)
Corn on the cob	Salt to season; addition of brine avoided
Corn, whole kernel	12–16 lbs. salt; 20–30 lbs. sugar may be added
Okra	8–10 lbs. salt
Peas, green	18 lbs. salt and 30–40 lbs. sugar
Peas, black-eyed	18–20 lbs. salt
Spinach	15–20 lbs. salt

For centuries, salt has been known to improve the palatability and acceptability of food. The physiological basis of this effect on food intake is discussed by Lepkovsky (1948). The addition of salt is known to improve the flavor and acceptability of many types of food, particularly meat, fish, poultry products, vegetables and even fruits. The enhancement of fruitiness in melon, watermelon, apple, pear and other products is well known. Fabian and Blum (1943) investigated the three basic flavors—saltiness, sourness and sweetness—and their influence on each other. They found that sodium chloride reduced the sourness of acids and increased the sweetness of sugars. Organic acids (such as malic, tartaric and lactic acids) increased the saltiness of sodium chloride, and the sweetness of sucrose but decreased that of fructose. All the sugars tested reduced the saltiness of sodium chloride. Sjöström and Cairncross (1955) reported that the addition of one per cent salt to sucrose solutions containing 3–10 per cent sucrose reduced sweetness but addition of 0.5 per cent salt to 5–7 per cent sucrose solutions increased sweetness. This interrelation between sweetness and saltiness has been used for many years by housewives in seasoning foods and is the basis of the commercial use of salt and sugar in preparing brines for canning vegetables such as peas. Salt not only enhances sweetness, and improves natural flavors but may weaken bitterness. The selection of the proper combination of the basic seasoning ingredients for specific products has been based and still is based on empirical trial and error procedures. More basic data of the above type are needed.

(2) As a flavoring ingredient and preservative in the curing of pork and other meat products, in brined herring, in smoked and dried fish and meat products and in fresh egg yolk to be frozen and used in preparation of other foods. Bacon and ham are prepared by soaking in a "pickle" (brine) containing salt, sugar and sodium nitrate or the brine may be distributed by artery injection. Beef is cured usually in a similar pickle; chopped meats for wieners, frankfurters, etc., are cured by mixing with salt and spices. Sliced bacon and sliced fish are prepared by rubbing and sprinkling salt on the flesh. Ground meats have a salt content of 2 to 4 per cent; bacon about 2.25 per cent; hams about 5 and corned beef about 6 per cent.

In the salt or brine processing of fish and meat products, the penetration of salt into and its absorption by the tissues is an important factor. While a considerable amount of data on absorption of salt by fish and marine products is available (Anderson 1956; Tressler and Lemon 1951) there is little data on accumulation of salt during the curing of meat. A recent investigation was that of Wistreich et al. (1959, 1960).

(3) As a flavoring ingredient and curing agent in hard cheeses such as cheddar and Swiss cheese. In cheese making, salt is mixed with the curd not only for flavor but also to aid in whey removal, hardening and shrinking the curd, retarding lactic acid fermentation, inhibiting undesirable fermentations and producing desirable texture. About three pounds of salt are added per 1000 lbs. of milk but only one-third of the added salt remains in the cheese. The ripened cheese contains about one per cent of salt.

(4) As a flavoring agent in butter and margarine. Although formerly salt was added only as a preservative in butter making, today salt is added primarily as a flavoring agent. The salt content of butter averages about 2.0 to 2.5 per cent.

(5) As a flavoring agent and for other uses in cereal products. In the baking of bread, salt is added to control and regulate fermentation by yeast of sugars and regulate the formation of the carbon dioxide. It checks the development of objectionable or "wild" types of fermentation, has a strengthening effect on gluten and assists in the production of the desired finer grain, softer texture, and whiter crumb. In the presence of added salt, the water mixed with the flour and retained in the bread can be increased. The salted bread has a longer storage life. Salt is added at the rate of 2 to 2.25 lbs. per 100 lbs. of flour used. In sweet rolls, coffee cakes, and biscuit mixes about two per cent of salt by weight of flour, and with doughnut flour about one per cent by weight are used.

(6) In the preparation and control of lactic acid fermentation of sauerkraut, pickles, green fermented olives and other vegetable pickles. The composition of brines used in pickling and holding vegetables is shown in Table 22. In the production of sauerkraut and pickles, dry salting,

TABLE 22

COMPOSITION OF BRINE USED IN PICKLING AND HOLDING VEGETABLES[1]

Product	Initial Brine	Desired Salt Concentration During Curing & Storage
Fermented Pickles	40° Salometer	20–25° Salometer
Sauerkraut	2.5% dry salt	2–3% salt
Salt stock	40° Salometer	Gradually increased to at least 60° Salometer
Olives (for ripe pickling)		
Large varieties (Sevillano & Ascolano)	2.5–5% salt	Gradually build up salt strength as these varieties are very susceptible to salt shrivel.
Smaller varieties (Manzanillo & Mission)	5–10% salt	Gradually increase salt content to 7–8 or even 10% for holding
Olives (Greek style)	7–10% salt	Increase to 15% or over
Olives (Green fermented)		
Sevillano variety	5% salt	Conduct fermentation at 4–7% salt
Manzanillo & Barouni	7–8% salt	Conduct fermentation at 4–7% salt

[1] After R. H. Vaughn (1954).

a combination of dry salt and brine and brine alone may be used. Particular care should be taken to distribute the dry salt uniformly and to obtain and maintain the brine at a uniform concentration throughout the barrell or vat. Figure 21 shows delivery of salt to pickle vats.

(7) In the brine storage of cucumbers and other vegetables, olives and other fruits for subsequent processing into canned, glass-packaged, or flexible packaging after suitable additional treatment. Production of "salt stock" and brine storage of olives, etc.

(8) In the brine storage of citrus peel (orange, lemon, citron, grapefruit) and of cut zucca melon for subsequent production of candied and glacéed products.

The ability of salt to inhibit microbial growth and activity in concentrations of ten per cent and above or to exert a selective inhibitive action at lower concentrations is widely used in the production of lactic acid fermented products which may be preserved by a combination of factors, reduction in fermentable sugar content, accumulation of lactic acid, and presence of salt. The salt used for this purpose should be low in carbonates and calcium and magnesium content and the concentration of salt should be adjusted to prevent or minimize shriveling and excessive wilting during storage in brine. In the preparation of salt stock, particu-

Courtesy of Leslie Salt Co.

Fig. 21. Brining Operation at a Pickle Plant

Vats are initially charged with pickles, brine and salt, and brine strength is maintained by adding salt. Salt is delivered to the vats pneumatically, using blower on tractor. Hopper holds over 3,000 lbs. of kiln dried salt.

lar care should be taken to gradually raise the salt concentration to the desired point without interfering with the fermentation and curing process and to avoid surface growth of salt tolerant aerobic organisms (molds and yeasts).

(9) For the temporary storage and handling of peeled and sliced or cut apples, potatoes, etc., to inhibit enzymatic browning and discoloration during preparation for canning, freezing or dehydration.

Salt, particularly when free from objectionable amounts of iron and copper impurities, has a definite antioxidant effect of its own and also has the property of enhancing the inhibition of oxidation by other antioxidants. It improves the antioxidant action of sulfurous acid and the acid sulfites, ascorbic acid and other agents. For this reason mixtures of salt and antioxidant usually are more effective than either alone. Thus in preventing browning of a fruit like apple during freezing storage a mixture of sodium chloride, sodium bisulfite and ascorbic acid is particularly effective. The antioxidative effect of smoke constituents on meat and fish products is also improved by salt. Under some conditions however, salt may promote oxidations and the particular mixture of antioxidants must be carefully compounded and tested before it is used.

Salt also inhibits the activity of oxidizing enzymes such as the polyphenol oxidase involved in oxidative discoloration of peeled, cut or otherwise mechanically injured tissues of apples, potatoes and other products. Where salt absorption from brines is not harmful and even desirable, temporary storage and handling in brines is useful in preventing discoloration during preparation.

(10) Fish preservation. Freshly caught sardines on the Atlantic Coast are first salted on the boats and then held in brine at the port. Tuna fish are refrigerated in brine on board the ship in the Pacific and brought to port chilled or even frozen. Brine is used in processing shrimp, oysters, clams, crabs and lobster.

(11) In the quality grading of peas, beans, potatoes and other products which can be separated into different quality grades because differences in maturity and composition are reflected in differences in specific gravity of the product. Brine quality graders of various types are used for grade separation during preparation to reduce cost of sorting by hand. Brine separation is used also in determination of the grade of the final preserved product, both canned and frozen.

Canners class peas in three grades: No. 1 "fancy," No. 2 "choice," and No. 3 "standard." The difference is in the degree of tenderness. Young peas are most desirable and tender and are lighter than more mature peas.

There are several machines or types of equipment used for separating peas, but all depend on the specific gravity of brine to separate light tender peas from the harder, more mature peas since the lighter peas will float and the heavier ones will sink in a brine of a given density.

Normal brine densities used for peas are (using a Canner's Salometer Scale):

30° to 36°S for No. 1 fancy peas.
35° to 42°S for No. 2 choice peas.
38° to 46°S for No. 3 standard and larger peas.

For lima beans, normal densities are:

First Separation: 43° to 47°S.
Second Separation: 47° to 60°S.
Third Separation: 60° to 70°S.

The actual gravity is based on tenderometer readings which definitely establish the grade of the pea in terms of toughness for any batch.

For proper operation of a brine gravity separation system, a density control mechanism such as the Brine-o-stat and a constant source of saturated brine should be used. In this way, saturated brine and water will be proportioned to give a constant density brine in the grading equipment. Kiln dried salt may generally be used since the quantity of calcium absorbed will probably not be significant.

Some equipment such as the Food Machinery and Chemical Corporation's Lewis Quality Grader and Washer is equipped to clean the brine of scalpings and recirculate the brine, resulting in a saving in brine usage. This machine also is equipped to control density automatically. Older equipment may use brine only once so there would well be a considerable potential saving in installing more modern equipment.

(12) To prevent the undesirable effects of hard water on the texture of peas and beans during blanching. Salt water blanching has been used to prevent absorption by peas and beans of calcium and magnesium from hard water and to reduce losses by leaching of soluble constituents. The addition of 2 to 4 per cent of salt to hard blanching water results in marked softening of skins of these products. Salt blanching, however, is not in widespread use because of: (a) difficulties in maintaining the correct concentration of salt during continuous blanching, (b) necessity to compensate for salt pick-up during blanching in preparing brine for canning, and (c) accelerated corrosion of blanching equipment. Adequately controlled salt blanching is effective in preventing undesirable effects of hard water upon texture.

Closely related to salt water blanching is the use of hot brines for peeling certain root vegetables and pimientos. While limited in use, it has certain advantages.

(13) In the regeneration of zeolite or synthetic ion exchange water softener used for the preparation of soft boiler feed water and in the ion exchangers used in stabilizing wines.

(14) In refrigeration, salt is used extensively with ice in cooling refrigerated railroad cars and in maintaining the required low temperatures during the rail shipment of frozen foods. Salt brines are used as secondary heat transfer media in ice manufacture and in cooling air in meat coolers and other cold storage practices.

Commercial refrigeration depends on the great amount of heat absorbed by liquids on vaporization. For instance, when water boils, one pound of water vapor absorbs 1000 times as much heat as is required to raise the temperature of one pound of water one degree.

Primary refrigerants such as ammonia, carbon dioxide and the fluorinated hydrocarbons, such as Freon, will evaporate at low temperatures and pressures to absorb heat from the coils and surroundings. They are then recompressed and cooled to a liquid form to complete the cycle.

Brine is a secondary refrigerant and is cooled by the expansion coil containing the primary refrigerant. The lowest temperature possible with brine is $-6°F$. Brine, as a secondary refrigerant, is used in four kinds of commercial applications:

(a) **Cooling Bath.**—Cold baths are used for ice manufacture. Cans for ice are approximately 1 x 2 x 4 ft. deep, tapered slightly to the bottom. The primary refrigeration coil is submerged in the bath and an agitator circulates the brine around cans and coils. Most operators use a brine temperature of 12° to 18°F. This type of operation may use very little salt since the brine bath will last for years.

(b) **Unit Coolers.**—Unit coolers use brine outside of coils either as a spray or a cascade flow. The brine serves to keep coils defrosted and to increase the surface area available for heat transfer from the circulating air to the cold brine.

(c) **Cold Spray.**—Cold brine under pressure is forced through jets into the air stream, which may circulate by natural draft in smaller installations or by fan and duct in larger installations. This system is used in fruit holding installations. Smaller installations have been used in meat packing plants.

(d) **Car Icing.**—The quantity of salt used for car icing has greatly decreased because of increased popularity of mechanical refrigeration units. The principle involves the lower melting temperature of an ice-salt mixture as compared to that of ice without salt.

Some Considerations in Use of Brine for Refrigeration

(1) **Temperature Limitations of Salt Brine.**—The maximum concentration of brine for use in refrigeration is 88° Salometer, at which the freezing point is $-6°F$. At higher concentrations, salt forms a complex with water that freezes out of solution at a higher temperature. Note freezing points on brine charts. Brine is generally used for cooling air, ice or other products in the temperature range of 25° to 50°F. Below these temperatures, other refrigerating media such as calcium chloride and ethylene glycol may be used. An alternative to the use of the sec-

ondary refrigerant is periodic de-icing of the coils by electric resistance heating.

(2) **Humidity and Temperature Control in Unit Coolers.**—Brine tends to absorb moisture from air and the dry air picks up moisture from the product being stored. The higher the concentration of brine, the greater the tendency to absorb moisture. Refrigerating engineers in general plan to use as weak a brine as possible, consistent with cooling requirements.

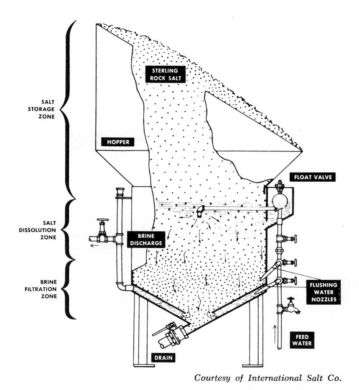

Courtesy of International Salt Co.

FIG. 22. THE LIXATOR AND HOW IT WORKS

(3) **Increase in Volume.**—Since brine tends to absorb moisture, the volume of brine in spray and cascade is continually increasing and the brine must be continually restrengthened. This can be accomplished by adding salt to the brine basin in each unit or, in the case of multiple unit coolers, the Lixator can be used to advantage to continually restrengthen a circulating stream of brine. Note that the Lixator does not make brine from fresh water but restrengthens a portion of the diluted brine (Fig. 22).

In these and other seasoning, preparative and preservative uses, it is necessary that care be taken in the selection of the salt that is most suitable for the product or process and to control its use adequately. Salt is obtained from various sources and is available in various degrees of purity and size and shape of crystals. Functional salts, tailored for the particular process or product, are now available (Simpson 1954). The storage, transport and dispensing of both dry salt and brine have been improved. The proper selection of salt or salt brine that is most economical and which is technologically better adapted to the product or process and its use in proper amounts or concentration is necessary to improve quality and reduce costs. Mechanized bulk handling and dispensing can lower costs and expedite use of salt.

In the stabilization of wine to prevent precipitation of excess cream of tartar, potassium bitartrate, sodium ion exchangers are used. The wine mixed with these or passed through columns packed with these exchangers gives up its potassium ion in return for the sodium ion supplied by the exchanger. Hydrogen exchangers and anion exchangers are used in stabilizing wine against copper and iron turbidity by elimination of excess copper and iron ions or removal of proteins present.

SOURCES, MANUFACTURE AND TYPES

Although food processors need not be familiar with details of the salt industry, a general knowledge of sources, impurities and methods of manufacture is useful in selecting salt best suited for specific applications and for avoiding difficulties. They should know how the source and method of manufacture affect the type of salt which is marketed and the impurities they can expect to encounter which may affect their product. Calcium sulfate, which occurs in the sea, is a particularly troublesome impurity to remove from salt.

In North America, commercial salt, in refined and unrefined form, is available from underground deposits of crystalline salt and from sea water or salt lakes. It is obtained from underground salt by mining and by circulating water through the deposits to produce brine which is evaporated. Solar evaporation in shallow ponds is the principal method for recovering salt from sea water.

Salt of high purity can be made by controlled crystallization from crude brine, but refined salt for food application is ordinarily made by thermal concentration of artificial brines made by dissolving crude salt. Chemical treatment is used to reduce undesirable impurities such as calcium sulphate. Methods of salt manufacture are described by Hester and Diamond (1955), Kaufmann (1960), Locker (1954) and by Tressler and Lemon (1951).

TABLE 23

SALT USES AND TYPE OF SALT RECOMMENDED

Baking	Vacuum Bakers[1]
Candy	Vacuum canners
Canning vegetables	Vacuum canners, salt tablets
Cereal & flour mixes	Vacuum 500 or 1000
Cooking, institutional	Vacuum bakers, table
Crackers	Vacuum grades
Dairy products	
Butter	Vacuum butter
Mayonnaise	Vacuum canners, butter
Cheese, cottage cheese	Vacuum cheese or canners
Fish	
Fillet curing	Vacuum butter or canners
Canning	Vacuum canners, tablets
Caviar, fish roe	Vacuum canners, butter
Oysters & clams	Brine from K. D. grades
Shrimp, canned	Vacuum canners
Meat	
Corned beef	Brine from K. D., vacuum grades
Bacon rubbing	Vacuum butter or canners
Ham, brining	Brine from K. D. vacuum grades
Ham, dry cure	Vacuum butter or canners
Pigs' feet	Brine from K. D. or vacuum grades
Salt pork	Vacuum butter or canners
Sausage mix, seasoned meats	Vacuum grades
Sausage casings	K. D. fine
Nuts & Popcorn	Vacuum, 500, 1000
Okra, curing	Brine from K. D.
Okra, canning	Brine from vacuum grades
Oleomargarine	Vacuum butter, canners
Olives, curing	Brine from K. D.
Olives, canning	Brine from vacuum grades
Pea blanching	Brine from K. D. grades
Peanuts (in shell)	Brine from K. D.
Peppers	Brine from K. D. grades
Pet food	K. D. fine
Poultry de-boning	Brine from K. D. grades
Pretzels	Vacuum grades
Quality grading	Brine from K. D. grades
Spice mixes	Vacuum 500 or 1000
Stabilization of wine	K. D. grades
Tomato products	Vacuum, brine from K. D. grades

[1] Leslie Salt Co. specifically recommends its vacuum grades for direct inclusion in a food product; however, many food processors do use the kiln dried grades.

Salt produced in vacuum pans consists of well defined cubical crystals known in the east as granulated salt and in the west as vacuum salt. Salt produced in a grainer pan is known as flake salt. Very fine flake salt is used for salting butter and also in cake mixes. Coarser flake salt is used for salting pretzels, crackers, peanuts and potato chips. Coarse flake and vacuum salt are used in brinemakers where brine is formed by flowing water through the salt.

Vacuum salt is screened to uniform granule size, free from fines so that the volume-weight relationship is constant and is used in canned foods, processed meats, cheeses, sauerkraut, baking, etc.

Salt from three main sources in North America (mined rock salt, solar evaporated sea salt, crude brine from salt wells or rock deposits) may be used in the unrefined form or further processed. Rock and solar salt are unrefined but are usually screened to coarse, medium or fine size grades. These are used where the presence of impurities, both soluble and insoluble, are not of primary concern. Most food salt, however, is granulated or flake. The flake salt can be produced with particles of a high dissolving rate. A coarse grade of grainer salt, known as GA or "ground alum" is produced for special purposes such as making sauerkraut and curing pickles and fish. Solar salt and evaporated salt can be produced with a high degree of purity.

TABLE 24

TYPICAL CHEMICAL ANALYSIS OF VACUUM SALT[1]
Used in both treated, untreated grades

		Rec'd, %	Dry, %
Water	H_2O at 1100 °F.	0.100	0.000
Calcium sulfate	$CaSO_4$	0.005	0.005
Sodium sulfate	Na_2SO_4	0.005	0.005
Insolubles	SiO_2 & R_2O_3	Trace	Trace
Magnesium chloride	$MgCl_2$	Trace	Trace
Sodium chloride	NaCl	99.890	99.990
		100.000	100.000

Heavy metals: Maximum 5 p.p.m.
Copper: Maximum 2 p.p.m.
Residual iron: Maximum 2 p.p.m.
Filter pad test—APHA Official Milk Sediment Standards, 1953—250 gm. sample:
Fine sediment: Less than 0.2 mg.
Coarse sediment: Less than 0.2 mg.

[1] Source: Leslie Salt Co.

TABLE 25

ADDITIVES USED FOR TREATED VACUUM SALT[1]

Treated Grades	Ingredient	Amount, %
Vacuum 1000, 500, popcorn	Tricalcium phosphate ($Ca_3(PO_4)_2$)	1.00
Vacuum 500 iodized	Tricalcium phosphate	1.00
	Sodium thiosulfate ($Na_2S_2O_3$)	1.10
	Potassium iodide (KI)	0.01
Vacuum table, bakers, granulated	Basic magnesium carbonate (3 $MgO \cdot Mg(OH)_2 \cdot 3H_2O$)	0.50
Vacuum free running, shaker	Basic magnesium carbonate	1.00
Vacuum table, iodized	Basic magnesium carbonate	0.50
	Sodium thiosulfate	0.10
	Potassium iodide	0.01
Vacuum shaker, iodized	Basic magnesium carbonate	1.00
	Sodium thiosulfate	0.10
	Potassium iodide	0.01

[1] Source: Leslie Salt Co.

FIGS 23A AND 23B. TYPES OF SALT AVAILABLE FOR FOOD USE

Coarse flake salt (A) and vacuum cheese salt (B). (A) Magnified six times; (B) magnified twelve times.

FIG. 23C. TYPES OF SALT AVAILABLE FOR FOOD USE
Kiln dried coarse magnified four times.

Particle size and purity affect flow properties of the salt and rate of solubility. The smaller the particle size, and the higher the ratio of surface area to volume of the particle, the faster is the rate of solution. Extremely fine salt, however, produces an undesirable "channeling" in brine tanks and a particle size should be chosen that is optimum for maximum rate of solubility without channeling. The appearance of the salt when used in dry-salting operations such as surface-sprinkler application on crackers or rolls, ease with which the dry salt can be mixed with a product to obtain uniform distribution of salt before solution as in preparing sauerkraut, and ease with which the dry salt can extract water from fish or meat in dry salt curing determine the particular particle size that is best for the product or process.

The particular particle size and shape, and the relative uniformity of particle in a given screen size (freedom from fines in medium or coarse salt) now can be readily obtained. Regulation of crystallization in evaporators (salt-brine slurry density, temperature, type and extent of agitation during crystallization), controlled screening for the more complete separation of fines, and controlled mechanical crushing or pulverization are employed commercially in obtaining the screen sizes desirable for a given product or process. The size grades that are usually preferable for a given product and process are shown in Table 23. Figure 23 shows the three types of salt commercially available (coarse flake, vacuum cheese and kiln dried coarse).

Typical chemical analysis of vacuum salt is shown in Table 24. Additives used in treated vacuum salt are shown in Table 25. The screen grades of vacuum salt are shown in Table 26.

TABLE 26

VACUUM GRADES[1]

Screen analyses reported as per cent passing

Mesh								
U. S. Standard	Tyler Standard	Leslie "1000"	Leslie "500"	Bakers	Granulated & Table	Butter	Canners	Cheese
20	20	...	...	100	100	100	100	100
30	28	...	...	99	98	99	98	89
40	35	...	100	96	59	96	59	11
50	48	100	99	57	7	57	7	1
70	65	99	79	11	1	11	1	...
80	80	98	47	...	...	...	...	...
100	100	97	17	1	1	1	1	...
200	200	83	...	...	...	...	...	...

[1] Source: Leslie Salt Co.

PURITY OF SALT

The type of impurities which may be present in crystallized salt will vary with the impurities present in the saturated brines from which the salt is obtained and the conditions of crystallization. The insoluble impurities (suspended bacteria, protozoa and other organic matter and suspended inorganic matter) occurring in natural salt deposits or growing in partly concentrated brines are removed during washing and refining. The soluble impurities (calcium sulfate, calcium chloride, magnesium chloride, magnesium sulfate and sodium sulfate) are more difficult to remove. Appreciable quantities of soluble impurities may occur in poorly refined salt. Soluble impurities include calcium and magnesium salts and iron, and copper and manganese salts in smaller amounts.

These impurities may affect the appearance, texture and keeping quality of the food to which they are added. The salt commercially available, particularly that developed for special food use, is much purer now than was true previously. Recently introduced improvements in refining, particularly the commercial development of chemical treatment of the brine prior to crystallization (Brighton and Dice 1931; Kaufmann 1960) has led to the production and distribution of salt of high purity. Even the modern rock salt prepared from clean crystal grade of crushed rock salt is marketed with an average purity of 98.95 per cent sodium chloride; solar salt with a minimum purity of 99 per cent and evaporated salt with a high minimum purity of 99.9 per cent are now commercially available. Sea salt containing all the chemical elements originally present in sea water but treated so that it is free-running is now available for special dietary uses (Lee 1955).

The extent to which salt manufacturers have been able to improve refining operations is best reflected in the changes that have occurred in the Federal Government Specifications for quality of refined salt. The table or dairy salt used by canners in the period shortly after World War I was "a fine-grained crystalline salt, containing, on a water-free basis, not more than 1.4 per cent of calcium sulfate, nor more than 0.5 per cent of calcium and magnesium chlorides, nor more than 0.1 per cent of matters insoluble in water." Bigelow and Stevenson (1923) pointed out that this specification permitted the presence of a total of 0.59 per cent calcium and would lead to a brine containing 17 lbs. of salt per 100 gal. which would have a hardness of 300 p.p.m. expressed as calcium carbonate; sufficient, when used as a brine in canning peas, to harden the product and reduce its commercial grade. They pointed out that in 1923 the majority of canners would be unable to secure a salt containing less than 0.3 per cent of total calcium. The last Federal specification still allowed the same degree of impurities on a moisture-free basis in table salt but canners and other food processors are now able to obtain salt of much greater degree of purity than the minimum of 98.0 per cent. Recognition of the effects of calcium and magnesium impurities in contributing to hardness of vegetables such as peas and beans (Bigelow and Stevenson 1923; Greenleaf 1932) of their role in altering flavor (enhancing bitterness) and particularly of the effect of trace amounts of iron and copper in promoting oxidative rancidity and other flavor changes in foods prone to oxidation has led to the demand for and the production of salt with a minimum of these impurities. Low-cost salt to meet the rigid tolerances set by a growing number of processors is now being produced. Straight sodium chloride crystals of over 99.9 per cent purity are now being produced commercially. The calcium and magnesium content in such salt has been reduced below the point where it can affect delicate flavors at the concentration in which it is used (usually two per cent) and the iron and copper content of such salt can be reduced to below two p.p.m. At this level the pro-oxidant effect of the impurities in salt is sufficiently low for usual storage conditions.

FUNCTIONAL OR TAILORED SALTS

Salts that are particularly adapted to a given product or process can be manufactured not only by carefully controlled elimination of undesirable impurities and proper size grading but also by the incorporation of chemical additives which may influence physical properties, enhance natural seasoning, improve palatability or keeping quality or meet specific problems.   One of the first additives was the addition of a chemical which would decrease the hygroscopic quality of salt (its ability to absorb water vapor) and thus prevent caking.   Originally starch was added to table salt for this purpose but was replaced by basic magnesium carbonate, tricalcium phosphate or calcium carbonate (Moss 1933A, B) and more recently sodium aluminum silicate.   Driers are usually added in amounts of $1/2$ to 1 per cent.   These driers coat the salt crystals and moisture is absorbed preferentially on them.   Calcium stearate is generally used in much smaller amounts, and its action seems to be the for-

TABLE 27

TYPICAL ADDITIVES TO SALT

Additive	Form of Product	Use
Antioxidant	Fine bulk Flake salt	Potato chips, nuts, French fried potatoes, shoestrings, to inhibit oxidative deterioration
Ascorbic acid	Tablets	Canning mushrooms, to improve color and flavor retention
Citric acid	Tablets	Canning bean sprouts, to improve color and flavor retention
Calcium chloride	Tablets	Canning white potatoes, whole tomatoes, for firming
Monosodium glutamate (MSG)	Tablets	Canning to intensify flavor
Tricalcium phosphate	Bulk salt	Cake and flour mixes, to prevent caking
Nitrites and nitrates	Bulk salt	Preservation of color in meat
Sugar	Bulk salt	Meat
Natural or artificial smoke	Bulk salt	Meat curing
Vitamins	Baking salt	Bread making

mation of a water repellent coating.   Recently it has been found that a few parts per million of sodium ferrocyanide changes the crystal habit of salt in such a way as to prevent caking.   The addition of potassium iodide (0.01 per cent) to salt for the control of goiter is another example of a tailor-made salt.   Its use in preventive medicine was based on the recognized widespread use of table salt.   At first, the potassium iodide was added alone and later when the instability of the added iodide was recognized, stabilizers which would prevent loss of added potassium iodide were required.   One-tenth per cent of sodium thiosulfate or dextrose is usually added with the iodide.   Iodized salt, however, generally should not be used in food processing because of the tendency of potassium iodide to decompose and form free iodine, with possible adverse effects on color and flavor of many food products (Simons et al. 1955).

Salt containing added calcium chloride or calcium sulfate is available for use in canned tomatoes, potatoes, and other products whose firming by added calcium is desired; salt containing added antioxidant is available for seasoning fried potato products and oil roasted nuts, and salt with added ascorbic acid for mushroom canning. It is possible to enhance natural seasoning by adding citric acid or monosodium glutamate. Table 27 lists the several additives that are now available.

HANDLING SALT IN THE PLANT

Dry Salt

The salt used in food processing is shipped as dry salt in multiwall paper bags of 10, 25, or 100 lbs. weight, in bulk bins on a flatbed, or in the bulk in hoppered or top loaded vans in trucks or railroad cars. Salt to be added to the food as dry salt or after dissolving in water must be protected against contamination during shipment and unloading. This is particularly true of the high purity sodium chloride which is evaporated from salt brines chemically treated to remove objectionable calcium and magnesium compounds. Although the paper bags in which pure salt is shipped have one ply of polyethylene as a protection against moisture absorption, they must be protected against damage during handling and must be stored properly to minimize caking or hardening. The bags of salt should be properly palletized and stored in a dry warehouse, away from damp floors, damp products or cold surfaces, particularly those likely to collect and drip condensate upon the salt. Salt stocks should be rotated and not allowed to remain in storage longer than necessary. Bags of salt showing indications of moisture absorption should be separated promptly from others. When moderate caking occurs the bags should be dropped or rolled into a free running condition. Salt stored in bags piled one on top of another should be restacked occasionally to prevent hardening of the lower sacks in the pile through compression due to the weight of the salt on top.

All vacuum grades of salt intended for human consumption should be shipped in bags or in coated dual stainless steel or aluminum alloy covered hopper cars or trucks or in covered portable bins. The cars or trucks may be unloaded mechanically by using belt conveyors, bucket elevators or screw conveyors, or pneumatically. All bulk handling systems tend to break down particle size, and to minimize this special designs are necessary in some cases. Hydraulic unloading is suitable for discharging salt into wet storage, such as brine pit or other large storage brine maker. The salt after unloading may be stored in customer owned portable bins, in bulk storage bins or in brine makers. In food grade salt storage, steel bins coated with an FDA-approved plastic coating or stainless steel, aluminum, or reinforced plastic may be used. The latter are more expensive than coated bins. To facilitate discharge, the bottom of the bins should be sloped to the discharge point at a grade of at least 45° and preferably 60° and the salt should be protected against absorption of moisture and caking. This can be done by the use of porous bagged silica gel desiccant (from 3 to 5 lbs.) in each two-ton bin.[1] Air pads installed in the discharge cone through which a small flow of dry air (about two cubic feet per minute per square foot of cross-sectional area in the bin) is maintained will maintain salt in free-flowing condition. Typical mechanical, pneumatic and hydraulic systems are shown in Figs. 24, 25 and 26.

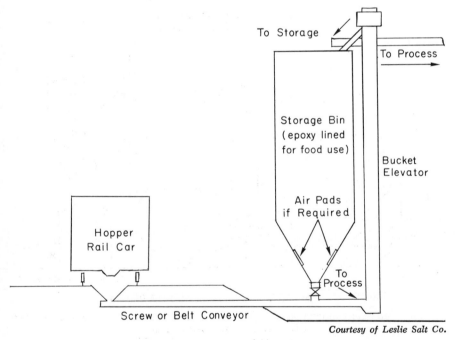

Courtesy of Leslie Salt Co.

FIG. 24.   MECHANICAL UNLOADING AND STORAGE OF DRY SALT

The handling of the dry salt in the plant can be greatly improved by suitable mechanization. For handling and dispensing batch amounts of salt, such as are needed in butter and cheese making and similar operations, specially constructed storage and dispensing bins are available. A bin designed of No. 316 stainless steel can be quickly washed and steri-

---

[1] Patent pending by Leslie Salt Co.

lized. Bottom salt is used first and the salt may be gate dispensed, thus eliminating need of returning excess salt.

Bulk salter machines for dispensing salt and other dry ingredients directly into cans also are available. These salters (Fig. 27) hold 50 lbs. of salt and dispense salt into tin or glass containers. The cans or glass containers, approaching the salter machine on a can line, furnish the power which turns its metering disk and causes a charge of clean dry salt to fall into each can. Even if the cans flow with uneven spacing, they will each receive the correct amount of salt. The machine has a speed of up to

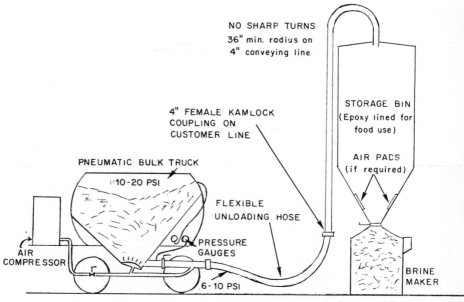

Courtesy of Leslie Salt Co.

FIG. 25. PNEUMATIC UNLOADING AND STORAGE OF DRY SALT

Pressuring air enters through aerating pad forcing salt through discharge nozzle where it is picked up by conveying air.

400 cans per min. on the smaller cans and up to 100 cans per min. on No. 10 cans. It will deliver up to 1200 grains of salt into No. 10 cans and up to 300 grains into the smaller cans. They should be protected against excessive exposure to steam or moisture which may cause clogging of the discharge spout.

The salt to be added per can of vegetables will vary with individual choice but usually is in the following range:

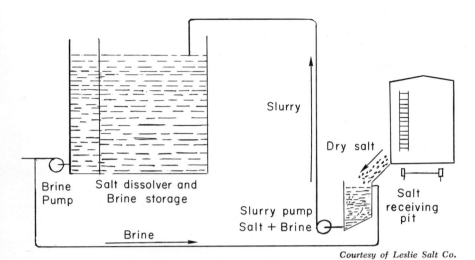

Courtesy of Leslie Salt Co.

FIG. 26. HYDRAULIC UNLOADING AND BRINE STORAGE OF SALT

Saturated brine circulates through the system picking up salt at the brine receiving pit. No fresh water is added and because brine is saturated, no salt is dissolved. Slurry will normally be 20–30 per cent solids. Recommended slurry pipeline velocity is 10 f.p.s.

Courtesy of Leslie Salt Co.

FIG. 27. DRY SALTERS FOR ADDITION OF (LEFT TO RIGHT)

(a) Dry seasoning. (b) Bulk salt. (c) Salt tablets.

Product	No. 2 Can, Grains	No. 10 Can, Grains
Asparagus	60–90	250–350
Corn	30–35	150
Tomatoes	30–35	150–200
Tomato juice	50–60	250–300
Green vegetables, string beans beets and mixed vegetables	50–75	250–300

Salt Tablets and Their Use

Salt tablets containing the exact amount of salt required for each container of a particular product, e.g., for each size of can, are available to better control flavor. Salt tablets varying from 5 to 400 grains in size, containing either pure salt alone, or mixtures of salt and other ingredients (calcium chloride and salt, ascorbic acid and salt, citric acid and salt, monosodium glutamate and salt, spices and salt, etc.) are available (Fig. 28). Salt and calcium chloride are used in tomato canning to give firmer, better appearing tomatoes. Salt is used in tomato juice and salt, sugar and spices are used in the packing of "stewed tomatoes." Salt and spice mixtures are used to flavor green beans. Salt and citric acid combinations are used to add flavor and prevent spoilage in many vegetable and fish products. Salt with anhydrous stannous chloride and citric acid is used to impart "tin" taste to glass packed vegetables as well as to maintain the natural looking color in the vegetables—primarily asparagus. These tablets must also be protected from moisture, to prevent hydrolysis and oxidation of stannous chloride. Tablets are packed in 50-lb. multiwall paper bags; made-to-order tablets are packed in 50- to 55-lb. corrugated shipping containers having six subdivided cartons. Salt tablet depositor machines fitted to operate with the more widely used fillers are available which mechanically deposit a salt tablet into each can or container before filling. These machines operate at speeds up to 700 tablets per min. and operate in various ways; from a simple star wheel feed to a high speed geared unit model with automatic electric controls. The star wheel driven depositor is used on hand packed fillers. The tablet is picked up by a pick-up disk and carried by the down-take disk to a point directly over the can where the tablet is dropped. The new model actuated by a star wheel but fitted with a down-take disk in place of a spout is shown in Fig. 27 (p. 99). Salt tablet dispensers should be protected against excessive exposure to steam or moisture.

Brine Preparation and Use

The handling of salt in the plant can be greatly expedited by the preparation of a saturated brine in a brine maker and pumping this to the point

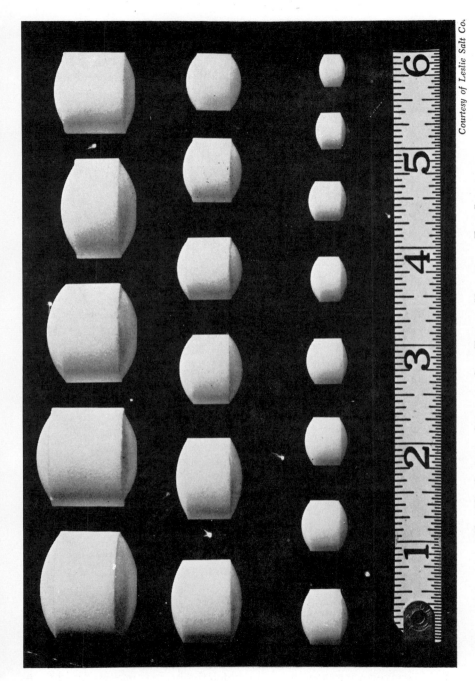

FIG. 28. SIZES AND SHAPES OF SALT TABLETS USED IN THE FOOD INDUSTRY

of use as such or after dilution with water to the desired degree. Brines used for quality grading of vegetables, brine peeling, and similar use can be prepared in a specially constructed tank or vat, filled with coarse salt, in which saturated brine is formed. The brine from the briner, which may be located at ground level at a distance from the operating area, may be readily and economically pumped to an upper level or wherever desired. Suitable mixer valves with flow control may be used to dilute it to proper strength before delivery.

Courtesy of Leslie Salt Co.

FIG. 29.   OVERHEAD SPRAYS USED TO CONVERT DRY SALT INTO
SLURRY FOR PUMPING INTO BRINE MAKER

Brine preparation and dispensing units can be used also to prepare the desired mixture of salt, sugar and other dry ingredients, and dilute this with water before addition to the can or glass containers. These depend on the design of efficient dry salt and ingredient automatic dispensing bins which discharge the dry ingredients in proper amounts through a suitable conveyor into a container in which the brine is prepared and from which it is pumped to the filling lines.

Combined brine and dry storage of salt makes salt handling even more efficient. In these large scale storage and dissolution tank installations salt is dumped into wet storage dissolving pits. The salt layer under the brine serves as a filter to produce clear saturated brine as it is withdrawn. The pits are made of concrete ànd may be placed in unused basement areas; brine-making is automatic and does not require close supervision. In these pits, the salt packs more than in dry storage and will have a bulk density of approximately 62.0 lbs. per cu. ft. in comparison with 60 lbs. for crude undried salt. The dissolved salt will weigh 10.4 lbs. per cu. ft. making a total weight of 101.5 lbs. per cu. ft. of combined storage of wetted salt and brine. The required storage volume will average about 27.6 cu. ft. per ton of total salt. In comparison crude salt will require 33.4 cu. ft. per ton of bulk storage and 40 cu. ft. per ton of bag storage space.

Specially constructed storage bins to meet the particular conditions existing may be designed through the assistance of local technical sales personnel. Tanks or vats already available may be reconverted into brine dissolvers and storage units. In one such operation, salt is received into a receiving tank and wetted with overhead sprayers before pumping as a slurry into a briner (Fig. 29).

Brine Concentration

The concentration of a solution of salt is usually measured by Baumé hydrometer or salometer. The Baumé hydrometer scale originally was calibrated as per cent of salt by weight, but as shown in Table 28 the present Baumé scale indicates appreciably less than the true per cent of salt. The salometer or salinometer scale originally was taken to indicate the per cent of saturation at 60°F. but was based on the assumption that a saturated salt solution contained 25 per cent by weight of salt. A saturated salt brine at 60°F. contains 26.395 per cent of pure sodium chloride and has a specific gravity of 1.204. For this reason, as shown in Fig. 30, the standard salometer degree is appreciably higher than 4 X per cent of salt by weight used in canners' salometer scale. Table 28 gives the weight of the brine in pounds per gallon and pounds per cubic foot and the weight of salt that must be added to 100 gal. of water to obtain the salt content desired.

The freezing point of water is depressed by addition of salt, and the freezing point of salt solution decreases from 32°F. for pure water to —5.8°F. for a solution containing 23.31 per cent salt. At this temperature and concentration both ice and salt crystallize out in a solid phase known as the eutectic mixture. This has a latent heat of fusion of 101.5 B.t.u. per lb. in comparison with 80 for ice. Sodium chloride brines, therefore,

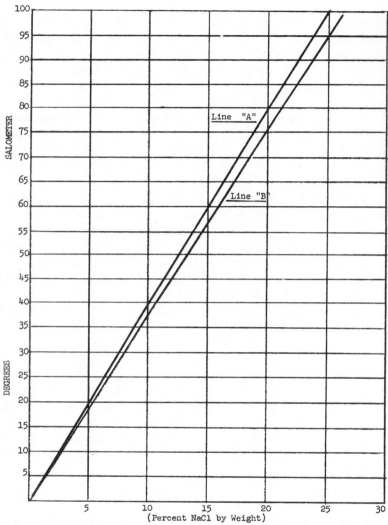

Line "A":   Canner's Salometer Scale (100° = 25% NaCl by weight at 60° F.)
Line "B":   Standard Salometer Scale (100° = 26.4% NaCl by weight at 60° F.)

Courtesy of Leslie Salt Co.

Fig. 30.   Chart Showing Relation Between Degrees Salometer and
Per Cent NaCl by Weight

can be used as secondary heat transfer mediums only above the eutectic
temperature in the usual ice making and brine spray cooling operations.
However because of the higher heat capacity of eutectic ice, salt and
water mixtures can be frozen in sealed cans and used as refrigerants in
transport and storage of smaller quantities of perishables.

TABLE 28

SPECIFIC GRAVITY, BAUMÉ, SALOMETER DEGREE AND FREEZING POINT OF BRINES OF VARIOUS
CONCENTRATIONS

Salt, by Weight, %	Specific Gravity, 68°/39.2°	Salometer Degrees, 59°F.	Baumé Degrees, 68°F.	Weight		Salt, Lbs. per 100 Gal. Water
				Lbs. per Gal.	Lbs. per Cu. Ft.	
0	6.9982	0.0	0.0	8.34	62.4	0.0
5	1.0341	18.2	4.8	8.62	64.6	43.9
6	1.0413	22.5	5.8	8.69	65.1	53.2
7	1.0486	26.0	6.8	8.76	65.5	62.7
8	1.0559	29.6	7.7	8.81	66.0	72.5
9	1.0633	33.5	8.7	8.86	66.5	82.5
10	1.0707	37.2	9.6	8.93	66.9	92.6
11	1.0782	41.1	10.6	9.00	67.4	103.0
12	1.0857	44.8	11.5	9.06	67.8	113.5
13	1.0933	48.7	12.4	9.12	68.3	124.5
14	1.1009	52.6	13.3	9.18	68.8	136.0
15	1.1081	56.8	14.2	9.24	69.3	147.0
16	1.1162	60.0	15.1	9.31	69.8	158.8
17	1.1241	64.0	16.0	9.38	70.3	170.8
18	1.1319	68.0	16.9	9.44	70.8	183.1
19	1.1399	71.7	17.8	9.51	71.3	195.7
20	1.1478	75.2	18.7	9.58	71.8	208.5
21	1.1559	79.1	19.6	9.64	72.3	221.8
22	1.1640	82.8	20.4	9.71	72.8	235.0
23	1.1722	86.8	21.3	9.78	73.3	249.0
24	1.1804	90.2	22.2	9.85	73.8	263.1
25	1.1888	94.0	23.1	9.91	74.3	278.0
26	1.1972	97.4	23.9	9.98	75.8	292.8

BIBLIOGRAPHY

ANDERSON, K. W. 1956. Absorption of salt by whole crayfish during cooking. Food Preservation Quarterly (Australia) *16*, No. 1, 14–15.

BIGELOW, W. D., and STEVENSON, A. E. 1923. The effect of hard water in canning vegetables. Natl. Canners Assoc., Res. Lab. Bull. *20L*.

BRIGHTON, T. B., and DICE, C. M. 1931. Increasing the purity of common salt. Ind. Eng. Chem. *23*, 336–339.

ESKEW, G. L. 1948. Salt the Fifth Element. J. G. Ferguson and Associates, Chicago, Ill.

FABIAN, F. W., and BLUM, H. B. 1943. Relative taste potency of some basic food constituents and their competitive and compensatory action. Food Research 8, 179–193.

GREENLEAF, C. A. 1932. Purity of salt important in quality pea separation. Food Inds. *4*, 211–213.

HESTER, A. S., and DIAMOND, H. W. 1955. Salt manufacture. Ind. Eng. Chem. *47*, 672–683.

JENSEN, L. B. 1953. Man's Foods. Garrard Press, Champaign, Ill.

KAUFMANN, D. W. (Editor) 1960. Sodium Chloride. The Production and Properties of Salt and Brine. Reinhold Publishing Corp., New York.

KOJIMA, N., and BROWN, H. D. 1955. The effect of iodized salt in processed fruits and vegetables. Food Technol. 9, 103–107.

LEE, J. A. 1955. Elements from sea captured by new process. Food Eng. *27*, No. 10, 90–91.

LEPKOVSKY, S. 1948. The physiological basis of voluntary food intake (appetite?). Advan. Food Res. *1*, 105–148.

LOCKER, C. D. 1954. Salt. In KIRK, R. E., and OTHMER, D. F. (Editors), Encyclopedia of Chemical Technology *12*, 67–82. Interscience Encyclopedia, New York.

Moss, H. T. 1933A. Tricalcium phosphate as a caking inhibitor in salt and sugar. Ind. Eng. Chem. *25*, 142–147.

Moss, H. T. 1933B. How to prevent caking in powdered foods. Food Inds. *5*, 133–135.

MURRAY, R. V., and PETERSON, G. T. 1951. Water for canning. Continental Can Co., Res. Bull. No. *22*, 1–27.

SIMONS, R. L., HOWE, R. N., and KLOMPARENS, K. 1955. Cut salt costs up to 3c./lb. Food Processing *16*, No. 18, 44–45.

SIMPSON, R. A. 1954. Tailored salts provide many plus-values. Food Eng. *26*, No. 7, 78, 79, 130, 133.

SJÖSTRÖM, L. S., and CAIRNCROSS, S. E. 1955. Role of sweetness in food flavor. Advan. Chem. Ser., No. *12*, 108–113.

TRESSLER, D. K., and LEMON, J. MC, W. 1951. Marine Products of Commerce. 2nd Edition. Reinhold Publishing Corp., New York.

VAUGHN, R. H. 1954. Lactic acid fermentation of cucumbers, sauerkraut and olives. In Underkofler, L. A. and Hickey, R. J. (Editors) Industrial Fermentations. Vol. *2*, 417–478. Chemical Publishing Co., New York.

WISTREICH, H. E., MORSE, R. E., and KENYON, L. J. 1959. Curing of ham: I. A study of sodium chloride accumulation. Food Technol. *13*, 441–443.

WISTREICH, H. E., MORSE, R. E., and KENYON, L. J. 1960. Curing of ham: II. A study of sodium chloride accumulation. Food Technol *14*, 549–551.

CHAPTER 5

R. L. Lloyd | Starches in Food Processing

INTRODUCTION

In 1962, Americans consumed 400 million pounds of starch in a variety of processed foods. A convenient, "gourmet" meal might include canned cream of mushroom soup, followed by a ready-to-serve beef pie, served with a (French-dressing-topped) green salad and hot rolls, followed by an instant pudding dessert.

Starches are important ingredients in each of these "convenience" foods, used to improve texture, consistency, shelf life, etc. Since there is a great variety in sources, modification and properties of starches, processors need to know the product best suited for specific applications. While the suppliers' chemists furnish dependable information, it is important for processors to understand the properties and applications of various starches when used in products in which they are interested.

The author's long experience in studying the functional uses of starch has revealed that there are numerous factors to be considered in selecting starch for a specific application: What is the starch intended to do? Under what conditions and in what equipment will the starch be combined with the food? What will be the storage conditions of products containing it?

To select the best starch, it is necessary to know the dispersion, gel and storage characteristics of many starches. Obviously, the same starch is not best suited for a clear, flowable cherry pie filling, for a clean-cutting, opaque chocolate cream pie, and for a creamy smooth salad dressing.

It is well for food processors to take the technical representative of the starch supplier into their confidence, because many factors affect the choice of the optimum starch ingredient for processed food. Formulations, methods and equipment used in processing, storage of processed foods, and even container size may influence the selection of a starch.

Many plants store starch as a source of carbohydrate and energy. Competitive cost of raw materials and manufacture, as well as physical properties influence the starch manufacturer's selection of starch sources. Commercial sources include the *grains:* regular (dent) corn, waxy maize, wheat, sorghum; certain *roots or tubers:* white (russet) potatoes, sweet

---

R. L. LLOYD is a Special Research and Development Consultant in Richmond, Calif.

potatoes, cassava (tapioca-mannioca) and arrowroot; and a *trunk,* the Sago palm.

Purified starch may be described as a white, dry granular material insoluble in alcohol and dispersible in hot water with the formation of a viscous sol or gel. Starch is used as the raw material for manufacturing adhesives, dextrin, corn syrups and dextrose.

Starch is an important ingredient in many food products including meats, desserts, salad dressing, baby foods, canned, frozen and baked specialties and confectionery. Table 29 indicates types of starch used

TABLE 29

SUMMARY OF STARCHES USED IN FOOD PROCESSING

Where It Is Used	What Is Used	What It Does and How It Behaves
Fruit pie fillings	Amioca-modified	Correct consistency; clarity; good flavor
	Common corn—untreated	Firm fillings
	Tapioca-untreated	Gummy texture
Cracker and cookie doughs	Common corn	Diluent; better flavor
Arrowroot cookies	Arrowroot	Indispensable ingredient
Ice cream cones and sugar wafers	Common corn Tapioca	Better texture
Soda crackers	Corn-pregelatinized	
Sandwich fillings	Corn-redried Tapioca Soya flour	
Icings	Amioca-pregelatinized	Absorbs moisture
	Common corn-pregelatinized	Thickener
	Tapioca-pregelatinized Wheat-pregelatinized Potato-pregelatinized	
Blintzes and knishes	Amioca-modified	Easy handling; better flavor
Flavored chips	Common corn Tapioca	Easy handling; better flavor
Dusting powder	Common corn	Sanitation; easy handling
Gum confections	Common corn—acid modified for thin boiling	Used extensively; fluid when hot; good gel, when cool
	Common corn-unmodified	Can be used; difficult to process
	Common corn-oxidized	Clear product; good gel
Marshmallows and nougats	Amioca	Stabilizer
	Common corn	Stabilizer; leaves starchy taste
Candy molding	Common corn—redried with added oils	Moisture absorber; shapes candy
Revolving pan goods	Common corn—redried	Moisture absorber; fills cracks
Chewing gum	Common corn—pregelatinized	Dusting
Sugar	Common corn-dried	Dispersing agent

TABLE 29 (*continued*)

Where It Is Used	What Is Used	What It Does and How It Behaves
Salad dressing	Blends of modified corn starches	Stabilizer; emulsifier good consistency; good storage life
Meat loaf	Corn—pregelatinized	Fat disperser
Bologna	Corn—pregelatinized	Fat disperser; binder
Frankfurters	Corn—pregelatinized	Water absorber
Pan grease	Common corn—pregelatinized	Prevents sticking
	Tapioca	
	Soya flour	
Baking powder	Common corn	Dispersing agent; protection during storage
	Rice	Good for prolonged storage
	Wheat	
Cream-style corn	Common corn—modified	Good consistency; stability
	Common corn—oxidized	Used in conventional processing operations
	Amioca-modified	Good consistency and stability
	Blends of Amioca and common corn	Used in high-temperature, rotary processing
Canned pie fillings	Amioca—modified	Resists acid; enhances flavor; stabilizer
	Tapioca	
Soups	Common corn	Consistency; stability
	Tapioca	
Chinese specialties	Amioca—cross-linked	Stability; clarity
Baby foods	Amioca—modified	Good consistency; stability; better flavor
Beer	Corn and rice (known as brewers grits)	Malt source; clarity
Frozen fruit pies	Amioca—pregelatinized	No cooking required; good stability; consistency, and flavor
Frozen meat pies	Amioca—varying degrees of modification with added wheat flour	Stability; consistency; good flavor
Prepared mixes for cakes and doughnuts	Common corn—pregelatinized	Tenderizer
	Wheat—pregelatinized	
Chocolate drink	Common corn—pregelatinized	Stabilizer
	Amioca—pregelatinized	
	Tapioca	
Cook-up puddings	Common corn	Good gel consistency
Instant puddings	Amioca—pregelatinized	No cooking required; choice of starch depends on gel strength preferred
	Potato—pregelatinized	
	Common corn—pregelatinized	
Tapioca pudding	Tapioca	
	Blend of amioca and common corn	
Packaging (in the future)	High amylose	Soluble packages

in various food products and the purpose served by the starch or by a flour containing a considerable percentage of starch. Although this table lists several starches, corn starch use predominates. About 90 per cent of all starch sold in the United States is from corn, and for this reason it is appropriate to insert a description of the method used in manufacturing this starch.

THE MANUFACTURE OF CORN STARCH

In obtaining starch from corn the various steps have been integrated into an orderly, continuous and efficient process.

The process, as outlined in Fig. 31, begins with shelled corn which is first cleaned to remove pieces of cob and any foreign substance. In these cleaners, strong currents of air blow out the unwanted light material, sifters remove heavy foreign particles, and electromagnets extract any stray bits of iron such as wire or nails that may have entered the corn after it was shelled or during transportation to the refining plant.

The cleaned corn goes first into huge vertical tanks, where it is soaked or "steeped" for about 40 hr. in warm water slightly acidified with sulfur dioxide, to prevent undesirable bacterial fermentation and help to extract soluble matter from the corn. This also softens the hull and loosens the protein-starch complex so the starch and other components can be separated more easily.

After steeping is complete, the "steepwater" is drawn off and softened kernels, in a stream of water, are run through degerminating or attrition mills which tear the kernels apart, freeing the germ and loosening the hull. From these mills, the wet mass of macerated kernels with freed germs is washed into tanks called germ separators. The germs, being lighter than the other parts of the kernel, float on the surface while other particles settle to the bottom. The surface-borne germs are then skimmed off, after which the remaining mixture of starch, gluten and hulls is finely ground in steel mills of special design.

The finely ground wet mash coming from these mills is first washed through a series of shakers to remove the particles of hull. The shakers are simply rectangular vibrating sieves made of nylon bolting cloth. Starch and gluten slurry passes through the sieves while bits of hull and fiber tumble off the end.

Only starch and gluten now remain to be separated. For many years this separation was accomplished by flowing the starch-gluten slurry over "starch tables," which were flat-bottomed shallow troughs about 2 ft. wide and 100 ft. long, sloping gradually to the discharge end. The starch-gluten slurry was introduced at the upper end and slowly flowed down the length of the table. Here, gravity accomplished the separation, the

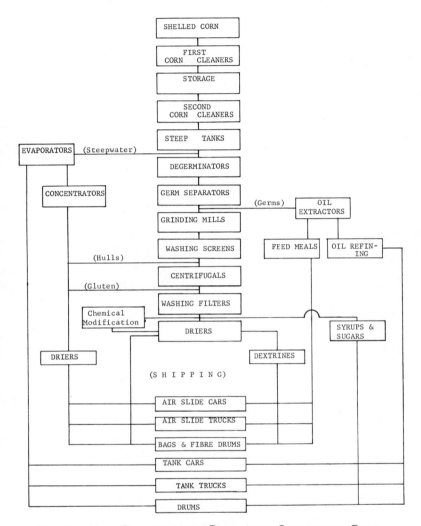

FIG. 31.   FLOW DIAGRAM OF THE RECOVERY OF STARCH FROM CORN

starch particles, being heavier, sank to the bottom and the gluten, being lighter, flowed over the lower edge.   Periodically, the starch deposited on the tables was flushed off, and then washed and dried.

Today, the old starch tables have disappeared in favor of centrifugal machines which separate the starch from the gluten more effectively.   In principle, these machines operate like a cream separator, the lighter gluten particles flowing out at the center and the heavier starch particles at the periphery.

After separation from the gluten, the starch, still in a slurry, is filtered and washed several times to remove remaining traces of nonstarch materials. After the final filtering, the starch may be dried and packaged for market or given further treatment to produce specialty starches.

Starch in dried form as it comes from the corn refining process and without further treatment is known commercially as regular, untreated or unmodified corn starch. In this form it is frequently referred to as pearl starch. When this starch is pulverized, it is known as powdered starch.

STARCH CHEMISTRY IN BRIEF

Many plants store starch as a reserve food supply, but few plants have a high enough starch content to make them commercially important sources of starch. Among the roots and tubers, potato, tapioca and arrowroot are processed commercially. A small amount of sago starch is recovered from the Sago palm stem. Of the grains—rice, wheat and maize—corn is the most important. About 90 per cent of the starch used in food is corn starch.

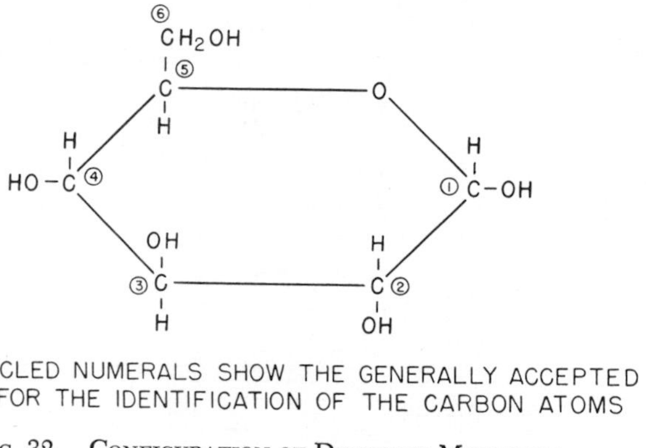

THE CIRCLED NUMERALS SHOW THE GENERALLY ACCEPTED ORDER FOR THE IDENTIFICATION OF THE CARBON ATOMS

FIG. 32.   CONFIGURATION OF DEXTROSE MOLECULE

Starches from each source differ in important respects, but they have one thing in common, the same general chemical composition. All can be broken down into dextrose—a simple sugar containing 6 carbon atoms, 12 hydrogen atoms and 6 oxygen atoms. When analyzed, starch is found to be composed of multiple units of anhydrous dextrose. Materials formed by chemical combination of four or more units of the same molecule are called polymers. The formula $(C_6H_{10}O_5)_n$ is the generic formula for starch. The n is the number of units in a particular dextrose polymer (starch).

To understand fully how starch behaves in food processing operations, the chemist must know how the dextrose anhydride units are arranged in the starch molecule. The arrangement and the number of units determine many of the industrially important properties of a specific starch. In dextrose the carbon, hydrogen and oxygen are arranged as shown in Fig. 32.

When nature combines some 250–400 dextrose units, a molecule of one of the starches is formed. Starches differ from one another in the number of dextrose units they contain and how they are joined. One way in which the dextrose units may be combined is in a straight chain, as

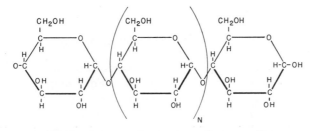

FIG. 33.   DEXTROSE UNITS COMBINED IN STRAIGHT CHAIN AS IN AMYLOSE

illustrated in Fig. 33. The starch having this straight chain structure is called amylose. No naturally occurring starch is composed exclusively of such straight chains.

In 1958, American Maize-Products Co. and the National Starch and Chemical Co. grew a special corn called Amylomaize which contains about 55 per cent of this straight chain type of starch. It is still too new to have many commercial applications, but starch chemists are confidently predicting a big future for Amylomaize.

Dextrose may also combine to form complicated chains with many side branches. This type of starch is called amylopectin and is found in waxy maize type corn as illustrated in Fig. 34. Commercially, amylopectin starch is called Amioca. Originally, waxy maize was grown only in China.

In 1936–1937, a high starch content waxy maize was developed by the Iowa Agricultural Experiment Station. Since then American Maize and National Starch have grown commercial crops of waxy maize and have conducted extensive research into its properties and industrial uses. It is now widely used in food products.

Some of the properties of waxy maize starches may be found in glutinous rice starch originally produced in China. Limited quantities now are grown in California.

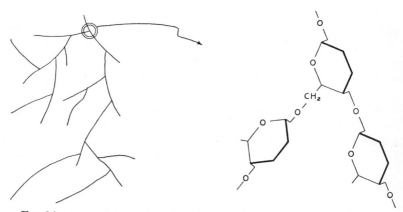

FIG. 34. ILLUSTRATING THE CONFIGURATION OF AMYLOPECTIN STARCH

All of the starches obtained from regular crops of grains and tubers are mixtures of both amylose and amylopectin. For example, corn starch is composed of 27 per cent amylose and 73 per cent amylopectin, while tapioca starch has 80 per cent of the branched chain starch and only 20 per cent of the straight chain type. Many of the properties important to the food processor are determined by the relative amounts of the two starch fractions present in the material being used. Table 30 gives the

TABLE 30

COMPOSITION OF USEFUL STARCHES

Starch	Amylose, %	%	Dextrose Units
Amioca	0	100	. . .
Amylomaize	55	45	250
Corn starch (ordinary)	27	73	250
Potato	25	75	500
Rice	15	85	. . .
Tapioca	20	80	450
Wheat	20	80	. . .

percentages of the two types of arrangement in common starches and the number of dextrose units that go to make up a molecule.

Because starch is often employed as a thickener and stabilizer in food, the gelling, flow and clarity of its solutions are of special interest. These properties depend on how the starch polymers are held together. Each plant organizes its starch into bundles and these form characteristically shaped granules. Corn granules are rather large and many-sided; rice grains look very much like corn, only smaller. Potato and sago particles are large with an oval appearance. The different shapes of some common starch granules are shown in Fig. 35. Strong attractive forces which hold the bundles together makes it difficult to break them apart and thus disperse the starch in water.

When a starch-water mixture is heated, the starch bundles separate slightly, permitting water to enter. As a result, the granule swells or gelatinizes, and the starch suspension becomes viscous. If heating is continued, starch suspensions composed of large amounts of amylose, corn starch for example, become thick. Suspensions of waxy maize or potato starch that have greater amounts of amylopectin become watery on continued heating. When the suspensions are cooled, they set or gel in varying degrees depending on the type of starch. Table 31 indicates the behavior of some starches when heated with water and then cooled.

TABLE 31

BEHAVIOR OF SOME STARCH SOLS WHEN HEATED AND COOLED

Starch	Beginning of Gelatinization (5% sol.), °F.	Clarity of Starch Paste	Texture of Starch Paste
Amioca	158.0	Clear to cloudy	Cohesive; nongelling on standing
Arrowroot	167.0	Clear to cloudy	Cohesive and fluid
Corn (ordinary)	176.0	Opaque	Gel
Potato	147.2	Clear	Cohesive and fluid
Sago	165.2	Clear to cloudy	Cohesive and fluid
Tapioca	145.4	Clear	Cohesive; gels on standing
Wheat	170.6	Cloudy	Fluid

With the new knowledge of the structure of starch, the chemist can manipulate starch molecules or parts of molecules to create starches with desirable properties for special purposes. If a more soluble, more stable starch is required, starch is treated with sodium hypochlorite. This oxidizes the OH group in the molecule (which makes it more soluble) and changes the structure so that molecules cannot unite with one another (which makes gelling more difficult). In general, oxidized starches have a shorter cooking time, are more fluid, give less turbid suspensions, and do not congeal as fast as unoxidized starches. One way to illustrate part of an oxidized starch molecule is shown in Fig. 36.

Gelling can be made almost impossible by connecting two adjacent starch molecules by use of a cross-linking agent, such as formaldehyde. Part of the material used to connect the starch molecules serves as a bridge between the two molecules. By careful control of the amount of cross-linking, it is possible to achieve the desired degree of gelling.

Another way in which clarity, gelation, film-forming and other colloidal properties can be profoundly changed is to substitute some other group—such as acid—for the OH (hydroxyl group) in the dextrose unit. When a substitution is made, the resulting compound is known as a starch derivative. At present, starch derivatives in which relatively few hydroxyl groups are replaced are most useful.

Besides adding or rearranging the starch molecules or atoms in the molecule, starch may be modified in other ways. When a starch suspension is heated with a small amount of acid at low temperatures, some of

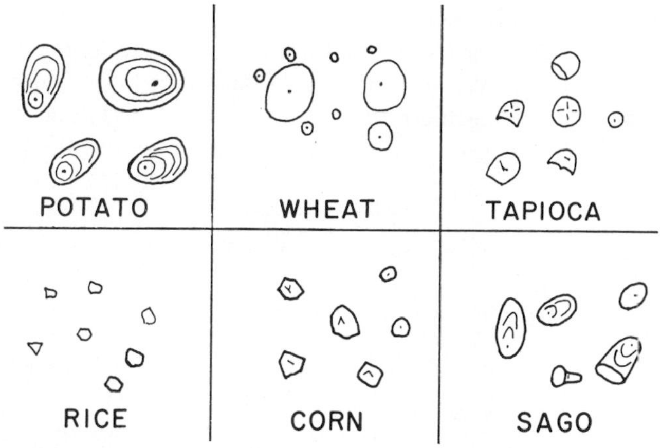

FIG. 35. APPEARANCE UNDER THE MICROSCOPE OF SOME COMMERCIAL STARCHES

the molecular chains are broken which weakens the force holding the starch bundles together. Starches treated in this way do not thicken as much as untreated types when the gelatinizing temperature is reached. These are the "thin-boiling" starches. By controlling the temperature and amount of acid, it is possible to obtain starches with varying viscosi-

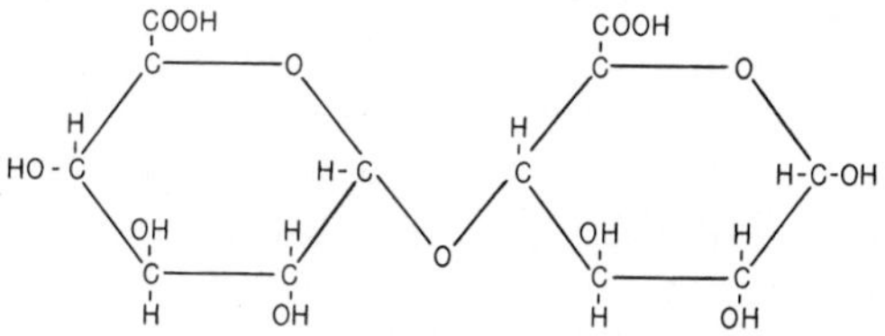

FIG. 36. EFFECT OF OXIDATION ON STARCH MOLECULE

ties or fluidities. This same breakdown of starches into simpler materials takes place through the action of naturally occurring chemical agents or enzymes. It is these enzymes that enable us to digest starch. Fruits and other foods contain enzymes that act on starch during processing operations.

Any kind of starch may be cooked and then dried, usually on hot rolls or drums. When water is added to such precooked starches, the original paste is reconstituted. Since the user does not have to cook or cool the starch, it is ready for immediate use, as in "instant" desserts, etc.

PROCESSING CONDITIONS IMPORTANT

In actual processing, the behavior of starch is affected by the other materials with which it is in contact and by operating conditions. Starch cooked with highly acid foods receives the same kind of treatment that is used to produce thin-boiling starches, if cooking time is prolonged. To maintain desired consistency, cooking time must be closely regulated.

Common ingredients such as sugar, corn syrups, fats, eggs and dry milk solids interfere with complete cooking of starch. If the starch granules are prevented from completely gelatinizing the starch is unstable. When the temperature is lowered, the undercooked starch releases water (weeps), and the viscosity of the product decreases.

Even completely cooked starches give up water under certain conditions. During cooling, the starch molecules recombine, thus squeezing water out of the granule. When dilute solutions are cooled, the recombined starch molecules may settle out as an insoluble precipitate. Cooling of hot concentrated solutions results in gels.

Use of high temperatures and new agitating cookers require starches that will remain stable under these conditions. Because high temperatures and vigorous agitation accelerate the breakdown of starch, cooking time, temperature, and agitation should be carefully controlled to produce satisfactory, uniform products.

Ordinary cooked starches are excellent media for bacterial growth. Sanitary precautions—including cleaning of hard-to-reach pockets and crevices—will prevent contamination. Specially treated, bacteria-free starches are available.

THE BAKING INDUSTRY

Consuming some 40 million pounds per year, the baking industry employs starch in many different roles, as an ingredient in pie fillings, in cracker and cookie doughs, etc., and in operating procedures, such as pan greasing and dusting. Forty-three million pounds per year are used in baking powder production.

Pies

Body, consistency and storage life of pies are in large measure determined by the type of starch chosen. For fruit filled pies, canned or frozen fruit forms the filling. The fruit is drained and the juice (with additional water, if necessary) serves as the solvent for sugars and as a gelantinizing medium for the starch. Sugar and corn syrup are added to the juice and heated to boiling. Starch is suspended in the syrup. Water is added and the mixture is cooked until a thick, clear liquid is formed. The thickened syrup is added to the drained fruit and the mixture is cooled to 80°F. before filling in pastry shells.

One of the primary problems of the pie baker is to make a filling that is of just the right fluidity without masking the fruit flavor and color. The consistency can be regulated to some extent by the type and quantity of starch. Tapioca has been used, but it tends to thin when heated. If unmodified root starches are used in excess, a gummy texture results. Untreated cereal starches, including corn starch, became firm and pudding-like on heating, masking the fruit color.

Specially prepared corn starches are available which overcome these difficulties. Acid-free starches which do not cloud and have high resistance to weeping are used. Several types of modified Amioca starches are most effective. Unlike unmodified common starch, the waxy maize starches do not form stiff bodies. One of these starches gives a heavy syrup-like consistency that maintains an even distribution of fruit throughout the filling. Cross-linked root starches are also being used.

In preparation of cream pie fillings, eggs are added to the starch suspension to prevent curdling during cooking; all other steps in preparation are the same as for fruit pies. Acids in lemon pie filling may hydrolyze the starch, which results in a thin filling. A mixture of acid resistant modified common corn starch and modified Amioca prevents running in these acid fruit pies. Since quality of custard pie fillings depends on gels, stability is even more important than in other pie fillings. Formation of a starch line during baking due to settling is a persistent hazard. This fault can be avoided by precooking the starch. Because of ability to hold water, modified waxy maize starches remain in suspension, and therefore are highly recommended for this application.

Considerable economies can be achieved by the use of pre-gelatinized waxy maize stabilizers in place of "cook-up" starch. These cooked-at-the-refinery types are ready to use simply by adding water. By cutting down processing time, and eliminating the need for cooking equipment, more pies are produced at lower cost. All the advantages of modified Amiocas are obtained by using the pregelatinized stabilizers.

Biscuit, Cracker and Specialty Doughs

Although a large percentage of the flour used in making bread is wheat starch, the other constituents, particularly the proteins, are of vital importance; flour in breadmaking is not an application of starch simply as starch. But starch does have important functions in many cracker and cookie doughs and in some specialty items.

It is not possible to make a real dough unless a certain amount of protein is present. If there is an excess of starch, a starch paste will result when the flour is added to the water. Most desirable flours for cookies, etc., are made from wheat flours that have about seven per cent protein. To get as close as possible to the optimum flour composition, it may be necessary to dilute the flour (if the protein content is too high). Sugar, shortening and corn starch have been used for this purpose.

Corn starch is the most popular choice among bakers as the necessary diluent or cutting agent (about 5 to 20 per cent is used). When corn starch is used for this purpose, less shortening, sugar and yeast are required. Economy is a factor, though not necessarily the deciding one. A better product is also obtained through improved and intensified flavor, clear color and better texture. Production is also made easier. Hard to handle flours can be made to give a smooth running dough which bakes without buckling.

For ice cream cones or wafers, the dough must be such as to yield a product that is neither crumbly nor brittle. It is almost impossible to obtain the proper flour at reasonable cost. By adding corn starch (or sometimes tapioca starch) to available flours, excellent wafer can be produced. Both starches have their partisans. Tapioca starch is said to give a more tender wafer with a somewhat better flavor, but corn starch with adjusted pH control will give more uniform results (Lloyd 1946).

An old standby in the cookie industry is the arrowroot cookie. Still popular because of its food value and as a baby pacifier, the arrowroot cookie is a standard item in large bakeries. As the name indicates, arrowroot starch is one of the essential ingredients.

Doughs for specialty products often require starches to improve quality or to facilitate handling. For example, dough for blintzes and knishes presents special problems. Knishes or blintzes are thin pancakes filled with meat, cheese or potatoes. The batter is placed in pans and is cooked by lowering a heated, revolving drum into the pan. As it rotates, a layer of partially cooked dough is formed on the drum. To keep the process moving, the dough must be continually removed from the drum. Sticking of dough interferes with the smooth flow of production. Corn starches, particularly waxy starches, give the dough greater flexibility so that it will not stick to the drum. A more tender, tastier product results.

Production Aids

Aside from its use as a component of doughs, starch does additional duty as an aid in production. In breadmaking, starch is used at several points as the baker's helper.

Dough for bread is usually prepared in two steps. Flour, yeast, yeast nutrients and water are mixed for about seven minutes and then allowed to ferment for $4^1/_2$ hr. After the fermentation period is over, additional flour, shortening, milk solids, salt and sugar are added and mixed; the dough is fermented for another half hour. It is now ready to be divided and baked.

A special machine divides the dough into loaf-size pieces. Each piece of dough is then rounded into a smooth ball by a rounder. After a rest period of ten minutes in which the dough expands, it is molded into a loaf and placed in tins. The pans containing the dough are proofed—allowed to rise in a warm, humid room—for about an hour. The dough is then baked in about 35 min.

Dough going to the rounder is still quite tacky and will stick to the machine unless it is dusted with a dry material. Wheat flour, ground cereal products and corn starch are used as dusting powders. Accumulations of flour or other cereals under the warm, humid conditions of the bakery are excellent breeding grounds for insect life. Meeting the need for more effective sanitation, corn starches have been developed for dusting baking equipment. Unlike cereals, corn starch will not support insect life. These starch dusting powders are designed to be used with the usual dusting hoppers.

As an aid to the release of baked goods, the baking pan is greased. In the production of bread or low-sugar goods, no special precautions are necessary. Cakes and sweet goods in general require a grease that will not be absorbed and cause sticking of product to the pan. Starches incorporated into the pan grease provide the interfacial coating necessary to prevent sticking and peeling. Pan-greasing corn starches are specially prepared for easy handling and storage and economy in operation.

Baking Powders

The light, airy breads and cakes are made possible by the incorporation of baking powder into the dough or batter. When baked, entrapped gas expands, forming small pockets in the baked goods.

Basically, baking powder is composed of sodium bicarbonate, acids, (monocalcium phosphate and sodium acid pyrophosphate), calcium lactate, and starch. In the presence of water, the bicarbonate and acid react to give carbon dioxide gas. Calcium lactate is added to control the release of gas, otherwise, the gas may be released before the dough is ready to hold the gas.

Starch acts as an inert dispersing agent permitting ease in handling and protection during storage. Contact between acid and bicarbonate in containers may result in release of gas, thus weakening the effect of the powder in baking—particularly if considerable free moisture is present.

Various starches have been tried. Rice and ground wheat starch are good for prolonged storage. Potato and coarse wheat starch are not recommended. Dried corn starch is the best and most practical carrier for baking powder ingredients. It is stable, will not add color, and is tasteless and edible. Most important, the particle size of corn starch is just right to cover the active ingredients, preventing their premature reaction. Its ability to absorb moisture prolongs storage. Handling is also made easier. Corn starch is a free-flowing powder which permits efficient feeding operations and gives a high volume per unit weight.

THE CANNING INDUSTRY

Canners are major users of starches. Suppliers of starch offer a wide variety of types to meet the needs of individual foods and processing conditions. Requirements for a canner's starch are rigorous and varied. It must maintain the consistency of the product after high temperature treatment and vigorous agitation; it should in no way damage the taste, and if possible, it should improve the flavor; it must be stable under different storage conditions; it must be bacteria-free.

How starches are able to solve some problems is demonstrated in the following examples.

Cream-Style Corn

In cream-style corn, starch is used to help give the product a creamy consistency. Because the starch-corn mixture is viscous, fairly high processing temperatures and vigorous agitation is required to achieve complete heat penetration. These conditions require special starches that will not thin out on continued heating or "weep" when cooled and stored.

Corn starches designed with cream-style corn in mind are widely used. In the past, common corn starch differed from batch to batch. With new processing techniques, a uniform product has been produced. This starch is sterilized to make it bacteria-free—a requirement of the National Canners Association. New methods of sterilization insure that these starches will not add a chemical taste to the corn. Oxidized common starches are giving good service when conventional canning methods are used. For longer shelf life and improved quality, modified waxy maize starches have superior performance. They have less tendency to gel and in addition, inhibit the gelling of other starches.

Where resistance to high temperature and physical stress are important, as in rotary batch and continuous, agitating, pressure cookers, waxy maize starches are most reliable, although there are oxidized pearl starches that do a good job. A combination of technical and economic considerations sometimes dictate the use of a blend of different starches. An economical blend of a modified waxy maize and common corn starches goes a long way toward meeting these exacting conditions. In general, the more waxy maize starch in the blend, the better the performance.

Canned Pie Fillings

A relatively new industry—canned pie fillings—is built on a starch foundation. Until suitable stabilizers were produced, prepared fillings were not practical because of processing and storage conditions. Continuing research by the starch industry has resulted in commercially effective starches. All the problems have not been solved, but there is a steady stream of new developments from the research laboratories.

Of first importance is the taste of the pie filling. To be useful, the starch must enhance the fruit flavor and maintain the correct consistency. The acidity of the fruit will affect the stability of the starch. Highly acid fruit fillings such as cherries, will be less stable than less acid fillings. If the pH is above 3.5, suitable starch will not break down.

Canned pie fillings are often stored in unheated warehouses and the cold parts of bakeries. Under these conditions, starch sols lose their ability to hold water. As a result, the pie fillings gel, become cloudy, or "water-off."

No stabilizer or starch-natural gum combination will remain stable indefinitely. Tapioca starch has been used with some success. Most effective stabilizer to date is a modified Amioca starch; it will not break down when stored at temperatures as low as 40°F. for 110 days. Other starches are effective at higher storage temperatures.

Other Canned Foods

Soups, like other canned goods, employ starch as a thickener. In cream soups, as asparagus, celery, mushroom, etc., consistency is most important. Improved starches do not thin out when processed or add a "starchy" flavor to soup. Cream of asparagus, celery and corn, green pea, vegetable and oyster soups include corn starch in the formula; in cream of mushroom, corn or tapioca starches are used.

Starch is an important ingredient in canned gravies, and sauces for baked beans and similar items. For chop suey and other Chinese-style foods, the starch paste must be exceptionally clear to improve the appearance of the vegetables. Stability of the gel and viscosity are also crucial. Purified cross-linked waxy maize starches are specially produced for use in Chinese specialties.

Canned Baby Foods

The production of canned and bottled baby foods is now a 250 million dollar industry.

Starches are included in baby food for the same reasons that they are required in other canning operations. Modified Amiocas help tickle baby's palate by providing the correct consistency and improving flavor and stability.

STARCHES IN CANDY MAKING

In candy making, as in baking, starch has a double function: As a vital *ingredient* in gum candies, fruit slices, spice strings, jelly bean centers, etc.; as a less important part of the recipe for marshmallow and similar candies—and as *part of the production process,* when used in molding fondants or in drying revolving pan goods, such as jaw breakers, Jordan almonds and the like.

Among confectioners, the manufacture of jelly candies is known as "gum work." Wheat, rice, tapioca, cassava and corn starches have been used. Because it is available in many forms and with varying properties at a low cost, corn starch is used almost exclusively in candy production.

Of all commercial food processes, candy making is still somewhat of an art, depending on individual skill and judgment. New ideas involving automatic and continuous methods are slowly being introduced. Open kettle methods of cooking under the watchful eye of an experienced candy technician are still used in the industry.

All jelly formulations include sweeteners—sugar, corn syrup, or dextrose—starch, water, cream of tartar, tartaric acid and flavoring. Other ingredients, such as coloring, coconut, etc., are added when necessary to make a particular kind of jelly. Sweeteners are dissolved in part of the water and brought to a boil in a steam-jacketed kettle. In the rest of the water, the starch is suspended to make a slurry and is slowly added to the boiling sweetener-water mixtures. More mechanized plants have electric mixers to obtain uniform starch suspensions and metering devices to feed the slurry into the boiling batch. Sufficient water and correct cooking temperatures are necessary to gelatinize the starches. Undercooked starch will result in candy that is unable to retain its moisture.

The usual batch is cooked for about 40-50 min. Complete mixing is achieved by electric agitators running at 35-40 r.p.m. Veteran jelly makers know when the cook is finished by testing its consistency with a paddle or knife. A more reliable technique is to determine the solids contents—which should be around 75 per cent—by means of a refractometer.

After the cook is complete, the jelly is placed in starch trays and put into a conditioning room at 140°–150°F. where the excess moisture is removed.

At first, only common corn starches were employed. They produced tender jellies with good shelf life but were difficult to process uniformly. Requiring long cooking times and close control of processing conditions, common starch jellies were expensive to produce because of the many substandard batches that had to be discarded. There is now a modified starch for every candy and process.

With the exception of Turkish pastes which are cut instead of molded, thin-boiling or fluidity corn starches have been found to give the best results. Thin-boiling starches for confectioners are acid-modified corn starches that flow easier when hot but have strong gels when cooled. This permits the jellies to be poured into molds after cooking but which have firm tender bodies when cooled. Maximum gel strength can only be obtained if the starches are thoroughly cooked. Complete cooking disperses the amylose molecules enough so that when they recombine on cooling, a tighter, closer arrangement results. Sugars interfere with the gelatinization of ordinary starches but have only a slight effect on the swelling of the acid-modified types.

In addition to providing a tender, stable, and free-flowing jelly, starches must give a clear candy. Oxidized starches with exceptional clarity and good gel strength are being produced commercially.

Only corn starches meet all the conditions of modern candy making. Tapioca gels lack strength. Sago starches are too cloudy.

Caramels, nougats and particularly marshmallows require starches to stabilize the other ingredients. To prevent separation of fat and to give a thicker body, powdered starch is added to the caramel formula. Marshmallows need the help of starches to stabilize the egg albumen and to bind goods which have a low gelatin content. Ordinary powdered corn starch will serve these purposes, although it may give a "starchy" taste to the product. Best for marshmallow work are the waxy maize starches. Bland in taste, they add no flavor of their own; more compatible with high-content sugar mixtures, they gelatinize completely when heated with sweeteners.

Molding Starches

The many attractive shapes of bonbons, creams, and Easter eggs are formed by pouring the hot candy into starch molds. Molding starches usually contain small amounts of edible oils or fats to help the starch maintain the desired shape. Another job for molding starches is to absorb the excessive moisture from the candy. Redried corn starches with low moisture content are required. Since the starches are used over and over again, they will in time lose some of their moisture holding ability. From time to time small amounts of additional starch are added to reinforce the existing stock.

Drying qualities of starch are also important in making revolving pan goods. Starch placed in the revolving pan absorbs moisture from the candy, helps maintain its shape, and fills small cracks or pin holes. Pure food grade common starch is normally used.

Low moisture starches are mixed with confectioner's sugar for the same reasons that they are incorporated in baking powders. Having the ability to hold water, they keep the sugar from caking during storage and maintain its free-flowing character.

SALAD DRESSINGS

The ability of starches to hold naturally immiscible materials together is utilized in manufacture of salad dressings. Many salad dressings are emulsions of oil in dilute vinegar, flavored with spices and sugar. Egg yolks serve as a primary emulsifying agent; vinegar serves as a preservative. Starches give dressings the correct body, in addition to stabilizing the emulsions.

Recommended procedure is to prepare the various phases separately and then combine them. Water, salt, sugar and vinegar are mixed and heated to about 160°F. A creamy, free-flowing starch slurry is prepared and added to the water-seasoning-acid mixture. All the ingredients are heated to 185°F. and held at this temperature for five minutes to insure complete gelatinization of the starch.

Overcooked starch will gel, particularly on standing, thus breaking the delicate emulsion; undercooked starch will impart foreign flavors to the dressing. A stainless steel, steam-jacketed kettle provides uniform heating without adding metallic flavors.

An emulsion base composed of egg yolk, sugar, salt, oil, water, vinegar and dry mustard is prepared. At first, small amounts of water and oil are added alternately to produce a well emulsified nucleus. The rest of the materials are then introduced. After the starch paste (which is about 35–65 per cent of the dressing) is added to the emulsion base, the dressing is fed to a mixer, homogenizer or colloid mill and thoroughly blended.

Salad dressing production is a good testing ground for starches. They must remain stable when heated with both sugars and acid and must withstand attrition of the homogenizers. Tapioca starches have good emulsifying properties but become very thin in acid-sugar solutions. Unmodified corn starches have a tendency to "weep" under these conditions; some corn starches will not gel in the presence of oil, while others gel too much when cooled.

Combinations of tapioca and corn starches have been used successfully. With an annual sales volume of about 238 million pounds, the salad dressing industry is big enough to receive special attention from corn starch producers. There are now available blends of corn starches that meet all the requirements for this application.

OTHER INDUSTRIAL USES

Both the meat processing and brewing industries are good starch customers. Whether it is a meat loaf or a hot dog, the starch serves as a binder and stabilizer. All processed meat products are composed of meat —usually ground—fat, and liquids (meat juices and water). During manufacturing, the ingredients must be held firmly together. Particularly, the fat must be dispersed to obtain a fine-grained, uniform product.

Ability to hold water is a major factor in choice of starch. Pregelatinized corn starches are excellent water absorbers. Starches with low gelatinizing temperatures, like potato starch, are good for soft salami and frankfurters. Flours (starch plus protein) have superior fat dispersing properties.

Beer, like many other foods, begins with starch—in brewer's grits. The starch is first converted to malt which is then fermented. Treated or gelatinized corn or rice starches are easily converted. Americans prefer clear beers served cold. Use of starches that have been roll-dried may result in a cloudy product when the beer is chilled.

Starches for Convenience Foods

Popularity of prepared, premixed and frozen foods is skyrocketing. Sharing the enthusiasm of the consumer for ready-to-use items, the food processor is not only meeting demands of his customers but is requiring convenience for himself.

Frozen Foods.—Using frozen fruit (packed with corn syrup solids or sugar) and precooked instant starch, makers of frozen fruit pies have cut processing operations to a minimum. Frozen fruit is defrosted just enough so it can be removed from containers. A blend of precooked starch, salt, sweeteners and seasoning is prepared. Undrained fruit and water are dumped into a mixer, the starch-sweetener blend is added, and the mixture agitated for a few minutes. Pastry shells are filled with the pie filling and frozen. The consumer simply heats the pie.

Precooked waxy maize stabilizers that swell in cold water are the starch bases. Experience with these materials and techniques indicate that pies with excellent consistency, flavor and stability are produced.

Ingredients for frozen meat pies are first cooked and then frozen. Starch thickening agents used in gravies must provide stable, smooth, gravies even after freezing and thawing. The meat (chicken or beef) is cooked in steam kettles, cooled and cut into small pieces or flakes. Broth from the cooking of meat, together with water, seasoning and spices serves as the gravy. A slurry of starch and wheat flour (for appearance and flavor) is prepared and added to the broth. The gravy is then heated to 190°F. for a few minutes.

Regular pie dough forms the crust. An automatic filler delivers the correct amount of gravy into each pie. Portions of meat are generally added manually. The amount of meat to be added is set by government standards. The top crust is applied by machine, and the finished pie is boxed and frozen.

Waxy maize starches modified in varying degrees are best able to withstand low temperatures. Slightly modified Amioca gives a more fluid gravy, while heavily modified waxy starch produces a thicker, firmer filling.

Dessert Puddings.—That old favorite, the pudding dessert, is essentially gelled corn starch with sweetener and flavoring. When the dessert mix is cooked with milk or water, the starch gels produce the familiar pudding. A common formula includes about 23–24 per cent common corn starch and 75 per cent sugar; the remaining ingredients are salt, flavor and coloring.

Many of the same instant starches used in frozen pie work are incorporated in new instant puddings. By simply mixing the pudding mix with cold milk the starch gel is reconstituted. These puddings have a somewhat higher starch content and are sweetened with dextrose as well as sugar. Several types of pregelatinized waxy starches are available. For reasons of economy, precooked oxidized potato starches have the major share of the instant pudding market. Economical puddings with a thicker consistency are obtained with precooked common corn starch.

Another long-time favorite is tapioca pudding, consisting of round pearls of tapioca starch in a pudding. A mixture of 90 per cent waxy maize and 10 per cent common corn starch also may be used for "tapioca type" puddings. When heated to about 160°F., common corn starch gels into pearls, while Amioca forms the surrounding thinner pudding.

Prepared Mixes.—Prepared cake and doughnut mixes are growing fields for starches. Used as emulsifiers, moisture conditioners, and tenderizers, new starches and starch blends are being offered to mix producers.

FUTURE DEVELOPMENTS

A general expanding economy with high demands for variety is a constant stimulus for research into new food applications for starch. Recently, a 55 per cent amylose starch was developed and plant scientists are talking about a 90 per cent amylose starch. One example of what the future holds is a water soluble food packaging film of amylose starch that will enable the housewife to cook without removing the food from the package.

About 90 per cent of all starch sold in the United States is corn starch. In the past, the root starches such as potato and tapioca were the only source of amylopectin in large amounts. When Amioca was developed for commercial use, a better source of clear, nongelling starches became available. The newer waxy maize starches and the many modifications of common corn starch meet most of the needs of the food industry.

Acknowledgment.—A list of all publications from which the author has accumulated information on starch chemistry would require more space than this entire chapter. However, special acknowledgment is due to publications by R. W. Kerr, and by the Corn Industries Research Foundation.

Of special interest to the general reader are publications listed in the following bibliography.

BIBLIOGRAPHY

AMERICAN CHEMICAL SOCIETY. 1954. Natural plant hydrocolloids. Advan. Chem. *11*. American Chemical Society, Washington, D. C.

AMERICAN CHEMICAL SOCIETY. 1955. Uses of sugar and other carbohydrates in the food industry. Advan. Chem. *12*. American Chemical Society, Washington, D. C.

ANON. 1955. Corn Starch. Corn Industries Research Foundation, New York.

BALL, C. O., and OLSON, F. C. W. 1957. Sterilization in Food Technology. McGraw-Hill Book Co., New York.

GREENWOOD, C. T. 1964. Structure, properties and amylolytic degradation of starch. Food Technol. *18*, 732–738.

HONEYMAN, J. (Editor). 1959. Recent Advances in the Chemistry of Cellulose and Starch. Heywood and Co., London.

KEER, R. W. 1950. Chemistry and Industry of Starch. 2nd Edition. Academic Press, New York.

LLOYD, R. L. 1946. Baking batters. U. S. Patent 2,394,791. Feb. 12.

MEYER, L. H. 1950. Natural and synthetic high polymers. 2nd Edition. Interscience Publishers, New York.

MEYER, L. H. 1960. Food Chemistry. Reinhold Publishing Corp., New York.

PIGMAN, W. W. 1957. The carbohydrates. Academic Press, New York.

RADLEY, J. A. 1954. Starch and its Derivatives. 3rd Edition, 2 vols. John Wiley and Sons, New York.

SCHOCH, T. J. 1959. Measuring the useful properties of starch. Staerke *11*, 156–162.

SCHOCH, T. J. 1961. Starches and amylases. Proceedings of the 1961 Annual Meeting of the Am. Soc. Brewing Chem., 83–92.

SCHOCH, T. J. 1962. Recent developments in starch chemistry. Brewers Digest *36*, No. 3, 35–40, 85.

WHISTLER, R. L., and SMART, C. L. 1953. Polysaccharide Chemistry. Academic Press, New York.

WHISTLER, R. L., and SPENCER, W. W. 1958. The past ten years of starch research. Baker's Digest *32*, No. 3, 38–41.

CHAPTER 6

H. E. Swisher and
L. H. Swisher

Use of Acids in Food Processing

ACID TYPES

The acids which are used in food processing include both the organic type, such as citric acid, and the inorganic, such as phosphoric acid. In addition, the salts of these acids, principally sodium, make it possible to control pH (active acidity) and taste, as well as contribute other desirable properties to the finished food products. The strong mineral acids, hydrochloric and sulfuric, are not discussed in this chapter since their general use in foods is limited due to the fact that they often produce abnormal flavors.

Because of the widely varying commercial sources of these edible acids, they are properly discussed according to their origin or method of manufacture. To produce the quality required for food use, these acids are obtained from natural, fermentation and synthetic sources as indicated below.

NATURAL ACIDS

Tartaric Acid (2,3-dihydroxysuccinic acid)
HOOC·CH(OH)CH(OH)COOH

Available as crystals, granules or powder, meeting the requirements for tartaric acid (Anon. 1960C). Formula weight—150.09. A dihydroxy dicarboxylic acid (dibasic). Somewhat hygroscopic. Good water solubility. Strong acid taste.

Lemon Juice

A natural juice whose principal acidic constituent is citric acid. Available as juice from fresh lemons or in a number of processed frozen and unfrozen juice products. A commonly used pasteurized concentrated lemon juice has an average volume concentration of 5.7 to 1 and contains not less than 2.91 lbs. of crystalline citric acid per gallon. Juice products are also available containing sulfur dioxide or sodium benzoate as preservatives.

H. E. SWISHER is Assistant Manager, Research and Development Division, and (Mrs.) L. H. SWISHER is formerly Research Librarian, Sunkist Growers, Inc., Ontario, Calif.

FERMENTATION ACIDS

Citric Acid (beta-hydroxytricarboxylic acid) HOOCCH$_2$COH(COOH)CH$_2$COOH

Available in two forms, monohydrate and anhydrous which meet the specifications of citric acid, USP (Anon. 1960A). Formula weight of anhydrous form—192.12, of hydrate—210.14. A monohydroxy tricarboxylic acid (tribasic). Translucent crystals, white granules or powder. Somewhat hygroscopic. Very good water solubility. Strong acid taste.

Lactic Acid (2-hydroxypropionic acid) CH$_3$CH(OH)COOH

Available in several food processing grades such as 50, 80 and 85 per cent lactic acid, USP, Formula weight—90.05. A monohydroxy carboxylic acid (monobasic). Colorless, almost odorless, syrupy liquid. Miscible with water in all proportions. Will absorb moisture from humid atmosphere. Moderately strong acid taste.

Vinegar

A sour liquid whose acidic constituent is acetic acid. Commercial vinegar contains from 5 to 8 per cent acetic acid. Distilled white vinegar contributes mainly simple sourness. Malt, wine and fruit vinegars contribute fragrance and flavor as well as sourness.

Fumaric Acid (trans-butenedioic acid) HOOCCH=CHCOOH

Available in a food-grade white crystalline powder. Formula weight—116.07. An unsaturated dicarboxylic acid (dibasic). Essentially non-hygroscopic. Poor water solubility. Strong acid taste.

SYNTHETIC ACIDS

Malic Acid (hydroxysuccinic acid) HOOCH$_2$CH(OH)COOH

Available as a food-grade white crystalline powder. Formula weight—134.09. A monohydroxy dicarboxylic acid (dibasic). Somewhat hygroscopic. Good water solubility. Strong acid taste.

Acetic Acid (ethanoic acid) CH$_3$COOH

Available in several grades, such as 80 per cent, 90 per cent as well as two USP grades, glacial and 36 to 37 per cent. Formula weight—60.05. A monocarboxylic acid (monobasic). Colorless liquid with a pungent odor. Miscible with water in all proportions. Volatile on boiling. Moderately weak acid with sour taste.

Phosphoric Acid (orthophosphoric acid) H$_3$PO$_4$

The standard acids of commerce are the 75 per cent food-grade and phosphoric acid N.F. (85 to 88 per cent). Formula weight—98.04. A tribasic inorganic acid. Will absorb moisture from a humid atmosphere. Miscible with water in all proportions. A clear, odorless, syrupy liquid with a very acid taste.

Adipic Acid (hexanedioic acid) $HOOC(CH_2)_4COOH$

Available in a food-grade white crystalline powder. Formula weight—146.14. A dicarboxylic acid (dibasic). Essentially nonhygroscopic. Fair water solubility. Strong acid taste.

SOURCES AND COMPOSITION OF ACIDS

Acids have played an important role in the diet of man from time immemorial. From the natural organic acids present in fruit, as in lemons and grapes, to the addition of acid foods and juices in the food products of the home kitchen, these culinary aids have been important. Historically the more recent commercial production of acids for use in food products, both for immediate consumption and foods that must be stored for a period of time, emphasizes the increasing importance of acids in modern food processing.

Natural Acids

Lemon Juice.—For generations fresh lemon juice has been used extensively in the home preparation of tasty foods, in which capacity it serves as a pleasing and healthful acidulant. Except for salt, lemon juice probably has been used more extensively to enhance and modify inherent food flavor than any other food substance. Of note is the fact that lemon juice contains a natural balance of the four components of taste; sweet, sour, salt and bitter.

Lemon juice is popularly associated with vitamin C (ascorbic acid) and it is also the best known fruit source of citric acid. Freshly extracted lemon juice is a buffered solution which contains organic acids, primarily citric and some malic acid along with mineral salts of these acids, predominantly potassium. Other components include sugars, vitamins, pectinous materials, protein and amino acids, flavonoids, enzymes and variable amounts of aromatic peel oil.

Tabulated data by Birdsall *et al.* (1961), as shown in Table 32, indicates the average composition of California lemon juice. It will be noted that fresh lemon juice contains about six per cent citric acid. In addition to being extremely low in sodium and relatively high in potassium, lemon juice also contains about 8.3 per cent soluble solids and 44 mg./100 gm. ascorbic acid.

As the need for lemon juice on a commercial scale developed, the production of concentrates from freshly extracted and screened juice was accomplished by evaporation of water under high vacuum. A number of lemon juice products are now available commercially which include frozen and unfrozen juices of various concentrations. These products are packed in bottles, tins, kegs and barrels.

TABLE 32

AVERAGE COMPOSITION OF FRESH LEMON JUICE[1]

Constituent	Quantity Found	
	gm./100 gm.	mg./100 gm.
Protein (Kjeldahl N x 6.25)	0.47	. . .
Amino nitrogen (Van Slyke)	0.04	. . .
Fat (ether extract)	0.19	. . .
Soluble solids, total	8.30	. . .
Sugar		. . .
Total	1.17	. . .
Sucrose	0.09	. . .
Reducing	1.09	. . .
Acid as anhydrous citric	5.98	. . .
Moisture	92.36	. . .
Ash, total	0.25	. . .
Potassium	. . .	102.0
Phosphorus	. . .	10.3
Calcium	. . .	6.1
Sulfur	. . .	2.7
Sodium	. . .	1.0
Iron	. . .	0.21

[1] WARF data—Birdsall *et al.* (1961).

Among the types of frozen lemon juices available are single strength, concentrate and lemonade products. Hot pack juices include single strength, concentrate for lemonade and concentrate products. A commonly used product is pasteurized concentrated lemon juice of 5.7 to 1 volume-concentration-ratio containing not less than 2.91 lbs. of crystalline citric acid per gallon.

Although preservatives are not normally required in lemon juice concentrates because of their high acidity, products are available containing either sulfur dioxide or benzoate for special uses. Details of the processing methods used by Sunkist Growers, Inc., are described by Kieser and Havighorst (1952).

Tartaric Acid.—Tartaric acid, which is less widely distributed than citric or malic acid, occurs naturally in several fruits and plants, but is found principally in grapes and the tamarind. It has been known since antiquity in the form of its acid potassium salt (cream of tartar), which deposits on the sides of the casks used for fermenting grape juice to wine. Its name, which derives from Tartarus, is of medieval alchemical origin.

Before the Civil War, tartaric acid and cream of tartar were imported, principally from France, where they were produced from the "argols" of the wine industry.

In 1862 an import duty was established making the manufacture of these products in the United States feasible. That year Pfizer began domestic production of high purity tartaric acid.

The present methods for producing tartaric acid and its salts involve the use of the crude tartars obtained as by-products of wine making.

In the manufacture of tartaric acid from these tartars, several processes are possible, which involve the recovery of tartaric acid, potassium acid tartrate (cream of tartar) or calcium tartrate. The crude potassium acid tartrate salt may be converted to calcium tartrate by treatment with such calcium salts as hydrated lime, calcium chloride or calcium sulfate. The resulting calcium tartrate is then converted to tartaric acid by treatment with a strong inorganic acid, usually sulfuric acid.

There are many variations used in tartaric acid plants to obtain good recoveries and minimize such impurities as salts of iron, lead, copper and aluminum. Details of these manufacturing methods are available from Chas. Pfizer (Anon.1954B) and also are given in the Encyclopedia of Chemical Technology (Anon. 1954A). Whereas the principal fruit acids, such as citric and malic are readily oxidized when ingested, tartaric acid is unique in that it is not metabolized.

The tartaric acid of commerce is the ordinary or natural dextro-rotatory form of 2,3-dihydroxysuccinic acid. It is manufactured to meet the specifications as described in the National Formulary (Anon. 1960C).

Fermentation Acids

Citric Acid.—Citric acid (Latin—*citrus*) is distributed widely in plants and animals, the most abundant source being the citrus fruit such as lemons and limes.

Until 1880, virtually all the citric acid used in this country was made in Europe. For a number of years thereafter, Chas. Pfizer and Co. produced the acid from imported Italian citrate of lime. Likewise, the acid became an important product from cull lemons in the early days of the lemon products industry in California, but this source is relatively unimportant now. Details of the manufacture of citric acid from lemon juice are described by Holton and Havighorst (1953).

In 1923, Chas. Pfizer opened the world's first successful citric acid fermentation plant and the world price of the acid dropped more than two-thirds!

Foster (1949) indicates that many strains of fungi, which belong to the genera Aspergillus, Penicillium (containing old Citromyces), Mucor, Botrytis, Coniophora and the like, may produce citric acid under suitable conditions. Oxalic acid also may be produced as a by-product during the fermentation. Strains belonging to *Aspergillus niger* have been used most frequently for the commercial production of citric acid. Yields average around 60 per cent and upward, based on sugar consumed.

In attempts to develop a more efficient strain, Miles Chemical Co. (Anon. 1962A) biologists exposed *Aspergillus niger* to intense ultraviolet radiation to produce mutations; and from the ten per cent of the exposed organisms which survived, they finally isolated a pale strain of Aspergillus. These organisms were found to be seven per cent more efficient in converting sugar into citric acid by deep-fermentation than those being used at that time!

Of interest is a recent U. S. patent issued to Kinoshita *et al.* (1961) describing methods for obtaining high yields of citric acid from such carbohydrate material as glucose, fructose, sucrose, maltose, waste molasses, dextrin and starch through the use of strains belonging to *Trichoderma viride.*

Citric acid is the most widely used organic acid for the acidification of foodstuffs. It is commercially available as a colorless, translucent crystal or white, granular or fine crystalline powder. This acid is available in both the anhydrous and hydrous (monohydrate) forms. Both anhydrous and hydrous are manufactured to meet the specifications in the U. S. Pharmacopoeia (Anon. 1960A). Unlike the anhydrous acid, the hydrated form contains water of crystallization, which accounts for 8.57 per cent of its weight. The two forms can be used interchangeably to produce the same acid concentration by employing the following equivalents:

1 lb. of citric acid, USP, anhydrous = 1.094 lbs. (1 lb., $1^1/_2$ oz.) of citric acid, USP, hydrous.

1 lb. of citric acid, USP, hydrous = 0.914 lbs. (14.6 oz.) of citric acid, USP, anhydrous.

Both forms are stable to light and air and can be stored in the dry form without difficulty. Because citric acid is hygroscopic, relative humidities up to 70 per cent at 70°F. are most suitable, thus preventing caking. Since hydrous acid has a tendency to lose varying amounts of moisture, depending on storage conditions, acid concentration may change over a period of time. Further technical details on the production and properties of citric acid are available from such manufacturers as Chas. Pfizer (Anon. 1949C), Miles Chemical Co. (Anon. 1960B) or from the Encyclopedia of Chemical Technology (Anon. 1949A).

In most cases, the anhydrous acid is preferred over the hydrous as there is no storage or shipping charge for this added water of crystallization, and further, anhydrous citric acid does not vary in moisture content.

Lactic Acid.—Lactic acid is one of the oldest known organic acids. It is the primary acid constituent of milk, from which it derives its name. Its structural formula reveals that it is not only an acid, but also an alcohol. The ordinary lactic acid of commerce is usually the racemic mixture of the two optically active forms.

Lactic acid is made in the United States by fermentation of organic substances. Peckham (1944) describes the process used by the Clinton Co., which involves the use of special strains of the lactic acid-producing bacteria (*Lactobacillus*). The procedure in general consists of the fermentation of a mash made up of a carbohydrate substrate, such as various grades of dextrose from starch hydrolyzates, together with suitable mineral and proteinaceous nutrients in the presence of an excess of calcium carbonate.

TABLE 33

TYPICAL ANALYSIS OF LACTIC ACID[1]
(As is or fresh basis)

	50 Per cent Acid	80 Per cent Acid
Free acid, %	47.0 (46.0 to 48.0)	68.5 (66.0 to 71.0)
Anhydride, %	3.0 (2.0 to 4.0)	11.5 (9.0 to 14.0)
Volatile acid as acetic (maximum), %	0.5	0.5
Ash (maximum), %	0.03	0.05
Iron, p.p.m. (maximum)	2.0	5.0
Copper, p.p.m. (maximum)	1.0	2.0
Lead, p.p.m. (maximum)	1.0	1.0
Specific gravity, 68°/68°F.	1.130	1.202
Wt./gal. 68°F. (pounds)	9.42	10.02
Lovibond color, 1 in. cell, caramel series	Less than 1	Less than 2

[1] From Clinton Co., Tech. Sales Data Sheet (Anon. 1960D).

Table 33 from data provided by the Clinton Co. (Anon. 1960D) gives a typical analysis of food processing grades for lactic acid. Food processing grades must meet quality standards regarding contaminants, color, flavor, odor, heavy metals, free sulfuric acid, and in some cases, chlorides. The USP lactic acid, 85 per cent, meets the requirements of the U. S. Pharmacopoeia (Anon. 1960A). For information on the physical properties of lactic acid, see Table 34 from Dupont (Anon. 1961F).

The food processing and USP grades of lactic acid are a clear syrupy liquid with little or no odor and are miscible with water in all proportions. Lactic acid, which is an acid of medium strength, is nonvolatile at atmospheric pressure and can be distilled only at high temperatures under reduced pressure.

TABLE 34

PHYSICAL PROPERTIES OF LACTIC ACID[1]

	Food Processing Grade			USP Grade
Lactic acid, %	50	80	88	85
Specific gravity, approx.	1.12	1.18	1.21	1.19
Lbs./cu. ft. approx.	69.5	73.4	75.7	74.0
Lbs./gal., approx.	9.3	9.8	10.1	9.9
Freezing point, approx.	3°F.	−40°F.	−40°F.	−40°F.

[1] From DuPont Production Information Bulletin (Anon. 1961F).

In many food processes, lactic acid is used as a direct additive or processing agent for neutralization of alkali, for pH and fermentation control, and as a flavoring agent. The amount of lactic acid used in food products to give the desired taste and pH is usually less than two per cent and in a pH range of 2.25 to 4.0.

Inasmuch as concentrated solutions of lactic acid are corrosive irritants in prolonged contact with the skin, proper precautions should be used in their handling.

Vinegar.—Vinegar (from the Latin *vinum*—wine), whose origin is lost in time, is a sour liquid containing acetic acid and is obtained by the fermentation of diluted alcoholic liquids such as cider, malt, wine, etc.

In the early colonial days, vinegar not only added pungency and savor to the year-round diet, but before canning and refrigeration were developed, it was the preservative used to keep meats, fish, vegetables and fruit.

There are a number of varieties of vinegar which vary in flavor and in strength. H. J. Heinz Co. (Anon. 1961H) describes six varieties of vinegar available in most markets: distilled white, tarragon, wine, cider, malt and salad.

Distilled white vinegar is ideal as a preserving medium and should have a mellow, delicate aroma that brings out the full flavors of foods without dominating them.

Cider vinegar, to be of top quality, should be made from the first pressing of sound, ripe apples and has a mellow fruit flavor that blends well with fruit and vegetable salads. It is clear and sparkling.

Tarragon vinegar is a blend of malt and white vinegars in which tarragon leaves have been steeped to give the herb fragrance. Subtly employed, it is perfect for sauces and for salads of greens, meats, eggs or fish.

Malt vinegar is a deep russet-colored liquid, brewed from barley malt. It has a rich, full-bodied flavor that is excellent for salads of meat, seafoods, macaroni or beans.   It adds savor and pungency to many a meat or fish sauce, too.

Wine vinegar is made from grapes.   It is nonalcoholic and carries the color of the grape pigments.

Salad vinegar is another blended vinegar.   Composed of two parts distilled grain, two parts rex amber corn sugar and one part malt vinegar, it was developed by Heinz as a vinegar for salads, but is also useful as an all-purpose vinegar.

Although not well known, orange vinegar, which contains about five per cent acetic acid and one per cent citric acid, has a very fine flavor.

While the legal minimum requirement for acetic acid is four per cent (W/V), most vinegars are standardized at five per cent acidity (50-grain).   Vinegar acidity may range from 4 to 8 per cent with wine vinegar usually containing 6 to 6.5 per cent.

Distilled white vinegar is produced by steeping rye and barley malt in hot water until all the starches of the grains are extracted and converted into malt sugar (maltose).   By yeast fermentation of the mash, the sugar is converted into alcohol.

After distilling, the alcohol is placed in generators, which are filled with beechwood shavings containing a culture of microscopic acetic acid-forming bacteria.   In the presence of oxygen, this culture converts the alcohol into vinegar.   Aging in wooden tanks improves the sharp acid taste of the raw vinegar.

The production of apple cider vinegar is similar to that of distilled white vinegar.   The juice is extracted by hydraulic presses and pumped into storage tanks to produce alcohol by natural fermentation.   The "hard cider" is filtered and converted into vinegar through the use of acetic acid-forming bacteria.   After aging in wooden tanks, the vinegar is standardized for acidity, clarified a second time, pasteurized and bottled.

Synthetic Acids

Phosphoric Acid.—Phosphoric acid (orthophosphoric acid) in a combined form is widely distributed in the fats, carbohydrates and proteins of animals and plants.

Food-grade phosphoric acid is prepared commercially by burning elemental phosphorus in air to produce phosphorus pentoxide, which upon hydration forms the acid.   Technical details of the process and properties of phosphates may be obtained from the Encyclopedia of Chemical Technology (Anon. 1953), or from such manufacturers as Monsanto Chemical Co. (Anon. 1961A).

TABLE 35

TYPICAL ANALYSES OF HIGH PURITY PHOSPHORIC ACIDS[1]

Phosphoric Acid—75%

Formula	H_3PO_4
Molecular weight	98
Total P_2O_5, %	54.50
Iron, %	0.0003
Fluorine	0.5 p.p.m.
Pb	0.2 p.p.m.
As_2O_3	0.1 p.p.m.
Specific gravity @ 59.9°/59.9°F.	1.584

Phosphoric Acid—85% NF Syrupy

Formula	H_3PO_4
Molecular weight	98
(In quality and purity, Phosphoric acid 85 per cent compares with Phosphoric acid 75 per cent. In connection with the greater strength of Phosphoric acid 85 per cent, these figures are significant):	
H_3PO_4, %	85.5
P_2O_5, %	61.9
Specific gravity @ 59.9°/59.9°F.	1.700

[1] Data from Monsanto Technical Bulletin (Anon. 1961A).

Phosphoric acid is a colorless, odorless, syrupy liquid with a strong acid taste. The two high-purity phosphoric acids which are sold commercially are food-grade (75 per cent) and NF Syrupy (85 per cent). In Table 35 will be found typical analyses for high-purity phosphoric acid.

In addition to their function of providing acidity or buffering action, phosphoric acid and the phosphates also have nutritive value in the diet.

Acetic Acid.—Acetic acid (Latin—*aceticum*) is one of the most common organic acids and has been known in its dilute form as vinegar, since ancient times. It is a colorless liquid with a pungent odor and in this respect is unlike the other edible organic acids discussed in this chapter.

Acetic acid may be made by the bacterial oxidation of ethyl alcohol to acetic acid using Acetobacter. The "quick vinegar" process, which is commercially applicable for manufacturing acetic acid, is similar to that for producing vinegar, which has been described elsewhere.

The complete synthesis of acetic acid depends upon the formation of acetaldehyde from acetylene and water followed by air oxidation to acetic acid. In the United States, the large-scale process of making acetic acid from ethyl alcohol via acetaldehyde is detailed in the Encyclopedia of Chemical Technology (Anon. 1947). Physical data on acetic acid is available from the Union Carbide Chemical Co. (Anon. 1962B).

When pure, in which form it is extremely irritating to the skin, it is called glacial acetic acid from the ice-like appearance of the crystals. Upon dilution it has a characteristic vinegar-like odor and a sour taste. Acetic acid is miscible in all proportions with water and unlike most other acids, is a good solvent for fixed oils and many essential oils. Acetic acid is available in several strengths, such as 80 and 90 per cent, glacial acetic, USP and acetic acid, USP (36 to 37 per cent).

Malic Acid.—Malic acid (1-hydroxysuccinic acid) is the fruit acid characteristics of apples and is found naturally in maple juice and in many fruits such as apples, cherries and peaches.

Commercially, the food-grade dl-malic acid, which is the racemic form, is made synthetically by the hydration of maleic acid obtained from the catalytic vapor oxidation of benzene.

In addition to having good solubility in water, malic acid also is very soluble in alcohol. It shows many of the chemical characteristics of both an acid and an alcohol, as would be expected from its structure.

According to data from Allied Chemical Corp. (Anon. 1962C), one of the most desirable properties of malic acid is its ideal blending power. They note that some food acidulants produce the undesirable sensation of two separate tastes with certain flavors, whereas malic acid combines to give a single agreeable flavor.

Malic acid does not absorb any significant amount of water up to a relative humidity of 83 per cent. Further data covering the physical properties of malic acid as compared to other organic food acids is given by Allied Chemical Corp. (Anon. 1961D).

New Food Acidulants

Several acids are now becoming fairly important in the food processing field which formerly had applications unrelated to foods. These include adipic, fumaric and succinic acids which are now produced in food-grade quality.

They may be used in nonstandardized foods as a replacement for such acids as citric and tartaric or potassium bitartrate. Interesting features of these acids are their relative nonhygroscopicity and low water solubility.

Adipic Acid.—Food-grade adipic acid is a white, non-hygroscopic, free-flowing powder with low water solubility. It is being used in such products as gelatin desserts, powdered concentrate for fruit-flavored beverages, soft drinks, candies, baking powders and refrigerated rolls and biscuits.

Fumaric Acid.—Food-grade fumaric acid is a white, free-flowing, nonhygroscopic material having very low water solubility. This acid is used in gelatin desserts, as a leavening agent, and to extend the shelf-life of dessert powders. In addition, it is reported to have synergistic antioxidant properties in combination with food antioxidants, and is recommended for use in small quantities to prevent rancidity from developing in fat-containing food products.

Succinic Acid.—Food-grade succinic acid is a white crystalline, nonhygroscopic, powder having low water solubility. Its uses are similar to those of adipic and fumaric acids. This acid occurs naturally in small amounts in several fruits as well as in sugar beets, cheeses, rhubarb and broccoli.

Detailed information on the various food applications of these three acids is available from the manufacturers. Food processors' technical data on adipic acid may be obtained from such producers as DuPont (Anon. 1957B), Monsanto Chemical Co. (Anon. 1961B) and Allied Chemical Corp. (Anon. 1957A); on fumaric acid, from Monsanto Chemical Co. (Anon. 1961C) and Allied Chemical Corp. (Anon. 1959); on succinic acid from Allied Chemical Corp. (Anon. 1961D).

STANDARDS OF IDENTITY AND QUALITY

The quality of an acid may be designated under one of the following classifications:

(1) USP means the acid complies with the standards listed in the U. S. Pharmacopoeia.

(2) NF refers to the quality standards of the National Formulary.

(3) Food-grade indicates a quality suitable for food use.

(4) Technical grade acids may be suitable for food use, depending upon impurities.

The U. S. Pharmacopoeia, 16th Revision (Anon. 1960A) gives the detailed requirements for USP acids. The requirements for NF grade phosphoric acid and tartaric acid are indicated in the National Formulary, 11th Revision (Anon. 1960C).

LEGAL STATUS OF FOOD ACIDS

In order to comply with the requirements of the "Food Additives Amendment of 1958" to the Federal Food, Drug and Cosmetic Act of 1938, acids used in foods must have Federal Food and Drug Administration (FDA) approval in one form or another. That is, they must be on the list of substances "generally recognized as safe" (GRAS), the subject of a specific regulation or the subject of a prior sanction or approval in effect immediately prior to September 6, 1958. Since there are two general classes of foods, standardized and nonstandardized, each group must be considered separately. Non-standardized foods are those which are not regulated by a definition and standard of identity (Anon. 1938).

Each of the acids discussed in this chapter enjoy GRAS status for use in all nonstandardized foods, with the exception of fumaric acid. The FDA has approved the use of fumaric acid as an acidulant, flavoring or leavening agent in food at concentration levels not to exceed 0.3 per cent as consumed. This approval has been extended by FDA until July 1, 1963. In this case, approval amounts to an extension of the effective date for the application of the Food Additives Amendment to this substance pending issuance of a specific regulation permitting its use under certain conditions. Future permissible amounts will depend upon final disposition made by FDA through the issuance or nonissuance of a specific regulation covering its use.

Where standards of identity for foods exist, the use of acids must conform to the FDA regulation. In order to use GRAS acids not presently included in a standardized food, petitioning FDA on a product-by-product basis is required.

As an example of a product regulated by definition and standard of identity, citric acid may be used as an acidifying ingredient for salad dressing, mayonnaise and French dressing in an amount not to exceed 25 per cent of the weight of the vinegar acids calculated as acetic acid.

The use of citric acid or lactic acid in relation to unstandardized foods might be exemplified by the use of these ingredients in diluted orange juice drinks such as orange juice drink, orange drink and carbonated orange beverages.

FUNCTIONS OF ACIDS IN FOOD PROCESSING

The use of acid fruit juices (such as lemon) and edible acids (such as phosphoric) in food processing depends upon one or more of the following functions which they perform:

(1) Depress sweetness and produce well-balanced tart flavors.

(2) Clarify and stabilize fruit and vegetable juices, fermented cereal and fruit products.

(3) Control the rate of thermal destruction of microorganisms and enzymes.

(4) Influence the properties of colloidal systems containing pectins, gums and proteins.

(5)   Scavenge and sequester harmful metals which accelerate deterioration of color and flavor and cause haze.

(6)   Make possible the utilization and control of microorganisms and enzymes.

(7) . Improve the texture of jellies and jams.

(8)   Cause inversion of sugars for increasing sweetness or hindering crystallization.

(9)   Prevent flavor reversion of edible oils.

(10)   Increase apparent flavor intensity.

(11)   Aid extraction of pectin, natural pigments, etc., from fruit and vegetable materials.

(12)   Increase the effectiveness of benzoate as a preservative.

(13)   Stabilize ascorbic acid.

SELECTION OF PROPER ACID

The choice of the particular acid for any specific food application is dependent upon a number of factors.   Since each acid has its own unique combination of physical and chemical properties, the choice should be made on the basis of the qualities required, as indicated in the section on **Functions of Acids in Food Processing** (p. 142).

The simplest possible use of a food acid involves decreasing the pH only.   As an example it might be desired simply to acidify a solution where pH adjustment is all that is required.   In this case, relative cost is most important so that phosphoric, the strongest and cheapest acid in this group, would normally be the acid of choice. A comparison of the relative costs of food acids is given in Table 36.

In many cases the selection is based upon the ability of the acid to bring out and enhance the food flavor in question.   For such purposes, compatibility and blending are important factors in the choice of acid.   Each acid behaves somewhat independently of pH and concentration so that the best acid for a particular type of use is not necessarily preferred for another.   Thus, citric acid is generally preferred for citrus beverages, tartaric acid for grape beverages, malic acid for apple beverages and phosphoric acid for cola drinks.   Since taste responses and stability cannot always be predicted, food products should be examined both before and after storage, when blending or substituting the acids used.

Certain applications require the use of those acids whose anion will form complexes with undesired metals such as copper and iron.   The desired cloud stability of juices and the freedom of wines from cloudiness depends upon the sequestering ability of such acids as citric and tartaric. Lemon juice, which contains citric acid, also falls in this category.

The relative volatility of the acids also may be an important consideration. In processes involving boiling at atmospheric or reduced pressure, such acids as vinegar or acetic acid are likely to lose strength by evaporation. In the thermal sterilization of low-acid foods, loss of acidity can be very important.

TABLE 36

RELATIVE COSTS OF FOOD ACIDS[1]

Acid	Type	Quality	Amount	Price, Cents/Lb.
Acetic	80%	. . .	Bbls, 100 lb.	9.41
	Glacial,		Drums, carload	
	synthetic	CP	dlvd. East	18.95
	Glacial	USP	Tanks, dlvd. East	13.00
Adipic	. . .	. . .	Carload, dlvd.	29.00
Citric	Anhydrous	USP	100 lb. bags, carload	29.50
	Hydrous	USP	100 lb. bags, carload	29.50
Fumaric	. . .	Food grade	Bags, carload	18.50
Lactic	50%	Food grade	Drums, tankcars	17.00
	50%	Technical	Drums, tankcars	14.00
	80%	Food grade	Tankcars	33.50
Malic	. . .	Food grade	Bags, carload	29.50
Phosphoric	75%	Food grade	Tanks, tankwagon	5.60
	80%	Food grade	Tanks, tankwagon	6.00
Tartaric	. . .	NF	Bags, carload	41.00

[1] From Oil, Paint and Drug Reporter 190, No. 20 (Nov. 14, 1966).

When selecting an acid for food use, the solubility of its salts should also be considered. In some cases, insoluble salts of such cations as calcium or iron form, which may require the use of greater amounts of acid, or cause the formation of an objectionable precipitate or water insoluble residue. When tartaric acid is added to the must in wine making, an appreciable amount of this acid is later removed as insoluble cream of tartar.

In the presence of relatively high amounts of calcium ion, possibly occurring in the food product or resulting from the use of hard water, several of the acids may form precipitates. By way of comparison, the relative solubility of the calcium salts of the acids, listed from most to least soluble, are acetate, lactate, citrate, malate, tartrate, phosphate. Thus, in the presence of high calcium ion, the use of phosphoric acid is the most likely to form a residue of insoluble calcium salt, whereas none should form with acetic or lactic acids because of the high solubility of their calcium salts.

Another consideration which is important relates to the hygroscopicity of the acid or its salts in such dehydrated food products as beverage bases and dessert formulations. Moisture pickup in food products by the acids may have deleterious effects ranging from simple agglomeration to premature release of the carbon dioxide in effervescent beverage preparations and baking powders. Of the solid acids, citric is the most hygroscopic, followed by malic and tartaric acids. On the other hand, adipic, fumaric and succinic acids are essentially non-hygroscopic.

Water solubility varies considerably among the food acids. The liquid acids, including vinegar and lemon juice, are miscible with water in all proportions. At room temperature, the remaining organic acids, arranged from most to least soluble in water, are citric acid, tartaric acid, malic acid, succinic acid, adipic acid and fumaric acid. Citric, tartaric and malic acids all have good water solubility, whereas the solubility of succinic and adipic acids is low. Fumaric acid has a solubility of only 0.6 gm./100 gm. water at 77°F., the lowest of all these acids. Low water solubility combined with nonhygroscopic qualities make these three acids of interest for specialized applications.

ACIDITY—RELATION OF QUANTITY AND ACTIVITY

According to the classical definition, an acid is a substance capable of yielding hydrogen ions (symbol H^+) in aqueous solution. Although present day knowledge indicates that hydronium ion (H_3O^+) is actually involved, for practical purposes we may consider the sourness or acidity to be dependent upon the amount of hydrogen ion in solution. The activity of the hydrogen ion is commonly referred to in terms of the logarithmic pH scale as developed by Sorenson. From this mathematical treatment, pH represents the negative logarithm of the hydrogen ion concentration (activity), or $pH = \log 1/(H^+)$. The pH of a food, then, is merely a number denoting the degree of effective acidity or alkalinity. Pure water, which has a pH of 7.0, is considered neutral. Acidity increases through the pH range 7 to 1 and alkalinity, also, increases from 7 through 14. Because the pH scale is logarithmic, a solution of pH 6.0 is ten times as acid as pure water at pH 7.0. Likewise, a solution of pH 5.0 is 100 times as acid as pure water. For a detailed discussion of the theoretical background concerning these concepts, the reader may consult any of a number of good reference books on the subject, such as Clark (1928).

In connection with the acidity of any food product, there are two important aspects to be considered: quantity of acid present and apparent hydrogen ion concentration. The total quantity of acid is determined by neutralization with a standard alkali, such as sodium hydroxide, to obtain the titratable acidity. From a knowledge of the particular acid present, and the formula weight, the exact amount of acid may be calculated. The total acidity ordinarily is expressed in terms of percentage, normality or grains per gallon.

The acid intensity or hydrogen ion concentration may be estimated by organic chemical indicators but is best measured by the use of such electrical instruments as pH meters. For details on pH measurement, the instrument manufacturers, or such references as Getman and Daniels (1940), or Gould (1957), may be consulted.

BUFFERING ACID SOLUTIONS FOR pH CONTROL

In many cases, particularly when using the stronger acids in foods and beverages, it is desirable to reduce the sharpness of the acid taste and thereby produce a smoother product with improved flavor. A practical means for reducing the active hydrogen ion concentration, or pH, and yet maintain the same total titratable acidity in a food product, is to add salts of that acid.

The sodium salts of the various acids such as citric, acetic or phosphoric acids are commonly used in the food industry for pH control. When the acids and their sodium salts are present together in a foodstuff, a "buffering" effect is obtained. Upon dilution with water or the addition of moderate amounts of acid (or base), but little effect upon the hydrogen ion concentration of the food is produced.

The application of these buffering principles to food processing is widely used in the manufacture of such products as juice beverages, jellies and gelatin desserts. As an example of the effect obtained by adding the buffer salt, sodium citrate, to citric acid solutions of various concentrations, reference is made to Table 37.

MEASURING UNITS OF ACID CONCENTRATION

The solid food-grade acids, which are available as crystals or powders, may be weighed directly for use in various formulations. Since some acids, such as citric, are available in both anhydrous (without water of crystallization) and hydrous forms, it is necessary to make allowance for the water content when substituting one form

TABLE 37

pH VERSUS CONCENTRATION CITRIC ACID—SODIUM CITRATE SOLUTIONS[1,2]

Sodium Citrate, %	Citric Acid, %										
	1	2	3	5	7	10	15	20	26	40	50
0.00	2.35	2.04	2.05	1.95	1.73	1.55	1.47	1.28	1.20	0.96	0.60
0.25	3.5	2.53	2.50	...	...	...	...	...	...	...	...
0.50	3.45	2.83	2.75	2.50	2.18	...	...	...	...	...	...
1.00	4.05	3.25	3.10	2.8	2.40	2.2	...	...	...	...	...
1.50	4.5	3.6	...	...	...	...	...	...	...	...	...
2.0	4.7	3.8	3.7	3.2	2.8	2.5	2.3	2.1	...	...	...
3.0	...	...	4.0	3.5	...	...	...	...	...	...	...
4.0	...	...	...	3.8	3.2	2.9	2.6	2.4	2.2	...	...
5.0	...	...	...	...	3.4	3.0	...	...	...	...	...
6.0	...	...	...	...	...	...	2.9	2.6	2.5	...	...
7.0	...	...	...	...	3.7	3.3	...	...	...	...	...
8.0	...	...	...	...	...	...	3.1	2.8	2.6	...	...
10.0	...	...	...	...	...	...	3.3	2.9	2.8	2.3	2.0
12.0	...	...	...	...	...	...	3.4	3.1	2.9	...	...
14.0	...	...	...	...	...	...	3.5	3.2	3.0	...	...
15.0	...	...	...	...	...	...	3.54	...	...	...	...
16.0	...	...	...	...	...	...	...	3.4	3.1	...	...
18.0	...	...	...	...	...	...	...	3.5	3.2	...	...
20.0	...	...	...	...	...	...	...	...	3.3	2.7	2.4
25.0	...	...	...	...	...	...	...	...	3.52	...	...
30.0	...	...	...	...	...	...	...	...	...	3.1[1]	2.6[1]
40.0	...	...	...	...	...	...	...	...	...		

[1] Exceeds solubility of sodium citrate. All values expressed as per cent by weight. Citric Acid Anhydrous USP. Sodium Citrate USP.
[2] Data from Chas. Pfizer and Co., Inc.

for the other. Since certain of these acids are hygroscopic (have the property of picking up moisture from a humid atmosphere), weights may be misleading if the acid has been improperly stored.

The acids supplied commercially in liquid form include lemon juice, vinegar, acetic acid, lactic acid and phosphoric acid. Since in each case varying amounts of water are present, the concentration of acid may be specified in such terms as per cent, pounds per gallon, grains per gallon, specific gravity, Baumé or normality. The Handbook of Chemistry and Physics, by Hodgman et al. (1961), contains a collection of tables relating several of these quantities for the liquid acids—acetic and phosphoric, as well as for citric and tartaric acids. Specific data on the several acids may be found elsewhere in this chapter, in the literature or from the manufacturer.

Normality of Acids

Of the various ways in which to express the quantity of acid in a solution, such as per cent or specific gravity, the technically trained person finds advantages in using normality, a term borrowed from the chemist. By normality is meant the concentration of acid as related to that of a normal solution and a normal solution, is one containing one gram equivalent of the acid per liter of solution. The normality of the acid, then, can be expressed as some whole or fractional multiple of this amount.

An equivalent of an acid is the amount required to furnish 1.008 gm. of hydrogen ion (H^+), if the acid were completely ionized. This would be a gram molecular (or formula) weight for acetic acid $(HC_2H_3O_2)$, half of a gram molecular weight for tartaric acid $(H_2C_4H_4O_6)$ and only one-third of a gram molecular weight for phosphoric acid (H_3PO_4). In the case of divalent acids, it is necessary to divide the molecular weight of the acid by two or, if trivalent, by three. For example, the weight of acid per liter in a normal solution of acetic acid would be the same as the molecular weight, 60 gm. For tartaric acid, containing two acid hydrogens, the amount is one-half the molecular weight, or 75 gm.

The advantage of using an acid solution of known normality is that it contains the same amount of total acid hydrogen as any other acid solution of equal normality. Furthermore, when determining titratable acidity, by neutralizing the acid with an alkali (or base), equivalent volumes of acid and base of the same normality exactly neutralize each other.

Determining Acidity and pH Value

Because of the necessity for accurate control of the total acid (titratable acidity) and the pH (active acidity) in food processing, it is important to measure these quantities.

Briefly, the usual procedure for determining the total concentration of acids is to titrate a measured sample of the product with a standardized solution of base (alkali) of known concentration or normality. The end point of the titration is reached when a chemically equivalent amount of the base just neutralizes the acid present in the sample. Although there has been considerable controversy regarding the proper end point pH value to use, many are adopting pH 8.1 which has long been proposed by the Association of Official Agricultural Chemists (1960). To determine the end point of this chemical reaction, either of two methods may be used. One of these depends upon a color change using an organic indicator such as phenolphthalein, which shifts from colorless to pink when the acid is neutralized. In the case of dark colored food products having too little acidity to allow dilution, methods other than colorimetric are required for a reliable determination of end point. More sophisticated methods include electrometric or potentiometric determinations which involve, respectively, the hydrogen ion concentration or the rate of change in potential when the reaction is completed.

Although the pH value of food products may be determined colorimetrically using selected indicators, most modern food plants use commercial pH meters of the glass electrode type. The industrial models usually have an accuracy in the range 0.01 to 0.05 pH and for research work very sensitive instruments are available which are accurate to 0.005 pH.

For a more detailed discussion relating to both theory and procedures of determining pH and acidity of food products, such references as Food Analysis by Joslyn (1950) should be consulted. The Association of Official Agricultural Chemists (1960) gives detailed procedures for determining pH and acidity of several classes of foods including beverages, fruit products, cereal foods, dairy products, oils and fats and sugar products.

RELATION OF ACIDITY TO TASTE

It is well known that the several acids have a different degree of sourness or taste intensity even though they are of the same concentration. This difference is quite apparent when phosphoric and acetic acids are tasted at equivalent concentrations. The sour reaction of acids, actually, is closely dependent on the hydrogen ion concentration (H^+) or pH value. In chemical terminology, such so-called "strong" acids, as phosphoric, more easily yield free H^+ ions in water and are said to be more completely ionized. By comparison, acetic acid is called "weak" or relatively undissociated because it has little tendency to yield free H^+ ions.

Qualitatively, the sour taste of acids is generally dependent upon the stimulation of the taste buds by H^+ ions. However, more recent data has been obtained to show that other factors are involved. At the same pH, organic acids usually give a greater apparent taste sensation than inorganic acids. In the case of wines, the sour taste is determined more by total acidity than by pH.

Since most foods are not a homogeneous mixture as eaten, the sourness of an acid flavor will be determined by the nature of the acid and the rate at which it is released from the food and mixed with saliva during mastication. In order to observe the direct effect of acid on the taste receptor, Beidler (1957) eliminated salivary effects by flowing the stimulus through a closed chamber surrounding the tongue. In such cases it was found that responses of equal sourness are not produced with acids of equal pH or equal normality. Interestingly enough, the sour sensation of an acid is directly related to its ability to be adsorbed by polyelectrolytes. The pattern of response was found to vary with the type and rate of release of the acid from the food.

USE IN FOOD PROCESSING
Effect of pH in the Sterilization of Foods

In the canning of foods, one of the most important factors affecting the sterilization times and temperatures is the actual pH of the food.

Since many of the delicate low-acid fruits and vegetables cannot withstand processing in a pressure cooker, pH control becomes essential to prevent spoilage.

Thermally processed canned foods must be treated at a temperature and for a time sufficient to destroy all pathogenic and toxin-forming organisms, such as *Clostridium botulinum*, as well as other more resistant types, which might be present and grow in the product, and produce spoilage under normal storage conditions.

Many processing studies in connection with the effect of acidity on the sterilization of canned fruits and vegetables have been conducted by the Research Laboratories of the National Canners Association (NCA) with the aid of other canning industry laboratories. Pertinent references include Townsend (1938), Spiegelberg (1939), Townsend and Powers (1942) and Gould (1957). All of these investigators have found that the pH of the product is an extremely important factor in determining processing conditions, because microorganisms are more readily destroyed or their growth inhibited, as the acidity of the product increases.

It is usually considered that a pH of 4.5 is the dividing line between acid and the so-called nonacid foods. This usually means with a product having a pH of 4.5 or less, that the growth after proper sterilization of bacterial spores from such public health hazard organisms as *Cl. botulinum*, will be inhibited.

Ordinarily, tomatoes are considered as an acid product (pH 4.5 or less), but through the introduction of (low-acid) new varieties in combination with lye peeling, Leonard *et al.* (1959) have observed a marked rise of pH values in canned tomatoes (5.0 to 5.6) and a concomitant increase in spoilage. These researchers suggest acidification with citric acid to a pH range 4.0 to 4.47. Similar studies and conclusions have been made by the NCA group.

Spoilage has been encountered in figs, whose natural pH varies from 4.8 to 5.1. Because of difficulty in sterilizing figs, some canners acidify with citric acid to a pH below 4.5 to inhibit the growth of thermophiles.

Because nonacid canned foods, especially those in the pH range 5.0 to 7.0, have been found to be a health hazard, much attention has been directed toward their sterilization. A cooperative study involving the NCA was made to determine the processing requirements of canned red pimientos, whose normal pH is in the range 4.7 to 5.2. Spraying or dipping blanched pimientos in a 0.5 per cent solution of citric acid or acetic acid (as vinegar) will lower the pH of the final product to about 4.7.

As an example of the problems involved in the safe processing of the different types of artichoke packs, Townsend and Powers (1942) have described this acidification procedure in some detail.

If food acids are to be added to canned vegetables, regulated by a definition and standard of identity, they must be an aid to processing and be added in a quantity not to exceed that to permit effective processing by heat, without discoloration or other impairment of the article. Acids are permitted in such products as asparagus, celery, Brussels sprouts, onions, cauliflower, etc. In artichokes, citric acid or a vinegar is a prescribed additive to reduce the pH to 4.5 or below.

Vegetable Products

As discussed in the prior section covering sterilization of foods, lower pH increases the resistance of canned goods to spoilage. Vegetable products, including juices, are ordinarily considered to be non-acid foods and therefore present a health hazard unless properly sterilized. Another important point is that the flavor of vegetable juices is usually improved by acidification.

Processing of several vegetable products such as tomatoes and pimientos have been discussed in the prior section. References also were given covering safe processing of artichokes. In the case of tomato juice, the growth of flat-sour organisms, which are responsible for off-taste, can be prevented by the addition of such acids as citric at levels which may be as low as 0.1 per cent. Other vegetable products in which acidification is indicated are asparagus, celery, Brussels sprouts, cauliflower, beans, onions, carrots, egg plant and such mixtures as vegetable juice cocktail and potato salad. According to Cruess et al. (1946), five per cent lemon juice greatly improved frozen pack tomato juice.

There can be little doubt but that the future uses for edible acids to control pH levels and to sequester trace metal contaminants in canned vegetables will expand greatly.

Factors which are important in the choice of acid for vegetable products and juices include buffering capacity and degree of coagulation of the product, rate of penetration of the acid (in solid products), and effect on taste. For acidification, the choice includes citric, tartaric, malic, lactic, phosphoric and acetic acids. Lemon juice and vinegar are also useful in many of these applications.

In general, the very strong inorganic acids such as hydrochloric, produce an abnormal flavor. However, Marsh (1942) found that the inorganic acid, phosphoric, was more satisfactory than lactic acid for acidifying carrot juice.

Acetic acid apparently arrests aerobic and anaerobic fermentation in foods and is widely used for preserving such vegetable products as pickles as well as fish and meats. Since acetic acid (or vinegar) is effective in preventing microbial spoilage, it is an essential ingredient in almost every variety of pickle with the exception of genuine dills. Vinegar is a big flavor contributor in tomato catsup (ketchup).

Lactic acid may be used in the manufacture of pickles, olives, sauerkraut and sandwich spreads to adjust pH and improve the keeping qualities.

In avocado product experiments, Cruess *et al.* (1951) found that a sandwich spread of avocado and pimiento, plus added distilled vinegar to keep it, has possibilities. In this product, pH value and total acetic acid content are vitally important.

Fruit Products

A general discussion concerning the effect of pH on heat sterilization of low-acid fruit products was presented in the prior section; "Effect of pH in the Sterilization of Foods."

Such acid fruits as plums, cherries and citrus juices have a pH below 4.0 and consequently present no problem in obtaining commercial sterility. However, other fruits such as pears, nectarines, figs, pineapples and peaches have a pH above 4.0 and which may exceed 4.5. Consequently, from a processing standpoint, products made from these fruits may require acidification. Fruit nectars are frequently low in acid and therefore require careful control in processing.

It is generally recognized that a consumer's acceptance of canned fruit juices and nectars is based largely upon the sweetness-acid-flavor relationship. The natural flavors of sweet juice products are greatly enhanced by the tang and tartness of added acid. If desired, such salts as sodium citrate may be used as a buffer to control pH in canned products.

When organic acids are added to such sweetened products as nectars, Valdés *et al.* (1956) found that the flavor was enhanced and palatability increased. The preferred soluble solids-acid ratios for sweetened apricot, peach and pear nectars with added citric acid were approximately 30, 40 and 160, respectively.

Using suprathreshold solutions of citric acid and sucrose, Pangborn (1961) found that citric acid, at concentrations ranging from 0.007 to 0.073 per cent, depressed the sweetness of 0.5 to 20.0 per cent sucrose.

In many cases lowered pH exerts a protective effect on fruit juice pigments. Acidification with citric acid will color-stabilize strawberry fountain syrup and malic acid is useful as a stabilizing agent for grape juice.

Cruess *et al.* (1946) report on the use of lemon juice in frozen pack punch syrups such as Concord grape juice and boysenberry juice. Frozen pack prune juice was also improved with lemon juice. In canned prune juice, either citric acid or lemon juice are included as permitted optional acidifying ingredients.

For acidifying fruit products citric acid is probably most often used. Other useful acids include tartaric, malic, lactic and phosphoric. Lemon juice is used in canned figs, prune juice and fruit nectars.

The problem of browning, which occurs in frozen sliced fruits such as peaches or apples, can be combatted through the use of citric acid solutions or lemon juice. When ascorbic acid is used, citric acid will stabilize the ascorbic acid, thus giving even better protection against atmospheric browning.

McColloch and Gentili (1958) found that a more stable cloud in stored frozen citrus juice concentrate can be obtained by the addition of 0.05 to 0.5 per cent fumaric acid.

Through the use of such acids as citric, the ferric casse in cider caused by an iron-tannin complex, may be eliminated.

Doesburg and DeVos (1959) have successfully prepared milk-flavored fruit juices through the use of high-ester pectins (degree of esterification about 50 per cent) to prevent the curdling of milk proteins. The best results generally were noted by acidifying to pH 3.8.

Soft Drinks—Carbonated and Still Beverages

The tart taste of soft drinks, other than those of the cola-type, is imparted by such organic acidulants as citric acid, malic acid, tartaric acid and lactic acid. In cola-type beverages the most commonly used acidulant is phosphoric acid. Buffering agents, generally the sodium salts of these acids, are frequently used to control the degree of acidity in soft drinks. The concentrations of acids and buffers employed are in a range to produce approximately the same pH as that of the natural fruit juice.

Citric acid is commonly used in ginger ale, and with citrus-fruit and berry-flavored drinks. Lemon juice makes up at least part of the acidity of lemon and lemon-lime beverages. For apple, celery, and cherry-flavored drinks, malic acid is preferred. Tartaric acid, the natural acid of grapes, serves with grape-flavored beverages.

Phosphoric acid has found wide use in the heavier leaf, root, nut or herbal flavors, such as the colas, root beer and sarsaparilla. In these drinks the bite and astringency of the acid serves to counteract the heaviness of the basic flavor. Low pH improves flavor and also contributes a preservative action.

The amount of acid used varies with the type of beverage. Soft drinks generally have a pH value of from 2.3 to 4.5 and the acid ranges from 0.02 to 0.24 per cent. Such beverages as Tom Collins and other mixers may go as high as 0.35 per cent acid. Cola flavors are usually in the range of 0.05 to 0.08 per cent phosphoric acid and may also contain citric acid. Both root beer and sarsaparilla contain around 0.01 per cent phosphoric acid with pH values approximating 5.0 and 4.5, respectively.

Citric acid, the most common of the fruit acids, adapts itself well to all light or fruity flavors. It is also indicated, for cereal beverages.

Malic acid is useful, according to information from Allied Chemical Corp. (Anon. 1962C), because of its ability to blend and bring out particular flavors. Also it does not affect the shade or permanence of the colors commonly used in food products nor cause a sediment with ordinary "acid proof" caramel.

Acids to be used for soft drink preparation are generally made up as 50 per cent stock solutions. The syrup is prepared by dissolving sugar in water and adding varying amounts of the prepared acid solution. Color, preservatives and flavor may be added as desired.

In addition to the primary purpose of obtaining the desired bouquet by modifying the sweet flavors, the acid also plays important secondary roles in beverage formulation. These functions include acting as a preservative in syrups and the finished beverage, sequestering harmful metals which cause haze and catalyzing sugar inversion to increase sweetness and body.

Although sodium benzoate is a good inhibitor of microorganisms, it is effective only in beverages having some acidity. It is generally recognized that between pH 5 to 7 benzoate is useless as a preservative in aqueous solutions. Starting at about pH 4.5, it becomes effective and the preservative action improves as acidity is increased. For use in citrus beverages, the product should be kept at least as acid as pH 4.2.

Recent tests were conducted at the Wisconsin Alumni Research Foundation (Anon. 1961G) to determine the relative value of citric, malic, lactic, adipic and fumaric acids in beverages. Citric and adipic acids were found to be equivalent in acid taste strength. Fumaric acid was of interest because it was of greater strength than other acids examined. However, because of solubility problems, special methods of incorporation would have to be developed before fumaric acid could prove useful in this field.

Details of beverage preparation with the several acids are described by Hale and Medbury (1944), Anon. (1949B) and Jacobs (1959).

Jams, Jellies and Preserves

Because certain fruits and other foods contain insufficient natural acidity for the preparation of jellies, jams or preserves, it is necessary to adjust the pH in the optimum range where pectin can act most effectively.

As pointed out by Joseph (1953), commercial preservers should recognize the tremendous effect pH has upon pectin gel formation. When sufficient pectin and sugar are present, no gel will form until the pH is reduced below some critical value near 3.6. This critical pH above which regular pectins will not form a gel, regardless of the amount of pectin, is sometimes termed the "marginal pH," although more correctly it should be called the "limiting pH."

Preservers get great variations in jelly strength, from batch to batch, when they operate near the critical pH region for each type of pectin. These variations are sometimes attributed to juice differences but most frequently are blamed on the pectins. Actually, the user can obtain more pectin economy and less fluctuation in product firmness by operating in the pH region below 3.2 for slow set pectin and 3.4 for rapid set pectin.

Most slow-setting pectins give optimum performance between pH 2.6 and 3.2, while rapid-setting pectins show their best behavior in the region of pH 2.9 to 3.4. Many times the addition of acid to lower the pH only 0.1 unit may be sufficient to prevent complete failure of a jelly batch.

Citric, tartaric and malic acids are used, as well as phosphoric and lactic acids, in these applications. Lemon juice is indicated for use in making all-fruit preserves and jellies. These acids control the acidity so as to produce the firmest pectin gel and also form a complex with heavy metal cations such as iron which, in the case of jelly, may give a dull color. Buffer salts, such as sodium citrate help to control the pH in jellies and preserves.

Phosphoric acid has been recommended for use in the production of very firm, nonsoaking jellies such as are required in jelly doughnuts, rolls and cake fillings.   The acid is not normally added until the final stages of cooking or preferably delayed until the product is put in the final container in order to minimize hydrolysis of the pectin.   Enough acid is used to lower the pH to an optimum of about 3.3.

Lactic acid is useful in this application because it produces a slower rate of gelling, allowing the elimination of air bubbles and slight overdoses do not impair taste or odor.

For specific use data refer to the manufacturers of each acid as indicated in the bibliography.

Candies and Confections

Edible acids, such as citric, tartaric, malic, lactic and phosphoric, are useful to give tartness and enhance the flavors of fruits and other flavor ingredients in the manufacture of candy.

In many cases, it is also desirable, by a process known as inversion, to convert sucrose (cane or beet sugar) to the two simple sugars, dextrose and levulose.   When such acids as citric or tartaric are added during the cooking process to "doctor" the batch, the sucrose is converted to these simple sugars which do not crystallize readily.   Sucrose is not as soluble as the inverted sugars and often causes graining due to crystallization of the sugar mass.   Thus, acid is added to cream centers to invert the sugar and prevent hardening.   In hard candies and taffies, cream of tartar is often used to obtain partial inversion and thus prevent undesirable crystallization.

For preparing slab or starch cast pectin gels, citric or tartaric acids and cream of tartar are useful, along with a buffer salt such as sodium citrate or acetate.   This treatment modifies the starch so that the product will flow freely while being cast.

Aspics and Low Methoxyl Pectin Gels

A new type product, known as low ester, low methoxyl, or Pectin L.M., has become of increasing importance to food processors during the past few years.   This product has the ability to form gels without regard for sugar concentration.   However, divalent metal ions such as calcium are needed to tie the pectin chains together.   The calcium requirement is associated with pH.

The acidity of gels with Pectin L.M. is not of great importance as it is with regular pectin gels.   As indicated by Joseph (1953), Pectin L.M. will make good gels with milk at pH of 6.5, with fruit or vegetable juices as low as pH 2.5. The desirable range of pH for most salad and dessert gels is 3.2 to 4.0. Citric and tartaric acids are most often used although such other acids as lemon juice are suitable.

Gelatin Desserts

In the manufacture of gelatin desserts, careful control of pH is extremely important, as the setting qualities of the gelatin are a function of pH. A suitable gelatin dessert powder may contain 0.75 to 2 per cent of acid. Citric, tartaric or malic acids are commonly used, but the high level of acid required (pH 3.0 to 3.5) to impart the desired degree of tartness may interfere with the setting time of the gel. Consequently, such alkali metal buffer salts as citrates, tartrates (cream of tartar), lactates and acetates are used in combination to repress the hydrogen ion concentration. At present it is estimated that adipic and fumaric acids control the bulk of the gelatin dessert market.

Adipic acid is reported by Ferguson (1953) to be superior in powdered gelatin compositions because of its nonhygroscopicity and effect on delaying the time required for the jelly to melt. Likewise, fumaric acid is used as an acidulant in gelatin desserts to provide a noncaking product having lengthened shelf-life. According to Stokes and Kennedy (1946), gel strength is also improved with two per cent less gelatin required in the finished product.

Dairy Products

Adjustment of acidity is a very important part of the production and use of several dairy products. Over a period of years Templeton and Sommer (1929, 1933, 1934 and 1935) Templeton (1937), as well as Gonce and Templeton (1930), studied the use of citric acid and its salts in milk and milk products. Their researches included starter cultures, infant feeding, whipping cream, butter making and processed cheeses.

Normal milk contains 0.16 to 0.18 per cent citric acid but the amount in finished dairy products varies due to processing treatments. Curdling is the greatest at pH 4.6, the isoelectric point of the casein in the milk.

Milk received at evaporating plants at different seasons and from different herds varies in stability to heat. This property is dependent upon the balance in the milk of the natural mineral salts, particularly the proportions of calcium, phosphate and citrate. It is often necessary, therefore, to add such buffer salts as disodium phosphate or sodium citrate to milk or ice cream mix in order to produce sufficient stability to prevent coagulation on heating. As an example, government standards allow the addition of disodium phosphate up to a level of 0.1 per cent by weight in finished evaporated milk.

According to Hammer and Babel (1957), 0.15 per cent citric acid or 0.26 per cent sodium citrate may be added to milk intended for culture to give the highly aromatic flavor of biacetyl. Hargrove *et al.* (1961) describes the phosphate heat treatment of milk to prevent bacteriophage proliferation in lactic milk cultures.

Excessive acidity, which may develop in cream, must be neutralized for satisfactory churning and to produce a butter of acceptable flavor and keeping quality. In the manufacture of buttermilk, citric or lactic acid may be used to give flavor tang. In unsalted butter, lactic acid is useful as a preservative.

For frozen dairy products citric and lactic acids are used. Citric acid is the primary acid used in acidifying sherbets and ices at levels usually sufficient to give a titratable acidity of 0.35 per cent or more. Lemon juice also has application for products in this area.

Recently, as indicated in Food Chemical News (Anon. 1961E), an industry group asked for amendments to the food standards for cottage cheese and creamed cottage cheese, which would permit the addition of citric, lactic or phosphoric acids.

Process cheese, although ideally of uniform flavor, color and consistency, must be made from natural cheeses that vary over a fairly broad range. The use of emulsifying agents such as citrates and phosphates up to levels of three per cent may be used in the preparation of process cheese. These materials improve homogeneity and smoothness after beating and help produce a uniform product. The emulsifying action also minimizes oiling off. Sodium citrate is used as an emulsifier in cheese products to produce smooth, evenly melting cheese that slices and spreads easily. Disodium phosphate is also quite commonly used in processing domestic cheeses.

Emulsification and a desired tartness in process cheese and cheese spreads may be obtained by the addition of acids such as citric, lactic, malic, tartaric and phosphoric.

In processing, calcium from raw cheese may form unwanted crystals of calcium citrate when using combinations of phosphates and citrates or disodium crystals when all phosphate emulsifiers are used. Tests carried on by Monsanto Chemical Co. (Anon. 1961B) show that sodium adipate used with sodium phosphate reduces crystal formation in the finished product.

Edible Fats and Oils

Natural edible fats and oils always contain metallic ions and during subsequent processing pick up additional contaminants from equipment. Because of their sequestering ability, certain of the edible acids are useful for the inactivation of iron, copper and nickel ions in edible fats and oils. The complexing of these ions by such acids as citric provides an edible oil product with improved stability and flavor retention. Complexing protects the color and flavor of treated soybean oil, and prevents reversion. The stability of hydrogenated fats is improved by complexing colloidal nickel and nickel soaps which result from the use of the nickel catalyst.

Data available from the technical bulletins of Pfizer (Anon. 1957C) and Miles Chemical Co. (Anon. 1960B) indicates that for various fats, the useful range of citric acid is between 0.002 and 0.05 per cent. According to Van Wazer (1961), phosphoric acid and phosphates are useful during processing of vegetable shortenings to control pH and tie up transition metal ions.

Certain acidic substances such as citric and fumaric acids enhance the properties of the widely employed antioxidants, butylated hydroxyanisole, butylated hydroxytoluene and propyl gallate, which are used to protect such fatty foods as lard, shortenings, crackers, nuts and potato chips.

Baking Industry

The acid ingredients used in chemical leavening agents by the baking industry include such compounds as tartaric, adipic, and fumaric acids, potassium acid tartrate and monocalcium phosphate.

Phosphoric acid is useful for buffering nutrient solutions to optimum pH in preparation of yeasts. This acid also serves as the source of phosphorus which is essential to the growth of the microorganisms involved.

Such acidic substances as acetic acid, lactic acid and monocalcium phosphate are effective in retarding the growth of molds and "rope" bacteria, which render baked goods inedible.

Mayonnaise and Salad Dressings

Although vinegar (acetic acid) is commonly used in this application, other edible acids are useful for obtaining special qualities.

Several food processors are now using citric acid, lemon juice or phosphoric acid to replace part of the vinegar in mayonnaise and salad dressing formulations.   Citric acid or lemon juice are ideal for this purpose since they complex harmful metal prooxidants in addition to adding desired acidity.   As was pointed out by Joseph (1929), lemon juice may be substituted for vinegar on a 25 to 50 per cent basis. Whereas acetic acid (the acid of vinegar) has high solubility in the oil phase, citric acid (from added acid or lemon juice), dissolves almost entirely in the aqueous phase.   These differences influence flavor as well as oxidative stability.

Sea Foods

The factors which affect the quality deterioration of seafoods include bacterial contamination, enzyme activity and rancidity.   Since the maintenance of low temperatures alone will neither prevent the growth of marine microorganisms nor stop protein breakdown (enzyme proteolysis), additional treatments are necessary for long storage.

Frozen Fish.—Frozen fish will discolor and develop off-flavors during storage and this deterioration is further hastened by the presence of harmful metal prooxidants which accelerate these undesirable changes.

Modern processing methods for fish, described by Pfizer (Anon. 1958) and Miles Chemical Co. (Anon. 1960B), include dipping and glazing baths using about 0.25 per cent each of both citric acid and either erythorbic or ascorbic acids.   Citric acid acts to inactivate certain natural enzymes and to sequester trace metals, which greatly accelerate proteolysis.   In addition, the ascorbic acid is more stable to atmospheric oxidation in the acid environment created by the citric acid.

Shellfish.—The discoloration of crustaceans, particularly those which are canned, may range from a faint gray to nearly blue or black. Copper combines with amines in crustacean meat to form a blue compound and with sulfur compounds to produce a black pigment.   Dipping the shellfish in a solution containing 0.25 to 1.0 per cent of citric acid, or its equivalent of lemon juice, is useful as a means for effecting a favorable pH reduction and the sequestration of copper.   In canned shellfish, Miles Chemical Co. (Anon. 1960B) recommends the addition of 0.7 per cent citric acid, 1 per cent salt and 1 to 2 per cent sugar to the brine to prevent the discoloration of the fish product.

Most packs of small shrimp canned in the Pacific Northwest are now acidified with citric acid.   Sufficient acid is added to reduce the pH to approximately 6.8.

Recent tests by Thompson and Waters (1960) on a type of Gulf of

Mexico shrimp called seabob, indicate that lemon juice has advantages over citric acid for the control of iron sulfide discoloration. Gallagher (1957) gives details for the use of lemon juice in commercial shrimp processing.

Wines and Fermented Juices

Wine-making is a very important industry in the United States, with many varieties of grapes coming from the different growing areas. As is indicated by Amerine and Joslyn (1951), several varieties, under California growing conditions, are quite often too low in acid, and their musts may have to be ameliorated by addition of acid or by blending with high-acid wines.

Amerine and Cruess (1960) indicate that acidification of low-acid grapes before fermentation results in better development of bouquet and flavor than if delayed until fermentation is complete. When tartaric acid is added to the must, a greater amount is required than of acids such as citric, because an appreciable amount of tartrate is later removed as insoluble cream of tartar. According to Amerine and Joslyn (1951), the addition of citric acid before fermentation is not recommended because it is possible that some may be converted to acetic acid during fermentation. Not only does the addition of acid to the must greatly affect the course of fermentation, but it also improves the resistance of the wine to spoilage. Additionally, the lower pH aids in the extraction of the pigments from the skins, in the case of colored grapes.

Although objective data is somewhat lacking, the amount of acid to be added will depend upon the original acidity of the must and upon the type of wine. Usually California white musts are brought to at least 0.7 to 0.8 per cent acidity before fermentation.

While tartaric acid would be the acid of choice for correcting the acidity of fermenting grape juices, it is seldom employed in the industry here. Citric acid, the principal acid used, serves for complexing iron to prevent the ferric type of turbidity caused by tannin-iron or phosphate-iron complexes. In white California wines, the addition of citric acid also slows browning. Oxalate-containing citric acid should be avoided since such acids lead to calcium oxalate cloudiness. Malic acid and lactic acids are both theoretically and legally possible, but apparently neither is used in California.

Citric acid is widely used to adjust the acidity of finished wines. The pH of finished dry wines should normally be between 2.7 and 3.8. According to Amerine and Cruess (1960), most California wines should be acidified with citric acid before carbonating, as consumer preference seems to be for sparkling wines of high acidity.   Some sugar should also be added.

Many possibilities exist for the production of fermented fruit juices from low-acid fruits.   For adjustment of acidity in such products citric acid with minor amounts of tartaric acid is used.   It is usually desirable to raise the total acidity to about 0.5 per cent prior to fermentation.

"Permission to use portions of the text of the *National Formulary*, Eleventh Edition, official October 1, 1960, has been granted by the American Pharmaceutical Association.   The American Pharmaceutical Association is not responsible for any inaccuracy of quotation, or for false implications that may arise by reason of the separation of excerpts from the original context."

BIBLIOGRAPHY

AMERINE, M. A., and CRUESS, W. V. 1960. The Technology of Wine Making. Avi Publishing Co., Westport, Conn.

AMERINE, M. A., and JOSLYN, M. A. 1951. Table Wines. The Technology of Their Production in California. Univ. Calif. Press, Berkeley and Los Angeles, Calif.

ANON. 1938. Food, Drug and Cosmetic Act. U. S. Dept. Agr., Washington, D. C.

ANON. 1947. Acetic acid. Encyclopedia of Chemical Technology, Vol. I. Interscience Encyclopedia, New York.

ANON. 1949A. Citric acid. Encyclopedia of Chemical Technology. Vol. IV. Interscience Encyclopedia, New York.

ANON. 1949B. Acid plays important roles in flavor. Food Inds. *21*, No. 10, 74–75.

ANON. 1949C. Citric acid. Tech. Bull. *78*, Charles Pfizer and Co., Brooklyn, N. Y.

ANON. 1953. Phosphates. Encyclopedia of Chemical Technology. Vol. X, Interscience Encyclopedia, New York.

ANON. 1954A. Tartaric acid. Encyclopedia of Chemical Technology. Vol. XIII. Interscience Encyclopedia, New York.

ANON. 1954B. Tartaric acid. Tech. Bull. *79*. Charles Pfizer and Co., Brooklyn, N. Y.

ANON. 1957A. Adipic acid. Tech. Bull. *1–12R*. Allied Chemical Corp., New York.

ANON. 1957B. Adipic acid and its derivatives. Tech. Bull. *A-5322*. E. I. du Pont de Nemours and Co., Wilmington, Del.

ANON. 1957C. Citric acid–edible oils. Tech. Bull. *79*. Charles Pfizer and Co., Brooklyn, N. Y.

ANON. 1958A. Food Additives Amendment 1958. U. S. Dept. Health, Education, and Welfare, Washington, D. C.

ANON. 1958. Ascorbic and citric acids for processing seafoods. Tech. Bull. *28*. Charles Pfizer and Co., Brooklyn, N. Y.

ANON. 1959. Fumaric acid. Tech. Bull. Allied Chemical Corp., New York.

ANON. 1960A. U. S. Pharmacopoeia. 16th Edition. U. S. Pharmacopoeial Convention, Inc., Washington, D. C. Mack Publishing Co., Easton, Pa.

ANON. 1960B. Citric acid USP. Tech. Bull. Miles Chemical Co., Elkhart, Ind.

ANON. 1960C. National Formulary. 11th Edition. American Pharmaceutical Assoc., Washington, D. C.

ANON. 1960D. Food processing grade lactic acid data sheet. Technical Sales and Service Dept., Clinton Corn Processing Co., Clinton, Iowa.

ANON. 1961A. Sodium phosphates for industry. Tech. Bull. Monsanto Chemical Co., St. Louis, Mo.

ANON. 1961B. Food-grade adipic acid. Tech. Bull. Monsanto Chemical Co., St. Louis, Mo.

ANON. 1961C. Food-grade fumaric acid. Tech. Bull. *FPD-1*. Monsanto Chemical Co., St. Louis, Mo.

ANON. 1961D. National food acids. Tech. Bull. *TS-10*. Allied Chemical Corp., New York.

ANON. 1961E. Industry group asks amendment to cottage cheese standard. Food Chem. News *3*, No. 35, 12.

ANON. 1961F. Lactic acid. Production Information Bull. E. I. du Pont de Nemours and Co., Wilmington, Del.

ANON. 1961G. Research data as reported in Monsanto Food Processor's Tech. Data Rept. *FPD-2*. WARF (Wisconsin Alumni Research Foundation). Monsanto Chemical Co., St. Louis, Mo.

ANON. 1961H. What you want to know about vinegars. News From the Home of the 57 Varieties. H. J. Heinz Co., Pittsburgh, Pa.

ANON. 1962A. Creative research and *Aspergillus niger*. Miles Chemical Co. Science *135*, 119.

ANON. 1962B. Physical properties—synthetic organic chemicals. Tech. Bull. Union Carbide Co., New York.

ANON. 1962C. Malic acid. Tech. Bull. Preprint. Allied Chemical Corp., New York.

ASSOCIATION OF OFFICIAL AGRICULTURAL CHEMISTS. 1960. Official Methods of Analysis. 9th Edition. Assoc. Offic. Agr. Chemists, Washington, D. C.

BEIDLER, L. M. 1957. Facts and theory of the mechanism of taste and odor perception. *In* Chemistry of Natural Food Flavors. Edited by J. H. Mitchell *et al.* QM Food and Container Institute, Chicago, Ill.

BIRDSALL, J. J. *et al.* 1961. Nutrients in California lemons and oranges. II. Vitamin, mineral and proximate composition. J. Am. Diet. Assoc. *38*, 555–559.

CLARK, W. M. 1928. The Determination of Hydrogen Ions. 3rd Edition. Williams and Wilkins Co., Baltimore, Md.

CRUESS, W. V. *et al.* 1946. Experiments on frozen citrus juices and syrups. Fruit Prod. J. *26*, No. 1, 8–10, 25.

CRUESS, W. V. *et al.* 1951. Avocado products experiments. Canner *112*, No. 3, 14–17, 20–21.

DOESBURG, J. J., and DeVos, L. 1959. Pasteurized mixtures of fruit juices and milk with a long shelf life. Proc. 5th Int. Fruit Juice Congress, Vienna.

FERGUSON, L. R. 1953. Gelatin composition. U. S. Pat. 2,657,996. Nov. 3.

FOSTER, J. 1949. Chemical Activities of Fungi. Academic Press, Inc., New York.

GALLAGHER, L. C. 1957. Fresher and better shrimp. Ref. No. *478*. Sunkist Growers, Inc., Product Sales Department, Ontario, Calif.

GETMAN, F. H., and DANIELS, F. 1940. Outlines of Theoretical Chemistry. John Wiley and Sons, New York.

GONCE, J. E., and TEMPLETON, H. L. 1930. Citric acid-milk in infant feeding. Am. J. Diseases Children *39*, 265–276.

GOULD, W. A. 1957. Quality lab must take accurate pH readings. Food Packer *38*, No. 9, 22–23, 36–37.

HALE, J. F., and MEDBURY, H. E. 1944. Memorandum on acidulants. Natl. Bottler's Gaz. *63*, No. 745, 63–67.

HAMMER, B. W., and BABEL, F. J. 1957. Dairy Bacteriology. 4th Edition. John Wiley and Sons, New York.

HARGROVE, R. E. *et al.* 1961. Phosphate heat treatment of milk to prevent bacteriophage proliferation in lactic cultures. J. Dairy Sci. *44*, 1799–1810.

HODGMAN, C. D. *et al.* 1961. Handbook of Chemistry and Physics. 43rd Edition. The Chemical Rubber Publishing Co., Cleveland, Ohio.

HOLTON, H. H., and HAVIGHORST, C. R. 1953. Their waste-salvage process balances multi-product operation. Food Eng. *25*, No. 6, 58–60, 162–165, 175, 177.

JACOBS, M. B. 1959. Manufacture and Analysis of Carbonated Beverages. Chemical Publishing Co., New York.

JOSEPH, G. H. 1929. Mayonnaise and other salad dressings. Spice Mill *52*, 1887–1889.

JOSEPH, G. H. 1953. Better pectins. Food Eng. *25*, No. 6, 71–73, 114.

JOSLYN, M. A. 1950. Methods in Food Analysis Applied to Plant Products. Academic Press, New York.

KIESER, A. H., and HAVIGHORST, C. R. 1952. They use every part of fruit in full product line. Food Eng. *24*, No. 9, 136–139.

KINOSHITA, S. *et al.* 1961. Method of producing citric acid by fermentation. U. S. Pat. 2,993,838. July 25.

LEONARD, S. *et al.* 1959. The pH problem in canned tomatoes. Food Technol. *13*, 418–419.

MARSH, G. L. 1942. Vegetable juices—1942 model. Canner *95*, No. 9, 7–8, 12–13; No. 10, 15–16.

McCOLLOCH, R. J., and GENTILI, B. 1958. Stabilization of citrus juices with fumaric acid. U. S. Pat. 2,845,355. July 29.

PANGBORN, R. M. 1961. Taste interrelationship. II. Suprathreshold solutions of sucrose and citric acid. J. Food Sci. *26*, 648–655.

PECKHAM, G. T., JR. 1944. The commercial manufacture of lactic acid. Chem. Eng. News *22*, 440–445.

SPIEGELBERG, C. H. 1939. *Cl. pasteurianum* associated with spoilage of an acid canned fruit. Food Research *5*, 115–130.

STOKES, W. E., and KENNEDY, M. H. 1946. Food Product. U. S. Pat. 2,412,-305. Dec. 10.

TEMPLETON, H. L. 1937. The use of citric acid and sodium citrate in milk and milk products. Research Bull. *133*, 1–44. Agr. Expt. Sta., Univ. Wis., Madison, Wis.

TEMPLETON, H. L., and SOMMER, H. H. 1929. The use of citric acid and sodium citrate in starter cultures. J. Dairy Sci. *12*, 21.

TEMPLETON, H. L., and SOMMER, H. H. 1933. Studies on whipping cream. J. Dairy Sci. *16*, 329–345.

TEMPLETON, H. L., and SOMMER, H. H. 1934. Studies on whipping cream. J. Dairy Sci. *17*, 307–319.

TEMPLETON, H. L., and SOMMER, H. H. 1935. The use of citric acid and sodium citrate in butter making. *J. Dairy Sci. 18*, 97–104.

THOMPSON, M. H., and WATERS, M. E. 1960. Control of iron sulfide discoloration in canned shrimp (*Xiphopenus sp.*). Comm. Fisheries Rev. *22*, No. 8, 1–7.

TOWNSEND, C. T. 1938. Spore-forming anaerobes causing spoilage in acid canned foods. Food Research *4*, 231–237.

TOWNSEND, C. T., and POWERS, M. J. 1942. Control of pH in canning acid foods. Food Inds. *14*, 52–55.

VALDÉS, R. M., *et al.* 1956. Effect of sucrose and organic acids on apparent flavor intensity. II. Fruit nectars. Food Technol. *10*, 387–391.

VAN WAZER, J. R. *et al.* 1961. Phosphorus and its Compounds. Vol. II. Interscience Publishers, New York.

CHAPTER 7

John H. Kilbuck

Seasoning for the Food Manufacturer

INTRODUCTION

From the laboratories of the food processing industry come hundreds of new products each year—each aimed at filling a need created by the modern housewife for better tasting, more appealing foods, which require minimum preparation in the home. Since many of these new products contain spices to impart a desired characteristic flavor, the food manufacturer not only must be a preserver of foods, but must be adept at seasoning his products, an art essential in successful food preparation.

The value of spices imported for United States consumption in 1960 was about 43 million dollars (Table 38). The domestically grown spices—the capsicum spices (paprikas, chili peppers and red peppers), mustard seed and a few herbs increase the value consumed to over 50 million dollars per year. Though the spice industry in the United States is not large, the food in which spices are used represents a several hundred-fold greater value than the spices.

WHAT IS A SPICE?

Terminology in the food industry, and more specifically in the spice field itself, is somewhat confusing as the word "spice" may be used (as in this discussion) to include all aromatic botanical substances used in foods. "Spices" (as cinnamon, cloves, mace) can also be used as a sub-classification of these aromatic substances along with aromatic seeds (as coriander, celery, cumin) and herbs (oregano, bay, thyme). Spices have been defined by the Food and Drug Administration as "aromatic vegetable substances used for the seasoning of food. They are true to name and from them no portion of any volatile oil or other flavoring principle has been removed."

"Seasoning" is a comprehensive term applied to blends of spices which may or may not contain other ingredients such as onion, garlic, monosodium glutamate, salt and sugar. The various seasoned salts (onion salt, garlic salt and celery salt) are seasonings, as are chili powder and curry powder.

JOHN H. KILBUCK is Manager, Western Division, Stange Co., Oakland, Calif.

A relatively small quantity of spices used in the food industry are whole spices. Celery and mustard seeds and mixed pickling spice (a blend of 10 to 20 spices) are used primarily for appearance in some pickles and pickled products. Considerable quantities of whole sesame and poppy seed are used in the baking industry. The meat industry uses a whole black pepper in several meat items. Very often some other form of spicing is used with whole spices for flavor strength and uniformity of flavor, but whole spices usually do not compete with the other forms of spicing. They will not be considered further in this discussion.

GROUND SPICES

Since the beginning of recorded history ground spices have been used extensively to season foods, but more recently other forms of spicing have become well recognized because of some desirable characteristics. In addition to ground spices, the food processing industries use considerable quantities of "soluble" spices and essential oils and, to a lesser extent, aromatic chemical compounds.

Of great importance are the ground spices (Table 39) which are used widely, especially in bakery, meat and canned products. Ground spices are available in a wide range of particle sizes varying from cracked spices (as pepper) to very finely milled spices averaging 10 to 50 microns. Many methods of grinding spices are commonly used but the factors which determine which method is used for a particular spice include (1) grinding rate, (2) power requirements, and (3) the amount of heat generated and transferred to the ground spice. The amount of heat and aeration determine, to a large extent, the loss of volatile constituents during the grinding operation. Some of the very oily spices such as nutmeg, are difficult to grind to a fine mesh size with conventional grinding techniques and this oily character makes sieving to a fine mesh size nearly impossible.

SOLUBLE SPICES

"Soluble" spices are made by mixing spice extractives from one or a number of spices with a soluble carrier, such as sucrose, dextrose, salt or monosodium glutamate. Either the volatile oils from distillation, or the oleoresins from solvent extraction, or both, are mixed with a soluble carrier in approximately the same concentrations as they occur in nature (Table 40). Since the characteristic flavor comes from both the volatile oil and the oleoresins in most spices, a blend of both fractions will result in a soluble spice with a truer flavor than when either is the sole source of spice flavor. Spice extractives have

TABLE 38

UNITED STATES IMPORTS OF SPICES FOR CONSUMPTION[1]—1960

	Weight, lbs.	Value
Paprika, ground or unground		
Spain	4,708,159	$1,267,473
Hungary	1,317,390	276,756
Other	2,084,208	388,438
Celery seeds		
India	2,291,805	348,510
France	186,255	62,199
Other	200	182
Cinnamon and cinnamon chips, unground		
Ceylon	363,667	224,281
Seychilles	136,062	18,660
Other	70,431	23,405
Caraway seed		
Netherlands	6,198,150	1,056,067
Poland	307,837	42,520
Other	92,486	13,505
Cardamom seed		
Guatemala	100,281	224,352
India	57,519	147,443
Other	24,953	47,418
Capsicum or red pepper, unground		
Mexico	2,559,756	687,352
Japan	2,028,846	478,969
Other	1,081,626	263,647
Cassia buds, unground		
Indonesia	8,569,860	1,919,223
Vietnam	2,272,244	843,636
Other	312,576	71,095
Cloves and clove stems, unground		
Br. East Africa	1,834,151	592,818
Madagascar	793,618	242,349
Other	41,594	38,880
Ginger root, unground		
Jamaica	1,102,503	272,336
Nigeria	628,551	71,240
Other	1,354,710	231,950
Mustard seed, whole		
Canada	21,743,024	1,406,950
Denmark	6,298,795	509,125
Other	371,796	37,038
Mustard, ground or prep.		
United Kingdom	795,590	304,046
West Germany	54,392	30,719
Other	59,841	38,575
Nutmegs, unground		
Indonesia	2,579,409	2,505,478
West Indies	542,373	635,793
Other	1,319,118	533,126
Mace, unground		
Indonesia	549,349	684,398
Singapore	44,297	56,970
Other	9,952	10,753

TABLE 38 (*continued*)

	Weight, lbs.	Value
Pepper black, unground		
India	21,135,454	9,615,866
Indonesia	12,644,388	6,725,666
Other	3,187,762	1,658,100
Pepper, white, unground		
Indonesia	2,455,369	1,572,778
Brazil	503,943	332,334
Other	207,890	135,081
Pimento, unground		
Jamaica	976,412	567,419
Mexico	217,020	111,131
Other	151,889	77,398
Anise seed		
Turkey	82,997	16,350
Spain	49,288	8,158
Other	5,993	1,674
Cumin seed		
Iran	2,971,690	567,397
India	300,459	46,990
Other	245,402	44,686
Fennel seed		
India	446,923	56,387
Argentine	73,458	8,900
Other	57,244	7,144
Coriander seed		
Morocco	1,881,944	123,901
Rumania	738,549	40,706
Other	232,421	19,760
Laurel and oregano leaves		
Greece	1,001,572	146,414
Turkey	417,761	51,492
Other	890,656	227,929
Sage, ground		
Yugoslavia	1,324,478	436,174
Albania	431,523	58,349
Other	421,841	68,612
Sesame seed		
Nicaragua	13,259,950	2,046,436
San Salvador	1,952,278	193,917
Other	2,165,955	254,097
Poppy seed		
Netherlands	3,457,964	597,226
Poland	1,928,928	314,840
Other	1,832,959	226,788
Turmeric		
India	1,776,688	284,812
Taiwan	275,575	25,199
Other	246,571	30,493
Other spices, blends, etc.		
Other	572,719	98,677

[1] From U. S. Dept. of Commerce—Bureau of the Census.

Table 39

IMPORTANT SPICE VARIETIES

Spice	Scientific Name	Family	Major Varieties	Plant Part Used
Allspice	*Pimenta officinalis*	Nutmeg	Mexican Jamaican	Unripe berry
Anise	*Pimpinella anisum*	Carrot	Spanish Mexican	Seed
Basil, Sweet	*Ocimum basilicum*	Mint	Italian Domestic	Leaf
Bay (Laurel)	*Laurus nobilis*	Laurel	Turkey Yugoslavia	Leaf
Caraway	*Carum carvi*	Carrot	Dutch Polish	Seed
Cardamom	*Elettaria cardamomum*	Ginger	Guatemala Indian	Seed
Cassia	*Cinnamomum cassia* *C. loureirii, C. burmanni*	Laurel	Batavia Korintji	Bark
Cayenne	*Capsicum frutescens* or *C. boccatum*	Potato	Mombassa Hontaka	Fruit
Celery Seed	*Apium graveolens*	Carrot	French Indian	Seed
Chili Pepper	*Capsicum*	Potato	Ancho Anaheim	Fruit
Cinnamon	*Cinnamomum zeylanicum*		Ceylon Seychelles	Bark
Cloves	*Caryophyllus aromaticus*	Myrtle	Zanzibar Penang	Flower buds
Coriander	*Coriandrum sativum*	Carrot	Moroccan Argentine	Seed
Cumin	*Cuminum cyminium*	Carrot	Iranian Moroccan	Seed
Dill	*Anethum graveolens*	Carrot	Indian Domestic	Seed
Fennel	*Foeniculum vulgare*	Carrot	Indian Roumanian	Seed
Fenugreek	*Trigonella foenumgraecum*	Pea	Moroccan	Seed
Ginger	*Zingiber officinale*	Ginger	Cochin Jamaican	Rhizome
Mace	*Myristica fragrans*	Nutmeg	Siauw West Indies	Aril
Marjoram	*Marjorana*	Mint	French Chilean	Leaf
Mustard, Black	*Brassica nigra*	Mustard	Canadian Montana	Seed
Mustard, Brown	*Brassica juncea*	Mustard	Canadian Montana	Seed
Mustard, Yellow	*Brassica alba*	Mustard	Montana English	Seed
Nutmeg	*Myristica fragrans*	Nutmeg	East Indian West Indian	Seed
Oregano	*Origanum vulgare*	Mint	Mexican Greek	Leaf
Paprika	*Capsicum annum*	Potato	Spanish Domestic	Fruit
Pepper, Black	*Piper nigrum*	Pepper	Malabar Sarawak	Fruit
Pepper, White	*Piper nigrum*	Pepper	Muntok Sarawak	Fruit w/o pericarp
Poppy	*Papaver somniferum*	Poppy	Dutch Polish	Seed
Rosemary	*Rosmarinus officinalis*	Mint	French Spanish	Leaf
Sage	*Salvia officinalis*	Mint	Dalmation Albanian	Leaf
Savory	*Satureia hortensis*	Mint	French Spanish	Leaf
Sesame	*Sesamum indicum*	Sesanum	Nicaraguan Salvadoran	Seed
Thyme	*Thymus vulgaris*	Mint	French Spanish	Leaf
Turmeric	*Curcuma longa*	Ginger	Alleppy Madras	Root

TABLE 40

SOME IMPORTANT FLAVOR CONSTITUENTS OF SPICES

Spice	Average Volatile Oil, %	Major Volatile Oils	Average Nonvolatile Ether Extract, %	Important Nonvolatile Compounds
Allspice	3.5	Eugenol Eugenol methyl ether Cineole	5.5	Quercitannic acid
Anise	2.0	Anethole Methyl chavicol Anisketone	20.0	...
Basil, sweet	0.4	Methyl chavicol d-Linalool	3.6	...
Bay	1.0	Cineol α-Pinene	7.0	...
Caraway	5.0	d-Carvone d-Limonene	15.0	...
Cardamom	4.0	Limonene Cineole	...	...
Cassia	2.5	Cinnamic aldehyde Cinnamyl acetate	4.0	...
Cayenne	...	...	15.0	Capsaicin (pungent principle)
Celery	2.0	d-Limonene Selinene Sedanolide Sedanonic acid	16.0	...
Chili pepper	...	...	16.0	Capsanthin (pigment) Carotene (pigment) Capsaicin (pungent principle)
Cinnamon	.75	Cinnamic aldehyde Eugenol	...	...
Cloves	16.0	Eugenol Eugenol acetate	7.0	...
Coriander	0.3	d-Linalool d − α-Pinene	16.0	...
Cumin	2.5	Cumaldehyde Dihydrocumaldehyde	20.0	...
Dill	3.0	Carvone d-Limonene	17.0	...
Fennel	3.0	Anethole Fenchone d − α-Pinene	15.0	...
Fenugreek	trace	...	7.0	Trigonelline and choline
Ginger	2.0	Zingiberene α + β-Phellandrene d-Camphene	5.0	Zinegerone (pungent principle)
Mace	12.0	d + (α)-Pinene β-Pinene d-Camphene	23.0	Trymyristin
Marjoram	1.0	Terpinene d − α-Terpineol	4.5	...
Mustard, black	0.6	Allyisothiocyanate	33.0	...
Mustard, yellow	none	...	25.0	Sinalbin mustard oil (pungent)
Nutmeg	6.5	See mace	28.0	See mace
Oregano	4.0	Thymol Carvacrol	6.0	...
Paprika	...	...	15.0	Capsanthin (pigment) Carotene (pigment) Capsorubin (pigment)
Pepper, black	2.5	α-Pinene β-Pinene 1-α Phellandrene	5.5	Piperine (pungent) Chavicine (pungent) Piperdine (pungent)
Pepper, white	2.0	Same as black	5.0	Same as black pepper
Poppy	...	...	48	...

also been mixed with nonsoluble carriers such as dehydrated onion and garlic, other spices and occasionally with drying agents such as calcium silicate.

SPICE OILS

Spice oils include the essential oils and a nonvolatile fraction known as oleoresin. The yield of volatile oil collected from steam distillation is often around two per cent but ranges from a trace to 15 per cent. Essential oils are commonly used in pickle products and to a limited extent in catsup. Oleoresins are not only complex flavoring substances but contain the pungent or "heat" principles of black pepper, red pepper and ginger, and the coloring compounds found in paprika, turmeric and saffron. These are usually extracted from the spice using one of several low-boiling solvents, then separated from the solvent by fractional distillation. The Food and Drug Administration recently established the following solvent residue tolerances in spice extractives in parts per million: acetone 30; methanol 50; isopropanol 50; methyl chloride 30; and trichlorethylene 30.

The use of aromatic chemical compounds to extend or to replace spice oils has been practiced for many years. Some essential oils of spices such as anise and cassia, contain one predominant compound whose flavor resembles the complete oil. For instance, oil of anise contains appreciable quantities of anethol. Cinnamic aldehyde is a major constituent of oil of cassia. These synthesized compounds are usually much cheaper than the natural volatile oils and are often used for this reason.

Detection of additions of these compounds to spice extractives is difficult even with newer techniques such as gas chromatography, unless gross quantities are used with the natural oils.

FACTORS CONTROLLING FORMS OF SPICES USED BY FOOD MANUFACTURERS

The food manufacturer has four forms of spice flavors with which to season his products: ground spices; soluble spices; essential oils and aromatic chemicals. His choice will depend upon the product to be seasoned, the physical and chemical characteristics of each form and other factors such as cost and label declaration. The more important considerations are enumerated as follows:

Flavor

(a) **Ground spices** are usually very good unless they are exceptionally old or have picked up off-flavors during storage.

(b) **Soluble spices** can be very good, providing the essential oils and/or the oleoresins are of good quality. The particular solvent used for extraction can have a very important effect on flavor of the resulting oleoresins and its soluble form. The better soluble spices contain well-rounded oleoresin fraction as well as essential oils. These blends tend to have the truest flavor.

(c) **Essential oils** can be good, but the addition of oleoresins usually improves the flavor, making it resemble the original spice flavor more closely.

(d) **Aromatic Chemicals.**—Generally the poorest of the four types. They are used on occasion to "extend" essential oils as cinnamic aldehyde in oil of cassia. In the hands of an expert, they can be blended with spice oils or even other chemicals to closely approximate many spice flavors.

Flavor Stability

(a) **Ground spices** are considered the most stable of these four forms of spices but exposure to air and light can cause considerable loss of flavor in storage, especially in the very finely ground material.

(b) **Soluble spices** will vary considerably in flavor stability and occasionally have a very short life when the carrier contains appreciable quantities of copper and iron. Salt, with some drying agents such as calcium silicate or tricalcium phosphate which can be a major source of heavy metals, can be especially troublesome. For this reason, sucrose, dextrose and monosodium glutamate usually are better carriers than salt. Inclusion of the oleoresins with the essential oils often improves their stability because the solvent will extract some natural antioxidants from the ground spices.

(c) **Essential Oils.**—This group varies with the individual oils and is also dependent upon such factors as presence of oxygen, light and heavy metals during storage. No natural antioxidants are present.

(d) **Aromatic Chemicals.**—These react much the same as essential oils but often cinnamic aldehyde will change to a mixture having a bitter almond taste.

Flavor Variability

(a) **Ground Spices.**—Flavor and flavor intensity can vary considerably in spice removed from one plant. Other common causes of variation include variety, area of production, annual variation during growing and, apparently, even harvesting and drying techniques. There can be important differences in flavor and flavor strength in various lots of spices, but these can be minimized by blending.

(b) **Soluble spices** can vary as much as ground spices, but since they are compounded there is ample opportunity for standardizing the flavor. Soluble spices can be much more uniform than ground spices.

(c) **Essential Oils.**—Same as for soluble spices.

(d) **Aromatic Chemicals.**—Should be the most uniform of all forms of spice.

Flavor Release in the Food Product

(a) **Ground Spices.**—Generally rather slow but this is an advantage in some products which are exposed to high temperatures, but are not in sealed containers. Bakery products are usually spiced with ground spices because of this slow flavor release.

(b) **Soluble Spices.**—Flavor is released as soon as the carrier dissolves. Evaporation losses from prolonged heating in an open vessel can be very serious. Because of this, most spicing is added at the end of the heating period.

(c) **Essential Oils.**—Same as for soluble spices.

Flavor Distribution

(a) **Ground Spices.**—Flavor distribution is not normally a problem if original mixing has been adequate. However, in some thin-bodied liquids, ground spices can settle out.

(b) **Soluble Spices.**—Usually not a problem, but in thin-bodied liquids the oleoresins can separate and form unsightly gummy droplets at the top or bottom. This can be minimized by solubilizing agents such as Polysorbate 80, or other additives permitted by the Food and Drug Administration.

(c) **Essential Oils.**—Can be better than soluble spices since they do not contain an oleoresin fraction, but these are often "solubilized" with a surface active agent.

(d) **Aromatic Chemicals.**—Same as for soluble spices.

Appearance

(a) **Ground Spices.**—In some foods, ground spices are used as much for their appearance as they are flavor. A good example is bakery goods such as pumpkin pie or as a topping on sweet rolls.

(b) **Soluble Spices** can be used where specks would detract from the appearance. In mayonnaise, a soluble pepper is commonly used so that there is no specking. Extractives of turmeric and paprika are used primarily for coloring a product evenly.

(c) **Essential Oils.**—Do not impart color to food products.

(d) **Aromatic Chemicals.**—Same as for essential oils.

Contamination

(a) **Ground Spices.**—Various types of contamination can be a problem in ground spices as with most dry vegetable products since washing is generally not practical. Various cleaning techniques can remove some types of contamination, and "sterilization" with ethylene oxide can reduce microbial populations to around one to ten thousand per gram. Still, much needs to be done in the area of preventative sanitation before many of these imported spices are comparable to those few produced in the United States. All imported spices are subject to FDA inspection upon arrival but not all lots receive a thorough checking. Rejected lots can be cleaned in many cases so that FDA will permit their import. Cleaning several times is not an uncommon procedure to bring the lot up to the standards required by the FDA and/or the buyer. Cleaning losses can be as much as 25 to 40 per cent for some leafy herbs.

(b) **Soluble Spices.**—There is no reason why this form of spice should not be as clean as the carrier used—providing the handling and mixing is done under reasonably sanitary conditions.

(c) **Essential Oils.**—Practically free from contamination.

(d) **Aromatic Chemicals.**—Same as for essential oils.

Tannins

(a) **Ground Spices.**—Since many spices are from plant parts (bark, twigs, and leaves) normally high in tannins, it is not surprising that spices can be an important source of tannins in foods. Where discoloration of the product from oxygen, iron and tannins is a problem, the use of ground spices is decreasing.

(b) **Soluble Spices.**—No tannins present.

(c) **Essential Oils.**—Same as soluble spices.

(d) **Aromatic Chemicals.**—Same as for soluble spices.

Cost

(a) **Ground Spice.**—Relatively high usually when compared with other forms of spices.

(b) **Soluble Spices.**—Occasionally higher, but usually less than ground spices.

(c) **Essential Oils.**—Generally cheaper than soluble spices.

(d) **Aromatic Chemicals.**—Generally the cheapest form of spicing.

Handling Problem

(a) **Ground Spice.**—Relatively easy to handle and measure accurately as there is sufficient quantity of ground spice added to large batches of food product to be easily measured.

(b) **Soluble Spices.**—Same as for ground spices.

(c) **Essential Oils.**—The quantity used is often only one to five percent of the amount of ground or soluble spice used. Sometimes this poses a problem of accurately measuring the liquid. It is not uncommon for the amount left in the measuring container to cause important flavor variation.

(d) **Aromatic Chemical.**—Same as for essential oils.

Label Declaration

Most food products for which there are Standards of Identity, permit the addition of "spices" and/or flavoring. On nonstandardized foods where declaration is necessary, following declarations are usually considered acceptable:

(a) **Ground spices** are declared as "spices."

(b) **Soluble spices** are declared as "spice extractives" or "flavoring."

(c) **Essential oils** are declared same as soluble spices.

(d) **Aromatic chemicals** can be declared two ways, depending on their use. "Imitation flavoring" and sometimes "flavoring" are accepted terms.

Standards of Identity

(a) **Ground spices** are permitted in most standardized products.

(b) **Soluble spices** usually can be used in lieu of ground spices.

(c) **Essential oils** same as for soluble spices.

(d) **Aromatic chemicals** not generally permitted.

TABLE 41

FOOD AND DRUG ADMINISTRATION DEFINITIONS AND STANDARDS OF SPICES

Anise	The dried ripe fruit of *Pimpinella anisum* L. It contains not more than 9 per cent of total ash, nor more than 1.5 per cent of ash insoluble in hydrochloric acid.
Caraway	The dried ripe fruit of *Carum carvi* L. It contains not more than 8 per cent of total ash nor more than 1.5 per cent of acid-insoluble ash.
Cayenne pepper	The dried ripe fruit of *Capsicum frutescens* L., *C. baccatum* L., or some other small-fruited species of *Capsicum*. It contains not less than 15 per cent of nonvolatile ether extract, not more than 1.5 percent of starch, not more than 28 per cent of crude fiber, not more than 8 per cent of total ash, nor more than 1.25 per cent of ash insoluble in hydrochloric acid.
Cardamom	The dried, nearly ripe fruit of *Elettaria cardamomum Maton.*
Cardamom seed	The dried seed of Cardamom. It contains not more than 8 per cent of total ash, nor more than 3 per cent of ash; insoluble in hydrochloric acid.
Celery seed	The dried fruit of *Celeri graveolens.* (L.) Britton (*Apium graveolens* L.). It contains not more than 10 per cent of total ash, nor more than 2 per cent of ash insoluble in hydrochloric acid.
Cinnamon	The dried bark of cultivated varieties of *Cinnamomum zeylanicum* Nees or of *C. cassia* (L.) Blume, from which the outer layers may or may not have been removed.
Ceylon cinnamon	The dried inner bark of cultivated varieties of *Cinnamomum zeylanicum* Nees.
Saigon cinnamon, cassia	The dried bark of cultivated varieties of *Cinnamomum Cassia* (L.) Blume.
Cloves	The dried flower buds of *Caryophyllus aromaticus* L. They contain not more than 5 per cent of Clove stems, not less than 15 per cent of volatile ether extract, not less than 12 per cent of quercitanic acid (calculated from the total oxygen absorbed by the aqueous extract), not more than 10 per cent of crude fiber, not more than 7 per cent of total ash, nor more than 0.5 per cent of ash insoluble in hydrochloric acid.
Coriander seed	The dried fruit of *Coriandrum sativum* L. It contains not more than 7 per cent of total ash, nor more than 1.5 per cent of acid-insoluble ash.
Cumin seed	The dried fruit of *Cuminum cyminum* L. It contains not more than 9.5 per cent of total ash, nor more than 1.5 per cent of ash insoluble in hydrochloric acid, nor more than 5 per cent of harmless foreign matter.
Dill seed	The dried fruit of *Anethum graveolens* L. It contains not more than 10 per cent of total ash, nor more than 3 per cent of ash insoluble in hydrochloric acid.
Fennel seed	The dried fruit of cultivated varieties of *Foeniculum vulgare* Hill. It contains not more than 9 per cent of total ash nor more than 2 per cent of ash insoluble in hydrochloric acid.

TABLE 41 (continued)

Ginger	The washed and dried, or decorticated and dried, rhizome of *Zingiber officinale* Roscoe. It contains not less than 42 per cent of starch, not more than 8 per cent of crude fiber, not more than 1 per cent of lime (CaO), not less than 12 per cent of cold-water extract, not more than 7 per cent of total ash, not more than 2 per cent of ash insoluble in hydrochloric acid, nor less than 2 per cent of ash soluble in cold water.
Jamaica ginger	Ginger grown in Jamaica. It contains not less than 15 per cent of cold-water extract, and conforms in other respects to the standards for Ginger.
Limed ginger, bleached ginger	Whole Ginger coated with carbonate of calcium. It contains not more than 4 per cent of carbonate of calcium nor more than 10 per cent of total ash, and conforms in other respects to the standards for Ginger.
Laurel (bay) leaves	The dried leaves of *Laurus nobilis* L.
Mace	The dried arillus of *Myristica fragrans* Houtt. It contains not less than 20 per cent, nor more than 30 per cent of nonvolatile ether extract, not more than 10 per cent of crude fiber, not more than 3 per cent of total ash, nor more than 0.5 per cent of ash insoluble in hydrochloric acid.
Macassar mace, papua mace	The dried arillus of *Myristica argentea* Warb
Marjoram, leaf marjoram	The dried leaves, with or without a small proportion of the flowering tops, of *Marjorana hortensis* Moench. It contains not more than 16 per cent of total ash, not more than 4.5 per cent of ash insoluble in hydrochloric acid, nor more than 10 per cent of stems and harmless foreign material.
Mustard seed	The seed of *Sinapis alba* L. (white Mustard), *Brassica nigra* (L.) Koch (black Mustard), G. *juncea* (L.) Cosson, or varieties or closely related species of the types of B. *nigra* and B. *juncea*. *Sinapis alba* (white Mustard) contains an appreciable amount of volatile oil. It contains not more than 5 per cent of total ash nor more than 1.5 per cent of ash insoluble in hydrochloric acid. *Brassica nigra* (black Mustard) and B. *juncea* yield 0.6 per cent of volatile Mustard oil (calculated as allyl isothiocyanate). The varieties and species closely related to the types of B. *nigra* and B. *juncea* yield not less than 0.6 per cent of volatile Mustard oil, similar in character and composition to the volatile oils yielded by B. *nigra* and B. *juncea*. These Mustard seeds contain not more than 5 per cent of total ash, nor more than 1.5 per cent of ash insoluble in hydrochloric acid.
Ground mustard seed	Unbolted, ground Mustard seed, conforming to the standards for Mustard seed.
Mustard flour	The powder made from Mustard seed, with the hulls largely removed and with or without the removal of a portion of the fixed oil. It contains not more than 1.5 per cent of starch, nor more than 6 per cent of total ash.

TABLE 41 (*continued*)

Prepared mustard	A paste composed of a mixture of ground Mustard seed and/or Mustard flour and/or Mustard cake, with salt, vinegar, and with or without sugar and/or dextrose, spices, or other condiments. In the fat-, salt- and sugar-free solids it contains not more than 24 per cent of carbohydrates, not more than 12 per cent of crude fiber, nor less than 5.6 per cent of nitrogen, the carbohydrates being calculated as starch.
Nutmeg	The dried seed of *Myristica fragrans* Houtt, deprived of its testa, with or without a thin coating of lime (C_aO). It contains not less than 25 per cent of non-volatile ether extract, nor more than 10 per cent of crude fiber, not more than 5 per cent of total ash, nor more than 0.5 per cent of ash insoluble in hydrochloric acid.
Macassar nutmeg, papua nutmeg, male nutmeg, long nutmeg	The dried seed of *Myristica Argenteca* Warb, deprived of its testa.
Paprika	The dried ripe fruit of *Capsicum annum* L. It contains not more than 8.5 per cent of total ash, nor more than 1 per cent of ash insoluble in hydrochloric acid. The iodine number of its extracted oil is not less than 125, nor more than 136.
Hungarian paprika	Paprika having the pungency and flavor characteristic of that grown in Hungary. (a) Rosenpaprika, rosapaprika, is Hungarian Paprika prepared by grinding specially selected pods of Paprika, from which the placentae, stalks, and stems have been removed. It contains no more seeds than the normal pods, not more than 18 per cent of non-volatile ether extract, not more than 23 per cent of crude fiber, not more than 6 per cent of total ash, nor more than 0.4 per cent of ash insoluble in hydrochloric acid. (b) Koenigspaprika, king's Paprika, is Hungarian Paprika prepared by grinding whole pods of Paprika without selection, and includes the seeds and stems naturally occurring with the pods. It contains not more than 18 per cent of nonvolatile ether extract, not more than 23 per cent of crude fiber, not more than 6.5 per cent of total ash, nor more than 0.5 per cent of ash insoluble in hydrochloric acid.
Spanish paprika, pimienton, pimiento	Paprika having the characteristics of that grown in Spain. It contains not more than 18 per cent of non-volatile ether extract, not more than 21 per cent of crude fiber, not more than 8.5 per cent of total ash, nor more than 1 per cent of ash insoluble in hydrochloric acid.
Paradise seed, grains of paradise, guinea grains, melegueta pepper	The seed of *Amomum melegueta* Roscoe.
Black pepper	The dried immature berry of *Piper nigrum* L. It contains not less than 6.75 per cent of non-volatile ether extract, not less than 30 per cent of starch, not more than 7 per cent of total ash, nor more than 1.5 per cent of ash insoluble in hydrochloric acid.

Table 41 (*continued*)

Ground black pepper	The product made by grinding the entire berry of *Piper nigrum* L. It contains the several parts of the berry in their normal proportions.
Long pepper	The dried fruit of *Piper longum* L.
Red pepper	The red, dried, ripe fruit of any species of *Capsicum*. It contains not more than 8 per cent of total ash, nor more than 1 per cent of ash insoluble in hydrochloric acid.
White pepper	The dried mature berry of *Piper nigrum* L. from which the outer coating (or the outer and inner coatings) have been removed. It contains not less than 7 per cent of non-volatile ether extract, not less than 52 per cent of starch, not more than 5 per cent of crude fiber, not more than 3.5 per cent of total ash, nor more than 0.3 per cent of ash insoluble in hydrochloric acid.
Pimento, allspice	The dried, nearly ripe fruit of *Pimenta officinalis* Lind. It contains not less than 8 per cent of quercitannic acid (calculated from the total oxygen absorbed by the aqueous extract), not more than 25 per cent of crude fiber, not more than 6 per cent of total ash, nor more than 0.4 per cent of ash insoluble in hydrochloric acid.
Saffron	The dried stigma of *Crocus sativus* L. It contains not more than 10 per cent of yellow styles and other foreign matter, not more than 14 per cent of volatile matter when dried at 212°F., not more than 7.5 per cent of total ash, nor more than 1 per cent of ash insoluble in hydrochloric acid.
Sage	The dried leaf of *Salvia officinalis* L. It contains not more than 12 per cent of stem (excluding petioles) and other foreign material.
Savory, summer savory	The dried leaves and flowering tops of *Satureia hortensis* L.
Star anise seed	The dried fruit of *Illicium verum* Hook. It contains not more than 5 per cent of total ash.
Tarragon	The dried leaves and flowering tops of *Artemisia dracunculus* L.
Thyme	The dried leaves and flowering tops of *Thymus vulgaris* L. It contains not more than 14 per cent of total ash, nor more than 4 per cent of ash insoluble in hydrochloric acid.
Turmeric	The dried rhizome or bulbous root of *Curcuma longa* L.

METHODS OF ANALYSIS OF SPICES

There are two important collections of methods of analyses for spices. One is the Association of Official Agricultural Chemists, which describes chemical and physical methods for examination of spices, their constituents and contaminants. The American Spice Trade Association published a booklet in 1960, "Official Analytical Methods," which includes both general methods of analysis as well as methods for specific spices (as piperine content of pepper). But, the results of these analyses by themselves have little meaning unless the values are compared against a standard. The Food and Drug Administration established advisory standards in 1936 in the Service

TABLE 42

CHEMICAL CHARACTERISTICS OF GOOD COMMERCIAL SPICES

Spice	Max. Crude Fiber, %	Max. Total Ash, %	Max. Ash Insol. in HCl, %	Min. Volatile Oil, %	Max. Moisture, %	Min. Total Ether Extract, %[1]	Min. Starch
Allspice	25.0	4.5	0.2	3.5	10.0	8.0	...
Anise	12.0	7.0	0.5	2.0	8.0	22.0	...
Basil, sweet	...	15.0	1.0	0.4	8.0	4.0	...
Bay	30.0	4.5	0.5	1.0	7.0	8.0	...
Black pepper	11.0	6.0	0.5	2.5	12.0	8.0	30
Caraway	18.0	7.0	0.5	2.5	9.0	18.0	...
Cardamom, green	30.0	10.0	1.0	3.0	9.0	4.0	...
Cardamom, decorticated	30.0	5.0	3.0	4.0	13.0	4.0	...
Celery seed	...	12.0	1.5	2.0	10.0	18.0	...
Chili pepper	28.0	6.0	0.5	None	10.0	12.0	...
Cassia	20.0	5.0	0.5	2.0	11.0	6.0	...
Cloves	10.0	5.5	0.5	17.0	7.5	20.0	...
Coriander	25.0	6.0	0.5	0.3	8.0	18.0	...
Cumin	7.0	9.5	0.5	2.5	8.0	25.0	...
Fennel	14.0	9.0	0.5	2.0	7.5	19.0	...
Ginger	8.0	5.0	1.0	2.0	12.0	8.0	42.0
Mace	4.0	3.0	0.5	12.0	6.0	35.0	...
Marjoram	22.0	13.0	3.5	1.0	10.0	6.5	...
Nutmeg	4.0	3.0	0.5	6.5	7.5	35.0	...
Oregano	...	10.0	1.0	4.0	10.0	10.5	...
Paprika (Spanish)	21.0	8.5	1.0	None	10.0	7.0	...
Red pepper	28.0	8.0	1.25	None	7.0	15.0	...
Sage (Dalmatian)	...	10.0	1.0	1.5	7.5	13.5	...
Thyme	...	7.5	1.5	1.5	9.0	9.0	...
Turmeric	5.5	7.0	0.5	4.0	9.0	10.0	...
White pepper	5.0	2.0	0.3	2.0	15.0	7.0	52.0

[1] Moisture-free basis.

and Regulatory Announcements and where the spice has drug use they are listed in the U. S. Pharmacopoeia and National Formulary. The definitions and standards quoted from the regulatory announcements are not official legal standards but are still used in an advisory fashion.

The values found in the Food and Drug Administration's definitions and standards (Table 41) are generally minimum and maximum values and these differ from the values representing spices generally recognized as good commercial quality. These values are shown in Table 42.

In addition to these official methods of analyses, the spice industry uses specific chemical tests such as the determination of pungency in red peppers and the determination of color intensity in turmeric.

Gas chromatography is being widely used as a research tool and in quality control procedures.

Some large food manufacturers who use considerable quantities of spices, have established their own specifications. Some of these specifications bear only a faint resemblance to FDA specifications and those values which are generally recognized to represent good commercial spices. However, it cannot be emphasized too strongly that physical and chemical characteristics are only guides in considering quality of spices. Final acceptability can only be determined by organoleptic evaluation.

Smelling the spice in the container in which it has been stored can be misleading. For best results, a small amount of the spice should be placed in a clean dry dish. If two spices are to be compared then care must be taken to insure samples are comparable—amounts being smelled, surface area exposed, grind, temperatures, etc.

Spices are most easily tasted using a neutral diluent that is thick enough to prevent settling or floating of the spice. A thin-bodied white sauce heated to disperse the starch can be used for many spices. The best concentration of the spice or seasoning will vary considerably, but it is considered best to taste the spice when it is at a flavor level comparable to its own normal use—0.2 to 1.0 per cent.

DETERIORATION OF SPICES DURING STORAGE

Storageability of spices is important since they are harvested seasonally. Some spices are used in food manufacturing within a month or two after harvesting but it is more common for the spices to be 4 to 14 months old before use. In most instances spices held in the whole form in cool dry storage do not deteriorate to any serious extent during this period of time. An exception is color loss in the capsicum spices, especially paprika. For this reason paprika is usually held in cold storage and then blended to the desired color value prior to shipping.

Information on flavor and color loss of ground spices is not generally available but it is usually recognized that ground spices deteriorate much more rapidly than spices in the whole form. Ground spices should be held in tight containers, such as fiber drums with polyethylene liners, and kept as cool as possible.

Soluble spices have much the same storage characteristics as ground spices unless the carrier has some detrimental effect on flavor or color. Storage stability of soluble spices on a salt carrier is usually much less than when dextrose or onion and garlic are used as a carrier.

Compatibility of spices in storage, whether whole, ground or soluble, is not usually a problem because flavor transfer is not great between whole spices under normal storage conditions. Ground and soluble spices should be stored in tight containers. That flavor transfer which does occur among whole spices is usually so slight that it is masked completely when the spice is blended with other spices prior to use in food. The pickup of a musty character from a damp storage area can cause serious flavor changes which will make the spice unsuitable for use.

BLENDING SPICES

Few food manufacturers blend their own spices as most rely on suppliers specializing in seasoning blending. These suppliers offer three types of blends to food manufacturers: (1) one of many standard spice formulations; (2) a standard formulation modified to meet the particular flavor and color requirements of the food manufacturer; or (3) a formula developed by the food manufacturer but blended by the seasoning supplier for his sole use. These are known as "private formulas."

The cost of buying a blend of spices should be little, if any, more than the cost of the individual spices. Sometimes it is less expensive.

It is becoming more common for food manufacturers to purchase their seasoning in batch size units (one bag of ten pounds of onion, garlic, red pepper and spice extractives will season a 500-gal. batch of catsup). This eliminates many errors of under and over spicing that can so easily occur in large scale food production. This is especially true in the production of seasonal foods, such as fruits and vegetables, where cook room labor is not always infallible.

BIBLIOGRAPHY

ANON. 1960. Official Analytical Methods of the American Spice Trade Association. American Spice Trade Assn., Inc., New York.

ARCTANDER, S. 1961. Perfume and Flavor Materials of Natural Origin (Privately published.) P.O. Box 114, Elizabeth, N.J.

CARTWRIGHT, L. C., and NANZ, R. A. 1948. Comparative evaluation of spices. Food Technol. 2, 330–336.

GUENTHER, E. 1948–1952. The Essential Oils. 6 Vols. D. Van Nostrand Co., New York.

MERORY, J. 1960. Food Flavorings, Composition, Manufacture and Use. Avi Publishing Co., Westport, Conn.

MILORADOVICH, M. 1954. The Art of Cooking with Herbs and Spices. Doubleday and Co., Garden City, N. Y.

PARRY, J. W. 1945. The Spice Handbook. Chemical Publishing Co., New York.

PARRY, J. W. 1953. The Story of Spices. Chemical Publishing Co., New York.

Suzuki, J. I., Tausig, F., and Morse, R. E. 1957. Some observations on red pepper. 1. A new method for determination of pungency in red pepper. Food Technol. *11*, 100–104.

Wallis, T. E. 1957. Analytical Microscopy. 2nd Edition. Little, Brown and Co., Boston, Mass.

Warrell, L. 1951. Flavors, Spices, Condiments. *In* The Chemistry and Technology of Food. Vol. *2*. Interscience Publishers, New York.

CHAPTER 8

George K. Parman and
Gerald J. Salinard

Vitamins as Ingredients in Food Processing

INTRODUCTION

Food processors have always had a fundamental interest in improving the nutritive value of products.   Advances in the technology of canning and freezing made it possible to retain much of the appeal and nutritive value of freshly harvested foods, regardless of season.

However, technology has limitations.   Processing can never make a food product more complete, or better balanced in nutrients than the starting material, or compensate for irregularity in the amounts of naturally occurring nutrients, antioxidants or color in food.   Processing may, of necessity, reduce or remove essential nutrients.

The availability of essential vitamins, in pure crystalline form, from large-scale chemical or biological synthesis has provided the food industry with important and widely applicable means for compensating for seasonal variations and processing limitations.   Many pure vitamins are used to restore or enhance nutritive value.   Others are effective antioxidants and, another group provides excellent food colors.

The food industry, through intelligent use of vitamins in foods, has made important contributions to public health.   Vitamin enriched flour (or bread) is the largest single source of B vitamins in the American diet.   Were it not for enrichment, the diet of a sizable segment of our population would be seriously deficient in vitamin B_1, vitamin B_2, niacin and iron.   Thousands of people, once in mental hospitals in Southern states, are now leading useful lives because of the addition of a few milligrams of the B vitamin, niacin, to their staple food, corn grits.   Iodized salt, baby foods, milk which is widely fortified with vitamins D and A, and margarine have made other equally important contributions.

The food industry has also found intelligent addition of vitamins to products to have a powerful appeal to nutrition-conscious consumers who are appreciative of the widening variety of foods which provide them with better nutrition.

GEORGE K. PARMAN is Executive Secretary, Committee on Marine Resource Development, Food and Nutrition Board, National Academy of Sciences, National Research Council, Washington, D. C., and GERALD J. SALINARD is Food Industry Manager, Fine Chemicals Division, Hoffman LaRoche Inc., Nutley, N. J.

TABLE 43

MAJOR VITAMIN CHART[1]

Recommended Daily Allowance	What It Does	Major Dietary Sources
Vitamin A, 2,500–5,000 Int. Units	Important for normal growth. Necessary for good vision. Essential for healthy skin, eyes and hair and all the epithelial structures of the body.	Milk, butter, fortified margarine, eggs, liver and kidney, leafy green and yellow vegetables.
Vitamin B₁, 1.0–1.6 Mg.	Necessary for proper function of heart and nervous system. Early signs of deficiency include loss of appetite, constipation, insomnia, irritability. Required to obtain energy from food.	Enriched cereals, enriched bread, fish, lean meat, liver, milk, pork, poultry, dried yeast, whole grain cereals.
Vitamin B₂, 1.5–2.5 Mg.	Necessary for healthy skin. Helps prevent sensitivity of the eyes to light. Essential for building body tissues.	Eggs, enriched bread, enriched cereals, leafy green vegetables, lean meats, liver, dried yeast, milk.
Vitamin B₆, 1.0–2.0 Mg.	Important for healthy teeth and gums, the health of the blood vessels, the red blood cells and the nervous system.	Wheat germ, vegetables, dried yeast, meat and whole grain cereals.
Vitamin B₁₂, 2.0–5.0 Micrograms	Helps prevent certain forms of anemia. Contributes to health of nervous system.	Liver, kidney, milk, saltwater fish, oysters and lean meat.
Folic Acid, 0.2–0.4 Mg.	Helps prevent certain forms of anemia. Essential for the intestinal tract.	Leafy green vegetables, food yeast, meats.
Pantothenic Acid, 7.0–10.0 Mg.	Essential for synthesis of adrenal hormones, the health of the nervous system and production of antibodies.	Present in all plant and animal tissues.
Niacin, 7.0–10.0 Mg.	Necessary for converting food to energy. Aids for nervous system. Helps prevent loss of appetite.	Lean meats, liver, dried yeast, enriched cereals, enriched bread, eggs, dried yeast.
Biotin, Requirement unknown	Necessary for the skin and mucous membranes and for health of red blood cells and cardiovascular systems.	Liver, kidney, eggs and most fresh vegetables.
Vitamin C, 70.0–75.0 Mg.	Essential for healthy teeth, gums, and bone. Builds strong body cells and blood vessels.	Citrus fruits, tomatoes, green vegetables, peppers, new potatoes.
Vitamin D, 400 Int. Units	Necessary for strong teeth and bones. Prevents rickets. Helps utilization of calcium and phosphorus.	Vitamin D fortified milk, cod liver oil, salmon, tuna, egg yolk.
Vitamin E, 5–30 Int. Units	Prevents abnormal peroxidation of tissue fats. Essential for integrity of red blood cells.	Vegetable oils, wheat germ, whole grain cereals, lettuce.
Vitamin K, about 1.0 Mg.	Necessary for normal blood clotting.	Leafy vegetables.

[1] Courtesy of National Vitamin Foundation, New York.

The value of, and interest in, vitamins in foods is by no means decreasing. Vitamins are an important ingredient in popular foods for dieting. Certain vitamins may play significant roles in the cholesterol-atherosclerosis-heart disease complex. The special problems of geriatric foods, a neglected segment of the food industry, will involve careful consideration of vitamin requirements. The geriatric group is increasing in size yearly and already contributes a sizable market.

WHAT ARE VITAMINS?

The vitamins are specific chemical substances which the body requires in small, but fairly regular, amounts to carry out certain important metabolic functions. The body does not make these vitamins but must obtain them through the diet. The body will store fat-soluble vitamins, but water-soluble vitamins are not stored in significant quantity. Most of the well-known vitamins are essential parts of specific enzyme systems which, in turn, cause certain essential metabolic reactions to take place.

The amounts of the vitamins required are small. For example, the daily need of vitamin B_1 is one milligram, about $1/_{28,000}$ of an ounce. The daily need for vitamin C is approximately 50 to 75 mg.

The term "vitamin" was coined originally by Casimir Funk from "vital amines," since the early work in the field appeared to indicate that they were amines, that is, nitrogen-containing products. This turned out not to be the case but the term has remained. Similarly, before the individual vitamins were isolated, letters of the alphabet were used for identification of the vitamin "factors," hence, vitamins A, B, C, etc. This nomenclature led to some confusion, since it was found that vitamin B was actually several factors, so numerical subscripts were added, vitamin B_1, vitamin B_2, etc. Then it was found that some vitamins were identical to others.

Vitamin G and vitamin B_2, for example, were found to be the same substance. Other vitamins, such as pantothenic acid and niacin, were never given a letter designation. Today, the chemical names and the letter designation are used interchangeably in the scientific literature but the layman is probably more familiar with the letter designations.

THE ESSENTIAL AND THE IMPORTANT VITAMINS

Table 43 lists the essential information for all of the vitamins currently considered important for human nutrition. Of this group, the U. S. Food and Drug Administration has designated, by regulation and order, the following vitamins as essential in human nutrition:

Vitamin A (including provitamin A)	Niacin (a B vitamin)
Vitamin D	Vitamin C
Vitamin B_1	Vitamin B_{12}
Vitamin B_2	Vitamin E
Vitamin B_6	

More of the important vitamins may be listed as essential as more knowledge is gained as to their functions in the body.   Vitamin E, and vitamin B_6, for example, are fairly recent additions.

CHARACTERISTICS OF THE VITAMINS

Vitamin A (chemical name—axerophtol)

This vitamin is available in pure form by chemical synthesis as vitamin A acetate and vitamin A palmitate.   It is also available as a concentrate from molecularly distilled fish oils and in more dilute form in refined fish oil.   In foods the pure forms are almost universally used because of their purity and freedom from fishy odors.

Vitamin A is a yellowish oily material which, in pure form may crystallize into yellowish, needle-like crystals.

Vitamin A, *per se*, is fat-soluble but through use of emulsifiers or other water-dispersible formulations, it can also be incorporated into nonfat or low-fat foods.   Vitamin A is quite stable under the heat conditions normally encountered in food processing but is easily destroyed by oxidation.   It is not affected by most metals or metal salts encountered in food processing, nor by reducing conditions.   It is stable to mild acid and alkaline conditions.

Vitamin A is usually expressed in terms of International Units or USP units.   The two terms are identical.   The International Unit is defined as the activity of 0.6 microgram of pure beta carotene or 0.3 microgram of pure vitamin A alcohol.

Very high daily dosages of vitamin A, taken for several months, can lead to toxic symptoms including upset of calcium metabolism. At levels used in foods, it would be almost impossible to attain a sufficiently high intake to bring any risk of these symptoms.

Provitamin A

As the name implies, provitamin A is converted to vitamin A in the body.   In most diets, the majority of vitamin A is supplied in the form of provitamin. There are several provitamin A products but the main commercially available compound is beta carotene.

Beta Carotene

Beta carotene is an important provitamin A and also an excellent food colorant. This compound is the main coloring ingredient in carrots, good summer butter, and is present, though not visible, in most green leafy vegetables. It is widely distributed, in smaller amounts, in many other foods, along with many other carotenoids. The carotenoids are a very extensive series of natural coloring agents but only beta carotene and a few others have vitamin activity. Of these, beta carotene is the most active provitamin A and, in fact, the principal source of vitamin A in the American diet.

Beta carotene is available from chemical synthesis, from biological synthesis, or from extraction of carrots or palm oil. For ease in handling, the pure compound is usually supplied in the form of microcrystalline suspensions in vegetable oil, or in water-dispersible formulations.

In pure form, beta carotene occurs as shiny, purplish red crystals. It is soluble in most fats and oils to a limited but practical extent. Chemically, beta carotene is two vitamin A molecules joined together. Like vitamin A, beta carotene is sensitive to oxidation, but is otherwise stable to the conditions encountered in most food processing. The sensitivity to oxidation is most marked in the crystalline form but becomes less marked when the beta carotene is suspended or dissolved in oils or fats.

The conversion of beta carotene to vitamin A is quite complex. It is not split, as might be expected, into two vitamin A molecules which would give two units of vitamin A activity per microgram. Instead, less than two molecules of vitamin A are formed, so that one microgram gives 1.66 units of vitamin A activity.

Unlike vitamin A, excessive doses of beta carotene do not cause any symptoms, other than some coloring of the fatty deposits in the body. The body appears to convert what it needs and eliminates the rest.

Vitamin D

This fat-soluble vitamin is available in two, closely related, forms designated as vitamin D_2 and vitamin D_3. Both are complex sterols.

Vitamin D_2 is obtained by irradiating the plant sterol, ergosterol, with ultraviolet light. Vitamin D_3 is made by irradiating 7-dehydrocholesterol with ultraviolet light.

Both forms are stable to most conditions encountered in food processing except oxidation, and are accelerated by heat and minerals. While both forms are oil-soluble, they can be incorporated into dry or aqueous foods by suitable techniques.

Their activity is designated in terms of International Units, defined as the biologic activity of 0.025 microgram of vitamin D_3.

Vitamin E (chemical name—alpha-tocopheryl acetate)

Vitamin E is an oily liquid, obtained from molecular distillation of by-products from vegetable oil refining, or by chemical synthesis. The product obtained from the natural sources is a dextro (d) isomer, that is, it will cause a beam of polarized light passing through it to rotate clockwise because of the characteristic of its molecule. The vitamin E from synthesis is a dextro-levo (dl) or racemic product, which is composed of equal parts of right and left twisting molecules so that there is no apparent effect on the beam of polarized light.

While the levo isomer does not have the full biological activity of the dextro form, the ease of purifying the racemic product, and its stability, has led to the International Unit of vitamin E being defined as one milligram of dl-alpha-tocopheryl acetate. All other forms are sold on the basis of their activity in relation to this standard.

Unesterified alpha-tocopherol, either d- or dl- form, has limited use as a nutrient because of susceptibility to oxidation. This product is used as an antioxidant in foods because of this characteristic.

Alpha-tocopheryl acetate is very stable under conditions found in food processing. It is available in various dry forms for greater flexibility of use. Another ester is alpha-tocopheryl acid succinate, which has found application in some dry mixes.

Vitamin E is also available in the form of a concentrate in mixed tocopherol preparations, which are oily liquids consisting of alpha-tocopherol together with the other nonactive tocopherols. Since the nonvitamin active tocopherols tend to be more active antioxidants, the mixed tocopherols are also used as an antioxidant product.

The Vitamin B Complex

Vitamin B_1 (chemical names—thiamin hydrochloride and thiamin mononitrate.)—Vitamin B_1 is a white crystalline powder with a characteristic yeast-like odor. It is fairly stable to heat and oxidation at a pH range of 6 or less, becomes less stable at a neutral pH, and unstable under alkaline conditions. Sulfur dioxide and sulfites rapidly destroy the vitamin. It may be degraded by some mineral salts in aqueous foods but this reaction does not always occur.

Vitamin B_1 is now made by chemical synthesis. It is available in pure form as the hydrochloride and mononitrate salts. Both conform to USP specifications. The hydrochloride is used where the vitamin is dissolved in the food. The mononitrate is used in flour and other mixes with relatively high moisture content because of its greater stability under those conditions.

The vitamin is also sold in wafers and premixes for cereal enrichment purposes.

The vitamin activity is expressed in terms of milligrams of vitamin. No units are used.

Vitamin B_2 (chemical name—riboflavin).—Riboflavin is an intense orange colored crystalline product having limited solubility in water. It is stable under most food processing conditions but, like vitamin B_1, is unstable under alkaline conditions. Vitamin B_2, in solution, is also very sensitive to light, particularly in the presence of vitamin C. Amber glass containers, metal cans or similar protective measures must be used to protect riboflavin from light when it is used in many foods.

All pure riboflavin is obtained by chemical synthesis or from fermentation. The latter is usually in the form of a concentrate rather than the pure material.

Vitamin B_2 activity is listed as milligrams of pure riboflavin present.

Vitamin B_6 (chemical name—pyridoxine).—Pyridoxine is available commercially as pyridoxine hydrochloride, a white crystalline powder conforming to USP specifications. It is stable under most conditions found in food processing.

The vitamin activity is expressed in terms of milligrams of pyridoxine present.

Niacin, Niacinamide.—In Europe, niacin and niacinamide have been designated as vitamin PP, for "pellagra preventive." Both are white, water-soluble, crystalline powders and both possess full vitamin activity. At the levels used in foods, the two compounds are interchangeable. Niacin will cause a harmless but very noticeable flushing and "pins-and-needles" effect if taken in pure or concentrated form. While this does not occur at normal use levels, it has led to some preference for niacinamide.

Both forms are very stable under the conditions encountered in food processing. Their vitamin activity is expressed in terms of milligrams of the compound used.

Vitamin B_{12} (chemical name—cyanocobalamin).—Vitamin B_{12} is a water-soluble reddish crystalline compound obtained through a fermentation process. It is available in crystalline form and as a standardized concentrate.

The structure of this vitamin is complex.   While it is stable in many foods, it can react with a number of the other vitamins and food substances.   Adequate stability testing should be carried out on any food product containing vitamin B_{12} to determine the proper overage needed to support label claim.

The activity of the vitamin is expressed as micrograms (one-thousandths of a milligram) of the compound.

Vitamin C (chemical name—ascorbic acid)

Vitamin C is a white crystalline compound, readily water-soluble, with a characteristic pleasantly tart acidic taste.   It is available commercially as ascorbic acid, USP, sodium ascorbate and ascorbyl palmitate.   The latter is a fat-soluble form.

Ascorbic acid, and salts, are stable to most conditions encountered in food processing, but they are easily oxidized.   The ease with which these compounds are oxidized has led to their extensive use as food antioxidants.   Oxidation of ascorbic acid is enhanced by certain metals, particularly copper and nickel, by riboflavin and by certain dyes.

Because it is a strong reducing agent, i.e., a ready accepter of oxygen, ascorbic acid may fade or alter the color of some food colors if it is present in too high a concentration.

Vitamin activity is listed as milligrams of ascorbic acid.

HUMAN VITAMIN REQUIREMENTS

It is difficult to give an exact statement of the daily required intake of the vitamins because of individual variations.   Some quantitative expression is needed, however, as a guide.   For this purpose, two statements are available.

For many of the vitamins which they have listed as essential, the Food and Drug Administration has indicated the Minimum Daily Requirement (MDR).   Table 44 is the current compilation of this listing, which also includes certain essential minerals.

By definition, the MDR is the daily intake of a particular vitamin or mineral which will just prevent the appearance of deficiency symptoms.   The MDR list is of importance for labeling purposes, as discussed later.   Being a minimum guide, it lacks considerable nutritional usefulness.

As a guide to optimum nutrition, the National Research Council— National Academy of Sciences publishes a Recommended Daily Allowance (RDA) table.   Table 45 is the latest revision.

The levels recommended for various nutrients are calculated to

TABLE 44

MINIMUM DAILY REQUIREMENTS OF SPECIFIC NUTRIENTS[1]

	Infants	Children 1–5 yrs., Inclusive	Children 6 yrs. and Over	Adults	Pregnancy or Lactation
A, USP units	1500	3000	3000	4000	...
B_1, mg.	0.25	0.50	0.75	1.00	...
B_2, mg.	0.60	0.90	0.90	1.20	...
Niacin, mg.	...	5	7.5	10	...
C, mg.	10	20	20	30	...
D,[2] USP units	400	400	400	400	...
Calcium, gm.	...	0.75	0.75	0.75	1.50
Phosphorus, gm.	...	0.75	0.75	0.75	1.50
Iron, mg.	...	7.5	10.0	10.0	15.0
Iodine, mg.	...	0.1	0.1	0.1	0.1

[1] Source: U. S. Food and Drug Administration.
[2] Cow's milk containing 135 units of vitamin D per quart, and evaporated milk containing 7.5 USP units per avoirdupois ounce, usually will prevent clinical rickets when fed to normal infants in customary quantities.

maintain good nutritive health. The levels take into account normal individual differences. They do not take into account increased needs due to illness, or stress except in the case of pregnancy.

The Recommended Daily Allowances are a sound nutritional guide for a healthy person. The levels are guides for planning the proper amount of nutrients in foods. The list does not, however, have any legal status as regards labeling.

The Food and Nutrition Board (Anon. 1958) gives not only the listing, but also a concise discussion of how the levels were arrived at and a good discussion on other vitamins and nutrients for which there is insufficient data to arrive at a recommended daily allowance. Every interested food packer should have a copy of this publication which can be obtained from the National Academy of Sciences at 2101 Constitution Avenue, Washington 25, D. C.

SUGGESTIONS FOR FURTHER READING

"The Heinz Handbook of Nutrition," (Anon. 1959) is an excellent general reference book on nutrition. It provides a great deal of material in succinct, understandable form without becoming too scientific in tone.

For a more exhaustive and technical approach, the three volumes, "The Vitamins," Sebrell and Harris (1954) are perhaps best.

From the medical point of view, the book "Modern Nutrition in Health and Disease," Wohl and Goodhart (1960) is an excellent reference text.

TABLE 45

FOOD AND NUTRITION BOARD, NATIONAL RESEARCH COUNCIL RECOMMENDED DAILY DIETARY ALLOWANCES,[1] REVISED 1958

Designed for the Maintenance of Good Nutrition of Healthy Persons in the United States

(Allowances are intended for persons normally active in a temperate climate)

	Age, yr.	Weight, kg., lb.	Height, cm., in.	Calories	Protein, gm.	Calcium, gm.	Iron, mg.	Vitamin A, I.U.	Thiamin, mg.	Riboflavin, mg.	Niacin[2], mg. equiv.	Ascorbic Acid, mg.	Vitamin D, I.U.
Men	25	70 (154)	175 (69)	3,200[3]	70	0.8	10	5,000	1.6	1.8	21	75	….
	45	70 (154)	175 (69)	3,000	70	0.8	10	5,000	1.5	1.8	20	75	….
	65	70 (154)	175 (69)	2,550	70	0.8	10	5,000	1.3	1.8	18	75	….
Women	25	58 (128)	163 (64)	2,300	58	0.8	12	5,000	1.2	1.5	17	70	….
	45	58 (128)	163 (64)	2,200	58	0.8	12	5,000	1.1	1.5	17	70	….
	65	58 (128)	163 (64)	1,800	58	0.8	12	5,000	1.0	1.5	17	70	….
	Pregnant (second half)			+300	+20	1.5	15	6,000	1.3	2.0	+3	100	400
	Lactating (850 ml. daily)			+1,000	+40	2.0	15	8,000	1.7	2.5	+2	150	400
Infants[4]	0–1/12, 2/12–6/12	6 (13)	60 (24)	kg. × 120		0.6	5	1,500	0.4	0.5	6	30	400
	7/12–12/12	9 (20)	70 (28)	kg. × 100	4	0.8	7	1,500	0.5	0.8	7	30	400
Children	1–3	12 (27)	87 (34)	1,300	40	1.0	7	2,000	0.7	1.0	8	35	400
	4–6	18 (40)	109 (43)	1,700	50	1.0	8	2,500	0.9	1.3	11	50	400
	7–9	27 (60)	129 (51)	2,100	60	1.0	10	3,500	1.1	1.5	14	60	400
	10–12	36 (79)	144 (57)	2,500	70	1.2	12	4,500	1.3	1.8	17	75	400
Boys	13–15	49 (108)	163 (64)	3,100	85	1.4	15	5,000	1.6	2.1	21	90	400
	16–19	63 (139)	175 (69)	3,600	100	1.4	15	5,000	1.8	2.5	25	100	400
Girls	13–15	49 (108)	160 (63)	2,600	80	1.3	15	5,000	1.3	2.0	17	80	400
	16–19	54 (120)	163 (64)	2,400	75	1.3	15	5,000	1.2	1.9	16	80	400

[1] The allowance levels are intended to cover individual variations among most normal persons as they live in the United States under usual environmental stresses. The recommended allowances can be attained with a variety of common foods, providing other nutrients for which human requirements have been less well defined.

[2] Niacin equivalents include dietary sources of the preformed vitamin and the precursor, tryptophan. 60 mg. tryptophan equals 1 mg. niacin.

[3] Calorie allowances apply to individuals usually engaged in moderate physical activity. For office workers or others in sedentary occupations they are excessive. Adjustments must be made for variations in body size, age, physical activity and environmental temperature.

[4] The Board recognizes that human milk is the natural food for infants and feels that breast feeding is the best and desired procedure for meeting nutrient requirements in the first months of life. No allowances are stated for the first month of life. Breast feeding is particularly indicated during the first month when infants show handicaps in homeostasis due to different rates of maturation of digestive, excretory and endocrine functions. Recommendations as listed pertain to nutrient intake as afforded by cows milk formulas and supplementary foods given the infant when breast feeding is terminated. Allowances are not given for protein during infancy.

WHY ADD VITAMINS TO FOODS?

The primary purpose for the addition of vitamins to any food is to make that food more beneficial to the consumer by enhancing its nutritive value as well as by improving its taste, texture or color.

Enhancement of nutrition is the main reason for adding vitamins to foods. The addition can be considered from four approaches, restoration and/or enrichment, fortification, standardization and dietary supplementation.

"Restoration" is adding back to a particular food the essential vitamins and nutrients lost during processing. "Enrichment" is the word reserved for the restoration of vitamins B_1, B_2, niacin and iron to white bread, flour, macaroni products, corn grits, corn meal and rice. The levels added are approximately those lost in processing although, in the case of cereal enrichment, somewhat higher levels are added to provide a better intake.

By implication, restoration involves only the vitamins and nutrients which occur naturally in the unprocessed food. "Fortification" is the addition of vitamins, and other nutrients, to foods which are not good sources of the vitamins in the unprocessed state. In this case, fortification is done for two reasons. One, the food is a good carrier for a nutrient which is needed in greater amounts in the diet. Iodized salt is a good example. Two, the food replaces or substitutes for some other food which is a good source of the nutrient. Margarine, for example, replaces butter in the national diet to an ever increasing extent. Butter is an important source of vitamin A in the national diet. If margarine was not fortified with vitamin A to the level of summer butter, our diet might be low in vitamin A.

"Standardization" is a new concept. This is the addition of a pure vitamin to a food to standardize the varying content of the same vitamin in the food throughout the harvest and processing season. It is particularly applicable to fruit juices. Such juices are considered as good sources of vitamin C, but, as shown in Fig. 37, the actual vitamin C content varies widely, due to such factors as stage of ripeness, varietal differences, amount of sunlight and processing variables.

The amount of naturally occurring vitamin C in a batch of fruit juice can be quickly determined and sufficient pure vitamin C added to bring the content up to an optimum figure, which may be the average maximum found during a typical harvest season or some other nutritionally significant level.

Standardization of the vitamin C content of fruit juices benefits the consumer by providing him with significant vitamin C regardless of his choice of juice.

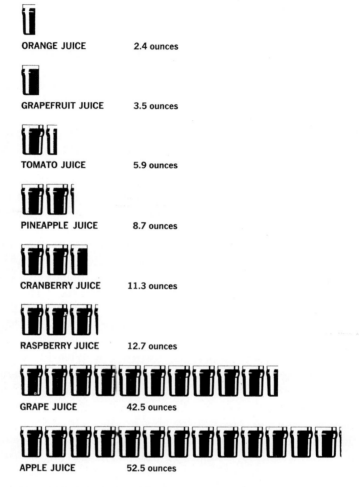

ORANGE JUICE   2.4 ounces

GRAPEFRUIT JUICE   3.5 ounces

TOMATO JUICE   5.9 ounces

PINEAPPLE JUICE   8.7 ounces

CRANBERRY JUICE   11.3 ounces

RASPBERRY JUICE   12.7 ounces

GRAPE JUICE   42.5 ounces

APPLE JUICE   52.5 ounces

The volume of various fruit juices* in 4 ounce glasses
required to supply 30 milligrams of vitamin C.

*Calculated from the average content as shown in published data

FIG. 37. THE VOLUME OF VARIOUS FRUIT JUICES IN 4-Oz.
GLASSES REQUIRED TO SUPPLY 30 MG. OF VITAMIN C

"Dietary supplementation" is the addition of several important vitamins for a special purpose, either to provide the complete vitamin needs in such foods as infant foods, or to present the food as an appealing carrier for the vitamins. In the latter case, the food becomes, in effect, a substitute for multivitamin tablets, capsules, etc. This form of vitamin addition to foods is, currently, of importance in infant and children's foods.   It will undoubtedly also be of importance in geriatric foods.

ADDITION OF VITAMINS TO FOODS FOR ENHANCING NUTRITION—HOW AND WHERE

The addition of vitamins to foods to enhance nutrition does not involve any complex techniques.   A number of vitamins are being routinely added to a great variety of foods by many food processors without difficulty.   It would take a volume to cover, in detail, all the techniques of addition.   However, the chemical and physical characteristics and the processing, storage and cooking procedures of the food must be considered in choosing the best method of addition.

The chemical characteristic of the food can affect the stability of added vitamins.   Alkalinity, as in pretzels and many crackers, or presence of sulfur dioxide, can be very destructive to vitamin B_1. Rancidity, high air content and presence of copper salts are other adverse factors.

The physical characteristic can complicate proper distribution of the vitamins.   It may be difficult to distribute vitamins uniformly over large food granules or to maintain uniform distribution during shipping and handling.

Processing conditions, such as high heat, excessive aeration, and presence of catalytic metals, can be destructive to added vitamins. It is equally important to analyze the processing method to determine the best point to add the vitamins.   Similarly, storage conditions, such as high heat, exposure to light and moisture can be adverse factors.   Finally, the way in which the food is cooked can affect the vitamins.   Precooking washing, cooking in excess water, high heat and excessively long cooking are points requiring special attention.

Most of these adverse factors can be eliminated or overcome through suitable techniques but their presence must be recognized.

The use of suitable antioxidants will greatly improve the resistance of vitamin A and beta carotene to oxidation and heat.   Deaeration of juices or drinks prior to filling aids in vitamin C stability.   Riboflavin must be protected from light.

Where the food presents adverse characteristics, the vitamins can be sprayed on the surface to minimize contact with the incompatible substances in the food.   Edible protective coatings can protect vitamins against moisture, heat or excess water.   Use of suitable overages provides, not only for long-term adherence to label claim, but provides a practical way of offsetting processing and/or cooking losses in many instances. In macaroni fortification, for example, the amount of vitamins present is approximately double that in enriched flour. The excess is to offset the approximately 50 per cent lost during cooking. Because of the low cost of vitamins, this excess is entirely feasible.

Methods of Adding Vitamins to Foods

There are, basically, four methods which have been developed for adding vitamins to foods. These are:

(1) **Tablets or Wafers.**—These are compressed tablets containing one or more vitamins, along with inert edible fillers, in sufficient amount to fortify a given quantity of food. The tablets are *always* dispersed in water, when used. Most white bread is enriched by wafers, each of which contains sufficient vitamins B_1, B_2, niacin and iron to enrich 100 lbs. of flour. One wafer for each 100 lbs. of flour in the dough is dispersed in the same water used in dispersing the yeast. The dispersion is then added to the dough.

Tablets of vitamin C and salt have been used to fortify vegetable juice products. Each tablet contains sufficient vitamin C and salt to fortify and season one 46-oz. (in this case) can. One tablet is added to each can by an automatic dispenser, just prior to sealing. The tablet dissolves shortly after addition. Normal handling provides sufficient agitation to insure uniform distribution.

Wafers and tablets simplify production by eliminating the need to weigh small quantities of vitamins and by enabling the by-passing of adverse processing conditions. On the debit side, the tablets must always be added to water, and they cannot be used in clear products because it is difficult to make tablets without a small amount of water-insoluble lubricants which will leave a haze. Bread wafers, which are made to standard formulations, are obtainable in small quantity. Any other formulation would have to be made up on special order by a private formula house and would be economical only if ordered in large quantity.

(2) **Powder Premixes.**—Getting uniform distribution of vitamins throughout a dry foodstuff can be difficult, particularly when the quantity of vitamin is small. The addition is made in the form of a premix to overcome this. The premix is simply a mixture of the vitamins with a carrier, usually a constituent of the food, at a greater ratio then required in the final food product. The appropriate amount of this mixture, called a premix, is then blended with the remainder of the food. The quantity of premix added can vary widely. White flour is enriched by adding premix continuously at a rate of from $1/4$

to 1 oz. per 100 lbs. of flour.   In other cases as much as one pound
or more of premix per 100 lbs. may be used.   Powdered premixes, or
standard formulations, are sold for enriching flour, semolina, farina,
rice and corn grits.   The premixes cling tenaciously to rice and corn
kernels and particles, resisting severe mechanical agitation, but not
rinsing with water.

Premixes for other foods are made up to specification.   Usually
this is best done by the food processor unless the quantity required
is large.

In enriching products like rice and corn grits which are traditionally
washed or rinsed prior to cooking, the vitamins must be protected
to prevent them from being rinsed down the drain.   This is accomplished by impregnating rice or corn grits with 200 or 400 times
the required amount of vitamins and iron, then coating the impregnated grits with an edible, cold-water insoluble coating.   One pound
of this protective premix is mixed into 199 or 399 lbs. of rice or grits.
The coating protects the vitamins during rinsing.   During cooking,
the coating breaks down and the nutrients are distributed throughout the whole portion.

(3)   **Sprays.**—Sprays of vitamin solutions or suspensions are a
variation of premixing.   The sprays are directed onto the surface of a
food or into liquid food products as a means of getting around difficult
processing conditions.   For example, toasted ready-to-eat breakfast
cereals are fortified by spraying a solution of the vitamins onto the
hot flakes just after toasting.   The heat of the flakes vaporizes the
water leaving an invisible residue of the vitamins.   For greater
uniformity, spraying is done by two or more separate spray applications with the bed of flakes being inverted and/or mixed between
each application.   Film-forming materials can be included in the
sprays to enhance stability of the vitamins.   Oil-soluble vitamins
have been successfully sprayed onto cereals by using water-dispersible
formulations with film-forming properties.

(4)   **Direct Addition.**—The direct addition of a vitamin to a
food is the most widely used approach.   The required amount of
vitamin is weighed out and added to the food with sufficient agitation
to insure uniformity.   For certain foods, such as margarine, the required amounts of vitamin A, beta carotene (or other color) and vitamin D may be obtained as a preweighed blend in a sealed can.   The
contents of the can, and rinsings, are added to a specific amount of
margarine oil and stirred until uniform color is obtained.

The point in the process at which the vitamins are added is important.   Ideally, the vitamins are best added as close to the end

of the process as possible. But this idea has to be tempered by practical considerations of production.

If the food itself does not present any stability problems for the added vitamins, addition is best made at that point in the process which will: (a) *provide sufficient agitation to insure that the vitamins are uniformly distributed;* (b) *present the food at some fixed, known, volume or weight to provide the proper ratio between vitamin and food;* (c) *provide for ease of addition;* and (d) *eliminate as many adverse processing conditions as possible.*

Where the food does present stability problems and/or processing conditions are very severe, spraying of the vitamins after processing may be the only available point of application.

Where addition of the vitamins is made on a batch basis, and no special equipment is required for addition, it is only necessary to know the weight of the food to which the vitamins are added.

Continuous addition of the vitamins can be done by pumping a vitamin solution through a proportioning pump at a rate governed by the rate of flow of the food stream. Suitable feeders are also available for dry powder premixes. There are a number of spraying devices available for dispensing accurate amounts of spray solutions in continuous or intermittent patterns.

EQUIPMENT—MATERIALS OF CONSTRUCTION

The materials used in processing equipment are of definite importance when vitamin C is being added to any food. Since copper, nickel and iron salts can catalyze the oxidative destruction of vitamin C, only stainless steel, plastic, aluminum or wood equipment should be used. Bronze, brass, copper, monel, cold rolled steel and black iron should be avoided. Copper, particularly, but also steel and iron may have an adverse affect on other vitamins, particularly vitamin A. Certain plastics may soften in contact with *concentrated* solutions of vitamin A.

Table 46 is a compilation of the methods of application and the usual point of addition used in adding vitamins to a variety of foods.

VITAMINS AS ANTIOXIDANTS

The oxygen in air is an enemy of flavor and color in many foods and beverages. Oxidation can cause rancidity in fat containing foods, "turpentine" flavor in many fruit-flavor beverages, and loss of color and flavor in many frozen fruits, in cured meats and other foods. These unfavorable changes can often be significantly retarded by

TABLE 46

METHODS OF APPLICATION AND USUAL POINT OF ADDITION USED IN ADDING VITAMINS TO FOODS

Food	Vitamins Added	Direct	Premix Powder	Premix Protective	Wafer or Tablet	Spray	Usual Point or Place of Addition	Remarks
White flour	B₁, B₂, niacin, iron	...	X	...	...	...	At mill	...
Semolina	B₁, B₂, niacin, iron	...	X	...	...	...	At mill	...
Farina	B₁, B₂, niacin, iron	...	X	...	...	...	At mill	...
Corn meal	B₁, B₂, niacin, iron	...	X	X	...	...	At mill	...
Corn grits	B₁, B₂, niacin, iron	...	X	X	...	...	At mill	...
Rice	B₁, B₂, niacin, iron	...	X	...	...	...	At mill	Vitamin B₂ optional because of color problems.
White bread	B₁, B₂, niacin, iron D, calcium	...	...	...	X	...	Yeast dispersion.	May also be done with enriched white flour.
Macaroni products	B₁, B₂, niacin, iron	...	X	...	X	...	Wafer dispersed in water to make paste.	Usual method is by mill enriched semolina and farina.
Toasted cereals	A, D, B₁, B₂, B₆, C, E, niacin	...	...	...	...	X	After toasting.	...
Crackers—biscuits	B₁, B₂, niacin, C	...	X	...	...	X	After baking.	May also be added to dough.
Margarine	A, D, beta carotene	X	...	...	...	...	Holding tank before churning.	...
Shortening and lard	Beta carotene	X	...	...	...	...	Holding tank.	...
Fruit juice drinks	C, mainly; also A and B vitamins	X	...	...	...	...	Holding tank prior to pasteurization and filling.	Also may be added to juice container as solution from dispenser or proportioning device.
Mellorine	A, Beta Carotene	X	X	...	...	...	To mix prior to freezing.	Water-dispersible form used.
Peanut butter	A, B₁, C	X	...	...	...	...	...	...
Dry baby foods	All important vitamins	X	...	...	...	...	...	...
Liquid baby foods	All important vitamins	X	...	...	...	...	...	...
Dry reducing foods	All important vitamins	X	...	...	...	...	...	...
Liquid reducing foods	All important vitamins	X	...	...	...	...	Syrup.	...
Beverages, carbonated	C, mainly	X	...	...	...	...	To candy mass on cooling slab.	...
Candy, hard	C, A, B, vitamins	X	...	...	...	...	Same as fruit juice drinks.	Same as fruit juice drinks.
Vegetable juice drinks	C, mainly	X	X	...	...	...	To chocolate or filling.	Also added at flavoring stage.
Candy, soft	All important vitamins	X	X	X	...	...	To batch with homogenization, if required.	...
Milk products, liquid	All important vitamins	X	...	...	...	...	Dry blend with batch.	...
Milk products, dry	All important vitamins	X	X	...	...	...	Dry blend with batch.	May also be added before instantizing or drying.
Dry milk modifiers	All important vitamins	X	X	...	...	...		May also be added before instantizing or drying.

the use of suitable antioxidants. Among these are two vitamins, ascorbic acid (vitamin C) and alpha tocopherol (vitamin E).

Vitamin C is widely used as an antioxidant in frozen fruits, cured meats and citrus type beverages, as well as in beer and other applications. It acts as a simple oxygen acceptor, preferentially removing oxygen which would otherwise cause flavor and/or color changes in the food. It provides protection so long as there is any unreacted ascorbic acid (or its salts) present. Vitamin C has unique features as a food antioxidant. It is a naturally occurring substance, a nutrient, and completely safe in addition to being highly effective. Its presence in foods is easily detected. It has no effect on bacterial decomposition, so that its use cannot hide dangerous bacterial contamination. Being water-soluble, it is easily added to most foods. Its principal applications are summarized below:

Frozen Fruits

Ascorbic acid is a well established antioxidant that inhibits enzymatic discoloration and loss of flavor in frozen peaches, apricots and other fruits of normally low ascorbic acid content. Such fruits will brown and lose flavor on thawing, often to such an extent as to be completely unusable. The browning of cut apples exposed to air is typical of this oxidative reaction. The presence of a sufficient amount of ascorbic acid retards this reaction for a significant and practical length of time.

The ascorbic acid addition is usually made at the rate of 120 to 250 mg. per pound of fruit *and* syrup. The ascorbic acid may be dissolved in the syrup used with the fruit or mixed with the dry sugar used in preparing "dry-sugar" packs. In either case, it is important that the fruit be kept submerged below the syrup and that it be frozen as soon as possible after the ascorbic acid addition. This procedure works well for peaches, apricots, plums and nectarines. Cherries also are benefited, primarily in protecting from a color change. The results with strawberries are more variable because of variation in the natural ascorbic acid of the fruit and also probably by a variable reaction of the natural coloring pigment in the berry.

Frozen apples and pears can also be very effectively protected from browning during thawing, but the porous nature of these fruits makes it necessary to get the ascorbic acid solution into intimate contact with all parts of the fruit. This may be done by using thin conventional slices, or "julienne" slices. When the thicker wedge-shaped conventional slice is used, the fruit must be submerged in an ascorbic acid-containing syrup and subjected to vacuum. This procedure draws the syrup into the fruit. The treated fruit is drained, packed, covered with additional ascorbic acid-containing syrup and frozen.

Frozen fruit treated with ascorbic acid can be thawed and held for significant periods of time without losing the flavor and color of fresh fruit. Both retail and larger packs (for bakers, etc.) benefit from this treatment in providing a finer looking product of improved quality.

Suggestions for Further Information.—More specific data, on the use of ascorbic acid in frozen fruits can be obtained from the suppliers of ascorbic acid. An excellent reference in two volumes has been prepared by Tressler and Evers (1957). Additionally, numerous articles have been published in trade journals.

Cured Meats

Ascorbic acid and sodium ascorbate find very wide application as curing aids and antioxidants in cured meat products of all kinds.

Cured meats depend for their particular flavor on curing salts, spices and the smoking or cooking they undergo. The distinct color of cured meat is due to a reaction between nitric oxide gas and a muscle pigment in the meat, myoglobin, closely related to hemo-globin. The nitric oxide gas comes from the sodium nitrite contained in the curing salts.

Before the use of ascorbic acid, the sodium nitrite reacted with natural reducing substances in the meat to produce nitric oxide. This was a variable reaction and failures to develop cured color in a reasonable time were not infrequent in production.

The nitroso-myoglobin, source of the characteristic color of cured meat, is quite easily oxidized to the unappetizing gray-brown color of met-myoglobin. Light accelerates the oxidation. When cured meats were sliced by the butcher, the discoloration was a minor problem. The advent of self-service meat counters, preslicing and the use of brightly lit display cabinets made the discoloration a major problem, which could be largely overcome by use of ascorbic acid or sodium ascorbate.

The addition of up to three-fourths ounce of ascorbic acid or seven-eighths ounce of sodium ascorbate for every 100 lbs. of meat used in preparing a cured meat product, or the use of up to $87^1/_2$ ounces of sodium ascorbate per 100 gals. of curing pickle will improve curing and provide a level of ascorbic acid or sodium ascorbate in the finished product furnishing significant protection for the color. The presence of the ascorbate compounds provides reliable and adequate reaction with the sodium nitrite to cause quick and uniform development of the cured meat color. The remaining, unreacted, ascorbate acts as an antioxidant for the color during display.

In the case of chopped cured meats, the ascorbates are added, in a solution or dry, to the meat during chopping or mixing. Good distribution is important. Often the ascorbates are mixed with the spices. In whole cured meats, sodium ascorbate is pumped in with the curing pickle, or dissolved in the cover pickle. Sodium ascorbate is *always* used in curing pickles to minimize reaction with the sodium nitrite prior to pumping. To further reduce the reaction, the pickle should be kept at a temperature of 50°F. or less.

Ascorbic acid, in the form of a ten per cent solution, may also be sprayed onto the surface of sliced cured meats to provide color protection during retail display. This spraying may be done automatically by various spraying devices, or by hand sprayers in store cutting and packing areas. The spray should be fine so as not to leave any visible moisture on the meat.

The use of ascorbic acid and sodium ascorbate is permitted in cured meats to the maximum levels discussed above by the Meat Inspection Division of the Agricultural Research Service, U. S. Department of Agriculture.

Erythorbic acid and sodium erythorbate may be used interchangeably with ascorbic acid and sodium ascorbate in cured meats. These compounds are chemically identical to ascorbic acid and its salts, but have little or no vitamin C activity.

Suggestions for Further Information.—Suppliers of ascorbic acid are a good source for further data. Various publications of the American Meat Institute Foundation, 939 E. 57th St., Chicago 37, Ill., are good reference works.

Other Uses.—Ascorbic acid is of value as an antioxidant in the following applications:

Beer.—Three to three and three-tenths grams per barrel is effective in preventing oxidized flavor in beer. This treatment is particularly valuable in canned beer and in beer subject to long or adverse storage and shipping conditions.

Fresh Milk.—Thirty to forty milligrams added per quart will prevent the "cardboard" flavor which often develops in milk from cows on poor pasture. This flavor is prevalent when summer pasture goes dry. It can be accelerated as a result of the growing use of bulk holding tanks. Addition of the ascorbic acid should be made as soon as possible after the milk has been drawn from the cow, since onset of the oxidized flavor is rapid. The required quantity of ascorbic acid may be added dry, with good stirring, or in the form of a concentrated aqueous solution. Slight curding at the point of addition may be noticed, but the curds are quickly dispersed with stirring.

Frozen Shrimp and Crab.—Ascorbic acid retards darkening of frozen shrimp and crab. The addition of 0.1 to 0.2 per cent ascorbic acid to the cooking water will help to retard discoloration of crab meat during processing. Ascorbic acid will also help to retard the development of "black spot" in shrimp. The procedure is to dip the shrimp into a five per cent solution of ascorbic acid for about five minutes immediately after the shrimp have been cleaned. Following the dip, the shrimp are packed in crushed ice and handled in the usual manner.

Frozen Fish.—High fat fish, such as mackerel, salmon and trout can develop rancidity, even when frozen. Dipping such fish in a one per cent ascorbic acid solution just prior to freezing, or glazing the frozen fish with the solution effectively retards this rancidity.

Dips must be handled so as to minimize bacterial build-up. Use of minimum quantities of dip, frequent replenishment, and keeping the solutions as cold as possible are recommended.

Ascorbyl Palmitate

Ascorbyl palmitate is an ester, a reaction product between ascorbic acid and a fat, palmitic acid. Its oil solubility, while limited, has made it of interest as a fat antioxidant, particularly for unsaturated fats. The work by Somogyi (1961) has indicated that this product, at levels of 0.006 to 0.036 per cent, has been more effective than phenolic antioxidants in certain polyunsaturated fats such as sunflower and cottonseed oil. Further work is in progress at this writing, but present indications are that this compound can be of interest in the protection of unsaturated fats.

Vitamin E

Vitamin E, in form of the free, unesterified, alpha tocopherol has antioxidative properties. Like many fat-soluble antioxidants its effectiveness appears to depend greatly on the type of fat it is protecting. In lard and similar fats of low natural tocopherol content, it is fairly effective, particularly when used in conjunction with ascorbyl palmitate. Alone, or in combination with ascorbic acid, alpha tocopherol has found usefulness as an antioxidant in flavoring emulsions.

In fats, use of 0.05 to 0.1 per cent is suggested, together with 0.025 to 0.05 per cent ascorbyl palmitate. In flavoring emulsions, 0.02 to 0.1 per cent should be tried. The pronounced effect of the fatty substance being protected on the effectiveness of alpha tocopherol as an antioxidant requires an experimental approach to determine the best use level for any particular product.

As with ascorbic acid, the advantage of alpha tocopherol as an antioxidant lies in its safety and nutritive value. In certain countries, Germany, for example, tocopherol and ascorbyl palmitate are the only fat-soluble antioxidants permitted.

VITAMINS AS FOOD COLORS

Two vitamins qualify as food colors. Vitamin B_2, because of its intense orange color, has been used to a limited extent in foods, particularly in Europe. However, its distinct greenish cast and sensitivity to light has made its use extremely limited.

Of much more practical significance is beta carotene, which is widely used as a source of a color in many foods. Beta carotene is provitamin A. It gives, in solution, a pleasant yellow to orange color. Beta carotene is the same compound as the principal color in summer butter, in carrots, and in many other vegetables.

Beta carotene is fat-soluble only, and only to a limited extent. Its coloring power, however, is very strong so that only a small amount is required to produce the usual color range desired. For example, in margarine, three milligrams of beta carotene per pound is sufficient to produce a pleasant yellow shade, and at the same time, provide 5,000 units of vitamin A activity.

It is also possible to color nonfat foods with beta carotene through use of suitable emulsifiable preparations. This approach is being used to color fruit drinks, etc.

As a food color, beta carotene offers the unique advantage of safety and nutritive value. It is also of value since it is not affected by pH in the range encountered in foods, by metals, by acids, and by light and heat, in the absence of air. It does fade, however, through oxidation. In fatty foods, such as margarine and shortening, the oxidation is not of significance. In nonfat foods, the fading becomes of significance only where it is difficult to protect the carotene from air. Dry mixes, for example, with their very large exposed surface, are particularly difficult to color with beta carotene. Oxidation can be kept to a minimum by excluding air through packaging, use of antioxidants, or by deaeration of the food.

General Methods of Application

Fatty Foods.—In **margarine,** the usual practice is to add a pre-weighed blend of beta carotene and vitamin A to the oil prior to churning to handle both fortification and coloring. The oil is usually held in a tank at 105° to 120°F. At this temperature, adequate stirring quickly dissolves the beta carotene.

For **shortening,** a suspension of beta carotene is added directly, and in required amounts, to a known quantity of melted fat. With stirring, the beta carotene quickly dissolves.

Popcorn seasonings are colored in similar fashion. The severe conditions met in corn popping necessitate the use of specially prepared beta carotene suspensions containing special antioxidant combinations.

Butter poses a special problem. In continuous churn methods, suspensions of beta carotene may be added directly to the heated butterfat in the holding tanks. In the conventional churn method, the low temperatures require either the use of very dilute suspensions of beta carotene, about one per cent, in vegetable oil, or special forms developed for butter coloring. Butter may also be colored by using a water-dispersible form of beta carotene, dispersed in a small quantity of water and adding this dispersion at the salting stage.

Other **fat-containing foods** can be colored by coloring the fat portion separately, where possible, or by using water-dispersible forms of beta carotene to color the aqueous phase.

Cheeses are colored by adding suspensions of beta carotene to process cheese or water-dispersible forms to a natural cheese. The process cheese is colored during mixing, the natural cheese is colored by adding the dispersed beta carotene just prior to curding. Six to 8.0 mg. per pound of cheese provides the usual range of color. However, this color is yellow to orange. While it is a good natural appearing color, it does not have the reddish tone frequently desired. Newer carotenoids, which are expected to be available in the near future, will provide the redder shades.

Beverages of all kinds may be given a good orange color by using water-dispersible forms of beta carotene. Levels used are in the range of 7.0 to 7.5 mg. per quart. Since coloring is done through use of emulsions, slow separation of the beta carotene will occur if the specific gravity differs from that of the beverage. In canned beverages, this slight separation is not of significance, since it cannot be seen, and the usual agitation on opening and pouring the container is sufficient to redisperse the emulsion. In glass bottles, the problem is more serious. Here beta carotene emulsions weighted with brominated oil to the proper specific gravity should be used.

Other foods which can be colored with beta carotene are:

Toppings—Colored in fat phase.

Mellorines—Colored with water-dispersible forms.

Pastries—Shortening colored, or water-dispersible beta carotene used.

Suggestions for Further Information.—The suppliers of beta carotene can provide detailed suggestions for specific applications. Bauernfeind (1953), Bauernfeind *et al.* (1958), and Bunnell *et al.* (1958) provide many interesting applications for the use of beta carotene to color fat-base and water-base foods.

LEGAL ASPECTS—LABELING

When vitamins are added to foods for vitamin activity, the provisions of the Federal Food and Drug Act, and its regulations as well as applicable state and municipal laws, must be complied with. In general, the regulations require that the label state:

(1)   The amount of each vitamin present, in terms of percentage of the minimum daily requirement provided by a suitable portion or serving of the food product.

(2)   A listing of each vitamin in the appropriate place in the list of ingredients.

The details of labeling are covered in the Food and Drug Administration regulations which may be obtained from the Food and Drug Administration, Department of Health, Education and Welfare, Washington 25, D. C.   The Federal requirements are not stringent but are designed to be informative and helpful to the consumer. It is always advisable to review all proposed label copy with legal counsel or with the Federal or state Food and Drug regulatory agencies.

In June, 1962, a new set of proposed regulations covering vitamins, proteins and minerals in foods was issued by the Food and Drug Administration.   At the time of writing, the proposed regulations were subject to comments and possibly hearings.   As proposed, the regulations do not appear to require drastic changes in labeling. The food manufacturer should, however, keep informed on this and other regulatory changes which may affect his operations.   The Food and Drug Administration will send copies of all proposed changes in regulations, petitions on food additives, etc. to any interested party.   Requests should be addressed to the Food and Drug Administration, Department of Health, Education and Welfare, Washington 25, D. C.

PACKAGING, HANDLING AND STORAGE OF VITAMINS AND VITAMIN PREMIXES, TABLETS, ETC.

The packages used by the manufacturer to ship vitamins and vitamin products have been designed to provide adequate protection under normal storage conditions. In many cases, instructions for proper storage are provided on the package label and should be followed.

In the absence of specific instructions, all vitamins and vitamin concentrates are best stored in a cool, dry place. If air-conditioned space is available, it should be used, particularly where high heat and humidity are ambient conditions.

Unless specifically stated on the label, refrigerated storage is not necessary. An exception is concentrated vitamin A and beta carotene forms which have to be stored for several months. Here it is advisable to store in metal containers, under refrigeration. The containers should be taken out of the refrigerator and allowed to warm to room temperature before being reopened for intermittent withdrawals.

In handling, weighing, and using the vitamins, personnel should be trained to wipe off the containers before opening, to use clean utensils in handling, to carefully recover all containers after use, and to make sure the labels remain legible so as to minimize any risk of contamination. Packages of vitamin A and beta carotene products should be used within four to six weeks after opening. It is advisable, but not essential, to flush the containers of vitamin A and beta carotene with nitrogen before resealing if the product is to be stored for a week or more before reuse. The dry crystalline vitamins do not need to be given any treatment of this kind.

With the possible exception of the flushing caused by niacin, none of the vitamins is in any way harmful or corrosive, and thus present no hazard in handling.

SUGGESTIONS FOR FURTHER REFERENCE

Bauernfeind (1953) has reviewed in detail the use of ascorbic acid in processing foods. Practical suggestions for adding vitamins to a particular food can be obtained from the suppliers of vitamins. These firms have experienced technical service groups who will work with food processors on application of the vitamins to foods. Their services include suggested procedures, initial assays, stability tests, and assistance in setting up production and control procedures, etc.

The state experiment stations throughout the country can provide assistance. Private consulting laboratories should also be considered both for specific product development or for continuous technical assistance, control or guidance. Other sources of excellent technical service are the can and container suppliers and equipment manufacturers.

BIBLIOGRAPHY

ANON. 1958. Recommended daily allowances. Food and Nutrition Board, National Academy of Sciences, Washington, D. C.

ANON. 1959. The Heinz Handbook of Nutrition. H. J. Heinz Co. McGraw-Hill Book Co., New York.

BAUERNFEIND, J. C. 1953. Advances in Food Research 4, 359–431. Academic Press, New York.

BAUERNFEIND, J. C., SMITH, E. G., and BUNNELL, R. H. 1958. Coloring fat base foods with β-Carotene. Food Technol. 12, 527–535.

BUNNELL, R. H., DRISCOLL, W., and BAUERNFEIND, J. C. 1958. Coloring water base foods with β-Carotene. Food Technol. 12, 536–541.

SEBRELL, W. H., JR., and HARRIS, R. S. 1954. The Vitamins. Three Vols. Academic Press, New York.

SOMOGYI, J. C., and KUNDIG-HEGEDUS, H. 1961. The stabilization of poly-unsaturated oils and other fats used as foods. Mitteilungen aus dem Gebiete der Lebensmitteluntersuchung und Hygiene 52, 104–115.

TRESSLER, D. K., and EVERS, C. F. 1957. The Freezing Preservation of Foods. Two Vols. Avi Publishing Co., Westport, Conn.

WOHL, M. G., and GOODHART, R. S. 1960. Modern Nutrition in Health and Disease. Lea and Febinger, Philadelphia, Pa.

CHAPTER 9

John T. R. Nickerson | Preservatives and Antioxidants

PRESERVATIVES

Introduction

There is some question as to what should be called a food preservative and what should be excluded from this category. Insecticides are used to prevent infestation, hence deterioration of growing plants; fumigants are used to destroy insects in harvested cereals and fruit. The Food and Drug Administration of the U. S. Department of Health, Education and Welfare has set up tolerances in foods for many compounds which might be included in one or the other of these groups. However, insecticides and fumigants are not generally considered as preservatives.

Tetracycline compounds may be used to treat eviscerated poultry or eviscerated, but otherwise uncut fish. These compounds are used to destroy or inhibit microorganisms which would otherwise grow on these products and cause spoilage. The Food and Drug Administration prescribes a tolerance for tetracyclines in the uncooked flesh of poultry or fish but only on the basis that these compounds will be destroyed on cooking. Therefore, there is no tolerance for tetracyclines in foods as they are eaten.

The chief use of nitrites in foods is in cured, or cured and cooked meats. In this application the main purpose is to develop what is considered a desirable color. There is no doubt that in the curing methods used today, in this country, the use of nitrites in meats has little significance related to spoilage by microorganisms. The application of nitrites to fish, on the other hand, has been primarily for the purpose of either preventing the growth of microorganisms or to modify the type of end-products produced by bacterial growth.

Other instances could be cited to illustrate difficulties which may be encountered in classifying chemical compounds according to whether or not they are applied to foods as preservatives. Because of the difficulty of making an absolute separation on the basis of the term "preservative," in this discussion a food "preservative" will be defined as a

JOHN T. R. NICKERSON, Professor, Department of Nutrition and Food Science, Massachusetts Institute of Technology, Cambridge, Mass.

chemical compound or mixture of compounds applied for the specific purpose of preventing spoilage due to the growth of bacteria, yeasts or molds, after the raw material or materials have been harvested.

It must not be expected that because a compound has been declared as "GRAS," (Generally Recognized as Safe for Use in Foods), that this compound can be added to foods in any amounts. The Food and Drug Administration considers that such approved materials should be used in foods at levels which are in accordance with good manufacturing practice and the use of levels beyond such amounts would be considered in violation.

The Food and Drug Administration has also set up standards for maximum quantities of a number of compounds which may be added to specific foods (Anon. 1960). Such standards are based on the toxicity of the additive (a safety factor is included) together with the quantity of the food eaten by a consumer in a given period. Since the amount allowed is calculated in this way a compound approved for a food in amount "x" might not be allowed in any amount in another food. For instance, suppose that 100 mg. of compound "Y" taken daily were found to be toxic, and, based on a safety factor, 20 mg. of this compound per pound were allowed in fruit juice, considering that not more than one-half pound of juice would be consumed by the average individual daily. This compound might be disallowed for use in some other food product because of the possibility that the daily total consumption of the compound by the individual might be such that the tolerance would be exceeded.

Preservatives with which foods may be treated or which are allowed in foods according to the regulations of the Food and Drug Administration or the Meat Inspection Branch of the Department of Agriculture are listed in Table 47.

THE EFFECT OF PRESERVATIVES ON MICROORGANISMS

Although speculation exists as to the action of some preservatives, in most cases little is known of the mechanism by which bacteria, yeasts or molds are inhibited or destroyed by the action of chemicals. It is obvious that lactic acids (produced through fermentation) or acetic acid, added to some foods, may lower the pH sufficiently to limit or prevent the growth of some spoilage organisms. Dunn (1957). There are few if any foods in which this type of treatment may be used to preserve foods without the added inhibitive effect of refrigeration. Prevention of microbial growth in most cases involving the use of acid may be due to other factors than lowering of the pH.

It is generally considered that with acids of the fatty acid group such as acetic, propionic and caprylic, the undissociated part of the molecule is more effective in preventing the growth of certain bacteria and molds than is the change of pH brought about by the addition of these compounds. It is believed (Wyss 1948) that fatty acids may inhibit the growth of microorganisms through the destruction of cell membranes or through inhibition of some of the enzyme systems of the cell.

It has been theorized (Wyss 1948) that benzoates and related compounds may destroy cell membranes in inhibiting microorganisms or may compete with coenzymes necessary for enzyme action. Recent investigations (Bosund 1959, 1960) would indicate that these compounds may interfere with the utilization of acetate in the formation of energy-rich compounds required for cell metabolism.

Borates and boric acid are believed to interfere with enzymes involved in the metabolism of phosphate compounds (Wyss 1948).

Oxidizing agents such as those which liberate chlorine are believed to destroy S-H groups in the proteins of some enzymes essential to the metabolic processes of microorganisms (Wyss 1948).

It has been shown (Castell 1949; Tarr and Sunderland 1939A and B) that nitrites inhibit bacterial growth in fish but that these compounds are effective in this respect only when the pH of the flesh is below 6.4. The mechanism of this inhibition is not known. Regardless of the fact that, in concentrations of 200 p.p.m., nitrites do not inhibit bacterial growth on fish when the pH is near neutrality, these compounds have been shown to retard the spoilage of fish in which the pH is much higher than 6.4. The latter effect appears to be due to a preferential reduction of nitrite, the bacteria reducing the nitrite instead of trimethylamine oxide. A limited storage life extension is therefore obtained since, while the nitrite is present, trimethylamine (the main compound causing off-flavors in fish of the cod family prior to putrefaction) is not formed (Castell 1949). The situation in this case is therefore one of preventing the formation of compounds causing off-flavors rather than that of bacterial inhibition. Tarr and Sunderland (1940).

The reasons for the inhibitive effect of sorbic acid in preventing the growth of microorganisms, especially molds, has been fairly well established (Deuel et al. 1954A and B; Melnick and Luckmann, 1954A and B; Melnick et al. 1954A). Sorbic acid is metabolized by experimental animals as are fatty acids; its toxicity to humans is therefore not a matter of concern.

In molds and in catalase positive bacteria, sorbic acid prevents growth by inactivating dehydrogenase enzymes necessary for the

TABLE 47

CHEMICAL PRESERVATIVES ALLOWED IN FOODS OR USED TO TREAT FOODS DURING PROCESSING

Compound	Formula	Amounts Allowed in Foods
Acetic acid	CH_3—COOH	GRAS—may be added in accordance with good manufacturing practice
Sodium diacetate	CH_3—C(—OH)(—O⁻ N⁺aO)=C—CH_3	GRAS—0.4 part per 100 parts of flour—in bread
Caprylic acid	CH_3—$(CH_2)_6$—COOH	GRAS—may be added in accordance with good manufacturing practice
Propionic acid	CH_3—CH_2—COOH	As above
Calcium propionate	CH_3—CH_2—C(=O)—O—Ca—O—C(=O)—CH_2—CH_3	GRAS—0.32 part per 100 parts of flour—in bread
Sodium propionate	CH_3—CH_2—C(=O)—ONa	GRAS—may be added in accordance with good manufacturing practice 0.32 parts per 100 parts of flour—in bread
Benzoic acid	(benzene ring)—COOH	1,000 p.p.m. or 0.1 per cent in foods 0.3 per cent or 3,000 p.p.m. in vitamin preparations
Sodium benzoate	(benzene ring)—COONa	1,000 p.p.m. or 0.1 per cent in foods
Parahydroxybenzoic acid (Paraben)	(benzene ring)—COOH, —OH	1,000 p.p.m. or 0.1 per cent in foods

Compound	Structure	Status
Methyl parahydroxybenzoate (Methyl paraben)	$COOCH_3$, benzene ring, OH	1,000 p.p.m. or 0.1 per cent in foods
Propyl parahydroxybenzoate (Propyl paraben)	$COOCH_2CH_2CH_3$, benzene ring, OH	1,000 p.p.m. or 0.1 per cent in foods
Sodium salt of propyl parahydroxybenzoate	$COOCH_2CH_2CH_3$, benzene ring, ONa	1,000 p.p.m. or 0.1 per cent in foods
Vanillic acid	$COOH$, OCH_3, OH on benzene ring	Not allowed in foods
Methyl ester of vanillic acid	$COOCH_3$, OCH_3, OH on benzene ring	Not allowed in foods
Propyl ester of vanillic acid	$COOCH_2CH_2CH_3$, OCH_3, OH on benzene ring	Not allowed in foods
Boric acid	H_3BO_3	Not allowed in foods
Diethylpyrocarbonic acid	$CH_3-CH_2-O-C-O-C-O-CH_2-CH$ (with $=O$ groups)	Presently not allowed—being evaluated Decomposes to ethyl alcohol and carbon dioxide
Hexamethylene tetramine (hexamine)	(tetramine cage structure)	Not allowed in food—allowed in packaging material considered safe
Sodium hypochlorite	$NaOCl$	Not specified Reacts with food materials

TABLE 47 (*continued*)

CHEMICAL PRESERVATIVES ALLOWED IN FOODS OR USED TO TREAT FOODS DURING PROCESSING

Compound	Formula	Amounts Allowed in Foods
Potassium nitrite	KNO_2	0.02 per cent or 200 p.p.m. in meat
Sodium nitrite	$NaNO_2$	0.0007 per cent or 0.7 p.p.m. in canned fish 0.02 per cent or 200 p.p.m. in cured fish
Diphenyl		110 p.p.m. or 0.011 per cent on citron, grapefruit, kumquats, oranges, tangelos, tangerines and other citrus fruit
Sodium chloroorthophenate		Not allowed in food
2-4 Dichlorophenoxyacetic acid (2-4-D)		5 p.p.m. or 0.005 per cent in or on apples, citrus fruits, pears or quinces
2-4-5 Trichlorophenoxyacetic acid (2-4-5 T)		Not specified Probably not allowed
Sorbic acid	$CH_3-CH=CH-CH=CH-COOH$	GRAS—may be added in accordance with good manufacturing practice Has been used as 0.025 per cent or 250 p.p.m. to 0.2 per cent or 2,000 p.p.m. of foods
Calcium sorbate		As above

Name	Structure	Notes
Sodium sorbate	$CH_3-CH=CH-CH=CH-\overset{\displaystyle O}{\overset{\|}{C}}-ONa$	As above
Sulfur dioxide	SO_2	GRAS—but not allowed in meat
Potassium metabisulfite	$\begin{array}{c}O=S-O-K\\ \| \\ O=S-O-K\end{array}$	As above
Sodium metabisulfite	$\begin{array}{c}O=S-O-Na\\ \| \\ O=S-O-Na\end{array}$	As above
Chlortetracycline (aureomycin)	(structure of chlortetracycline)	0.0007 per cent or 7 p.p.m. in uncooked tissues of poultry 0.0005 p.p.m. in uncooked tissues of whole, headed or gutted fish, shucked scallops or un-peeled shrimp
Oxytetracycline (tenamycin)	(structure of oxytetracycline)	As above

metabolism of carbohydrates and fatty acids (Melnick *et al.* 1954B). This compound is ineffective against microorganisms which have a multiplicity of dehydrogenase enzymes, such as the strict anaerobes.

Sulfur dioxide cannot be used in sufficient concentration in foods to effectively inhibit the growth of microorganisms through a lowering of pH. The chief inhibiting effect of this compound is believed to be due to the reaction with aldehydes in carbohydrate dissimilation and through the reduction of S-S linkages in enzyme proteins (Joslyn and Braverman 1954).

THE APPLICATION OF PRESERVATIVES TO FOODS

Acetic acid and acetates are used in a number of instances as a preservative or partial preservative for foods. Part of the process of curing sweet or sour pickles involves the holding for several days in a solution of vinegar containing 4 to 6.5 per cent of acetic acid. The final solution in which sour pickles are packed contains 2.5 to 3.5 per cent of acetic acid. Sweet pickles are packed in a solution which contains 4 to 4.3 per cent of acetic acid when equilibrium is reached. Pickles of these types generally are not heat processed after packing. Onion, cauliflower, string bean and green tomato pickles may be prepared and packed in much the same manner as are cucumber pickles (Cruess 1958).

Catsup and chili sauce are usually packed hot or pasteurized after they are bottled. However, these products are oftentimes not sterile and there is also the problem of recontamination after opening. Regardless of this, little trouble is encountered due to spoilage of these condiments. In the manufacturing process vinegar or diluted acetic acid is added to catsup and chili sauce in amounts sufficient to raise the final content of acetic acid to 1.5 per cent or higher. It has been stated (Cruess 1958) that acetic acid is the most active ingredient involved in the preservation of these products and that certain of the spice oils may be somewhat active in this respect.

Pickled fish are pretreated and packed in solutions containing vinegar and various spices with or without sugar. Oftentimes these products have been presalted and held for some time, but in such instances they are freshened prior to holding in vinegar solutions and are finally packed in solutions the final acetic acid content of which may be as low as 0.5 per cent or as high as 3.5 per cent. Herring is most often preserved in this manner but alewives, anchovies, salmon, mackerel, king mackerel, sturgeon, oysters and shrimp are also prepared as pickled products.

Pickled fish cannot be held at room temperature without undergoing bacterial decomposition; they must be held at suitable refrigerator temperatures above freezing in order to prevent spoilage. Whereas the acetic acid, and in some cases the relatively high sodium chloride content, will not prevent the growth of spoilage bacteria in these products when held at room temperature, they will inhibit the growth of spoilage bacteria at refrigerator temperatures. In this case, therefore, acetic acid may be considered as a factor in the preservative action since without it pickled fish would spoil even if refrigerated.

Dykon, a white powder consisting of a complex of sodium acetate and acetic acid (42.25 per cent available acetic acid in water) is sometimes added with the dry ingredient as a component of bread. Used in this manner it inhibits mold growth and also ropiness due to the growth of *Bacillus mesentericus*, *B. subtilus* and *B. panis*.

Capryllic acid is sometimes used as a mold inhibitor in cheese. Ordinarily this is used as a component of the wrapper with which the cheese is covered. It may be added as a component of the wax used to impregnate the paper wrapper or as a component of some coating such as nitrocellulose used to coat a plastic film (cellophane or other plastic) with which the cheese is wrapped.

Propionic acid, calcium propionate or sodium propionate may be added to bread or cake to prevent molding or the formation of rope. Usually the calcium or sodium salt is used (Mycoban) and is added as a component of the dry ingredients (baking powder in the manufacture of cakes).

Benzoic acid, sodium benzoate, parahydroxybenzoic acid and related compounds as well as vanillic acid and the methyl and propyl esters are white crystalline compounds. These materials may be added to foods as a powder mixed intimately with the product, as a dusting powder dispersed in an inert carrier such as starch or they may be dissolved in water in which the food is immersed for purposes of application. However, the vanillic acid compounds are not allowed in food in this country.

Since benzoic acid is not very soluble in water, the sodium salt is most often used.

The use of sodium benzoate in ice used for the refrigeration of fresh fish has been suggested but there appears to be no application of this kind at the present time. Sodium benzoate is used to extend the storage life of salt cod (40 to 45 per cent moisture), in which case it is dusted on the product after mixing with an inert carrier. Sodium benzoate may be used as a preservative for pickled fish or caviar, in which case it is added during presalting, as a powder mixed with salt, or dissolved in the cover solution with which the product is packed.

It has been shown that the benzoates are most effective in acid foods (pH 4.0 or below) (Cruess and Richert 1929). For this reason the greatest use of such materials has been in fruit juices, fruit concentrates, jellies, preserves, syrups, toppings and similar products. When used in such foods the sodium salt is dissolved directly in the product.

The paraben compounds are more soluble than benzoic acid and the sodium salts of these compounds are even more soluble. It has been stated (Anon. 1962) that the paraben compounds are effective over a much broader microbiological spectrum than are the benzoates and are active even in foods which are essentially neutral in pH (7.0). (Neidig and Burrell 1942; Von Schelhorn 1901).

In Europe the paraben compounds have been used by dissolving directly in fruit juices, fruit juice concentrates, horseradish preparations, pickles, pickled beets and pickled tomatoes. There has been less use of these compounds in this country, probably because of a lack of information concerning their properties. It would appear that, for the preservation of many foods, paraben analogues might be more efficacious than benzoates. In a recent article (Anon. 1962) it was suggested that the paraben compounds be used by adding directly to the ingredients during comminution, when preparing the emulsion for frankfurters or for the preservation of salad dressings with a cheese base. For prevention of spoilage of peeled, sweet or white potatoes it was suggested that these compounds be applied by dipping in aqueous solutions.

Vanillic acid and the esters of this compound are more soluble in water than is benzoic acid. The use of these compounds as a preservative for fruits, bread and cheese spreads has been suggested (Evans and Curran 1948). Some care must be taken that the addition of vanillic acid or its esters does not affect the flavor of the food product in which they are used (Gillespie *et al.* 1955). (Pearl and McCoy 1945).

In the United States boric acid is not allowed in foods; however, there has been some use of this compound in treating citrus products which are to be shipped as fresh fruit. This application consists of a wash in an eight per cent solution of the acid prior to waxing. It thus serves as an inhibitor of spoilage due to molding without contacting the food itself. The skins of fruit treated in this manner cannot be used for candied peel products.

Diethylpyrocarbonic acid may be added directly to food products in which it is to be used. It has recently been used for the preservation of foods in Europe and its use has been suggested for food products produced in the United States. This compound is a liquid which, when added to foods, shortly decomposes to ethyl alcohol and carbon dioxide.   The application of this compound has been proposed for flesh-type foods, which are to be held under refrigeration, and for fruit juices.   A concentration of 100 p.p.m. has been suggested for refrigerated foods.   As yet the Food and Drug Administration has not made a ruling on the use of this compound in foods.

Chlorine, as such or as liberated from sodium hypochlorite, is quite often applied to foods such as fish fillets or may be applied to such foods as unpeeled citrus fruit.   No tolerance has been set up for chlorine and it would not be possible to analyze for its presence in a food because of the fact that it reacts with food components.   This compound is considered as "GRAS" by the Food and Drug Administration.

In applying chlorine to fish, the fillets are usually conveyed through a weak brine (approximately 3 to 5 per cent NaCl) containing 3 to 5 p.p.m. of available chlorine.   Immersion is for approximately ten seconds.   Concentrations of 6,000 p.p.m. of available chlorine are sometimes used to wash unpeeled citrus fruit.

The nitrites are applied to meat products as a component of pickle or added directly as a solid in preparing the meat emulsion for cooked sausage products.   Sodium or potassium nitrite may be added in maximum amounts of 2 lbs. per 100 gal. of pickle, 1 oz. for each 100 lbs. of meat in dry cure or $1/4$ oz. per 100 lbs. of chopped meat or meat by-products (Anon. 1952).

A concentration of ten p.p.m. of nitrites is allowed in canned fish. Presumably this is for canned tuna frankfurters and would be added directly to the frankfurter emulsion during comminution of the ingredients.   In cured fish, where 200 parts of nitrite are allowed, this material is mixed directly with salt used to preserve the fish as a salted product.

Although the Canadians have allowed the application of sodium nitrite to fresh fish for some years this has not been approved by the Food and Drug Administration in this country.   In Canada, sodium nitrite in concentrations of a maximum of 200 p.p.m. in the product has been applied by dipping fillets in solutions.

Diphenyl has been used to impregnate the oiled paper liners with which individual fruits of the citrus group are sometimes wrapped. The purpose of this application is to prevent decay caused by mold growth (Hopkins and Loucks 1947).   This compound is not allowed in foods.

Sodium chlorophenate has been used to disinfect the peel of oranges, lemons or grapefruit after washing.   This may be applied as a rinse after spray residues have been removed or it may be applied in the sodium silicate solution used to remove spray residues. When used as a rinse or in the sodium silicate solution, a concentration of 0.4 per cent is applied (Kineholz 1948, Pryor 1950). This compound is not allowed in food by regulatory agencies.

In other applications, fruit may be washed with a solution of 2 per cent sodium chloro orthophenate, 1 per cent hexamine and 0.5 per cent soap.

The compounds 2-4 dichlorophenoxyacetic acid and 2-4-5 trichlorophenoxyacetic acid have been applied to lemons which are shipped as fresh fruit to prevent deterioration by molding (Amer. Soc. Refrig. Engineers 1959). These compounds may be dissolved in the wash water or in the wax applied to the fruit after washing and before polishing. The compound 2-4-5 trichlorophenoxyacetic acid appears not to have been approved for foods.

Sorbic acid or its potassium or sodium salts is used primarily to prevent mold growth in foods. These materials may be added to foods by means of several types of applications. This compound is considered as "GRAS" by the Food and Drug Administration.

Various suggestions have been made for the application of sorbic acid or its salts to food products (Anon. 1961B). Some of the suggested applications are listed in the following:

Up to 0.2 per cent of sorbic acid may be added to certain types of cheese or cheese foods. It has been suggested that this be added directly or incorporated into the paper, waxed or coated plastic, with which the cheese is wrapped.

Concentrations of 0.03 to 0.07 per cent by weight of sorbate have been suggested as a direct addition to creamed cottage cheese but this material has not been approved by federal agencies for this type of cheese.

The addition of sorbic acid in a concentration of 0.1 per cent of the batter weight has been proposed to prevent molding of cakes. The addition of sorbate to bread and to brown-and-serve products has also been suggested; again it should be pointed out that this compound is not included in federal standards of identity for bread rolls and buns, hence the addition of this material to these foods would not be allowed if the final product were to be shipped interstate.

For pickle products sorbic acid has been recommended as a component of the liquid (vinegar and sugar solution or brine), in concentrations of 0.025 to 0.1 per cent by weight, used as a cover pickle.

The addition of 0.02 per cent by weight of sorbic acid or potassium sorbate to grape juice to be held in bulk under refrigeration or to refrigerated apple juice or cider (0.035 per cent of the acid, 0.05 to 0.1 per cent of the potassium salt) has been found to extend storage life.

Other suggestions for the addition of sorbic acid to foods have been: 0.02 to 0.04 per cent in bulk stored wine, 0.025 to 0.05 per cent in soft drinks, 0.1 to 0.15 per cent to chocolate, corn and maple syrup, 0.05 to 0.1 per cent to frankfurters and 0.05 to 0.1 per cent to salted or smoked fish. The latter application would have to be made by mixing the sorbic acid with the salt used in curing or by dipping the cut fish in solutions prior to smoking.

Fruit juices, especially those in which the pH is comparatively low and in which contamination with microorganisms is also low, may be preserved by adding sulfur dioxide. The juice of strawberries, black currants, and other berries and especially citrus juices may be preserved by the addition of 350 to 600 p.p.m. of sulfur dioxide as such or as the sulfite (Joslyn and Braverman 1954). In certain cases it may be necessary to also add sodium benzoate to obtain the desired extension of storage life. In the case of citrus concentrates which are not to be frozen, the amount of sulfur dioxide or the equivalent which are added may be as great as 1,000 to 1,500 p.p.m.

Fruit pulp and purées either cooked or uncooked are preserved with sulfur dioxide in Europe. In this country freezing is generally used to preserve material of this type.

Sulfur dioxide is used in wine making and in vinegar manufacture to sanitize equipment and to prevent the growth of molds and undesirable types of yeast. It is also used to prevent bacterial spoilage in wine held in bulk storage (Mills and Wiegand 1942; Yang and Wiegand 1949). Solutions of sulfur dioxide or sulfites may be used to clean holding tanks; 50 to 100 p.p.m. may be added to the must prior to fermentation in wine making; 50 to 75 p.p.m. may be maintained in bulk stored wine or 50 p.p.m. in vinegar stock.

The chlortetracycline and oxytetracycline antibiotics have been approved for addition to poultry, some fish and shellfish in the United States (Anon. 1960). This has been done only on the basis that the antibiotic would be destroyed when the fish or poultry is cooked. Since some fish are eaten without cooking, the use of these compounds has been approved only for whole, headed or gutted but otherwise uncut fish. The tetracyclines are not allowed for treating fish fillets. Due to these regulations these antibiotics may be applied to fish only as a component of the ice used to hold the product in refrigerated storage or as a prewash or dip for the eviscerated but otherwise uncut fish prior to storing in ice.

It has been found that the addition of tartaric or other acids may be necessary to solubilize some oxytetracycline compounds when used in alkaline waters (Downing *et al.* 1955-1956A; Downing *et al.* 1955-1956B). Also, if any of these compounds are to be used as a component of ice it has been found necessary to add some colloidal substance such as carboxymethyl cellulose or carrageen to the water, in order to obtain uniform distribution of the antibiotic throughout the ice (Gillespie *et al.* 1955).

In fresh eviscerated or cut poultry, a concentration of seven p.p.m. of the tetracycline antibiotics has been allowed. This may be applied by dipping in solutions of such strength and for periods of time that will provide for an accumulation of not more than the allowed concentration in the flesh.

The over-all attitude of some investigators concerning the use of antibiotics in foods (Vaughn *et al.* 1957) appears to be that these additives are of limited use in extending the refrigerated storage life except under special conditions. These special conditions include the use of good plant sanitation and the application of relatively low temperatures (above freezing) for purposes of storage.

ANTIOXIDANTS

Introduction

Several different types of compounds are commonly called antioxidants, yet only one class of compounds truly belong in this group. An antioxidant is an ortho or para diphenol, or has a similar electronic configuration. However, some compounds, not of the antioxidant type, are synergistic to the action of antioxidants and some antioxidants have a synergistic effect on the protective action of other antioxidants in preventing the oxidation of fats. Also, some compounds which are neither synergists nor of the antioxidant type may be effective in preventing oxidation of fats. Because of the wide use of various compounds in foods for purposes of preventing rancidity, all of the different types of so-called antioxidants will be considered in this discussion.

In order to understand the manner in which antioxidants, synergists, and other compounds prevent oxidation of fats it is first necessary to know something about the mechanism of fat oxidation. The type of problems encountered are also interesting.

Some of the fatty acids in essentially all food fats are subject to deterioration through autoxidation with the subsequent development of oxidative rancidity. Fat-containing foods such as fish, meat and poultry, when handled in the fresh or fresh-refrigerated state, do not often deteriorate through the development of oxidative rancidity, since the fats contained therein are sufficiently stable to remain comparatively unchanged during the usual shelf life at refrigerator temperatures above freezing.   The shelf life in this case is determined primarily by the growth of bacteria and other microorganisms.   There are some notable exceptions to this and fresh pork sausage is an example of a fresh, refrigerated food which frequently spoils through the development of oxidative rancidity.   The reason for this is that fresh pork sausage is high in (common) salt which has an accelerative effect on the oxidation of the fats of pork.

When foods are preserved, as by freezing or drying, deterioration because of the development of rancidity may occur during processing or during subsequent storage.   This may be obviated in some cases by treating under special conditions, the incorporation of antioxidants, synergists or other effective compounds in the food, or by special methods of packaging.

Bacon sometimes becomes rancid before it is eaten but relatively fast curing methods and the incorporation of antioxidant compounds through smoking have all but eliminated this problem.   On the other hand, the outside portions of salt pork are usually rancid when used for home consumption or in some commercially prepared foods.   During commercial use of salt pork, processing such as canning may cause further reactions to take place involving compounds causing rancidity, resulting in relatively tasteless compounds.   Lard has always been subject to the development of oxidative rancidity and in recent years has been stabilized by the incorporation of antioxidants.

Shelled nuts often become rancid, especially when packaged by methods which do not provide a high vacuum or an inert atmosphere. The addition of common salt in many cases probably accelerates the rancidification of shelled nuts, since common salt has been shown to be a pro-oxidant (Dubois and Tressler 1943, Wiesman and Ziemba 1946) for the fats of certain foods.

Potato chips which are not protected by inert atmospheres or vacuum packaging may go rancid and the storage life of this product is either predicated by the length of time it may be held without becoming rancid or by the period required for the absorption of sufficient moisture to cause staleness.   Antioxidants may be used to prevent the rancidification of potato chips.

Low moisture-content baked products which may have to be stored for some time are subject to deterioration through the rancidification of the fat contained therein.   Prevention of this type of deterioration may be brought about by the use of saturated fats, the addition of antioxidants or by both methods.

Various vegetable oils are subject to the development of rancidity. This is especially the case after the container has been opened and part of the contents removed. When oils are incorporated into precooked products such as chicken or fish sticks which are to be frozen, they are also subject to oxidation during frozen storage. It is probable that some storage stability may be achieved in this case by the addition of antioxidants although there is some likelihood that these compounds may be inactivated during the heating involved in frying.

Most of the foods or food products with which problems involving the rancidity of fats may arise have been briefly discussed in the foregoing. However, some problems of this type may also be encountered with such foods as mayonnaise, salad dressings, cereal flakes and others.

Mechanism of Fat Oxidation

The degree to which a fat is subject to autoxidation depends, among other things, on the composition of the fatty acids contained therein. The more unsaturated fatty acids oxidize at a faster rate than those with fewer double bonds. Thus a fatty acid having a formula such as $HOOC-(CH_2)_7-CH=CH-CH_2-CH=CH-(CH_2)_4-CH_3$ would be much more subject to autoxidation than one which had the following formula: $HOOC-(CH_2)_{16}-CH_3$. The stability of the fatty acids found in foods, therefore, depends generally on the degree of saturation or unsaturation of these acids. Arranged in order of decreasing stability to oxidation we have the following: stearic and other saturated acids; oleic, linoleic, linolenic, acids more unsaturated than linolenic.

Since unsaturated fatty acids are more readily oxidized than saturated types, it can be said that generally liquid-type fats are less stable than those which are solid or semisolid at room temperature, since the unsaturated fatty acids have lower melting points than saturated fatty acids having the same number of carbons (Hilditch 1949). No absolute statement of this kind can be made, however, since fats such as coconut oil, though containing very small proportions of unsaturated fatty acids, are composed of a relatively high proportion of fatty acids with fewer carbons than 18, and short chain fatty acids also melt at comparatively low temperatures (Bailey 1951). Coconut oil, therefore, though soft or semisolid at room temperature, is fairly stable to autoxidation. Also, the rate at which the fatty acids in a natural fat become oxidized may depend upon the configuration of the unsaturated acid or the relative position of the double bonds, the presence or absence of anti-oxidants, the presence or absence of pro-oxidants and on other factors.

In considering the autoxidation of a fatty acid, if RH represents a pentadiene system ($-CH=CH-CH_2-CH=CH-$), h_v a quantum of energy (light, heat or chemical energy), ROOH an hydroperoxide and R_* a pentadiene system with free radical, then, including only some of the initiating and propagating reactions, we may illustrate the mechanism as follows (Blanch 1955, Dugan 1961):

$$RH + h_v \rightarrow R_* \text{ Initiating}$$

$$\left.\begin{array}{l} R_* + O_2 \rightarrow RO_{2*} \\ RO_{2*} + RH \rightarrow ROOH + R_* \end{array}\right\} \text{Propagating}$$

Several things should be noted about this type of reaction. Chemical changes of this type involve a kind of chain mechanism in which the energy of activation of an already activated molecule can be passed along to an unactivated molecule, thus continuing the series of oxidation reactions. Secondly, the first step in the process requires the abstraction of hydrogen, activating an atom in the molecule and causing it to be especially labile to the addition of oxygen. Finally, it is evident that any compound which interferes with the initiating or propagating mechanisms of these reactions will have a relatively great effect on the overall process even though a comparatively small amount of this compound (enough to terminate a limited number of reactions) is present, since each terminated reaction accounts for a relatively large amount of energy of activation.

Energy for the initiation of the reactions causing oxidation of fats can be obtained from heat. Generally it can be said that the higher the temperature at which a fat is held the faster the rate of oxidation. Light energy also accelerates the oxidation of fats. Visible light has some effect but ultraviolet light is much more active in accelerating the oxidation of fats. Light with the longer wave lengths (brown, green and red) have little activity in promoting the oxidation of fats. Chemicals such as ozone, peroxides and peracids also accelerate oxidation of fats; and certain metals, especially copper or iron and their salts, are active in this respect. Certain enzymes, the lipoxidases, will catalyze the oxidation of fats (Lea 1961), and these enzymes appear to be activated at temperatures below freezing. However, in many fats or fat-containing foods these enzymes either are not present, have been inactivated by processing or have been removed from the product. Lipoxidase enzymes do not supply energy for the initiation of the fat oxidation reaction but lower the energy required for the initiation of the reaction to the point that the amount of energy necessary to start the process can usually be picked up from the environment even though the fat be stored at low temperatures.

Compounds Preventing the Oxidation of Fats

Several different types of chemical compounds are usually included among the antioxidants. This method of classification is confusing since some of the compounds are true antioxidants; some have a synergistic effect increasing the total protective effect of true antioxidants but by themselves are not active; and others may simply tend to exclude oxygen from the fat by preferentially reacting with it.

Compounds which are true antioxidants are ortho or para diphenols or have a similar electronic configuration. A simple illustration of an

$$HO\langle\ \rangle OH$$

antioxidant would be hydroquinone (not allowed in foods).

The manner in which the antioxidant breaks the chain mechanism of fatty acid oxidation may be illustrated as follows:

$$HO\langle\ \rangle OH + R_* \rightarrow HO\langle\ \rangle-O_* + RH$$

$$HO\langle\ \rangle OH + RO_{2*} \rightarrow HO\langle\ \rangle-O_* + ROOH$$

$$HO\langle\ \rangle-O_* + HO-\langle\ \rangle-O_* \rightarrow HO\langle\ \rangle OH + O=\langle\ \rangle=O$$

The antioxidant, therefore, forms nonactivated fatty acid products from those which have been activated, hence tend to terminate reactions once they have been initiated. Under such conditions small amounts of true antioxidant compounds will prevent the oxidation of fats over a comparatively long period of time. Also, it should be noted that the radical antioxidant products formed during the termination of the fat oxidation reactions are of the type which may react with each other but which, under normal circumstances, do not react with fatty acids or their oxidation products.

If too much antioxidant of the type illustrated above is added to fats an acceleration rather than an inhibition of oxidation of fatty acids may be the result. This is believed to be due to the fact that under such conditions antioxidants promote the decomposition of fatty acid hydroperoxides, forming radical by-products which cause the oxidation of unactivated fatty acids.

Probably partly because of the pro-oxidant effect of an excess of antioxidants, the addition of these compounds to foods has been limited by regulatory agencies to a maximum concentration of 200 p.p.m. in most cases, this amount being based on the weight of fat or of oil present.

Synergists and other compounds preventing, or assisting some other compound in preventing the oxidation of fats, cannot be classified according to the manner in which they act, since in most cases the mechanism of action is unknown. However, several mechanisms have been proposed. There are also instances in which mixtures of true antioxidants such as combinations of nordihydroguiairetic acid and butylated hydroxytoluene (Lea 1961) may have synergistic effects in preventing the oxidation of fats.

It has been fairly well established that synergists such as citric acid, the various phosphoric acids and phosphates, amino acids and ethylenediamine tetra acetic acid may chelate metals, such as copper and iron, which would otherwise act as pro-oxidants. On the other hand, citric acid and ascorbic acid could also have other effects. One theory is that synergists may supply electrons and protons to provide for the regeneration of antioxidants once these compounds have taken part in breaking the chain of oxidation. This mechanism may be illustrated as follows:

$$HO\langle\bigcirc\rangle OH + R_* \longrightarrow RH + HO\langle\bigcirc\rangle -O_*$$

$$HO\langle\bigcirc\rangle -O_* + \text{Synergist} \longrightarrow HO\langle\bigcirc\rangle OH$$

Finally, there seems to be no doubt that some compounds, not of the phenolic type, such as ascorbic acid or thiodipropionic acid, when present in foods, may preferentially react with oxygen, thus causing it to be unavailable for the oxidation of fats. It should be pointed out that ascorbic acid and related compounds may in some cases act as a pro-oxidant, accelerating the rate of oxidation of fats (Krukovsky 1949). This has been found to be the case when used with meat tissues low in tocopherol (Watts 1954; Watts and Wong 1951).

Some Properties of Antioxidants and Synergists

The formulas and solubilities of antioxidants and synergists have been listed in Tables 48 to 50.

Phenolic-type antioxidants are sufficiently soluble in oil (0.5 to 2.5 per cent) to provide the desired concentration but are essentially in-

TABLE 48

PHENOLIC-TYPE ANTIOXIDANTS

Name	Formula	Approximate Solubilities		Allowed in
		Oil	Water	
Butylated hydroxy anisole (BHA)	(chemical structure: OCH_3, CH_3, $C—CH_3$, CH_3, OH) or (chemical structure: OCH_3, OH, $C—CH_3$, CH_3, CH_3)	Readily	0.0015 per cent @ 77°F.	Fats and oils—200 p.p.m. or 0.02 per cent based on the weight of fat in the food Chewing gum as 100 p.p.m. or 0.01 per cent of weight Breakfast foods, cereals, de hydrated potatoes as 50 p.p.m. or 0.005 per cent of weight Mixed, dried and glazed fruits as 40 p.p.m. or 0.004 per cent of weight Potato flakes as 20 p.p.m. or 0.002 per cent of weight Potato granules as 10 p.p.m. or 0.001 per cent of weight
Butylated hydroxy toluene (BHT)	(chemical structure: OH, CH_3, $C—CH_3$, CH_3, OH_3C, CH_3)	1.5 per cent	Insoluble[1].	Fats and oils as 200 p.p.m. or 0.02 per cent or in same concentration based on the weight of fat in foods
2,4,5 Trihydroxy butyrophenone	(chemical structure: $O=C—CH_2CH_2CH_3$, OH, HO, OH)	2.5 per cent	0.5 per cent @ 122°F.	Fats and oils as 50 p.p.m. or 0.005 per cent or in same concentration based on weight of fat in foods In packaging materials in concentrations which do not provide for the addition of more than 0.005 per cent to foods

Gum guaiac	....	Insoluble	Insoluble[1]	Edible fats and oils as 1,000 p.p.m. or 0.1 per cent of weight
Propyl gallate	COOCH$_2$CH$_2$CH$_3$ / OH / HO OH	0.5–1 per cent @ 77°–122° F.	1.8 per cent @ 122°F.	Edible fats and oils—breakfast cereals 200 p.p.m. or 0.02 per cent based on weight of oil
Nordihydroguaiaretic acid (NDGA)	CH$_3$ CH–CH$_2$–CH$_2$–CH / OH OH / HO HO	0.5 per cent	Insoluble	Edible fats and oils—lard, shortening 200 p.p.m. or 0.02 per cent
α-Tocopherol (There are 7 known tocopherols —natural and synthetic. α-Tocopherol is the most active as an antioxidant.) (Vitamin E)	CH$_3$ OH$_3$ / C—C$_{16}$H$_{33}$ / O CH$_2$ / CH$_3$ CH$_2$ / CH$_3$ HO CH$_3$	Insoluble	Soluble	GRAS—may be added at levels in accordance with good manufacturing practice

[1] Anon. 1961A Tenox food grade antioxidant: Advertising brochure, Eastman Kodak Co.

TABLE 49

COMPOUNDS OF THE NON-PHENOLIC TYPE WHICH RETARD OXIDATION OF FATS

Name	Formula	Solubilities		May Be Added To
		In Oil	In Water	
l Ascorbic acid		Insoluble	33 per cent @ 68°F.	GRAS—may be added to foods at levels in accordance with good manufacturing practice
Sodium ascorbate		Insoluble	Very soluble	As above
Calcium ascorbate		Insoluble	Very soluble	As above

Name	Structure	Solubility	Solubility	Uses
Ascorbyl palmitate	$CH_2OOC(CH_2)_{14}-CH_3$ structure (ascorbic acid ester)	Soluble	Soluble	GRAS various foods—may be added to foods at levels in accordance with good manufacturing practice
d-isoascorbic acid (erythorbic acid) (also the salts of d-isoascorbic acid)	ascorbic-type ring structure with HCOH, CH_2OH	Insoluble	Very soluble	GRAS—may be added to foods at levels in accordance with good manufacturing practice
Thiodipropionic acid	CH_2-CH_2-COOH / S / CH_2-CH_2-COOH	Soluble	3.5 per cent @ 77°F.	Various foods—fats and oils at 200 p.p.m. or 0.02 per cent based on weight of oil
Dilaurylthio-propionate	$CH_2-CH_2-C-O-CH_2-(CH_2)_{10}-CH_3$ / S / $CH_2-CH_2-C-O-CH_2-(CH_2)_{10}-CH_3$	Soluble	Insoluble	Various foods—fats and oils as 200 p.p.m. or 0.02 per cent based on weight of fat or oil
Distearylthio-propionate	$CH_2CH_2-C-O-CH_2-(CH_2)_{16}-CH_3$ / S / $CH_2CH_2-C-O-CH_2-(CH_2)_{16}-CH_3$	Soluble	Insoluble	Various foods—fats and oils as 50 p.p.m. or 0.005 per cent based on weight of fat or oil. In packaging materials in concentrations which do not provide for the addition of more than 0.005 per cent to foods

TABLE 50

SYNERGISTS AND SEQUESTERANTS

Name	Formula	Solubilities		May Be Added to
		In Oil	In Water	
Citric acid	CH_2-COOH $HOC-COOH$ CH_2-COOH	0.005 per cent	Greater than 60 per cent @ 68°F.	GRAS various foods—may be added to foods at levels in accordance with good manufacturing practice
Isopropyl citrate (monoisopropyl citrate)	$CH_2-C-OCH_3$ $HOC-COOH$ CH_2-COOH	Slightly soluble	Soluble	As above
Stearyl citrate (mono stearyl citrate)	$CH_2-C-O-CH_2-(CH_2)_{16}-CH_3$ $HOC-COOH$ CH_2-COOH	Slightly soluble	Soluble	Various foods, edible fats and oils as 1,500 p.p.m. or 0.15 per cent based on weight of fat or oil
Mono-glyceride citrate	$CH_2-C-O-CH_2$ $CHOH$ $HOC-COOH$ CH_2OH CH_2-COOH	Slightly soluble	Soluble	Various foods, fats and oils as 200 p.p.m. or 0.02 per cent of weight of oil
Ortho-phosphoric acid	$HO-P=O$ OH OH	Insoluble	Very soluble	GRAS various foods—may be added at levels in accordance with good manufacturing practice

Name	Structure			Uses
Sodium mono-hydrogen phosphate	$NaO-P(=O)(ONa)(OH)$	Insoluble	4.15 per cent @ 68°F.	As above
Sodium dihydrogen phosphate	$NaO-P(=O)(OH)(OH)$	Insoluble	59.9 per cent @ 68°F.	As above
Pyrophosphoric acid (also salts)	$HO-P(=O)(OH)-O-P(=O)(OH)-OH$	Very slightly soluble	Very soluble	As above
Metaphosphoric acid (also salts)	$(HPO_3)_n$	Insoluble	Very soluble	As above
Calcium disodium ethylene-diamine tetra acetic acid (Calcium disodium versenate)	(structure of calcium disodium EDTA)	Very slightly soluble	Very soluble	100 p.p.m. or 0.01 per cent as a component of potato salad or sandwich spread; 75 p.p.m. or 0.0075 per cent as a component of french dressing, mayonnaise, sauces, salad dressing, nonstandardized dressing, oleomargarine
Disodium ethylene-diamine tetra acetic acid (Disodium versenate)	(structure of disodium EDTA) .2H$_2$O	Very slightly soluble	Very soluble	75 p.p.m. or 0.0075 per cent in nonstandardized dressings; 100 p.p.m. or 0.01 per cent in sandwich spreads; 75 p.p.m. or 0.0075 per cent in sauces

soluble in water.   An exception to this is propyl gallate which at 122°F. has a solubility of 1.8 per cent in water (Lea 1961).   On the other hand, most chelating agents are essentially insoluble in oil but readily soluble in water.   An exception to this is calcium disodium ethylenediamine tetra acetic acid which is slightly soluble in oil (Anon. 1953).

Some phenolic-type antioxidants are more stable, hence most effective, under neutral or slightly acid conditions; others under slightly alkaline conditions.   The choice of antioxidants may, therefore, depend upon the characteristics of the food product with which it is to be used.

Water soluble antioxidants such as propyl gallate may discolor food products in the presence of metals such as iron unless metal chelating agents are present (Lea 1961).   The so-called hindered monophenol (ortho or para substituted) do not discolor in the presence of iron salts.   (Lea 1958).

Most phenol-type antioxidants are decomposed under conditions of baking or deep fat frying but butylated hydroxy anisole and butylated hydroxy toluene are said to be fairly stable to heat, hence are more often used in foods which are to be processed by heating.   This particular property is called "carry over value."

Application of Antioxidants

The method of application of antioxidants and synergists will depend upon the solubilities of the antioxidant in oil or water, and upon whether synergists are to be included in the antioxidant mixture.   The solubility of poly-phenol type antioxidants, such as propyl gallate or nordihydroguiairetic acid, is such that it would be difficult to add the material to oil or fat, dissolve it and obtain an even distribution of the antioxidant in a reasonably short time.   This is also the case when synergists such as citric, phosphoric or ascorbic acids are to be included with the antioxidant or synergist mixture.   In such instances it is necessary to dissolve the antioxidant mixture in some carrier which is miscible with fat or oil.   Usually propylene glycol has been used as a carrier for antioxidant or antioxidant and synergist combinations.

The difficulty of applying antioxidant combinations to flesh-type foods is that these foods are composed largely of water in which the antioxidant is not soluble and the fat which may be exposed on surfaces will take up the antioxidant only with difficulty.   One method which has been used in such instances is to prepare an emulsion of water containing synergists and the antioxidant in oil or propylene glycol and a stabilizer of the gum, tween or span or lecithin type.

In other instances in which antioxidants are to be applied to foods of high water content, it may be possible to dip the food in oil containing the antioxidant mixture, the antioxidants being dissolved directly in the oil or dispersed by means of a carrier solvent.

Some methods which have been suggested for the application of antioxidants and/or synergists to specific foods are listed in the following: Bentz *et al.* (1952); Dugan *et al.* (1950); Kraybill *et al.* (1949); Stuckey (1956), Stuckey and Gearhart (1957).

In adding to cream, butter, candy, pastry premixes, essential oils, vitamin A solutions in oil, oleoresins and melted fats, dissolve the antioxidant mixture in a carrier such as propyl gallate or propyl gallate and oil and add directly to the food or food preparation with mixing.

For corn and wheat germ meal, butter and peanut butter, add the antioxidant mixture directly and mix thoroughly. Best results are said to be obtained with such applications when the antioxidant selected is fat soluble.

For bacon, hams, meat, or fish which are to be frozen or otherwise processed, paint or dip the product in oil in which the antioxidant mixture has been dissolved with or without the aid of a carrier solvent.

For cereals, nuts or shredded coconut, spray with an emulsion of the antioxidant mixture made up in water or in ethyl alcohol. In applications of this type it is necessary to air-dry the product after the application has been made (Tappel 1954).

For hams, bacon and cured fish products, inject with an emulsion of the antioxidant mixture made up in water and stabilized with a gum.

For potato chips (Magaffin and Bentz 1949), fried chicken, meat or fish products which are to be frozen, dissolve the antioxidant in a carrier solution and mix with the oil in which the food is to be fried.

There is need for research to determine more effective methods of applying antioxidants to food products, especially to those foods with a high moisture content. There is also need for oxidation-retarding compounds of the non-phenolic type which are sufficiently soluble in both fat and water to provide for ease of application to flesh-type foods. Such compounds would be useful only if they could be shown to be of low toxicity and to contribute essentially no flavor or odor to the products to which they were to be applied.

BIBLIOGRAPHY

AM. SOC. REFRIG. ENG. 1959. ASRE Air Conditioning—Refrigeration Data Book—Refrigeration Applications. Amer. Soc. Refrig. Eng., New York.

ANON. 1952. Regulations governing the meat inspection of the U. S. Department of Agriculture. U. S. Govt. Printing Office, Washington, D. C.

ANON. 1953. Versenes. Bosworth Chemical Co., Framingham, Mass.

ANON. 1960. Compilation of regulations for food additives, Food and Drug Administration, U. S. Dept. of Health, Education and Welfare, Washington, D. C.

ANON. 1961A. Tenox food grade antioxidants. Advertising brochure, Eastman Chemical Co., Kingsport, Tenn.

ANON. 1961B. Sentry food preservatives—sorbic acid—potassium sorbate. Union Carbide Chemicals Co., New York.

ANON. 1962. Parabens inhibit food spoilage molds, yeast and bacteria at any pH. Food Processing 23, 64.

BAILEY, A. E. 1951. Industrial Oil and Fat Products. Interscience Publishers, New York.

BENTZ, R. W., O'GRADY, T. S., and WRIGHT, S. B. 1952. Antioxidants and food preservation. Food Technol. 6, 302–304.

BLANCK, F. C. 1955. Handbook of Food and Agriculture. Reinhold Publishing Corp., New York.

BOSUND, I. 1959. The bacteriostatic action of benzoic and salicylic acids. I. The effect on the oxidation of glucose and pyruvic acids by Proteus vulgaris. Acta. Chem. Scand. 13, 803–813.

BOSUND, I. 1960. The bacteriostatic action of benzoic and salicylic acids. II. The effect on acetate metabolism. Acta Chem. Scand. 14, 111–125.

CASTELL, C. H. 1949. Nitrite-reducing bacteria on cod fillets. J. Fisheries Res. Board of Can. 7, 528–535.

CRUESS, W. V. 1958. Commercial Fruit and Vegetable Products. McGraw-Hill Book Co., New York.

CRUESS, W. V., and RICHERT, P. H. 1929. Effects of hydrogen ion concentration on the toxicity of sodium benzoate to microorganisms. J. Bacteriol. 17, 363.

DEUEL, H. J., JR., ALFIN-SLATER, R., WEIL, C. S., and SMITH, H. F., JR. 1954A. Sorbic acid as a fungistatic agent for foods. I. Harmlessness of sorbic acid as a dietary component. Food Research 19, 1–12.

DEUEL, H. J., JR., CALBERT, C. E., ANISFELD, L., McKEEHAN, H., and BLUNDEN, H. D. 1954B. Sorbic acid as a fungistatic agent for foods. II. Metabolism of α,β-unsaturated fatty acids with emphasis on sorbic acid. Food Research 19, 13–19.

DOWNING, H. E., HARDIE, W. B., McMAHAN, J. R., and BILLMAN, D. C. 1955–56A. Antibiotic preservation of meats. III. Intraperitoneal injection of oxytetracycline in sheep. Antibiot. Ann., 734.

DOWNING, H. E., McMAHAN, J. R., and BAKER, C. 1955–56B. Antibiotic preservation of meats. IV. Intraperitoneal injection of oxytetracycline in hogs. Antibiot. Ann., 737.

DUBOIS, C. W., and TRESSLER, D. K. 1943. Seasonings, their effect on maintenance of quality in storage of frozen ground pork and beef. Proc. Inst. Food Technol. 202–207.

DUGAN, L. R. 1961. Development and inhibition of oxidative rancidity in foods. Food Technol. 15, 10–16.

DUGAN, L. R., JR., KRAYBILL, H. R., IRELAND, L., and VIBRANS, F. C. 1950. Butylated hydroxy aniscle as an antioxidant for fats and foods made with fat. Food Technol. 4, 457–460.

DUNN, C. G. 1957. Food preservatives. In Antiseptics, Disinfectants, Fungicides and Sterilization. Edited by C. F. Reddish. Lea and Febinger, Philadelphia, Pa.

EVANS, F. R., and CURRAN, H. R. 1948. Esters of vanillic acid as spore controlling agents. Food Research 13, 66–69.

GILLESPIE, D. C., BOYD, J. W., BISSETT, H. M., and TARR, H. L. A. 1955. Ices containing chlortetracycline in experimental fish preservation. Food Technol. 9, 296–300.

HILDITCH, T. P. 1949. Industrial Fats and Waxes. 3rd Edition. Balliere, Tindall and Cox, London.

HOPKINS, E. F., and LOUCKS, K. W. 1947. The use of diphenyl in the control of stem-end rot and mold in citrus fruits. Citrus Ind. 28, No. 10, 5.

JOSLYN, M. A., and BRAVERMAN, J. B. S. 1954. The chemistry and technology of the pretreatment and preservation of fruit and vegetable products with sulfur dioxide and sulfites. Advances in Food Research 5, 97–160.

KIENHOLZ, J. R. 1948. Chemicals aid Hood River pears. Better Fruit 43, No. 2, 18.

KRAYBILL, H. R., DUGAN, L. R., JR., BEADLE, B. W., VIBRANS, F. C., SWARTZ, V., and REZABEK, H. 1949. Butylated hydroxyanisole as an antioxidant for animal fats. J. Am. Oil Chemists' Soc. 26, No. 9, 449–453.

KRUKOVSKY, V. N. 1949. The influence of tocopherols and cod liver oil on stability of milk. J. Dairy Sci. 32, 196.

LEA, C. H. 1958. Some nutritional and allied problems confronting the food manufacturer: technological aspects of antioxidants. J. Sci. Food Agr. 9, 621–632.

LEA, C. H. 1961. Some biological aspects of fat deterioration. Food Technol. 15, 33–40.

LEA, C. H., and WARD, R. J. 1959. Relative antioxidant activities of the seven tocopherols. J. Sci. Food Agr. 10, 537–548.

LUNDBERG, W. O. (Editor). 1961. Autoxidation and Antioxidants, Vol. I., Interscience Publishers, New York.

MAGAFFIN, J. E., and BENTZ, R. W. 1949. The use of antioxidants in potato chipping. J. Am. Oil Chemists' Soc. 26, 687–690.

MARCUSA, R. 1954. Fat rancidity. J. Agr. Food Chem. 2, 126.

MARCUSA, R. 1958. On the use of antioxidants in foods. Presented at a Symposium on Foreign Materials in Foods, International Commission of Agricultural Industries, July 14–19.

MELNICK, D., and LUCKMANN, F. H. 1954A. Sorbic acid as a fungistatic agent for foods. III. Spectrophotometric determination of sorbic acid in cheese and cheese wrappers. Food Research 19, 20–27.

MELNICK, D., and LUCKMANN, F. H. 1954B. Sorbic acid as a fungistatic agent for foods. IV. Migrations of sorbic acid from wrappers into cheese. Food Research 19, 28–32.

MELNICK, D., LUCKMANN, F. H., and GOODING, C. M. 1954A. Sorbic acid as a fungistatic agent for foods. V. Resistance of sorbic acid in foods to oxidative deterioration. Food Research 19, 33–43.

MELNICK, D., LUCKMANN, F. H., and GOODING, C. M. 1954B. Sorbic acid as a fungistatic agent for foods. VI. Metabolic degradation of sorbic acid in cheese by molds and the mechanism of mold inhibition. Food Research 19, 44–58.

MILLS, D. R., and WIEGAND, E. H. 1942. Effect of storage on sulfur dioxide in wine. Fruit Prods. J. 22, 5–9.

NEIDIG, C. P., and BURRELL, H. 1944. The esters of parahydroxybenzoic acid as preservatives. Drug Cosmetic Ind. 54, 408, 481.

PEARL, I. A., and McCOY, J. F. 1945. Vanillic acid esters as food preservatives. Food Inds. 17, 1458.

PRYOR, D. E. 1950. Reduction of post-harvest spoilage in fresh fruits and vegetables destined for long distance shipment. Food Technol. 4, 57–62.

STUCKEY, B. N. 1956. Which antioxidants for your fat-containing foods? Food Eng. 28, 76.

STUCKEY, B. N., and GEARHART, W. M. 1957. Trihydroxybutyrophenone—a food grade antioxidant. Food Technol. 11, 676–679.

TAPPEL, A. L. 1954. Effect of antioxidants on cereals, induced antioxidation. J. Agr. Food Chem. 2, 197.

TARR, H. L. A., and SUNDERLAND, P. A. 1939A. The preservation of fresh and lightly smoked fish with special reference to the use of nitrites and their influence on the color of the treated products. Progr. Rept. *40*, 14–17. Pacific Fisheries Experimental Sta., Fisheries Research Board of Canada.

TARR, H. L. A., and SUNDERLAND, P. A. 1939B. A note on preservative ice containing sodium nitrite. Prog. Rept. *41*, 15–16, Pacific Fisheries Experimental Sta., Fisheries Research Board of Canada.

TARR, H. L. A., and SUNDERLAND, P. A. 1940. Conditions under which nitrites inhibit bacterial spoilage of fish. Prog. Rept. 44, 16–17, Pacific Fisheries Experimental Sta., Fisheries Research Board Canada.

VAUGHN, R. H., NAGEL, C. W., SAWYER, F. M., and STEWART, G. F. 1957. Antibiotics in poultry meat preservation. A comparison of the tetracyclines. Food Technol. *11*, 426–429.

VON SCHELHORN, M. 1901. Control of microorganisms causing spoilage in fruit and vegetable products. Food Research *3*, 429–482.

WATTS, B. M. 1954. Oxidative rancidity and discoloration of meat. Advances in Food Research *5*, 1–52.

WATTS, B. M., and WONG, R. 1951. Some factors affecting the antioxidant behavior of ascorbic acid with unsaturated fats. Arch. Biochem. *30*, 110.

WIESMAN, C. K., and ZIEMBA, J. V. 1946. How to prevent rancidity in frozen pork sausage. Food Inds. *18*, 1863.

WYSS, O. 1948. Microbial inhibition by food preservatives. Advances in Food Research *1*, 373–393.

YANG, H. Y., and WIEGAND, E. H. 1949. Possibilities of secondary fermentation in light sweet wines. Fruit Prods. J. *28*, 134.

CHAPTER 10

M. A. Joslyn | Enzymes in Food Processing

INTRODUCTION

As received by processors, meats, fish, fruits, vegetables, milk and grains contain many enzymes involved in normal life processes plus those contributed by microorganisms present in or upon these raw products. These enzymes may be "exo-cellular," occurring in freely soluble form in such fluids as gastric juices, plant sap, milk, blood, etc. Soluble, dispersed enzymes may also be present as secretions from microorganisms, or may be released by crushing, chopping, cutting, warming or freezing and thawing plant or animal cells. "Endocellular" enzymes are active inside cells in which they are confined.

It has been long recognized that the naturally occurring tissue enzymes are of major importance in producing changes in color, flavor, texture and nutritive value of foods and food products during processing and storage. The changes produced by microbial contaminants which occur are brought about also by enzyme activity either endocellularly or exocellularly. These changes may be either desirable and result in improvement in quality, or undesirable and result in loss in quality. Many of the processes and operations used in food preparation and processing depend essentially on promoting desirable enzymatic changes occurring during the post-harvest physiological changes in plant tissues and during the post-mortem changes in animal tissues as a result of the activity of naturally occurring enzymes. Other processes depend on the addition and use of industrially available enzyme preparations. The control of undesirable enzyme activity either by naturally occurring enzymes or of those adventitiously introduced by contaminating microorganisms and from other sources is also well established.

Although the utilization and control of microbial activity in food processing is authoritatively discussed in several recent text and reference works, until recently similar texts dealing with enzyme activity were not available. Excellent text and reference works on the chemistry of enzymes and enzyme action are available, but texts on enzyme technology, particularly as regards enzymatic aspects of food technology are not.

The growing interest in this field is indicated by the fact that a

M. A. JOSLYN is Professor of Food Technology, Department of Nutritional Sciences, University of California, Berkeley, Calif.

Symposium on Food Enzymes was arranged by the Department of Food and Dairy Technology, Oregon State College, in September, 1959 (Schultz 1960), and a symposium on production and application of enzyme preparations in food manufacture by the Food Group of the Society of Chemical Industry in London, England, in October, 1959.

Enzymes may be characterized as potent catalyzers that promote vital activity. They may occur as free or soluble enzymes, as enzymes bound to particular cell constituents and as integrated multi-enzyme systems. Enzymes promote chemical change because of their power of specific activation of substrate. Their ability to activate the substrate is shown schematically in Fig. 38. All the enzymes which

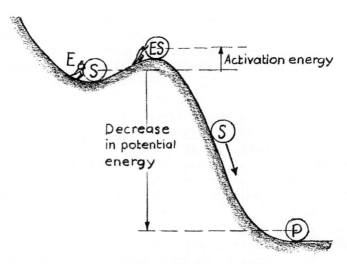

FIG. 38.   Schematic Diagram Illustrating Modes of
Action of Enzymes

have been obtained in the pure state have proved to be proteins, and enzymes generally, whether isolated or not, possess properties characteristic of proteins, e.g., thermolability. Enzymes as catalytic proteins may be classified as simple proteins, metallo proteins, or conjugate proteins, as shown in Table 51. The coenzyme components of conjugate proteins may be loosely or firmly bound to the enzyme protein. Many of the coenzymes are vitamin derivatives. Asimov (1959) elegantly describes enzyme activity in simple, readily understandable terms. He characterized a chair as catalyst which hastens shoelace tying reaction. An ordinary kitchen chair is quite

TABLE 51

ENZYMES AS CATALYTIC PROTEINS

Simple proteins
  Polypeptides
  Reactive linkages—peptide bonds
  Proteases: pepsin, trypsin, papain
  Hydrolases: esterases, lipases, amylases, glycosidases
Metallo proteins
  Cu—proteins: Phenol oxidases
  Mo—proteins: Aldehyde mutase
  Zn—protein: Carbonic anhydrase
  Mg—protein: Hexokinase
  Mn—protein: Arginase
  Mn, Mg—protein: Pyruvate decarboxylase
Conjugate proteins
  Enzyme protein + coenzyme
    Co-carboxylase: Thiamin pyrophosphate
  Enzyme protein: prosthetic group
    organic, metallo-organic
Vitamin components
  Thiamin   Co-carboxylase
  Nicotinomide   Phosphopyridine nucleotides
  Lactoflavine   Flavin nucleotides
  Pyridoxal   Pyridoxal phosphate
  Pantothenic acid   Coenzyme A

TABLE 52

DEFINITION OF TERMS

Enzyme.—Specific thermolabile protein catalysts which occur in all living plant and animal tissues and in microbial cells. They promote changes which occur during growth, development, and decomposition of living and dead organisms. Each individual enzyme usually promotes a specific change under specific conditions (as of moisture, pH, temperature, etc.). They may act only in the presence of living cells (cell dependent) or in the absence of cells (cell independent). Their action may be desirable or undesirable, and consequently to be encouraged or discouraged. They may occur naturally in a raw material or may be added for a specific purpose.

Thermolabile.—Subject to destruction by heat.

Biochemical.—Pertaining to the chemistry of life (plants and animals).

Catalyst.—An agent which promotes or accelerates specific chemical changes and is usually regenerated in the process so that a small quantity can stimulate transformation of much larger quantities of substrate.

Substrate.—The particular substance subject to change by a specific enzyme.

Protein.—Complex nitrogenous constituents of living cells, high molecular weight compounds of amino acids. They may be altered by heat, acids, alkalis, etc. They may be converted by hydrolysis progressively into polypeptides, peptides, and amino acids.

Amino Acids.—Organic acids containing nitrogen in amino groups (NH_2) adjacent to a carboxyl group (COOH).

pH.—A measure of active ionized acidity, related to the logarithm of the hydrogen ion concentration. pH ranges progressively from 0 to 7.0 in acid solutions, and from 7 to 14 in alkaline solutions.

adequate as a catalyst with which to accelerate the tying of shoe-laces. An enzyme catalyst is likened to a specially designed chair with back, arm rests and foot rests that are motorized and capable of automatic motion. As you sit down, your weight upon the seat closes a contact and up flies one of the foot rests lifting your foot to just the right height. Simultaneously the back moves forward, while the arm rests move around binding your arms at the elbow and gently forcing your hands together.

Enzyme technology can best be discussed in specialized terms. To facilitate ready understanding, these terms are defined in Table 52.

Characteristics of enzymes of special importance to food processors are summarized in Table 53. It may be noted that maximum activity for most enzymes lies between pH 4 and pH 8, reaching a peak around pH 6. Pepsin, however, is active at a pH as low as 2 and blood phosphatase is active at a pH as high as 9.

The pH in food products ranges from a low of 2.2 in lemon and lime juice to 7.8 for hominy. The flesh of animals and fowl is normally in the range between pH 6 and pH 6.5; fruits range from 2.2 to 4.8 and the so-called nonacid vegetables from 5.2 to 6.3.

It will be apparent that one means of controlling undesirable enzyme action would be by adjusting the pH, as, for example, adding lemon juice or fruit acids to inhibit discoloration by phenolase.

Conversely, desirable enzyme action may be promoted by adjusting temperatures, concentration, pH, substrate availability, etc., to conditions which are favorable. Pears, bananas, peaches and other fruit harvested when firm-ripe are softened, sweetened and colored by storage in rooms in which temperature, humidity and composition of the atmosphere are controlled. Composition of atmosphere is controlled by removing gases exhaled by fruit, by introducing fresh air or carbon dioxide, and by using respiratory stimulants such as ethylene.

Green chlorophyll in the peel and occasionally in the flesh is broken down. Fruits like lemons, bananas, peaches, pears, berries and tomatoes change from green to yellow or red. Starch present in tissues of unripe bananas is converted into sugars and fruits soften as a result of decomposition of pectic constituents. Loosening of the hulls of walnuts and almonds and blanching of celery are other examples of enzymatic changes.

Proper aging of meats by storage under conditions which promote enzymatic breakdown of proteins in connective tissue and muscle fibers results in tenderization and improvement in flavor. Aging must be carried out under conditions which prevent undesirable growth of microorganisms. By maintaining good sanitation, chilling carcasses promptly and thoroughly and maintaining ultraviolet radiations in aging rooms, it is possible to protect meat against spoilage losses. Tests of the radiation of carcasses with accelerated electrons, and of the use of broad spectrum antibiotics, indicate possibilities for new techniques in avoiding spoilage.

Tenderizing of cut meats may be promoted by treatment with proteolytic enzymes but this is limited by the poor diffusion of the enzyme into the interior of the meat tissue. Surface applications of proteases results in tenderization of surface areas only. Recently such tenderization has been improved by injection of specially prepared proteases into the animal before slaughter. This ante-mortem treatment results in more uniform distribution of proteases through the blood stream into all the muscular tissue and thus more uniform tenderization.

In cells, multiple enzymes often are present in integrated packets. Several enzymes act simultaneously in promoting a series of sequential reactions. Life depends on orderly functioning of these systems. A substrate is changed through a series of intermediates, the formation and utilization of each being catalyzed by a specific enzyme. Under abnormal conditions the balance between these reactions may be disrupted and result in undesirable changes. Thus, if potatoes are stored at too high temperatures, starch is converted into sugars which are oxidized, and the potatoes soften. At too low storage temperatures, oxidation of sugars may be slowed down more than conversion of starch and the potatoes become objectionably sweet. Grapefruit stored at too low temperatures will develop pitted areas on the peel. Unfavorable changes in the atmosphere may cause abnormal changes in color and flavor. Storage at low oxygen concentrations results in such abnormal suboxidative changes as internal browning in potatoes and in some fruit. Some fruits and vegetables rapidly develop objectionable off-flavors under suboxidative conditions. Superficial scald develops in some varieties of apples apparently caused by accumulation of respired volatiles in air surrounding fruit when circulation and ventilation are inadequate.

Enzyme activity varies quantitatively with the growth and development of fruits and vegetables.

In general, enzyme activity in dormant plant seeds is low but increases during sprouting. Sprouting of cereal seeds such as wheat, barley and oats, is accompanied by increased formation of amylase.

TABLE 53

CHARACTERISTICS OF ENZYMES DISCUSSED IN THIS CHAPTER

Name	Substrates	End Products	Optimum, pH	Nature of Change Produced
Amylase				
(a) Liquefying	Starch	Dextrins and maltose	5.0–7.0	Conversion of relatively insoluble into soluble starch
(b) Saccharifying	Starch	Maltose and limit dextrins	5.0–7.0	Conversion of starch to fermentable sugar
Anthocyanase	Anthocyanin	Anthocyanidin and glucose	3.0–4.5	Decoloration of berry and grape juices by conversion of natural pigment into less soluble form
Ascorbic acid oxidase	Ascorbic acid and molecular oxygen	Dehydroascorbic acid, H_2O	...	Oxidative destruction of vitamin C
Catalase	Hydrogen peroxide	Water, oxygen	6.8	Decomposition of hydrogen peroxide
Chlorophyllase	Chlorophyll	Chlorophyllide, phytol alcohol	6.0	Stabilization of green color of spinach leaves
Dextrinase	Dextrin	Maltose	6.0	Conversion of soluble starch into fermentable sugar
Glucose oxidase (and catalase)	Glucose and molecular oxygen	Gluconic acid, water	5.6	Removal of sugar from egg whites or of dissolved oxygen from juices
Glucosidases	Glucoside	Sugar, nonsugar residue	4.4–6.0	Hydrolysis of bitter glycosides which may lead to loss of bitterness
Invertase	Sucrose	Glucose, fructose	4.6–5.0	Conversion of sucrose into invert sugar
Lipases	Triglycerides	Glycerol, fatty acids	5.0–8.6	Conversion of neutral oils and fats into fatty acids
Lipoxidase	Unsaturated oils + molecular oxygen	Peroxides of linolenic acid	6.5	Oxidative rancidity of oils and induced destruction of carotene

Enzyme	Substrate	pH	Products	Action
Maltase	Maltose	4.5–7.2	Glucose	Hydrolysis of disaccharide into reducing sugars
Pectin esterase	Pectinates	4.0–7.0	Methyl alcohol, and pectates	Conversion of soluble pectinic acids into calcium precipitable pectic acid
Pectin poly-galacturonase	Pectates	3.5–8.0	Oligogalacturonides and monogalacturomic acid	Degradation of pectic acid into lower molecular weight constituents
Polymethyl-galacturonase	Esterified pectic substances	6.0	Oligogalacturonides and β-unsaturated galacturonides	Degradation of polymethyl galacturonides into lower molecular weight constituents
Peptidases	Peptides	6.0–7.4	Amino acids	Complete hydrolysis of proteins
Peroxidases	Hydrogen peroxide and phenolic compound	5.0–6.0	Quinone and other oxidation products	Oxidation of chromogens in absence of oxygen
Phosphatases	Esters of phosphoric acid	3.0–10.0	Phosphoric acid	Hydrolysis of phosphate esters
Polyphenol-oxidase	Molecular oxygen and phenolic constituents	5.0–7.0	Quinone and other oxidation products	Oxidation of chromogens leading to browning and induced oxidation of ascorbic acid
Proteases (Bromelin, papain, pepsin, trypsin, renin)	Proteins	1.5–10.0	Polypeptides and dipeptides	Partial protein hydrolysis
Thiaminase	Thiamine	5.0–8.0	Pyrimidine + thiazole (Varies with purity and source of enzymes)	Destruction of vitamin B_1 activity
Urease	Urea	7.0	Carbon dioxide, ammonia	Hydrolysis of urea into ammonia
Cellulase	Cellulose	3.5	Cellulodextrins and glucose	Hydrolysis of cellulose to produce additional fermentable sugar, improve texture and appearance

In growing plants, enzyme activity is greater in young, rapidly growing, physiologically active cells than in the older cells or structural tissues. It is most intense in the tissues where respiratory activity is highest.

Post harvest enzymatic changes in vegetable tissue are usually undesirable. In corn kernels, continuing synthesis of starch from sugars results in loss of sweetness and toughening of texture. Asparagus stems harvested in the tender stage convert carbohydrates into lignin and become tough. Enzymatic conversion of pectic constituents may occur, resulting in formation of soft spots or in general softening.

Lipid constituents of vegetable tissues may be converted into glycerin and free fatty acid by hydrolysis catalyzed by naturally occurring lipases. Accumulation of free fatty acids in peanuts, soybeans, etc., during storage is objectionable. Lipase-catalyzed, hydrolytic rancidity of oils and fats may be pronounced in seeds and nuts infected by mold, or in olives and walnuts subjected to freezing injury, either before or after harvest. Oxidation of unsaturated fatty acids may be catalyzed by naturally occurring lipoxidase in soybeans, peas, asparagus and other vegetables and this leads to the accumulation of peroxides and objectionable oxidation products.

A peculiar off-flavor which occasionally develops in frozen orange and grapefruit concentrate and in frozen grapefruit sections characterized by a "tallowy" taste and a "cardboard" or "castor-oil-like" odor, the so-called "COF effect," has been ascribed to activity of enzymes involved in lipid synthesis. Citrus fruit harvested before the natural process of conversion of sugars into fatty acids is completed contains intermediates which give to citrus products prepared from them this peculiar off-flavor. These intermediates occur also in unrefined vegetable oils.

Not all enzymes and enzyme systems present in intact living tissue are active. Some naturally occurring enzymes are inactive because of physical separation of enzyme and substrate. In wheat, enzymes present in the seed are largely confined to the germ and to a lesser extent in the aleurone layer, while the endosperm contains much of the substrate. In oats the lipase is present almost entirely in the outer pericarp. In sugar cane the juice is rich in sucrose while the plant tassel contains invertase.

Lack of substrate is another factor in natural control of enzyme activity. Thus the jack bean is rich in urease but lacks urea. When soybeans rich in urease are used in mixed feeds containing added urea, this may be hydrolyzed to ammonia and carbon dioxide. Certain fruit (figs, pineapple, cantaloup and papaya), contain relatively high concentrations of proteases but are low in protein. Catalase is widely distributed in plant and animal tissue but its substrate, hydrogen peroxide, does not accumulate under normal conditions. In some cases enzymes occur in the form of precursors from which the enzymes are formed. Thus, pepsin occurs as pepsinogen in gastric mucosa and is converted into pepsin by hydrochloric acid. Proteolytic enzymes in living tissue do not act on living protein, either because they are unable to act chemically on native protein, or because they are prevented from doing so by the presence of antienzymes such as antitrypsin. Oxidizing enzymes such as polyphenol oxidase, peroxidases, ascorbic acid oxidase, may occur in relatively high concentration but are inactive because the conditions within the cells of normally respiring tissues are so strongly reducing that neither oxygen nor hydrogen peroxide accumulates in appreciable concentrations.

When the cells of living tissues are damaged by cutting, bruising, adverse storage conditions, insect or fungus attack or any other treatment which kills cells without destroying soluble enzymes, these are liberated. Rapid and extensive enzymatic changes may take place. Hydrolysis of naturally occurring pectic substances by pectic enzymes in crushed apples and grapes increases yield of juice and facilitates pressing and clarification. In vegetables such as garlic and onions, naturally occurring enzymes promote the formation of flavors from tasteless precursors. Under certain conditions the naturally occurring amylases may convert starch into sugars.

Desirable changes in crushed or ground tissue may be slow and may be hastened by the addition of commercially available enzymes from other sources. Pectic enzymes are used to speed up clarification of fruit juices. Malt and fungal diastases are used in the conversion of starch to sugar. Proteolytic enzymes are used in tenderizing meats and in the hydrolysis of proteins in beer. Soybean lipoxidase is used to bleach flour. Fungal anthocyanase is used to decolorize grape and berry juices. Glucose oxidase is used to remove excess sugar from egg white from drying and to remove oxygen from packaged foods and beverages, etc.

Methods for promoting enzyme reactions are given in Table 54.

UNDESIRABLE ENZYME CHANGES

Bruising, cutting or crushing the tissues of fruits and vegetables such as occur during harvesting and transport and in peeling, pitting,

TABLE 54

PROMOTION OF DESIRABLE ENZYME REACTION BY

---

(1)   Providing favorable conditions.
       (A)   Controlling ripening of pears in storage rooms.
       (B)   Tenderizing beef by natural enzymes under controlled storage temperatures.
       (C)   Releasing flavor compounds from precursors during rehydrating dried onions and garlics.
       (D)   Coloring citrus fruits with ethylene to stimulate respiration.

(2)   Adding enzyme preparations or microorganisms which secrete enzymes.
       (A)   Using proteinases (pepsin, pancreatin, trypsin, ficin, papain, bromelin, rennet, etc.) to tenderize meat, or form a curd in producing cheese, or modify the texture of dough in bakeries, or clarify beer against chillhaze, or to produce protein hydrosates as soy sauces, seasonings, amino acids, etc.
       (B)   Using carbohydrases (such as amylase, maltase, invertase, lactase, dextrinase, etc.) to convert starch to dextrose, maltose, and dextrins, maltose to dextrose, sucrose to dextrose and fructose, or lactose to dextrose and galactose, etc. (Commercial applications include malting of grain in fermentation industries, production of corn sweeteners and gums, production of breakfast cereals, and in baking, candy making and ice cream production.)
       (C)   Using pectic enzymes to aid in extracting juices (as from grapes) and in clarifying juices (as grape and apple); to prevent jellying of concentrated juices, to remove the coating from coffee beans, etc.
       (D)   Using enzymes to release flavor constituents from precursors in reconstituting dried vegetables (such as cabbage) in which enzymes have been inactivated by blanching.
       (E)   Using glucose oxidase to avoid darkening in dried egg white during storage by converting glucose to gluconic acid.
       (F)   Using enzymes to remove oxygen from carbonated beverages, juices, cheese, and other products after packaging.
       (G)   Using cellulase to produce additional fermentable sugars from grain mash in brewing and distilling, to remove cellulose fibers from vegetables in canning and freezing.
       (H)   Using lipase to improve whipping quality of dried egg albumin and to improve flavor of cheese and milk chocolate.
       (I)   Using selected microorganisms which secrete enzymes to promote fermentation in producing beer, wine, vinegar, pickles, kraut, etc., converting fermentable carbohydrates into alcohol, acetic and lactic acids, etc.

---

halving, slicing or puréeing operations in the food processing plant may result in undesirable changes. These include:

(1) Darkening of peeled and cut apples, bananas, pears, peaches is due to the activity of polyphenol oxidases which, in the presence of molecular oxygen, convert naturally occurring phenolic substrates into brown or red pigments. The reddening and subsequent darkening of the butts of cut lettuce, darkening of cut potatoes, browning of Brussels sprouts and bluing of horse beans are similar.

(2) The formation of off-flavors in bruised vegetables is noticeable in vined peas and green beans, in cut corn and in bruised asparagus.

(3) Undesirable clarification of citrus juices and tomato juice by naturally occurring pectic enzymes acting on dispersed pectic con-

stituents causes rapid settling of suspended insolubles to which these juices owe color and flavor. In tomato products like catsup, paste and concentrate, this results in loss in desired consistency. In frozen citrus concentrates it may result in gel formation and poor reconstitution.

(4) Rapid decrease in ascorbic acid occurs in bruised, crushed or cut tissues of fruit exposed to air. In fruits that brown, this loss may be complete due largely to the activity of phenolases. In fruit like the tomato and in vegetables like the turnip this is due to the activity of the specific ascorbic acid oxidase. In cereal and other products, loss or destruction of carotene (or vitamin A), may be induced by lipoxidase enzyme. Vitamin A itself may be destroyed by oxidation catalyzed by lipoxidase. In certain fresh water fish, especially in shellfish like clams, and in crab and lobster tissue, thiaminase may rapidly and completely destroy vitamin B_1.

(5) In leafy green vegetables, discoloration owing to the conversion of chlorophyll into brown pheophytin may be reduced by enzyme action. In spinach, for example, a naturally occurring enzyme, chlorophyllase, *may* convert native chlorophyll into a derivative, chlorophyllide, which is more stable to destruction by heat.

(6) The tissues of some plants contain appreciable quantities of cyanogenic glycosides which may be decomposed by enzyme action into constituents glucose, hydrogen cyanide and the aglycone. Amygdaline, which occurs in the kernels of bitter almonds and in apricot and peach pits, may be converted enzymatically into glucose, benzaldehyde and hydrogen cyanide. Linamarin, which occurs in flax and in certain native varieties of lima beans, is converted similarly into glucose, acetone and hydrogen cyanide. Other glycosides, in the presence of glycosidase enzymes, may be converted into products of hydrolysis which are bitter. Some naturally occurring glycosides are bitter before hydrolysis and are tasteless after. This is true of the bitter principle of olive, oleoeuropein.

These and other undesirable enzymatic changes can be inhibited by various means, as indicated in Table 55.

COMMERCIAL ENZYME PREPARATIONS

As outlined in Table 56 (p. 252), commercial enzyme preparations are used in the food industry. They are prepared from bacteria, yeast, fungi and other plant and animal sources by a variety of processes including grinding and drying selected tissues, and extraction from selected tissues for distribution in liquid or dried form. Drying is effected by precipitation, by combining with dry carrier, by drying

TABLE 55

PREVENTION OF UNDESIRABLE ENZYME CHANGES BY

---

(1) Providing storage conditions favorable for minimizing undesirable enzymic changes.
    (A) Avoiding excessively low (near freezing) temperatures in the storage of potatoes, papayas, bananas, grapefruit in which normal ripening processes are irreversibly disturbed by such conditions.
    (B) Using cold or frozen storage to slow or substantially halt undesirable enzyme changes, as in hydrocooling of shelled peas and lima beans to retard deterioration prior to processing.
    (C) Dehydrating, reducing moisture to below levels favorable for enzyme action.
    (D) Handling perishable foods, such as sweet corn, rapidly.
    (E) Avoiding mechanical, insect or freeze injury to raw products. Damaged tissue may be badly discolored or off in flavor. Freeze injury in oil seeds and fruit (peanuts, olives, etc.) may result in excessive amounts of free fatty acids. Enzymes activated by such damage may cause undesirable changes in sound material.
    (F) Excluding fruit or vegetables subjected to microbial attacks. Enzymes secreted by bacteria and fungi contaminate sound material; for example, damage of pickles by pectic enzymes present in infected blossoms attached to cucumbers.
(2) Using heat to inactivate enzymes.
    (A) Using hot break in extraction of tomato juice to prevent degradation of pectic compounds.
    (B) Blanching (steam or hot water scalding) of vegetables to be frozen, canned or dehydrated.
    (C) Blanching cut, peeled fruits such as peaches to minimize surface discoloration during canning.
    (D) Flash heating of citrus juices to stabilize cloud.
(3) Adding permissible inhibitors to inhibit enzyme action—sulfur dioxide, ascorbic acid, lemon juice, rhubarb juice, etc., to prevent darkening of cut fruits such as apples, peaches, bananas, and to reduce oxidation discoloration in fruit juices.
(4) Excluding constituents essential to undesirable changes by excluding oxygen from the surface of cut fruit by covering by water, brine or syrup. By vacuum closing packaged products, or by use of inert gas in head space, or by use of oxygen acceptors.
(5) Selecting varieties of fruits and vegetables, and harvesting at stages of maturity, in which undesirable enzyme action is at a minimum. Enzyme and substrate content both vary with variety and maturity.
(6) Taking proper care to minimize contamination of fruit and vegetable tissues with plant constituents containing high concentrations of enzymes such as wheat germ in flour, sugar cane tassels in cane milling and peel extractives in citrus juice extraction.
(7) Avoiding excessive mechanical bruising during peeling, pitting, halving or slicing.

---

under vacuum at temperatures above or below the freezing temperature of water.

Endo-cellular enzymes are difficult to extract and were originally used as ground, dried preparations of the cells. Invertase is now prepared by autolysis or self-digestion of yeast cells. Many endo-cellular and exo-cellular enzymes from microbial sources are available, in both dry and liquid form in varying degrees of concentration and activity. Usually commercial preparations contain stabilizers and inert ingredients such as sugar, starch, gelatin, etc., for standardization. Those used in food products must be reasonably free from other enzymes and contain no ingredients unacceptable in food.

Some commercial enzymes listed in Table 56 are considered here in detail.

Yeast invertase liberated from yeast cells by autolysis was one of the first commercially available endo-cellular enzymes. It hydrolyzes sucrose to dextrose and fructose and was used to prepare invert sugar syrup until replaced by acid inversion. It is now used in preparing soft cream candy centers, permitting sugar concentrations sufficiently high (80 per cent) to inhibit gas formation and bursting of confections by sugar tolerant yeasts and bacteria.

Amylases from a variety of plant, bacterial and fungal sources are used in the milling, baking, brewing and distilling industries, in the conversion of starch to dextrins and sugars, in the clarification of juices, in the textile industry in sizing and desizing fabrics. There are two types: alpha amylases liquefy starch to dextrins, while beta amylases convert starch into fermentable sugars, maltose and dextrose. Maltase and dextrinase are usually present in commercial amylase. Recently a new amylolytic enzyme, amyloglucosidase, was introduced. This enzyme converts starch directly to dextrose without intermediate formation of dextrins and maltose. It can convert a corn starch slurry to a 93 D.E. syrup, containing as high as 90 per cent dextrose in 48 hr. at pH 4.1 and 140°F. (see Table 56, p. 252).

Pectic Enzymes.—Two commercial preparations include pectin esterase, usually obtained from tomatoes, and pectin galacturonidase from fungi. Separately and combined they are used for clarification of apple and grape juices and of wines, and for reducing the pectin content of juice prior to concentration to avoid jelling. Dry commercial products ordinarily contain filter aid, gelatin or sugar as diluent. Specialized mixtures are available for specific applications. Pectin esterase liberates methanol and pectic acid, and the latter may be precipitated by calcium or magnesium. Pectin galacturonidases hydrolyzes the glycosidal bonds in polygalacturonides into galacturonic acid and smaller molecular weight galacturonides. The hydrolysis may be by random or terminal mechanism and pectin may be attacked in preference to pectic acid or vice versa. A new enzyme degradation of esterified pectin into unsaturated galacturonic acid was reported recently.

Anthocyanase is prepared from fungus sources to convert antho-

Table 56

AVAILABLE COMMERCIAL ENZYMES AND THEIR APPLICATION

Type	Typical Use
Carbohydrases	Production of invert sugar in confectionery industry; production of corn syrups from starch; conversion of cereal starches into fermentable sugars in malting, brewing, distillery, baking industry; clarification of beverages and syrups containing fruit starches.
Proteases	Chill-proofing of beers and related products; tenderizing meat; production of animal and plant protein hydrolyzates.
Pectinases	Clarification of fruit juices; removal of excess pectins from juices such as apple juice before concentration; increase of yield of juice from grapes and other products; clarification of wines; dewatering of fruit and vegetable wastes before drying.
Glucose oxidase —Catalase	Removal of glucose from egg white before drying; removal of molecular oxygen dissolved or present at the surface of products wrapped or sealed in hermetic containers.
Glucosidases	Liberation of essential oils from precursors such as those present in bitter almonds, etc.; destruction of naturally occurring bitter principles such as those occurring in olives and the bitter principle glycosides in cucurbitaceae (cucumber and related family).
Flavor enzymes (flavorases)	Restoration and enrichment of flavor by the addition of enzymes capable of converting organic sulfur compounds into the particular volatile sulfur compounds responsible for flavor in garlic and onions, e.g.; conversion of alliin of garlic into garlic oil by alliianase; conversion of sulfur containing flavor precursors of cabbage and related spices (watercress, mustard, radish) by enzyme preparations from related rich natural sources of enzymes; addition of enzyme preparations from mustard seeds to rehydrated blanched dehydrated cabbage to restore flavor; production of natural banana flavor in sterilized banana puree and dehydrated bananas by naturally occurring banana flavor enzyme; improvement in flavor of canned foods by an enzyme preparation from fresh corn.
Lipases	Improvement in whipping quality of dried egg white and flavor production in cheese and chocolate.
Cellulase	Mashing of grain and brewing, clarification and extraction of fruit juices, tenderization of vegetables.

cyanin pigments into glucose and anthocyanidins (which precipitate). It is used to decolorize the red pigments in grape and berry juices.

Proteases.—Commercially available proteolytic enzymes include pancreatin recovered from glands of hogs, or less commonly, cattle; rennin from calves, papain from the latex of papaya fruit, bromelin from pineapple cannery residues. Two types of pineapple protease are now produced, bromelin from pineapple fruit tissue and bromelain from pineapple leaf and stem tissue. The latter differs markedly in proteolytic powers and in pH range from the former, ficin from fig latex and aesclutin from milk weed latex. Fungal and bacterial proteinases and peptidases are also available. The proteolytic enzymes for food use are mixtures of proteinases and peptidases. The proteinases or endopeptidases convert proteins into proteoses, peptones, and polypeptides and finally amino acids by hydrolyzing the internal peptide bonds. The exopeptidases hydrolyze surface peptide bonds and convert polypeptides into amino acids. By proper selection of enzyme and conditions (temperature, pH, time), either limited proteolysis or complete breakdown of most proteins to amino acids can be effected. The chief food use of these enzymes is in cheese manufacture, in chill-proofing beer (against haze) and in the baking industry. Their use for meat tenderization has been widely promoted in recent years, and is effective when proper contact and distribution is obtained.

Glucose-oxidase-catalase system from fungal sources is used (1) for converting glucose to gluconic acid (this is used in drying egg white to retard darkening); and (2) it may be used for reducing dissolved and heat space oxygen in packaged goods, containing glucose. In wines, beer and carbonated beverages, a preparation called "deoxygenase" is added (most commonly in canned soft drinks). Another use is in the wrappers of cheese and butter to retard surface oxidation. In dried foods, particularly milk, and in hermetically sealed containers, enclosure of a mixture of deoxygenase, butter and glucose in an oxygen permeable packet results in extension of storage life.

Catalase.—It has been suggested that milk might be sterilized with hydrogen peroxide and excess of oxygen could be removed by added catalase.

Enzymatic Liberation of Flavor Volatiles.—Volatile flavoring and aromatic constituents occur in many foods in nonvolatile combinations called precursors such as alliin in garlic and sulfoxyamino-acid in cabbage. Maceration often permits the enzymes which liberate the volatile compound to come in contact with the precursor. Empirical procedures are used in the perfume and essential oil industries to liberate and recover these volatiles. To illustrate, oil of wintergreen is obtained by chopping the leaves, covering them with water overnight at 120°F., then distilling off the oil. Sweet birch oil is recovered by similar methods, using the bark and branches of the birch. Bitter almond oil is recovered by a comparable process from apricot and bitter almond kernels. In garlic and onions, cutting, chopping and macerating bring the enzyme and precursor into increasingly extensive contact and speed up liberation of the pungent flavoring constituent. Onions and garlic for drying are sliced and dried rapidly with minimum maceration to retain both enzyme and precursor so the flavor can be liberated when the product is moistened for use. It has been demonstrated that cabbage which has been blanched and dehydrated can be made more flavorful by addition of an enzyme from rape seed which will split the purcursor.

TEMPERATURE VS. ENZYME ACTIVITY

While the temperature range for optimum activity of most enzymes is between 70° and 100°F., some enzymes reach or retain high activity at temperatures considerably outside this range. Nucleic acid hydrolyzing enzymes are highly heat resistant and reactive at higher temperatures. Starch liquefying enzymes tend to have higher optimum temperatures. The yield of maltose from starch peaks at 120°F. In brewing, malting with barley malt amylase is carried out at 150° to 170°F. in a single stage or at 100°, 120°, 140° to 145°, and 167°F. in multistages. With bacterial amylases, conversion of starch to lower molecular weight soluble polysaccharides may be carried out at temperatures as high as 180°F. This is particularly desirable in removing starch from sized fabrics, in the clarification of sorghum syrup, and in corn syrup and chocolate syrup manufacture.

Many esterases and certain lipases act best at high temperatures. Chlorophyllase in spinach converts chlorophyll to green chlorophyllin at 167°F. and pH of 6.0. By two-stage blanching, with the second stage at 212°F., the chlorophyllase is activated and the green color of the spinach is stabilized as a rich green instead of a bleached shade. Chlorophyllase does not occur in such green vegetables as English peas and green beans and the activity in spinach varies with variety and harvesting season.

CONTROL OF ENZYMES

Control of undesirable enzyme activity is of equal importance with promotion of desirable changes. Low temperature storage of raw products is the simplest method for retarding natural enzymic processes. Freezing temperatures and idiosyncracies of individual products impose limitations. For example, papayas and bananas cannot be stored at near freezing temperatures without complete disruption of desirable enzyme systems.

Blanching of vegetables is one of the most commonly applied methods for inactivating enzymes for canning and freezing storage. Inadequate blanching of vegetables may lead to darkening beneath the surface in frozen products or in canned products if canning is delayed. Even a short delay in heating crushed tomatoes results in undesirable enzyme action.

Dehydration slows undesirable enzyme action but it is not commercially practical to reduce moisture content of fruits or vegetables sufficiently to completely halt enzyme activity. With the exception of onions and garlic, blanching, sulfuring or other control techniques are applied before drying.

Freezing storage also slows enzyme action, but, at temperatures as low as $-50°F.$, vegetables containing active enzymes undergo deterioration.

Modifying the pH to a range unfavorable for enzyme action is another technique for controlling undesirable enzyme action. Lemon juice and other acid solutions, including sulfurous acid, are used to retard enzymatic darkening.

Some enzymes may be inactivated by oxidation. Proteinases in wheat flour are inactivated by bromate or other strong oxidizing agents. Other enzymes are inactivated by reaction with heavy metals.

Addition of antienzymes or removal of coenzymes may be used to retard undesirable changes. Inactivation of enzymes by ionizing or other radiations has no commercial applications. High dosages necessary to inactivate enzymes cause undesirable side effects.

APPLICATION OF ENZYME TESTS

Tests for enzyme activity are used as indices to the adequacy of heat treatments to destroy spoilage organisms or inactivate other enzymes. Such tests include:

(1)   Rate of thermal inactivation of phosphotase in milk.

(2)   Rate of inactivation of peroxidase or catalase in canning fruit, vegetables and pickles.

(3)   Rate of inactivation of invertase in pasteurizing beer.

Tests of enzyme activity may also be used as an index to microbial contamination. Such tests include:

(1)   Testing with peroxide for catalase as an index to mold contamination on sun-dried fruit.

(2)   Tests for bacterial dehydrogenase by addition of such oxidation-reduction indicators as methylene blue, resazurin and triphenyl dyes as an index to bacterial contamination of milk. Methylene blue and resazurin are colorless when reduced. Tetrazolium is blue in oxidized form, red in reduced form. An interesting application is its use as an index to the viability and germination of seeds which is used in grading barley for barley malt production.

Determination of enzymes including amylase, invertase and proteases in agricultural products is discussed in "Official Methods of

Analysis of the Assoc. of Official Agr. Chemicals," 9th edition, 1960, pp. 230–234. Test papers for detection of glucose are available for rapid assay of residual sugar in wines, pickled olives, etc. Test papers for peroxidase detection have been developed. Applications of enzyme analysis are described by Stetter (1951) and Neilands (1960). Methods for quantitative enzyme assay are described in a monograph edited by Colowick and Kaplan (1955–1957).

BIBLIOGRAPHY

ANDERSON, J. A. (Editor). 1946. Enzymes and their Role in Wheat Technology. Interscience Publishers, New York.

ANON. 1956. Enzymes and Metabolism. Elsevier Publishing Co., New York.

ANON. 1958. Proceedings International Symposium on Enzyme Chemistry. Maruzen, Tokyo.

ANON. 1959. Enzymes. Lectures held at the Conference on Enzymes and their Action, Wageningen, Holland, April 6–9.

ASIMOV, I. 1959. Enzymes and metaphor. J. Chem. Ed. 36, 535–538.

BALLS, A. K. 1934. Importance of enzyme analysis in agricultural chemistry. J. Assoc. Offic. Agr. Chemists 17, 531–534.

BALLS, A. K. 1950. Enzymes and enzymology. In Kirk, R. E., and Othmer, D. F. (Editors). Encyclopedia of Chemical Technology, 5, 735–762. Interscience Encyclopedia, New York.

BARTON, R. R., and LAND, C. E., JR. 1961. How latest enzymes sharpen your process control. Food Eng. 33, No. 9, 85–86, 87.

BECKHORN, E. J. 1960. Production of industrial enzymes. Wallerstein Lab. Commun. 23, No. 82, 201–212.

BOYER, P. D., LARDY, H., and MYRBÄCK, K. 1959–1960. The Enzymes. 2nd Edition. Academic Press, New York.

BURNET, F. M. 1956. Enzyme, Antigen, and Virus: A Study of Macromolecular Pattern in Action. Cambridge Univ. Press, England.

COLOWICK, S. P., and KAPLAN, N. D. (Editors). 1955–1957. Methods in Enzymology. Four Vols. Academic Press, New York.

CROOK, E. M. (Editor). 1958 Metals and Enzyme Activity. Cambridge Univ. Press, England.

CRUESS, W. V. 1958. Commercial Fruit and Vegetable Products. 3rd Edition. McGraw-Hill Book Co., New York.

DEANE, H. W., BARNETT, R. J., and SELIGMAN, A. M. 1960. Histochemical methods for the demonstration of enzymatic activity. Handbuch der Histochemie., 8. Enzymes. Pz. 1. G. Fischer, Stuttgart, Germany.

DEMAIN, A. L., and PHAFF, H. J. 1957. Recent advances in the enzymatic hydrolysis of pectic substances. Wallerstein Lab. Commun. 20, No. 69, 119–140.

DIXON, M. 1949. Multi-enzyme Systems. Cambridge Univ. Press, England.

DIXON, M., and WEBB, E. D. 1964. Enzymes. Academic Press, New York.

DORFMAN, R. I., and GOLDSMITH, E. D. (Editors). 1951. The influence of hormones on enzymes. Ann. N. Y. Acad. Sci. 54, 531–927.

EDSALL, J. T. (Editor). 1951. Enzymes and Enzyme Systems, Their State in Nature. Harvard Univ. Press, Cambridge, Mass.

GREENBERG, D. M., and HARPER, H. A. (Editors). 1960. Enzymes in Health and Disease. Charles C Thomas and Co., Springfield, Ill.

HARROW, B. 1950. One Family: Vitamins, Enzymes, Hormones. Burgess Publishing Co., Minneapolis, Minn.

HEINICKE, R. M., and GORTNER, W. A. 1957. Stem bromelain—a new protease preparation from pineapple plants. Econ. Botany *11*, 225–234.

HOWELL, E. 1946. The Status of Food Enzymes in Digestion and Metabolism. National Enzyme Co., Chicago, Ill.

JACOBS, M. B. (Editor). 1944. Enzymes and Enzymes in Food Processing. *In* The Chemistry and Technology of Food and Food Products. 2nd Edition, *1*, 221–259, *3*, 2346–2364. Interscience Publishers, New York.

JOSLYN, M. A. 1957. Enzymes—in food products manufacture. Western Canner Packer *49*, No. 12, 21–24, 29–32.

JOSLYN, M. A., and PILNIK, W. 1961. Enzymes and Enzyme Activity. Sinclair, W. B. (Editor). *In* The Orange. Its Biochemistry and Physiology. Univ. of California Press, Berkeley, Calif.

LARDLER, K. J. 1954. Introduction to the Chemistry of Enzymes. McGraw-Hill Book Co., New York.

LARDY, H. A. 1949. Respiratory Enzymes. Burgess Publishing Co., Minneapolis, Minn.

LANGLYKKE, A. F., SMYTHE, C. V., and PERLMAN, D. 1952. Enzyme Technology. *In* Sumner, J. B., and Myrbäck, K. (Editors). The Enzymes. Chemistry and Mechanism of Action. Vol. 2, Part 2. Academic Press, New York.

LINDERSTROM-LANG, K. 1952. Proteins and Enzymes. Stanford Univ. Press, Stanford, Calif.

MAKOWER, R. U. 1956. Influence of enzymes on the quality of processed vegetables and fruits. Econ. Botany *10*, 38–41.

MEHLER, A. H. 1957. Introduction to Enzymology. Academic Press, New York.

NEILANDS, J. B. 1960. Enzyme analytical reactions. Org. Analysis *4*, 65–90.

NEILANDS, J. B., and STUMPF, P. K. 1962. Outlines of Enzyme Chemistry. 2nd Edition. John Wiley and Sons, New York.

NORTHROP, J. H., KUNITZ, M., and HERRIOT, R. M. 1948. Crystalline Enzymes. 2nd Edition. Columbia Univ. Press, New York.

REED, G. 1950. Enzyme technology. A process frontier. Chem. Ind. *60*, No. 1, 30–35.

SCHULTZ, H. W. (Editor). 1960. Food Enzymes. Avi Publishing Co., Westport, Conn.

SMYTHE, C. V. 1951. Microbiological production of enzymes and their industrial application. Econ. Botany *5*, 126–144.

SMYTHE, C. V. 1955. Enzymes. *In* Handbook of Food and Agriculture. Blanck, F. C. (Editor). Reinhold Publishing Corp., New York.

SOC. CHEM. IND. 1961. Production and Application of Enzyme Preparations in Food Manufacture. Macmillan Co., New York.

STETTER, H. 1951. Enzymatische Analyse. Verlag Chemi. GMBH, Weinheim, Germany.

SUMNER, J. B., and MYRBÄCK, K. (Editors). 1950–1951. The Enzymes. *1* and *2*. Academic Press, New York.

SUMNER, J. B., and SOMERS, G. F. 1953. Chemistry and Methods of Enzymes. 3rd Edition. Academic Press, New York.

TAUBER, H. 1943. Enzyme Technology. John Wiley and Sons, New York. (Republished in 1949 as The Chemistry and Technology of Enzymes).

UNDERKOFLER, L. A., and FERRACONE, W. J. 1958. Commercial enzymes—potent catalyzers that promote quality. Food Eng. *29*, No. 4, 123–126, 130, 133.

WALLERSTEIN, L. 1939. Enzyme preparations from microorganisms. Ind. Eng. Chem. *31*, 1218–1223.

WHITAKER, J. R. 1961. Proteolytic enzymes. Wallerstein Lab. Commun. *24*, No. 83, 4–20.

CHAPTER 11

I. J. Pflug and
W. B. Esselen

Food Processing by
Heat Sterilization

INTRODUCTION

The canned food industry applies the principle that perishable foods can be preserved through proper application of a heat process. Progress in canning has been continuous since about 1809 when Nicholas Appert discovered that food could be preserved if it were placed in a sealed container and heated. Today's canning plants are efficient industrial operations where a single line may produce more than 600 containers per minute of wholesome nutritious food.

The manufacture of heat processed canned foods can be divided into three parts: (1) operations that prepare raw products for packing in containers; (2) operations involving the application of heat to "sterilize," rendering the product free of spoilage microorganisms and enzymes (in aseptic canning, heating precedes the filling and sealing operation); and (3) distribution of canned food products.

This discussion concentrates on the principles, operations and equipment used to heat-preserve food products, including: (1) principles of heat preservation; (2) vacuum-headspace; (3) equipment and procedures for heating foods in the container; (4) equipment and procedures for heat processing foods before placing in the container.

The symbols and technical terms used throughout this chapter are shown in Table 57.

PRINCIPLES OF HEAT PRESERVATION

Heat preserved canned food products include fruits, vegetables and meats.

A can or jar of "canned" food on a market shelf contains a "sterilized" product that at room temperature will remain unspoiled indefinitely from a microbiological standpoint and, depending on the type of food, will have a marketable quality shelf life from six months to two years. The majority of "canned" foods have been heat-

I. J. PFLUG is Professor, Food Science Department, Michigan State University, East Lansing, Mich.
W. B. ESSELEN is Head of the Department of Food Science and Technology, University of Massachusetts, Amherst, Mass.

TABLE 57

SYMBOLS AND DEFINITIONS

B = The process time in minutes measured from the time the retort reaches processing temperature (RT) until the steam is turned off and cooling begins.

CW = The cooling water temperature.

D_T = Decimal reduction time; time required to reduce the bacterial population by 90% at temperature T (°F.).

F, F_T^z, F_0 = The time in minutes required to destroy a stated number of organisms with a known z at temperature T. For example, F_{250}^{18} represents the time in minutes required to destroy a stated number of organisms at a temperature of 250°F. with a $z = 18$°F. F values are used to compare the sterilizing values of different processes, however, F values cannot be compared unless the z values are the same. When temperature is not specified, e.g., $F = 8.6$, it is understood that the temperature is 250°F.; the subscript 0 as in the term $F_0 = 7.4$ is used to indicate that the $z = 18$°F, and the temperature is 250°F.

f_h = The slope of the straight line portion of the heating curve. The slope is expressed as the number of minutes required for the curve obtained by plotting ($RT - T$) *vs.* t on semilogarithmic paper to traverse one logarithmic cycle [time required for ($RT - T$) to decrease by a factor of 10] (See Figs. 44 and 45).

f_2 = The slope of the second straight line portion of a broken heating curve (see Fig. 45).

f_c = The slope of the straight line cooling curve (see Fig. 46).

IT = The initial temperature of the canned food (the average temperature of the container contents at the time steam is turned on in the retort).

$I'T'$ = The temperature where the straight line portion of the heating curve intersects the corrected zero time line. The corrected zero time line is determined by the retort come-up-time (time from steam-on until retort reaches RT) and is located 0.58 x come-up-time (in min.) after the steam is turned on (see Figs. 44 and 45).

j = Lag factor for heating. $j = (RT - I'T')/(RT - IT)$.

L = The lethal rate in minutes at 250°F. per minute at T.

$$L = 10 \frac{(T - 250)}{z}$$

pH = A scale from 1 to 14 for expressing the degree of acidity or basicity of a solution. The pH is usually determined by measuring the potential of the solution using suitable electrodes or through the use of indicator solutions or papers. Pure distilled water has a pH of 7.0, 0.1N HCl has a pH near 1.0 and a 1.0 normal solution of strong alkali such as NaOH has a pH of near 14.

T = Temperature in °F.

t = Time in minutes.

x_{bh} = Time at which the break in a broken heating curve occurs. The x_{bh} is measured for the corrected zero time (see $I'T'$, and Fig. 47).

z = The slope of the thermal resistance curve. The z value is a measure of the effect of a change in temperature on the resistance of an organism and is the number of °F. required for the thermal resistance curve to traverse one log cycle (the °F. required for the thermal resistance to change by a factor of 10).

---

processed to prevent microbiological and enzymatic spoilage. The terms *sterilized, commercially sterilized* and *pasteurized,* are used to describe heat processes.

When a product is sterilized, it is free of viable microorganisms. Tanner (1944) suggests the term "commercial sterilization" to describe the heat process given canned foods which may contain viable spores of thermophilic organisms and, therefore, are not truly sterile. The terms "sterile" and "sterilized" will be used in this presentation to mean "commercially" sterile which is defined as "that degree of sterility at which all pathogenic and toxin-forming organisms have been destroyed as well as other more resistant types which, if present, could grow in the product and produce spoilage under normal storage conditions."

Frazier (1958) defines pasteurization as, "a heat-treatment that kills part, but not all of the organisms present and usually involves the application of temperatures below 212°F." In pasteurized canned foods, preservation is affected by a combination of a heat treatment and other factors such as a low pH, a high concentration of sugar, a high concentration of salt and storage at temperatures of 32° to 40°F. Canned foods preserved by a pasteurization process as defined are generally speaking, commercially sterile. Foods with a pH of less than 4.5 are often preserved by pasteurization at temperatures of 212°F. or below.

The lethal effect of heat on bacteria is a function of the time and temperature of heating and the bacterial population of the product. To design or evaluate an in-package heat process, it is necessary to know the heating characteristics of the slowest heating portion of the container, normally called the cold zone, the number of spoilage organisms present and the thermal resistance characteristic of the spoilage organisms.

Heat Resistance of Microorganisms.

Rates of Destruction of Bacteria.—The concentration of potential spoilage organisms in a food product is important because bacteria subjected to heat are killed at a rate that is in general proportional to the number of organisms present (Schmidt 1957). This characteristic of bacteria is usually referred to as a logarithmic order of death and means that in a given time interval the same percentage of the bacteriological population will be destroyed regardless of the population present. This fact is important in heat processing because if the number of microorganisms in the food increases, the heating time required to sterilize the product will also be increased. In Fig. 39 is

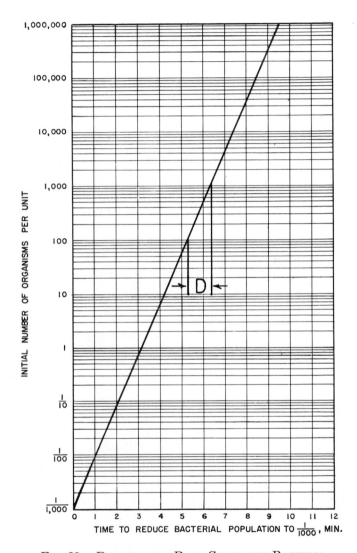

FIG. 39.   DESTRUCTION RATE CURVE FOR BACTERIA

Graph drawn to show that as the initial number of spoilage organisms per container of food increases, the time
required to reduce the population from the initial number
to 1 per 1,000 also increases.

shown a typical thermal destruction rate curve for bacteria; this graph is constructed so the time scale indicates the minutes required to reduce the bacteriological population from any assumed initial concentration to a concentration of one organism per one thousand units. (In thermal resistance studies the D value, which is the time in minutes to destroy 90 per cent of the microorganisms, is used as a measure of thermal resistance since it makes provision for variation in bacterial population.) The fractional survivor values in Fig. 39 are realistic and understandable only when applied to large numbers of units as in the canning industry where there are several thousand cans per retort load and where a single production line produces thousands of cans per hour. As a further explanation of this theory and Fig. 39, consider 1,000 cans, each containing 10,000 spoilage organisms that are heated so that the bacterial population per container or unit is reduced from 10,000 to 0.001 (7 D units). When the 1,000 cans are taken together as a unit, the initial bacteriological population is 10,000,000 the final population after a 7 D reduction will be "one organism" indicating one surviving organism per 1,000 cans and one spoiled can. The importance of sanitation and good housekeeping can be illustrated by a second calculation. Assume that due to the failure of some sanitation practice the initial number of spores per can in the above example increases from 10,000 to 100,000. The initial number for a 1,000 can unit is 100,000,000; a 7 D reduction leaves a final population of 10; if these are distributed 1 per can the spoilage rate would probably be 10 cans per 1,000.

The heat resistance of food spoilage microorganisms has been studied extensively and thermal resistance data are available for the more resistant organisms in a variety of products: Esty and Meyer (1922), Williams (1929), Townsend *et al.* (1938), Curran (1935), Gillespy (1947), Pflug and Esselen (1954), Reed *et al.* (1951), Schmidt (1955), Sognefest *et al.* (1948). The heat tolerance of microorganisms is greatly influenced by pH or acidity. Food products are divided for heat process design into groups of so-called acid foods, those with pH of less than 4.5; and low acid foods, those with a pH above 4.5. In Tables 58 and 59 are listed foods in the acid and low acid groups together with their pH values.

Low Acid Foods (pH greater than 4.5).—*Clostridium botulinum*, a heat resistant anaerobe, will produce under favorable conditions an extremely potent exotoxin that has a fatality rate in man of about 65 per cent (Dack 1956). This soil born organism is widely distributed in nature and must be assumed to be present on all raw products. The anaerobic conditions inside a hermetic food container are favor-

TABLE 58

CANNED FOODS WITH A pH OF LESS THAN 4.5 (ACID FOODS) AND THEIR pH VALUES

Canned Product	pH Value		
	Ave.	Min.	Max.
Apples	3.4	3.2	3.7
Apple sauce	3.6	3.2	4.2
Apricots	3.9	3.4	4.4
Blackberries	3.5	3.1	4.0
Blueberries	3.4	3.3	3.5
Cherries, black	4.0	3.8	4.2
Cherries, red sour	3.5	3.3	3.8
Cherries, Royal Ann	3.8	3.6	4.0
Cranberry sauce	2.6	2.4	2.8
Grape juice	3.2	2.9	3.7
Grapefruit juice	3.2	2.8	3.4
Lemon juice	2.4	2.3	2.8
Loganberries	2.9	2.7	3.3
Orange juice	3.7	3.5	4.0
Peaches	3.8	3.6	4.0
Pears, Bartlett	4.1	3.6	4.4
Pickles, fresh cucumber	3.9	3.5	4.3
Pickles, sour dill	3.1	2.6	3.5
Pickles, sweet	2.7	2.5	3.0
Pineapple juice	3.5	3.4	3.5
Plums, Green Gage	3.8	3.6	4.0
Plums, Victoria	3.0	2.8	3.1
Prunes, fresh prune plums	3.7	2.5	4.2
Raspberries, black	3.7	3.2	4.1
Raspberries, red	3.1	2.8	3.5
Sauerkraut	3.5	3.4	3.7
Strawberries	3.4	3.0	3.9
Tomatoes	4.3	4.1	4.6
Tomato juice	4.3	4.0	4.4
Tomato purée	4.4	4.2	4.6

able for growth and toxin production; therefore, destruction of the spores of this organism is the *minimum standard* for heat processing foods.

It is generally agreed that growth of *Clostridium botulinum* is inhibited in foods with a pH of less than 4.5 and is a potential health hazard only in foods with a pH above 4.5. Therefore, all low acid foods (pH greater than 4.5) should receive a process that is adequate to destroy *Cl. botulinum*. A thermal death time curve for *Cl. botulinum*, which is the time required to destroy this organism as a function of temperature, is shown in Fig. 40.

In general, canned foods receive a heat treatment that is more severe than that required to destroy *Cl. botulinum* since several other species of microorganisms have a greater heat resistance. PA (putrefactive anaerobe) 3679, a strain resembling *Cl. sporogenes*, is one of the most heat resistant sporeforming mesophiles and is widely used as a test organism in canned food heat processing studies. In Fig. 41 is

TABLE 59

CANNED FOODS WITH A pH GREATER THAN 4.5 (LOW ACID FOODS) AND THEIR pH
VALUES

Canned Product	pH Value		
	Ave.	Min.	Max.
Asparagus, green	5.5	5.4	5.6
Asparagus, white	5.5	5.4	5.7
Beans, baked	5.9	5.6	5.9
Beans, green	5.4	5.2	5.7
Beans, lima	6.2	6.0	6.3
Beans and pork	5.6	5.0	6.0
Beans, wax	5.3	5.2	5.5
Beets	5.4	5.0	5.8
Carrots	5.2	5.0	5.4
Corn, w.g., brine packed	6.3	6.1	6.8
Corn, cream-style	6.1	5.9	6.3
Figs	5.0	5.0	5.0
Mushrooms	5.8	5.8	5.9
Olives, ripe	6.9	5.9	8.0
Peas, Alaska	6.2	6.0	6.3
Peas, sweet wrinkled	6.2	5.9	6.5
Potatoes, sweet	5.2	5.1	5.4
Potatoes, white	5.5	5.4	5.6
Pumpkin	5.1	4.8	5.2
Spinach	5.4	5.1	5.9

shown a thermal resistance curve for PA 3679 in pH 7.0 M/15 phosphate buffer. A thermal resistance curve for *Bacillus stearothermophilus* (FS 1518) an extremely heat resistant thermophilic, facultative anaerobe is also shown in Fig. 41. The data from the curves in Fig. 41 can be converted to thermal death time data by multiplying the D value by the order-of-the-process factor. An order-of-the-process factor of 12 D is used in the commercial heat processing of low acid foods that do not contain preservation levels of salt or other bacteriolabile or bacteriostatic chemicals. (Hicks 1951, 1952; and Gillespy 1951.)

Acid Foods (pH less than 4.5).—A miscellaneous group of microorganisms including nonsporeforming and sporeforming aciduric bacteria, yeasts and molds are responsible for the spoilage of acid food products. In practically all cases these organisms can be controlled by a short heat process at or below 212°F.

The thermal resistance of microorganisms in acid foods is a function of the chemical composition of the product and other factors such as the amount and type of sugar present, pH and type of acid. The effect of organic acids on microorganisms is due to the toxicity of both the hydrogen ion and the undissociated molecule. An example of this effect is the work of Erickson and Fabian (1942) who found that the germicidal value of acid on bacteria was: lactic < acetic < citric, when the weight of acid was used as the criteria (the smallest weight of lactic was required) or acetic > citric > lactic when pH was used as the criteria (the acetic had the highest pH, the lactic the lowest for equal control). Certain spices also may exhibit a slight preservative effect in acid foods (Anderson *et al.* 1953).

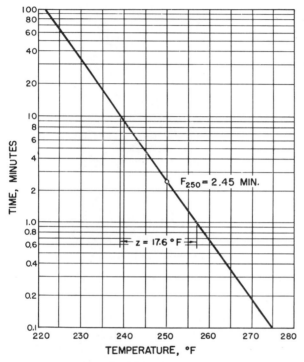

FIG. 40 THERMAL DEATH TIME CURVE FOR *Clostridium botulinum* IN PHOSPHATE BUFFER

Data from Townsend, Esty and Baselt (1938) who applied heating corrections to the data of Esty and Meyer (1922).

The contributory effect of the many components that go into acid foods compounded by the variations in formulation and manufacturing methods practically eliminates the possibility of having accurately determined thermal resistance data. The effect of sugars, acid, salt, total solids, and pH have all been studied either individually or in a two or three component system under laboratory conditions, but these data are not directly used in determining heat processes. Most processes for acid foods have been established by an experimental pack procedure.

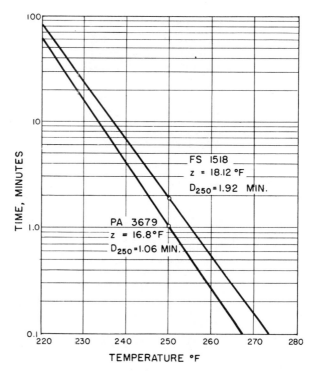

FIG. 41.   THERMAL RESISTANCE CURVES
FOR PA 3679 AND FS 1518

The heat processing requirements to preserve acid foods are very low when compared to the thermal death time of *Cl. botulinum*, PA 3679 or FS 1518.   The pH of the product is important in acid foods since lower pH levels are more toxic to bacteria.   The effect of pH on the process requirements of acid foods is not known precisely, but is demonstrated by comparing the process requirements of food products having different pH.   Fresh cucumber pickles (acetic acid brine, equalized pH 4.1) require an F_{160}^{18} process of about 36 min. whereas tomatoes at pH 4.5 require an F_{200}^{16} process of about 20 min.   Many factors must be considered in determining processes for acid foods. The effect of sugar in a covering liquid, the effect of packing an acid fruit in water, the effect of covering a nonacid vegetable with an acid brine all complicate the heat processing of acid foods.

The variations possible in methods of preservation for acid foods can be illustrated by citing the work of Bell and Etchells (1952) who found equalized sweet pickles could be adequately preserved using only sugar and acetic acid, providing the sum of the per cent sucrose and 20

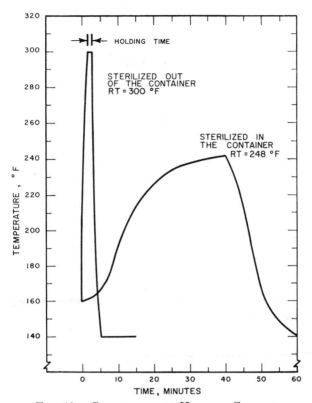

FIG. 42. COMPARISON OF HEATING CURVES

Heating (time-temperature) curve of a food product heated
and sterilized in the container compared with that of a
product continuously heated in a heat exchanger, held and
then cooled in a heat exchanger.

times the per cent acetic acid is equal to 80 (sugar + 20 acid = 80,
both per cent by weight).

Lethal rates.—In Figs. 40 and 41 it can be noted that when the
logarithm of time is plotted as a function of temperature, the resulting
graph is a straight line. It can also be observed from these thermal
death time or thermal resistance graphs that the time to achieve a
given sterilization varies with temperature. When food products are
heated in the container, the rate of temperature rise decreases as the
temperature in the container of food approaches the heating medium
temperature. With slow heating foods, it is possible to sterilize the
product before the product reaches the heating medium temperature
(Fig. 42). Therefore, in evaluating a thermal process, it must be
possible to add the lethal effect or lethality at many temperatures in a

procedure that will give the sum of the individual effects in terms of minutes at some reference temperature; 250 °F. is the standard reference temperature for low acid food processing.   Ball and Olson (1957) show through mathematical analysis how lethalities accumulated at different temperatures are additive.

The equation of the thermal death time curve is:

$$t = F \, 10^{(250 - T)/z}$$

or in logarithmic form:

$$\log t = {}^{(T - 250)/z} + \log F$$

However, the following equations are often used to describe the thermal death time curve:

$$\frac{t}{F} = 10^{(250 - T)/z} \text{ or } \log \frac{t}{F} = \frac{250 - T}{z}$$

The above equation lends itself to the development of the expression for the lethal rate.   The units of t/F are min. at T/min. at 250 °F.; the lethal rate is min. at 250 °F./min. at T or F/t, which is $10^{(T - 250)/z}$. Therefore, the lethal rate is a function of only the slope of the thermal death time curve z and the temperature T.   Values of the lethal rate, $10^{(T - 250)/z}$, for a z of 18 °F. over the range of temperatures used in processing low acid foods are listed in Table 60.

HEATING FOOD PRODUCTS

Introduction

In heating food products it is necessary to distinguish between heating the food in a heat exchanger prior to filling the product in the container and heating the food in the container.

Heating Foods in Heat Exchangers

Steam is usually used as the material to furnish heat to the product. Heat exchangers are normally designed for rapid heating where the product is heated from its initial temperature of 100 ° or 150 °F. to a sterilizing temperature of 250 ° to 300 °F. in a matter of seconds.   The final temperature to which the product is heated is usually sufficiently high that only a few seconds are required to achieve adequate sterilization with a safety factor of between 10 and 100.   After sterilization, the product is rapidly cooled in a second heat exchanger to the filling temperature which may be as low as 50 °F.

TABLE 60

LETHAL RATES[1] (MIN. AT 250°F. PER MINUTE AT T) FOR A z OF 18°F.

T, Temp. °F.	Min. at 250°F. Per Min. at T	T, Temp. °F.	Min. at 250°F. Per Min. at T	T, Temp. °F.	Min. at 250°F. Per Min. at T
214	0.010	232	0.100	250	1.000
215	0.011	233	0.114	251	1.136
216	0.013	234	0.129	252	1.292
217	0.015	235	0.147	253	1.468
218	0.017	236	0.167	254	1.668
219	0.019	237	0.190	255	1.896
220	0.022	238	0.215	256	2.154
221	0.024	239	0.245	257	2.448
222	0.028	240	0.278	258	2.783
223	0.032	241	0.316	259	3.162
224	0.036	242	0.359	260	3.594
225	0.041	243	0.408	261	4.084
226	0.046	244	0.464	262	4.642
227	0.053	245	0.527	263	5.275
228	0.060	246	0.600	264	5.995
229	0.068	247	0.681	265	6.813
230	0.077	248	0.774	266	7.743
231	0.088	249	0.880	267	8.800
				268	10.000

[1] Lethal rate $= 10^{(T-250)/z}$.

In general, foods heated in heat exchangers are sterilized at higher temperatures for correspondingly shorter times and retain more of the original quality than foods sterilized at lower temperatures for longer times. The improved quality of high temperature sterilized food is due primarily to the difference in the temperature coefficient of bacterial destruction compared to the destruction of flavor, color and heat labile nutrients. High temperature, short time sterilization utilizes this difference to produce a sterile product without materially affecting quality. An example of how quality losses during processing can be reduced by raising the processing temperature is illustrated in Fig. 43 where the loss of the heat-labile vitamin thiamin in strained vegetables is used as a representative quality factor (Data from Feliciotti and Esselen, 1957).

All points on the thermal death time curve in Fig. 43 will give a process equivalent to 6.0 min. at 250°F.; at 240°F. more than 20 per cent of the thiamin will be destroyed while at 280°F. less than one per cent will be destroyed. The comparative z values of thiamin and the bacterial thermal death time curve are 48.0° and 18.0°F., respectively. This phenomenon is responsible for the improved quality that results when some products are sterilized in high temperature agitating retorts instead of a conventional still cook.

The heating curve for products heated in heat exchangers using a condensing heating medium such as steam, is generally assumed to be a

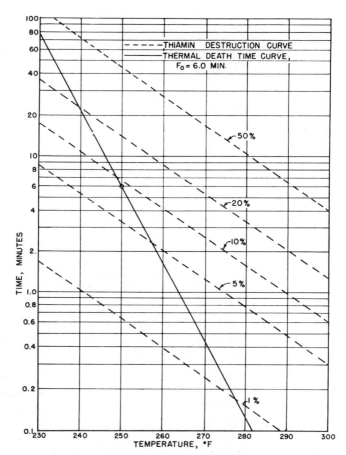

FIG. 43. THE TIME-TEMPERATURE STERILIZATION CURVE
FOR BACTERIA COMPARED WITH A 1, 5, 20 AND 50 PER CENT
DESTRUCTION OF THIAMIN

Data from Feliciotti and Esselen (1957).

straight line when plotted on semilogarithmic paper, according to the
methods described by Ball and Olson (1957). (See Blaisdell and
Zahradnik 1949; Kiratsous *et al.* 1962.)   The lethality accumulated in
the heat exchanger can be calculated if the rate of product flow and
volume capacity of the heat exchanger are known.

The heating curve for products heated in systems having a uniform
heat flux such as the direct injection of culinary steam, or electrical
resistance heated tubes, is a straight line on arithmetic coordinate
paper.

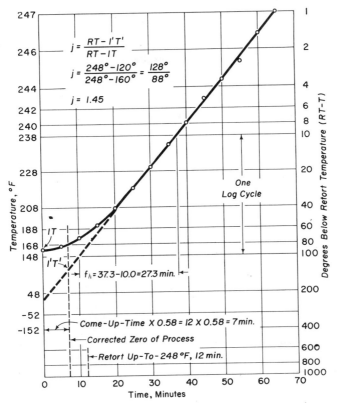

FIG. 44. CONVENTIONAL PLOT OF TIME-TEMPERATURE
HEAT PENETRATION DATA ON SEMILOGARITHMIC PAPER

Since the straight line portion of the curve can be presented
by a single straight line, this is called a simple logarithmic
heating curve.

Heating Foods in Containers

Heating of food products in containers is, in general, a slow and
inefficient process compared with heating in a heat exchanger. However, the problems encountered in manipulating and filling some
types of foods such as asparagus or pickles, and the inability to pump
other types of food products through heat exchangers due to their
physical consistency, are reasons why most foods are sterilized in the
container after packaging.

The rate of heating of food products in containers is a function of the
geometry of the container, physical properties of the food product,
heat transfer characteristics of the heating medium and the heat transfer characteristics of the container.

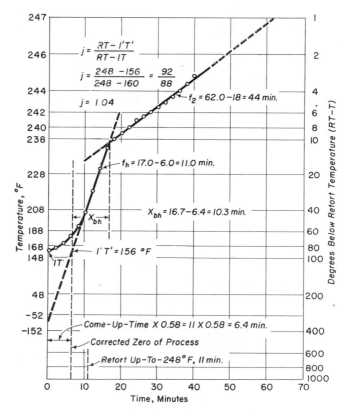

FIG. 45.   CONVENTIONAL PLOT OF TIME-TEMPERATURE
HEAT PENETRATION DATA ON SEMILOGARITHMIC PAPER

Since the initial straight line abruptly changes slopes or
breaks, requiring two straight lines to represent these data,
this is called a broken heating curve.

The nature or consistency of a food product, the presence of particles
of food and the use of starch and sugar in the covering liquids are some
of the factors that determine whether the product heats by conduction
or convection.   The effect of the nature of a food product on the rate
of heating can be illustrated by comparing the 6 min. f_h of peas in brine
with the 56 min. f_h of pumpkin or squash in 307 x 409 cans (the first
digit represents inches, the next two the fraction expressed as sixteenths of an inch with the diameter cited first followed by the height).
The f_h of conduction heating food products varies approximately as the
square of the container diameter or height (whichever is smaller).
The f_h of convection heating food products varies approximately as the
surface to volume ratio.   The external heat transfer characteristics of

the medium used to heat the container can be important, also the material from which the container is fabricated will affect the rate of heat flow.   The heat transfer through tin plate or metal containers is more rapid than that through glass or plastic containers; however, these heating rate differences are often minimized by the nature of the product itself (Pflug and Nicholas 1961).

Under a given set of product conditions, the time required for the food to accumulate the desired lethality can be decreased by (1) increasing the initial temperature of the contents of the container, (2) raising the heating medium temperature and (3) agitating the container during processing.   In the heat processing of food products in containers, the last few minutes of the heating cycle contribute the major part of the lethal or sterilizing effect of the process.   In some cases the last minute or two prior to turning off the steam, and the first two or three minutes of the cooling cycle contribute as much as 90 per cent of the total lethality.

Determining the Rate of Heating of Food Products

The rate of heating of a food product must be known before a thermal process can either be designed or evaluated.   Both glass and metal thermometers have been used in the past (Alstrand and Ecklund 1952) to determine the heating rates of food products in the container, but today most heat penetration tests are made using copper-constantan thermocouples and appropriate temperature indicating or recording potentiometers.   A thorough discussion of the equipment used for measuring temperature using thermocouples and potentiometers is presented by Ecklund (1949).

Plotting Heating and Cooling Data.—The curves in Fig. 42 (p. 267) typify the shape of heating and cooling curves obtained when temperature is plotted as a function of time on rectangular coordinate paper.   The majority of the heating and cooling curves when plotted on semilogarithmic paper can be represented by a straight line and described by two parameters f_h and j.   It is necessary to plot the logarithm of the difference in temperature between the product and the heating medium as a function of time to obtain this straight line type curve.   Typical heating and/or cooling curves of this type are illustrated in Figs. 44, 45 and 46; the straight line portion of these curves is described by the equation:

$$\log (RT - T) = -t/f_h + \log j(RT - IT)$$

The cooling curve must be plotted on a separate sheet but is plotted in the same manner as the heating curve.   The sheet of graph paper

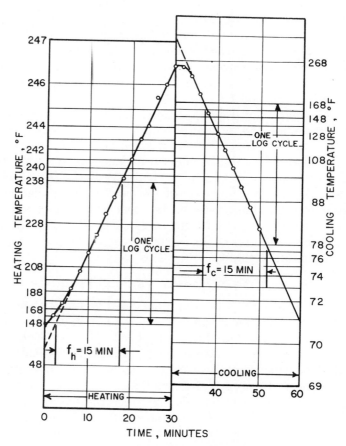

FIG. 46. CONVENTIONAL PLOT OF BOTH
HEATING AND COOLING DATA

The heating data and cooling data cannot be plotted on
the same graphic scale.

used to plot the cooling curve is not rotated 180°, since the bottom
line must represent 1°F. above the cooling water temperature. In
Fig. 46 are shown the curves for the heating and cooling data in
Table 61 (the heating curve scale is based on a heating medium
temperature of 248°F. and the cooling curve scale is based on a cooling
medium temperature of 68°F.). The heating rate f_h and cooling rate
f_c are also illustrated in Fig. 46.

Calculating Heating Rates

If the heating rate, f_h, is known for a food product in one size of container, the heating rate of the same food product in other sizes of con-

tainers processed under similar conditions can be calculated. Calculation is not a substitute for actual measurement of heating rates under processing conditions but is an expedient that can be used in an emergency. The j value is usually assumed invariable with can size changes.

Conduction Heating Products

The heating rate, f_h, of conduction heating products is a function of the size and shape of the container and a property of the food product called thermal diffusivity, f_h = can factor/thermal diffusivity. Thermal diffusivity can be considered a constant for a specific food formulation. Therefore, if the heating rate of a specific formulation f_{hA} in container A is known, the heating rate of the same formulation f_{hB} in container B can be calculated,

$$f_{hA} = \frac{\text{can factor } A}{\text{Thermal diffusivity } A}, \quad f_{hB} = \frac{\text{can factor } B}{\text{Thermal diffusivity } B}.$$

TABLE 61

HEATING AND COOLING DATA WITH CORRESPONDING LETHAL RATES

Time, Min.	Temperature, °F. Heating	Temperature, °F. Cooling	Lethal rate, $z = 18°F.$, Min. at $250°F./$ Min. at T
0	140	. . .	. . .
2	158	. . .	. . .
4	175	. . .	. . .
6	191	. . .	. . .
8	205	. . .	. . .
10	216	. . .	0.013
12	224	. . .	0.036
14	231	. . .	0.088
16	235	. . .	0.147
18	238.5	. . .	0.230
20	241	. . .	0.316
22	243	. . .	0.408
24	244	. . .	0.464
26	245.5	. . .	0.563
28	246	. . .	0.600
30[1]	246.5	. . .	0.640
32	. . .	247	0.681
34	. . .	222	0.028
36	. . .	181	. . .
38	. . .	152	. . .
40	. . .	129	. . .
42	. . .	113	. . .
44	. . .	102	. . .
46	. . .	93	. . .
48	. . .	86	. . .
50	. . .	81	. . .
		Sum of lethal rates =	4.214

[1] Steam off, cooling water on.

TABLE 62

CONDUCTION FACTORS B/A

Given Can Size, A	Desired Can Size, B											
	202 x 214	211 x 400	300 x 407	303 x 406	307 x 306	307 x 400	307 x 409	307 x 510	401 x 411	404 x 414	502 x 510	603 x 700
202 x 214	1.000	1.700	2.127	2.356	2.298	2.554	2.725	2.927	3.595	3.944	5.687	8.502
211 x 400	0.588	1.000	1.251	1.386	1.352	1.502	1.603	1.721	2.114	2.320	3.344	5.000
300 x 407	0.470	0.799	1.000	1.108	1.080	1.201	1.281	1.376	1.690	1.854	2.673	3.996
303 x 406	0.424	0.722	0.903	1.000	0.975	1.084	1.157	1.242	1.526	1.674	2.414	3.608
307 x 306	0.435	0.740	0.926	1.025	1.000	1.111	1.186	1.274	1.564	1.716	2.475	3.699
307 x 400	0.392	0.666	0.833	0.923	0.900	1.000	1.067	1.146	1.407	1.544	2.226	3.328
307 x 409	0.367	0.624	0.781	0.865	0.843	0.937	1.000	1.074	1.319	1.448	2.087	3.120
307 x 510	0.342	0.581	0.727	0.805	0.785	0.873	0.931	1.000	1.228	1.347	1.943	2.905
401 x 411	0.278	0.473	0.592	0.656	0.639	0.711	0.758	0.814	1.000	1.097	1.582	2.365
404 x 414	0.254	0.431	0.539	0.597	0.583	0.648	0.691	0.742	0.911	1.000	1.442	2.156
502 x 510	0.176	0.299	0.374	0.414	0.404	0.449	0.479	0.515	0.632	0.694	1.000	1.495
603 x 700	0.118	0.200	0.250	0.277	0.270	0.300	0.321	0.344	0.423	0.464	0.669	1.000

since for the same formulation, the thermal diffusivity of A = thermal diffusivity of B, and

$$\frac{f_{hA}}{\text{can factor } A} = \frac{f_{hB}}{\text{can factor } B}; \quad f_{hB} = f_{hA} \times \frac{\text{can factor } B}{\text{can factor } A}$$

This calculation can be further simplified by replacing the ratio can factor B/can factor A by a single conduction factor. The heating rate is now calculated as:

$$f_{hB} = f_{hA} \times \text{conduction factor } B/A$$

Can factors and conduction factors for all common sizes are listed in Olson and Stevens (1939). Conduction factors for some of the common can sizes are listed in Table 62. To use Table 62, consider, for example that a food product in a 303 x 406 can has an f_h = 50.0 min. and the f_h in a 603 x 700 can is desired. The conduction factor B/A for a 603 x 700 can when the f_h is known for a 303 x 406 can is 3.608. Using the equation above

$$f_{hB} = f_{hA} \text{ conduction factor } B/A$$

$$f_{hB} = 50.0 \times 3.608 = 180.4 \text{ min.}$$

In Table 63 are listed conduction factors for four sizes of glass jars. These data are the results of actual tests using 5 per cent bentonite as reported by Townsend et al. (1949).

TABLE 63

CONDUCTION FACTORS B/A FOR GLASS JARS[1]

Jar Size A	Jar Size B			
	Baby	Junior	No. 303	No. $2^1/_2$
Baby (202 x 309)	1.000	1.498	2.495	3.608
Junior (208 x 401)	0.669	1.000	1.670	2.411
No. 303 (303 x 411)	0.401	0.599	1.000	1.445
No. $2^1/_2$ (401 x 414)	0.278	0.415	0.692	1.000

[1] Data from tests using 5 per cent bentonite as reported by Townsend et al. 1949.

Convection Heating Food Products

The convection heating process in containers of food is not as fully understood as conduction heating. In general, homogeneous food products with viscosities not greatly different from water have heating rates proportional to the surface/volume of the container. Surface and volume can be incorporated into a can factor (Schultz and Olson 1938) which can be further simplified into a convection factor B/A.

TABLE 64

CONVECTION FACTORS B/A

Given Can Size, A	Desired Can Size, B											
	202 x 214	211 x 400	300 x 407	303 x 406	307 x 306	307 x 400	307 x 409	307 x 510	401 x 411	404 x 414	502 x 510	603 x 700
202 x 214	1.000	1.301	1.453	1.511	1.454	1.550	1.616	1.714	1.839	1.943	2.380	2.840
211 x 400	0.768	1.000	1.116	1.161	1.117	1.190	1.242	1.317	1.413	1.493	1.829	2.182
300 x 407	0.688	0.896	1.000	1.040	1.001	1.066	1.113	1.180	1.266	1.338	1.638	1.935
303 x 406	0.662	0.861	0.961	1.000	0.962	1.025	1.069	1.134	1.217	1.286	1.575	1.879
307 x 306	0.688	0.895	0.999	1.039	1.000	1.065	1.111	1.179	1.265	1.336	1.637	1.953
307 x 400	0.646	0.840	0.938	0.976	0.939	1.000	1.044	1.107	1.188	1.254	1.537	1.834
307 x 409	0.619	0.805	0.903	0.935	0.900	0.958	1.000	1.060	1.138	1.203	1.473	1.757
307 x 510	0.584	0.759	0.848	0.882	0.849	0.904	0.943	1.000	1.073	1.134	1.389	1.657
401 x 411	0.544	0.708	0.790	0.822	0.791	0.842	0.879	0.932	1.000	1.056	1.294	1.544
404 x 414	0.515	0.670	0.748	0.778	0.748	0.797	0.832	0.882	0.947	1.000	1.225	1.462
502 x 510	0.420	0.547	0.610	0.635	0.611	0.651	0.679	0.720	0.773	0.816	1.000	1.193
603 x 700	0.352	0.458	0.512	0.532	0.512	0.545	0.569	0.603	0.648	0.684	0.838	1.000

Convection factors for some of the common can sizes are listed in Table 64.   The new heating rate is calculated using the equation:

$$f_{hB} = f_{hA} \text{ x convection factor } B/A$$

Convection factors for glass jars (based on tests with 1 per cent bentonite (Townsend *et al.* 1949) are listed in Table 65.

TABLE 65

CONVECTION FACTORS B/A FOR GLASS JARS[1]

Jar Size A	Jar Size B			
	Baby	Junior	No. 303	No. $2^1/_2$
Baby (202 x 309)	1.000	1.230	1.760	1.989
Junior (208 x 401)	0.815	1.000	1.430	1.618
No. 303 (303 x 411)	0.568	0.699	1.000	1.130
No. $2^1/_2$ (401 x 414)	0.504	0.619	0.885	1.000

[1] Data from tests using 1 per cent bentonite as reported by Townsend *et al.* 1949.

TABLE 66

FACTORS FOR CALCULATING HEATING RATES[1] IN GLASS JARS WHEN HEATING RATES IN METAL CAN OF CORRESPONDING SIZE ARE KNOWN

Size of Container	Conduction Heating (5 per cent Bentonite)			Convection Heating (1 per cent Bentonite)		
	f_h		Factor, Jar/ Can	f_h		Factor, Jar/ Can
	Jar	Can		Jar	Can	
Baby can (202 x 214) to baby jar (202 x 309)	22.9	23.0	1.00	8.3	4.5	1.845
Junior can (212 x 210) to junior jar (208 x 401)	34.3	29.4	1.17	10.2	4.1	2.485
No. 2 can (307 x 409) to No. 303 jar (303 x 411)	57.1	56.0	1.02	14.6	5.1	2.861
No. $2^1/_2$ can (401 x 411) to No. $2^1/_2$ jar (401 x 414)	82.6	72.4	1.14	16.5	5.8	2.842

[1] Data from Townsend *et al.* 1949.

In Table 66 are listed factors for calculating heating rates in four sizes of glass jars when the heating rates in the four corresponding sizes of cans are known.   The equation below is used to make this conversion:

$$f_{h \text{ jar}} = f_{h \text{ can}} \text{ x factor jar/can}$$

Comparison of Heating Rate Data

Variation in the rate of heating of containers of food in the same lot and from lot to lot is important in both process design and control.

The only satisfactory method of comparing these data is to plot the heating rate and determine the f_h and j; if the curve is broken (Fig. 45) the f_2 and x_{bh} will also have to be determined. A tabulation of these variables will show trends and variations. These data can be treated statistically to determine mean heating rates and to determine the rate of heating of the slowest jar per thousand. In commercial practice, the thermal process design is based on the characteristics of the slowest heating container of the heat penetration test. Only 6 or 8 containers may be tested if the product is known to heat uniformly; however, considerably more containers must be tested if the product is new or if it exhibits peculiar or variable heating characteristics. Consideration must be given to packing procedure and formulation in evaluating heating characteristics.

Process Calculation

Evaluating and Designing Heat Processes for In-Container Sterilization.—The integrated sterilizing value of a process F_0 is the basis of comparison of thermal processes and the starting point in the design of a thermal process. Theoretically the F_0 of a process is determined from bacteriological considerations, however, a great deal of experience and judgment is needed in addition to scientific data and mathematical know-how. In many cases the sterilizing value of a process tends to evolve over many years of experience in processing a product rather than being determined analytically. A few representative F_0 values for low acid canned foods are listed in Table 67.

The sterilizing value of a heat process is obtained by integrating the lethal effect as the product is heated and then cooled. Three procedures have been developed for evaluating heat processes and are known as the general or graphical method (Bigelow *et al.* 1920) the formula method (Ball 1923 and 1928) and the nomogram method (Olson and Stevens 1939). Since all three methods are based on the same principle, only the general method will be discussed in detail.

Two sets of data are necessary to determine the sterilizing value of a process: (1) heating rate data; (2) a lethal rate table or graph. It has already been shown that the lethal rate is equivalent to $10^{\frac{T-250}{z}}$ and the units are min. at 250°F./min. at T (Table 60). The z-value of the thermal death time curve of the principal spoilage organism is used to determine the applicable lethal rate table. Two methods will be described for summing up the lethalities to arrive at the sterilizing value of the process. In the first method, the lethal rate

TABLE 67

CALCULATED STERILIZING VALUES (F_0) FOR SOME CURRENT COMMERCIAL PROCESSES[1]

Product	Can Sizes	Approximate Calculated Sterilizing Value, F_0
Asparagus	All	2 to 4
Green beans, brine packed	No. 2	3.5
Green beans, brine packed	No. 10	6
Chicken, boned	All	6 to 8
Corn, whole kernel, brine packed	No. 2	9
Corn, whole kernel, brine packed	No. 10	15
Cream style corn	No. 2	5 to 6
Cream style corn	No. 10	2.3
Dog food	No. 2	12
Dog food	No. 10	6
Mackerel in brine	301 x 411	2.9 to 3.6
Meat loaf	No. 2	6
Peas, brine packed	No. 2	7
Peas, brine packed	No. 10	11
Sausage, Vienna, in brine	Various	5
Chili con carne	Various	6

[1] Courtesy of American Can Co.

for each heating point is plotted on rectangular coordinate paper and then the area under the curve determined by measuring with a planimeter or counting squares. In Fig. 47 is a lethal rate curve using the heating data in Table 61 and the lethal rate data in Table 60 with a z of 18°F. The area under the curve ADE in Fig. 47 is 16.74 sq. in., and since one square inch is equal to 0.5 min. at 250°F., the area under curve ADE represents a sterilizing value at 8.37 min. at 250°F. The effect of reducing the process time 2 and 4 min., respectively, on the sterilizing value of a process can be obtained by assuming that the cooling rate for the shorter process will be similar and the new lethal rate curve will be parallel to the experimental lethal rate curve on the sterility diagram. This procedure should not be used if the temperature of the new steam-off time is more than 1°F. below the temperature of the experimental steam-off time. Reducing the process in Table 61 (p. 275) and Fig. 47 from 30 min. to 28 and 26 min. have the effect of reducing the sterilizing value of the process from 8.37 to 7.08 and 5.80 min., respectively. In this illustration the temperature actually rises 0.5°F. after the steam is turned off and cooling started; this is a frequent occurrence in products that have not reached the heating medium temperature when cooling begins.

A simplified procedure for determining the sterilizing value of a process when the z-value of the thermal death time curve is known and the heating rate data obtained at equal time intervals was described

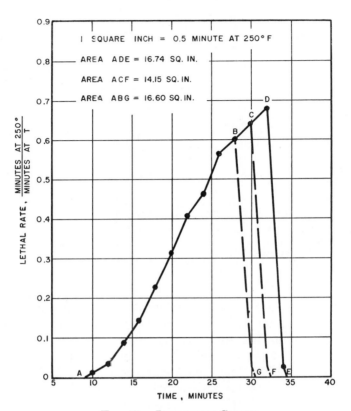

FIG. 47.   LETHALITY CURVE

The area under the curve is the product of time and lethal
rate which, when multiplied by the area factor gives the
sterilizing of F value of the process.

by Patashnik (1953).   This method is ideal for routine analysis of the
sterilizing value of heat processes.   The sterilizing value of a process
is the sum of the product of the lethal rates times the length of time
this rate is effective.

If the time intervals between temperature measurements are made
equal, then the sterilizing value can be obtained by first summing the
lethal rates and then multiplying this value by the common time unit.
The sum of the lethal rates in Table 61 is 4.214 and since the time
interval is 2.0 min. the sterilizing value of the process calculated by
this method is 8.4 min. compared to 8.37 obtained in Fig. 47 using the
graphical method.

Thermal processes may be designed by the inoculated pack or
direct method of process determination.   The inoculated pack method

takes account of the conditions as they exist in the food plant, and, therefore, is an ideal way to verify a calculated process.   The inoculated pack test must be carried out under known, controlled conditions that are reproducible if the results are to be of value.

The test is carried out by preparing inoculated containers of a food product with a heat resistant spoilage organism, processing these containers of food for varying lengths of time, cooling and then incubating the containers at a temperature that is favorable for growth of the spoilage organism used.   PA 3679 (discussed earlier) is commonly used as the test organism.   The inoculum is a spore suspension of known heat resistance standardized to contain 10,000 or 100,000 spores per ml.; 1.0 ml. of the spore suspension is incorporated into each container.   At least five process times should be used and these selected so that almost 100 per cent spoilage will occur at the shortest time with no spoilage at the longest time.   The interval between times should be about five minutes if the process is longer than 30 min. but less than 100 min.   At least 100 containers per time interval should be used in order to have results with sufficient precision for use in process design.   The processing conditions must be accurately known for correct interpretation of the results.   Containers size and shape, fill weight, headspace, initial temperature, vacuum, retort come-up-time, retort temperature, cooling time in the retort and cooling water temperature are a few of the process conditions that are necessary for correct interpretation and use of the results.

Thermal processes for foods in flexible packages may be designed using the same procedures as those presently used in determining processes for foods in metal or glass containers.   The same basic criteria regarding the requirements for commercial sterility of the product involved exist, regardless of the material from which the hermetic container is made.   Processes for food in flexible packages can be calculated by conventional methods from heating characteristics obtained by heat penetration tests and *the presently available sterilizing* (F_0) values known to be adequate for the specific product.   Flexible packages containing low acid foods must be processed in racks that will limit or restrict pouch thickness.   A vertical slot rack with heating medium space on each side of every slot is one method that can be used to ensure that each pouch heats as an individual unit and that the maximum thickness of all pouches are controlled.

The methods outlined above for evaluating and designing heat processes are most useful in giving the processor a method of determining the process actually being received by his product and to develop an awareness of factors that affect the lethal value of a process.

New processes are normally designed by experienced technologists and thoroughly evaluated before being recommended to the processor. Bulletins 26-L and 30-L of the National Canners Association give process times for many canned foods at several initial temperatures, retort temperatures and for several container sizes. Process times for some of the common vegetables in 307 x 409 cans and No. 303 glass jars are given in Table 68. Variations from these standard processing conditions require that a special process be designed. The National Canners Association and the major container manufacturers have technically trained staffs that can assist food packers in designing new processes.

Designing and Evaluating Heat Processes for Sterilization Prior to Canning.—When food products are heated in heat exchangers, the rate of heating is much faster than when the product is heated in the container. In Fig. 42 (p. 267) the heating and cooling curves for a food heated in a heat exchanger are compared with the same order of process where the food is heated in the container. When the product is heated in a heat exchanger, the major part of the lethal effect is accumulated at a constant temperature. Therefore, the sterilizing value is simply the product of the lethal rate at the holding temperature and the length of time it is maintained at this temperature in the holding tube. Both the come-up-time and cooling time contribute additional lethality. However, Townsend *et al*. (1956) indicate that the lethality of the cooling time is usually disregarded in process calculation and used as a safety factor. A first approximation of the lethal effect obtained during heating can be calculated by assuming that 0.42 of the time the product is in the heat exchanger is lethal time at the holding temperature.

TABLE 68

PROCESS TIME FOR VEGETABLES IN 307 x 409 CANS AND NO. 303 GLASS JARS[1]

	Initial Temp., °F.	307 x 409 Cans		No. 303 Jars	
Product		Time at 240°F.	Time at 250°F.	Time at 240°F.	Time at 250°F.
Green beans, whole or cut	70	21	12	25	. . .
Lima bean, succulent	70	40	20	45	. . .
Beets, whole, cut, diced	70	35	23	35	. . .
Carrots, whole, cut	70	35	23	30	. . .
Corn, cream style	160	100	80	105	80
Corn, whole kernel in brine	100	55	30	50	30
Peas in brine	70	36	16	45	25
Peas and carrots	70	45	20	45	. . .
Potatoes, white, small whole	70	35	23	35	25
Pumpkin or squash	160	80	65	80	65

[1] From National Canners Association Bulletin 26-L (8th Edition 1955) and 30-L (2nd Edition, 1955).

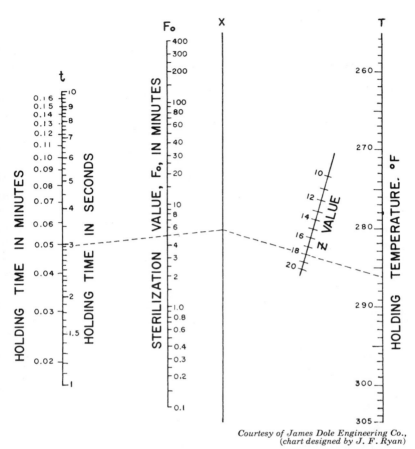

FIG. 48.   ALIGNMENT CHART FOR COMPUTING HIGH-TEMPERATURE
SHORT-TIME STERILIZATION PROCESSES

The nomograph in Fig. 48 can be used to find either the sterilizing value of a process when the holding time is known or if the sterilizing value is known, the holding time can be determined for high-temperature, short-time sterilizing processes.   This chart does not take into account the lethal effect obtained during heating and cooling.

When temperatures of 280° to 300°F. are used to sterilize foods, a process that is adequate from a bacteriological standpoint may be inadequate from an enzyme destruction standpoint.   Enzyme deterioration of high-temperature short-time sterilized foods can be significant if enzyme destruction tests are not used in the quality control program.

SPOILAGE DUE TO RECONTAMINATION OF CANNED FOOD FOLLOWING HEAT PROCESSING

Preservation of canned foods depends upon the fulfillment of two conditions: (1) the destruction by heat of bacteria capable of spoiling the food product; and (2) the prevention of heat processing bacterial contamination of the product through the use of a hermetic container. Serious spoilage of canned foods can result due to the entry of spoilage bacteria into the can of food product during post-processing can handling operations, thereby nullifying the effect of an adequate, well designed heat process.

The tendency in modern canning practice is to produce very high final vacuums in canned foods. Cans that have a high vacuum are susceptible to spoilage due to post-processing contamination if they are abused in the can handling operations following retorting. High speed automatic can handling equipment can produce the necessary impact between the double seams of adjacent cans or between the double seam of the can and the can handling equipment to cause the momentary deflection of the seam that is sufficient to allow spoilage bacteria to enter the can, if the can seams are in a wet condition.

The three main factors in spoilage resulting from post-processing can handling operations are: (1) the condition of the can double seams, (2) the presence of bacterial contamination in cooling waters or on wet can runways, (3) poor operation or adjustment of the filled can handling equipment.

The following recommendations will minimize the possibility of spoilage by post-processing contamination:

(1) Inspect can seams periodically to insure that they are properly formed.

(2) Do not allow cans to drop into crates from closing machine discharge tables.

(3) Do not overfill the retort crates. This will eliminate protruding cans which could be crushed by the crate bales or by crates placed on top of them in the retort.

(4) Prevent sharp impacts between filled crates or against protruding points during transfer on the overhead monorail.

(5) Operate crate dumps smoothly to prevent impact denting.

(6) Chlorinate all cooling waters to a point where there is one part per million chlorine residual at the discharge end of the can cooler. If chlorination renders the water corrosive, use a suitable corrosion inhibitor.

(7)   Periodically inspect the can handling system from the closing machine to the caser.   Where rough handling of the cans is apparent, smooth out the operation to minimize can seam damage.

(8)   Where the cans roll on their sides, install metal half rounds in the runways so that the can double seam will not contact wet or damp guides.

(9)   Where cans pass through felt driers or between belts on lowerators or elevators, cut away the contacting material so that the can double seams ride free of contact.

(10)   Replace all worn and frayed belting, can retarders, cushions, etc., with new nonporous material.

(11)   Thoroughly scrub and sanitize all tracks and belts which come into contact with the can seams at intervals frequent enough to prevent bacterial build-up.

(12)   Run cans through a can drier immediately on leaving the cooling system or allow them to dry in the retort crates before discharge into the can handling unit to lessen the recontamination hazard.

PRESSURE AND HEADSPACE IN CANNED FOODS

The unfilled volume of the hermetic food container, usually referred to as the headspace, is a most important part of the can-contents system.   There are three variables that deal with the headspace: (1) the type and relative gas concentration in the headspace; (2) the volume of the headspace; and (3) the vacuum (or pressure condition) in the headspace.   In packing a food product the specifications will normally establish limits for these three variables.

Headspace Gas

In the majority of canned foods, the headspace gas consists of air and water vapor.   In some special foods, the air present in the headspace and in the food may be pumped out and nitrogen or other inert gas added to replace the air.

Headspace Volume

The volume of the headspace is important and some provision is usually made for positive control.   It is generally assumed that headspace volume will not exceed ten per cent of the total can capacity since 90 per cent is the standard container fill promulgated under the U. S. Food and Drug Act for products with Standards of Identity and is a general requirement by the USDA-AMS.   In Table 69 are listed maximum gross headspaces for several metal container sizes and in Table 70 for four common jar sizes. The volume of the headspace can affect the thermal process, for example, in products sterilized in continuous agitating retorts, the rate of heating of the containers is reduced with an accompanying reduction in the F_0 of the process when the headspace is too small. Cans of food that are filled and sealed cold with no headspace may appear to be swelled and, therefore, unmarketable. If the headspace is too large, the product may appear to be slack-filled. The headspace volume can be controlled by using a filling machine that delivers a measured volume of product into each container or through the use of a headspacing machine. The product is first measured into the container either by volume or weight, then the container is filled to overflowing with the syrup or brine; the filled container then passes under the headspacing machine which displaces an amount of liquid equal to the desired headspace.

TABLE 69

MAXIMUM GROSS HEADSPACE FOR 90 PER CENT FILL OF METAL CONTAINERS

Can Size	Can Name	Maximum Gross Headspace, in.
211 x 400	No. 1 (picnic)	$18/32$
303 x 406	No. 303	$19/32$
307 x 306	No. 2 vacuum	$16/32$
307 x 409	No. 2	$19/32$
401 x 411	No. 2$1/2$	$20/32$
603 x 700	No. 10	$27/32$

TABLE 70

RECOMMENDED HEADSPACE FOR JARS[1]

Jars	Headspace in.
Baby jar	$3/16$
Junior jar	$3/16$
No. 303 jar	$3/8$
No. 2$1/2$ jar	$7/16$

[1] Data from NCA Bulletin 30-L.

The headspace of canned foods in glass containers is a volume measurement usually expressed in milliliters; one method of determining the headspace volume is to use a calibrated displacement gage. The headspace of metal containers is a distance measurement in thirty-seconds of an inch; net headspace is the distance from the can end to the product, gross headspace (GHS) is the distance from the top of the flange or end of the double seam to the product.

The Pressure in the Headspace of Food Containers

"Vacuum" is the term used to denote the pressure conditions inside a hermetic food container and is a measure of the extent to which air has been eliminated from the container. A zero vacuum indicates that the pressure in the headspace is equal to atmospheric pressure; a vacuum of 30 in. of mercury would indicate that all gas had been removed from the container. A vacuum gage measures the difference between atmospheric pressure and the pressure in the container and is usually calibrated to read in inches of mercury.

Many desirable effects have been attributed to vacuum in canned foods since canning processes were first developed; however, today the food canning industry recognizes only three attributes of a vacuum which are:

(1) It maintains the can ends or jar closures in a concave position during normal product life thereby giving a visual index to the condition of the contents.

(2) It reduces the quantity of oxygen in the container.

(3) It prevents permanent distortion of can ends and helps hold the closure on glass-packed products during thermal processing.

For a few food products, the adequacy of the thermal process itself is based on a rather high initial vacuum in the container.

A high vacuum is not a desirable attribute of all food products. In fresh cucumber pickles, for example, a high vacuum may cause the product to lose the desirable "whiteness."

The Measurement of the Vacuum in a Food Container.— Vacuum is usually measured with a Bourdon tube gage calibrated in inches of mercury. The measurement of the vacuum in canned foods is subject to several sources of error. These are:

(1) The accuracy of the vacuum gage.

(2) The amount of distortion of the can end or jar closure, brought about by the pressure necessary to pierce the container or closure.

(3) The temperature of the product.

(4) The volume of air at atmospheric pressure in the gage in relation to the volume of the headspace under reduced pressure.

The accuracy of measurement is directly related to the extent to which the possible errors are evaluated and the vacuum measurements correspondingly corrected. Boyd and Bock (1952) present a thorough discussion of vacuum measurement and give tables that aid in correcting the errors.

A vacuum gage has recently been described by Morpeth (1951) that largely overcomes errors due to air in the gage and variations in headspace volume through the use of a calibrated chamber inside the gage. After taking the initial reading, the passage to the calibrated chamber is opened, giving a change in reading as a function of this change in volume. A nomograph makes possible the rapid determination of the true vacuum from the two gage readings.

Methods of Producing a Vacuum in Food Containers

In present day canning practice there are three general methods of developing a vacuum in the container.

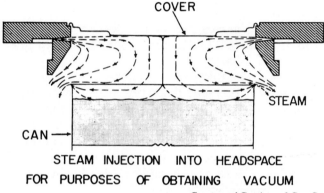

STEAM INJECTION INTO HEADSPACE
FOR PURPOSES OF OBTAINING VACUUM

Courtesy of Continental Can Co.

FIG. 49. STEAM INJECTION INTO HEADSPACE FOR
PURPOSES OF OBTAINING VACUUM

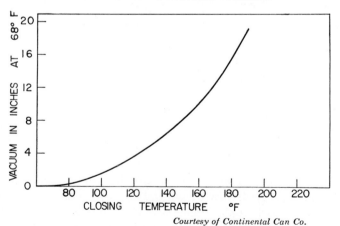

Courtesy of Continental Can Co.

FIG. 50. RELATION OF TEMPERATURE TO VACUUM
IN 307 x 409 CANS OF WATER

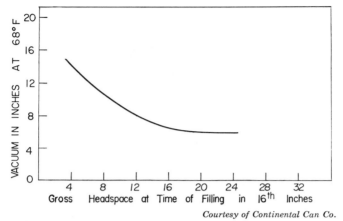

Courtesy of Continental Can Co.

FIG. 51. EFFECT OF HEADSPACE ON 307 x 409 CANS OF
WATER FILLED AT 180°F. AT TIME OF CLOSURE

(1) **Thermal Exhaust or Hot Filling.**—The contents of the container are heated to a temperature of 160° to 180°F., prior to closing the container. Contraction of the contents of the container after sealing produces the vacuum.

(2) **Mechanical.**—A portion of the air in the container headspace is pumped out by a gas pump.

(3) **Steam Displacement of Headspace Air.**—Steam is injected into the headspace in such a way as to sweep out air replacing it with steam. The container is immediately sealed. The vacuum is produced when steam in the headspace condenses (Fig. 49).

The effect of temperature or headspace volume is of secondary importance where the vacuum is produced by a mechanical method; however, the headspace is very important in both the thermal exhaust and steam displacement systems of producing a vacuum. The relationship of the product closing temperature (thermal exhaust system) and the vacuum measured at 68°F. is illustrated in Fig. 50. The vacuum at 68°F. is shown in Fig. 51 as a function of gross headspace for cans of water sealed at 180°F. Increasing the closing temperature or decreasing the headspace increases the vacuum produced by the thermal exhaust system.

The effect of headspace on the vacuum measured at 68°F. for cans of tomato pulp filled at 80°F. and sealed after a steam displacement system was used to sweep the air from the headspace is illustrated in Fig. 52. The effect of closing temperature on the vacuum produced by the steam displacement system is illustrated in Fig. 53. These data indicate that the steam displacement system is not very

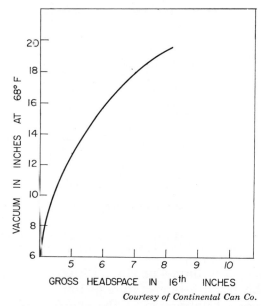

Courtesy of Continental Can Co.

FIG. 52. EFFECT OF HEADSPACE ON VACUUM IN 307 x 409 CANS OF TOMATO PULP FILLED AT 80°F. AND CLOSED AFTER INJECTING STEAM INTO HEADSPACE

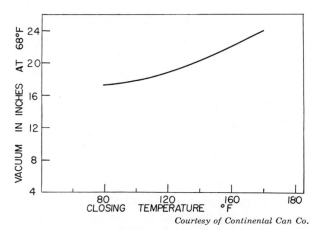

Courtesy of Continental Can Co.

FIG. 53. EFFECT OF CLOSING TEMPERATURE ON VACUUM 307 x 409 CANS OF TOMATO PULP FILLED TO $4/16$ IN. GROSS HEADSPACE AND CLOSED AFTER INJECTING STEAM INTO HEADSPACE

sensitive to the closing temperature but that an increase in headspace will increase the vacuum.

In Table 71 the three systems of producing vacuum are evaluated for five different operational factors. Product factors must also be considered; for some products the high closing temperature with thermal exhaust is deleterious to quality. In other products, it is not possible to use either mechanical or steam displacement methods since large quantities of dissolved and occluded gases are present in the product.

TABLE 71

COMPARISON OF THREE METHODS OF PRODUCING A VACUUM

Factors Evaluated	Thermal Exhaust	Mechanical Vacuum	Steam Displacement
Versatility	Good	Good	Fair
Sanitation	Fair	Good	Good
Space requirements	Large	Moderate	None
Suitability for high vacuums	Fair	Good	Good
Suitability to' high production speeds	Fair	Good	Good

The thermal exhaust system is best adapted to products that heat rapidly such as brine packed foods. It is not well suited for solid packed foods such as mince-meat, fish, pumpkin and other conduction heating foods.

Mechanical vacuum closing machines (for cans) are adapted to the widest variety of canned foods and will generally produce the highest vacuum of the three methods, but cannot be used effectively for products with large amounts of dissolved or occluded air. The use of a vacuum filling or vacuum syruping machine will often solve this problem.

The steam displacement system is usually limited to products that do not contain dissolved or occluded gases at the time of sealing. Adequate, controlled headspace is important for proper operation of vapor displacement systems.

In many operations a combination system of thermal exhaust and steam displacement, or of hot fill and steam displacement, or of vacuum filling followed by steam displacement is the most efficient and practical method for developing the desired vacuum.

Pressure in Canned Foods

Internal pressure is an important criterion during the retorting of canned foods, and is especially critical in sealed glass containers and in

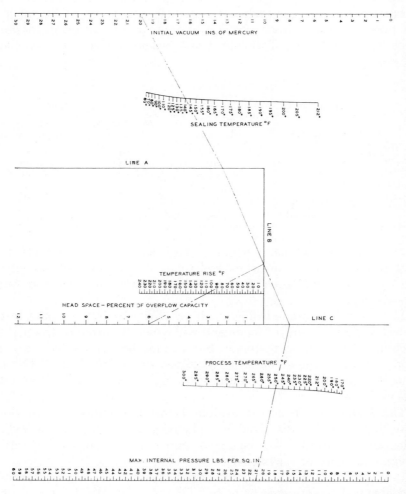

Courtesy of Emhart Manufacturing Co.

FIG. 54.   ALIGNMENT DIAGRAM

Pressure developed by heating sealed glass container.

sealed flexible packages. Excessive pressures in glass containers will tend to loosen the closure; consequently, the internal pressure must be balanced by air pressure to keep the closure in place during the heat processing operation.

Figure 54 shows an alignment diagram that makes possible the estimation of the maximum pressure in containers during heat processing as a function of the initial vacuum, sealing temperature, headspace, process temperature and temperature rise from sealing to processing.

TABLE 72

PRESSURE AT 250°F. OF THE NONCONDENSABLE GASES IN A FLEXIBLE PACKAGE AS A FUNCTION OF INITIAL CONDITIONS OF TOTAL GAS VOLUME AND TEMPERATURE AND VOLUME OF GAS SPACE AVAILABLE IN POUCH DURING PROCESSING

(Total pressure in package is sum of water vapor pressure and gas pressure)

Ratio: Volume Gas (Air) in Pouch — Volume of Gas Space Available in Pouch During Processing	Initial Air Volume Measured		
	at 100°F.	at 150°F.	at 200°F.
0.01	0.19	0.17	0.16
0.03	0.60	0.51	0.48
0.05	0.93	0.86	0.79
0.07	1.30	1.20	1.11
0.1	1.86	1.71	1.58
0.2	3.73	3.42	3.16
0.4	7.46	6.84	6.33
0.6	11.18	10.27	9.49
0.8	14.91	13.69	12.66
1.0	18.64	17.11	15.82

In flexible packages pressures must be limited during heat processing, and in Table 72 are shown the pressures produced by different pouch conditions. Since a vacuum cannot exist in a flexible package, the important criteria here are the ratios of the amount of space available for space expansion during heat processing, and the volume of air in the package at the time of sealing.

EQUIPMENT AND PROCEDURES FOR HEATING FOODS IN THE CONTAINER

Still-Retort

The nonagitating, noncontinuous retort or autoclave, has been in use for over 75 years as a device for processing low acid foods above the boiling temperature of water. In some canning operations the still-retort has been largely replaced by continuous-agitating retorts.

However, for the sterilization of conduction heating food products, for processing glass packed products and for small companies that cannot justify the cost of an agitating retort system, the still-retort is the primary piece of heat processing equipment. Still-retorts may be either of a horizontal design, with the door in the end, or of a vertical design with the door at the top. A typical vertical retort installation is illustrated in Fig. 55.

Horizontal retorts may be 10 to 20 ft. long, and 42 to 60 in. in diameter. Horizontal retorts normally have rectangular baskets and are loaded by pushing the basket, supported by trucks, into the retort.

Standard vertical retorts are 42 in. in diameter and either 72 or 96 in. high; however special vertical retorts 42 in. in diameter and

Courtesy of The Foxboro Co.

FIG. 55.   CONVENTIONAL VERTICAL STILL RETORT

Retort basket is conveyed by electric hoist controlled by operator's right hand.

140 in. high are in use in some plants.   Processing food in retorts is a batch operation; steel crates three feet in diameter and approximately 24 in. high with perforated or slatted sides and bottoms are used as the containers for moving the cans from the processing line into the retort and from the retort through the cooling system to the finished product line (Fig. 55).   Retort crates are usually handled in a combined system of three-wheeled dollies and an overhead monorail system.   The loading and unloading of retort crates has been mechanized to the point where a crate can be filled in less than a minute with a single man directing the filling operation.   One system for filling retort crates uses a hydraulic unit to elevate the removable bottom until it is level with the top which is also level with the can line.   The cans move onto the bottom steel sheet until it is filled. It is then dropped the distance of one can height plus the thickness of the divider plate and a second layer of cans is allowed to flow onto the plate.   This is continued until the retort crate is filled.   Normally, the crates are wheeled from the end of the filling line to the retort area.   Another method of transferring filled containers to the retort crates is through the use of a magnetic lifter.   In this system the filled containers are accumulated in a circular area that has the same diameter as the retort crate.   When the space has been filled, the head of the transfer machine is moved over the containers, the electrical magnet energized, and the containers moved from this accumulating space into the retort crate.   A divider is placed on top of containers and the operation is repeated.   The retort crates are unloaded by reversing the system.

Retort crates are usually loaded into vertical retorts by overhead steam or electrical hoisting systems although some plants use a special type of mechanical lift truck.   Standard vertical retorts are designed to hold either three or four crates, however, 140-in. retorts will hold five crates.   The approximate capacity of standard three and four crate vertical retorts for several can sizes is given in Table 73.

In modern canning plants, steam produced in remote steam boilers or steam generators is the source of the heat energy required in processing operations.   Steam at a line pressure of 100 to 125 p.s.i. should be available at the retorts for best results.   Steam production, flow and consumption is expressed in terms of boiler horsepower (h.p.); one boiler h.p. is equivalent to 33,479 B.t.u. hr.   According to Bock (1957) the peak heat demand of still batch retorts occurs during venting and for standard (42 in. x 96 in.) vertical retorts, or a horizontal unit of similar volume will vary from 80 to 200 h.p. for steam inlets in the range of 1- to 2-in. pipe size.   This peak demand exists

TABLE 73

CANS PER RETORT CRATE[1]

Number of Cans Per Retort Vertical Retorts—Cans Scrambled			Number of Cans Per Retort Vertical Retorts—Cans Stacked on End		
Can Size	Approximate No. Cans per Retort 3-Crate	Approximate No. Cans per Retort 4-Crate	Can Size	Approximate No. Cans per Retort 3-Crate	Approximate No. Cans per Retort 4-Crate
12 oz. oblong	1,120	1,500	211 x 109	6,250	8,330
202 x 214	3,000	4,000	200	4,310	5,750
211 x 109	4,700	6,200	212	3,360	4,480
200	3,200	4,300	300	2,880	3,840
212	2,500	3,300	400–414	1,920	2,560
300	2,150	2,900	600	1,440	1,920
400	1,500	1,950	300 x 108	4,470	5,970
414	1,450	1,900	206	2,720	3,630
600	1,080	1,400	308	1,710	2,280
300 x 108	3,300	4,500	400–414	1,370	1,820
206	2,000	2,700	509	1,030	1,370
400–411	1,050	1,400	303 x 406	1,200	1,600
509	760	1,000	509	910	1,210
303 x 406	975	1,300	307 x 203	2,590	3,450
509	680	900	306	1,440	1,920
307 x 203	1,980	2,590	400–409	1,150	1,330
306	1,080	1,440	510	860	1,150
400	900	1,200	401 x 411	730	970
409	850	1,140	404 x 307	820	1,100
510	650	850	414	660	880
			700	330	440
			603 x 700 (standard crate)	190 (top crate 3 layers)	240 (top crate 3 layers)
				160 (cans on side)	160 (cans on side)
			603 x 700 (no. 10 crate)	240	320
				160 (cans on side)	160 (cans on side)

[1] Data from Continental Can Co.

for only a relatively short period during each individual retort cycle. After the vent valve is closed and the retort reaches operating temperature, the steam consumption rate decreases rapidly to 3 to 5 h.p. and remains at this rate for the balance of the process. For processes up to 60 min., a total of approximately 300 lbs. of steam or 8.7 boiler h.p./hr. is consumed with half of this amount used during venting.

In Table 74 steam requirements are listed for processing several foods as well as for preparation for processing. Peak and operating demand for steam for several types of processing equipment in ad-

TABLE 74

STEAM REQUIREMENTS FOR PROCESSING VARIOUS PRODUCES[1]

Product	Pounds of Steam Per Case		
	Preparation	Retorting	Total
Asparagus cuts, No. 2's			
Cannery A	16	7.8	23.8
Asparagus cuts, No. 2's			
Cannery B	13	5.1	18.1
Asparagus cuts, No. 10's			
Cannery B	17.2	6.7	23.9
Corn, whole grain in brine, No. 2's	3	6.3	9.3
Corn, cream style, No. 2's	10	6.6	16.6
Peas, No. 2's	8.3	6.5	14.8
Apple slices, No. 10's	. . .	. . .	32
Applesauce, No. 10's	. . .	. . .	20

[1] Data from Bock and Newsome (1954).

TABLE 75

STEAM REQUIREMENTS FOR VARIOUS FOOD PROCESSING UNIT OPERATIONS[1]

Unit Operation	Peak Demand, lbs./hr.	Operating Demand, lbs./hr.	Ave. Lbs. Steam Used per Case
Retort			
1-in. steam inlet	2,500	100–150	6.5
1¹/₄-in. steam inlet	3,500	100–150	6.5
1¹/₂-in. steam inlet	4,500	100–150	6.5
2-in. steam inlet	6,000	100–150	6.5
Continuous pressure cooker	6,000	1,000–1,500	3.5–4.0
Open kettle (212°F.) processing			
60 min.	2,000	100–200	2–5
Blancher, reel	3,000	1,000	5–6
Blancher, tubular	3,000	1,200	5–6
Flash sterilizer T.J.-30 g./min.	950	750	1.8
Open kettle concentration tomato			
purée, 1.045	6,000	5,000	49 (6–10's)
Brine heating, 60° to 200°F.	. . .	. . .	3
Double batch mixer, cream style			
corn	1,800	750	3
Exhaust box, steam, 4 ft. x 20 ft.	500	500	3 (6–10's)

[1] Data from Bock and Newsome (1954).

dition to retorts is listed in Table 75. The rate of steam flow through several sizes of orifice are listed in Table 76.

The steam is fed into the retort through a system of steam spreaders or distributors designed to facilitate removal of air from the retort during venting. When steam is turned on, the void space in the retort is filled with air which must be displaced during the venting operation. All retort thermal processes are based on heating rate data where pure steam or hot water is the heating medium. Since steam-air mixtures have lower heat transfer rates than either steam or water, containers heated in steam-air mixtures will receive

TABLE 76

FLOW OF STEAM (POUNDS PER HOUR) THROUGH AN ORIFICE[1]

Steam Pressure, p.s.i. gage	Size of Orifice						
	$^1/_8$ In., 0.01227 sq. in.	$^3/_{16}$ In., 0.02671 sq. in.	$^1/_4$ In., 0.049 sq. in.	$^3/_8$ In., 0.110 sq. in.	$^1/_2$ In., 0.19635 sq. in.	$^3/_4$ In., 0.4418 sq. in.	1 In., 0.7854 sq. in.
5	7	20	58	80	145	315	580
10	10	30	52	120	216	480	850
20	14	40	76	175	316	690	1,230
30	20	50	100	215	384	840	1,510
40	26	60	125	260	450	980	1,780
50	33	70	150	300	520	1,125	2,050
60	38	85	175	345	590	1,270	2,330
70	44	95	200	390	660	1,415	2,600
80	50	105	225	430	730	1,560	2,880
90	56	115	250	475	800	1,700	3,170
100	61	130	275	520	870	1,850	3,450

[1] Data from Bock and Newsome (1954).

a less severe cook than containers heated in pure steam or water. An inadequately vented retort may contain steam-air mixtures or entrapped pockets of air which result in underprocessing and spoilage. Retorts are equipped with bleeders, small 1/8 or 1/4 in. petcocks, that remain open to remove any air that may accumulate during processing.

Listed below are the steps recommended in NCA Bulletin 32-L for a simple steam cook process:

Preparing for Come-Up

(1) Close the door or lid and check to determine if all the lugs are fastened securely.

(2) Check the temperature recorder to insure that it is working properly —clock wound, pen inked and chart firmly in place.

(3) Open the vents and bleeders, and close the drain and overflow (unless the overflow is used for venting).

Come-Up

(1) When the retort is ready for operation, admit steam by gradually opening both the controller and the by-pass lines.

(2) When the correct venting temperature has been reached and the specified time has elapsed, close the vents. Never vent less than recommended. Do not depend on agreement between mercury thermometer and pressure gage readings as a criterion for complete air elimination, because this is not necessarily a true indication of the desired condition. If the pressure gage is up but the temperature is low, it means there is still air in the retort and venting should be continued until agreement is reached.

(3) Gradually close the by-pass just before the processing temperature is reached. This will prevent a sudden drop in temperature which often occurs when the by-pass is closed too rapidly.

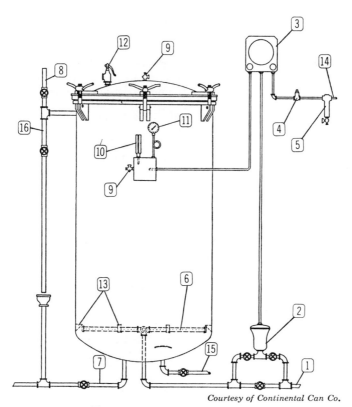

Courtesy of Continental Can Co.

FIG. 56. SIMPLE PROCESSING

(1) Steam, (2) regulating valve, (3) controller, (4) reducing valve, air, (5) air filter, (6) steam distributor, (7) drain, (8) vent, (9) bleeders, (10) indicating thermometer, (11) pressure gauge, (12) pop safety valve, (13) basket supports, (14) air for controller, (15) water, (16) overflow, ⊗ manual valves.

(4) When the retort has reached the processing temperature desired, check the temperature indicated on the mercury and recording thermometers. It is not serious if the chart indicates a temperature slightly lower than the mercury thermometer, but it must never be higher. When the temperature is correct, start timing the process. Use an accurate clock for this purpose, not a wrist watch or the recorder chart.

(5) At the start of the process, enter on the production record the time, the mercury thermometer reading, the pressure, and the temperature indicated by the recording thermometer.

(6) Keep a record of the come-up time to make certain it has been long enough to allow sufficient venting.

(7) With some vacuum packed products, it may be necessary to heat the cans sufficiently to dissipate the internal vacuum before the pressure in

the retort is permitted to become greater than 2 pounds, otherwise the cans may panel or even collapse.

Processing Period

(1) Maintain the retort temperature about one degree above the recommended processing temperature. This helps to compensate for unavoidable fluctuations.

(2) As the process continues, check the temperature from time to time to make certain it is holding properly.

(3) Leave all bleeders wide open during the entire process.

(4) When the recommended time for the process has elapsed, turn off the steam and immediately start the cool.

The design of the piping and control system for retorts has been standardized and these specifications are available from instrument suppliers, container manufacturers, and the National Canners Association. Figure 56 (p. 301) illustrates the piping and control system for a simple steam cook. Figure 57 illustrates the piping and control system for processing glass packed products in a still-retort.

Still-retorts may be operated manually with very simple instrumentation or automatically with temperature and time cycle controls. The expenditure that can be justified for instrumentation generally must be related to the complexity of the process. Steam cooking of small size metal containers is a rather simple operation and warrants

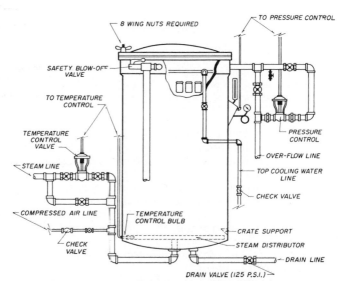

FIG. 57. BASIC REQUIREMENTS FOR VERTICAL
RETORTS USED IN PROCESSING GLASS

only a pressure control, whereas processing glass packed products under water with superimposed air pressure may require a pressure, temperature and time cycle control to achieve the same efficiency. When pressure controls are used, corrections must be made for altitude. Table 77 shows pressure-temperature relationships as a function of altitude.

TABLE 77

GAGE PRESSURE CORRESPONDING TO RETORT TEMPERATURE AT VARIOUS ALTITUDES

Temp., °F.	Sea Level	Feet Above Sea Level							Temp., °C.
		500	1,000	2,000	3,000	4,000	5,000	6,000	
200	....	....	....	....	....	....	....	....	93.3
205	....	....	....	....	....	....	0.5	0.9	96.1
210	....	....	....	0.4	0.9	1.4	1.8	2.3	98.9
212	0.0	0.2	0.5	1.0	1.5	2.0	2.4	2.9	100.0
215	0.9	1.1	1.4	1.9	2.4	2.9	3.3	3.8	101.7
220	2.5	2.7	3.0	3.4	3.9	4.4	4.9	5.3	104.4
225	4.2	4.5	4.7	5.2	5.7	6.2	6.6	7.1	107.2
230	6.1	6.3	6.6	7.1	7.6	8.0	8.5	9.0	110.0
235	8.1	8.3	8.6	9.1	9.6	10.0	10.5	11.0	112.8
240	10.3	10.5	10.8	11.3	11.7	12.2	12.7	13.1	115.6
242	11.2	11.4	11.7	12.2	12.7	13.1	13.6	14.1	116.7
245	12.6	12.9	13.1	13.6	14.1	14.6	15.0	15.5	118.3
248	14.1	14.3	14.6	15.1	15.6	16.0	16.5	17.0	120.0
250	15.1	15.4	15.6	16.1	16.6	17.1	17.5	18.0	121.1
252	16.2	16.4	16.7	17.2	17.7	18.1	18.6	19.1	122.2
255	17.8	18.1	18.3	18.8	19.3	19.8	20.2	20.7	123.9
260	20.7	21.0	21.2	21.7	22.2	22.7	23.1	23.6	126.7

In processing medium sized metal cans of food in still-retorts where steam is used as the heating medium and the cans are cooled with water either in the retort or in a cooling canal, it may be necessary to cool the cans under some pressure so that the ends of the cans remain concave during cooling. If the retort is blown down (pressure in the retort reduced to atmospheric pressure) immediately at the end of the heating time, the internal pressure inside large diameter cans may be sufficient to buckle the cans; therefore, it is necessary to maintain a pressure in the retort equal to pressure in the containers during the first few minutes of the cooling period. Steam may be used to maintain the pressure if the cold water is introduced from the bottom of the retort under a layer of hot water; a better solution is to use compressed air.

Products packed in glass containers must be processed under water with superimposed air pressure. The water level must be six inches above the top layer of jars during the entire come-up time, cook and cool; the retort should be equipped with some type of water level indicator or device to warn the operator if the water is below a safe level.   A minimum retort head space of 4 inches should be maintained between the water surface and the top of the retort.   Both steam and air are added at the bottom of the retort and are introduced through a suitable distributing system.   The superimposed air pressure should be controlled automatically so that the total pressure of 28 to 30 lbs. per sq. in. prevents venting or the loss of lids from the glass containers.   This pressure is maintained throughout the process including come-up, cook and cool.   In vertical retorts, the air is added with the steam and serves to create the turbulence necessary for uniform temperature during the come-up and cook.   A mechanical circulating system is used on horizontal retorts.   Glass-packed products are cooled in the retort under water until the temperature of the food product has been reduced below 150°F.   The remainder of the cooling may take place in a cooling canal.   The temperature of canned foods should be below 100°F. when cans are placed in the warehouse.

Flexible packages containing low acid food products must be restrained in a rack during the heat sterilization process.   A rack that supports pouches in the vertical postion in 0.75 in. slots is shown in Fig. 58.   The racks must be designed so there is a space for heat transfer medium between pouches.

Pflug (1963)

FIG. 58.   RACK WITH VERTICAL SLOTS FOR PROCESSING
LOW ACID FOOD IN FLEXIBLE PACKAGES

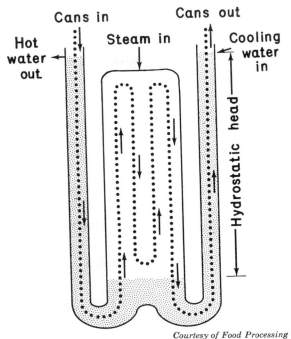

Courtesy of Food Processing

FIG. 59. HYDROSTATIC CAN COOKER AND COOLER

Dots represent cans traveling in the direction of arrows.
A 51.7 ft. head is equivalent to 20.7 p.s.i. gage or 260°F.

Agitating Discontinuous Pressure Sterilizer

This type of retort (Ft. Wayne and Berlin-Chapman Sterilizer)
was developed primarily for sterilizing evaporated milk.   The retort
contains one large, rectangular, revolving, perforated basket into
which the cans are stacked.   The can basket revolves on its own
axis and is driven by an externally located motor.   The rate of real
rotation is from 6 to 12 r.p.m. depending upon the size of the sterilizer.
Large numbers of these retorts are used in evaporated milk factories;
however, some of this equipment is being replaced by continuous
agitating pressure sterilizers.

Continuous Hydrostatic Pressure Cooker-Cooler System

In Fig. 59 is shown a diagram of the hydrostatic pressure cooker-
cooler system.   This system is unique in that it is open so far as
conveying is concerned, a single chain conveyor with can carrying
flights is continuous through the entire system.   A steam pressure of
approximately 10, 15 or 20 p.s.i. necessary for sterilizing at 240°,

250° or 260°F., is balanced by a hydrostatic or water head pressure in the heating and cooling water legs. Net water heads of 23, 34.5 and 46 ft., respectively, are necessary to produce pressures of 10, 15 and 20 p.s.i. The total tower height therefore varies with the temperature design; 40 ft. for 240°F., 50.5 ft. for 250°F., and 61 ft. for 260°F. A minimum amount of floor space is required; a unit with a capacity of over 1,000 cans per minute occupies only an area 13 × 26.5 ft.

Hydrostatic type cookers are usually designed so that several can sizes can be used without major equipment changes. In principle, the hydrostatic type cooker is the least complicated continuous pressure cooker in use today. However, to make this simple principle into a practical piece of food processing equipment requires considerable mechanical equipment in the way of feeders, unloaders, conveyors and controls.

Continuous Agitating Pressure Sterilizers

The continuous agitating pressure sterilizer system consists of separate units or components that are put together to form a sterilizing system. Components that are available are: preheater, pressure cooker, micro-cooler, pressure cooler and atmospheric cooler. In general, the system is tailor-made for a specific processing operation. In systems for sterilizing vacuum packed food products, it is necessary to have a preheater prior to the pressure cooker and a pressure cooler before the atmospheric cooler. The purpose of the preheating section (maintained at a moderate temperature and pressure) is to heat the product to a temperature of 180° to 210°F., so that the internal pressure is approximately one atmosphere (zero gage pressure). A 307 x 306 can, sealed with 20 in. of vacuum, will panel if abruptly subjected to pressures in the range of 20 to 25 lbs. per sq. in. A preheat treatment of only a few minutes at a temperature between 212° and 225°F., will raise the internal pressure a sufficient amount to prevent paneling of the cans when they enter the pressure cooker.

With some food products it is possible through a double valve system, called a Micro-Cooler, to cool the product sufficiently while the cans are in the valve mechanism that the remainder of the cooling cycle can be carried out at atmospheric pressure without danger of buckling the cans. In products where cooling proceeds more slowly, it is necessary to use a pressure cooler. The cooling rate determines the relative size of the pressure cooler and atmospheric cooler.

The preheating, pressure cooking, and cooling sections all operate

in the same manner.   Each section consists of a cylindrical pressure
tank inside of which is located a reel containing a helical track.
The containers of food enter through a valve; they roll, slide and are
carried around and around the unit until they reach the end of the
unit where they are valved out.   The containers receive a rather
unique rotational pattern as they proceed through the units in that
they are carried around the top portion of the cooker, slide a short
distance along the side, and then roll around the lower portion of the
unit.   Fig. 60 shows the general flow of cans through the valve and

Courtesy of Food Machinery and Chemical Corp.

FIG. 60.   CUT-AWAY VIEW OF A CONTINUOUS-
AGITATING PRESSURE STERILIZER

into the processing unit; in Fig. 61 is shown a diagram of the rotational pattern of the containers.   The agitation received by the
containers of food is sufficient to cause products that normally are
considered to heat by conduction, such as cream style corn, to heat
almost as fast as standard convection heating products.

Steam is used as the heating medium in the preheater and in the
pressure cooker.   Cold water is used as the cooling medium.   The
units are equipped with automatic temperature controls in the heating
sections and water level controls in the cooling section.   The heaters
and coolers are connected by conveyors to make a continuous processing system in that the cans come from the closing machines, are
conveyed into the first section, and on through one section after the
other until they have been sterilized and cooled, and are ready to be
conveyed to the warehouse.

The advantages of the continuous agitating pressure sterilizing
systems are: they are continuous, they reduce processing time and
costs, and a uniform cook is obtained.   High operating temperatures,

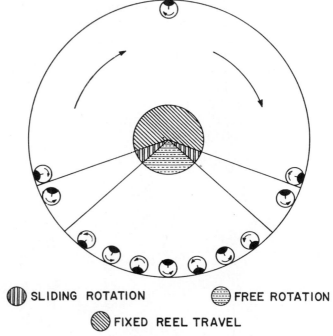

◉ SLIDING ROTATION   ◉ FREE ROTATION

◉ FIXED REEL TRAVEL

Courtesy of Food Machinery and Chemical Corp.

FIG. 61. AGITATION PATTERN OF A
CONTINUOUS AGITATING PRESSURE STERILIZER

260° or 280°F., plus agitation substantially reduces the processing time for convection heating foods. Certain food products that normally heat by conduction such as cream style corn, can be induced to heat by convection in the agitating cooker. This results in a major saving in time and improvement in quality.

Prior to 1950 the continuous cooker was restricted in use primarily to milk, peas in brine, and tomato products; however, since then, with the development of a new type of cream-style corn, it has been widely adapted for the processing of this product as well as brine packed corn, soups and formulated infant foods. A minimum headspace of one-fourth inch at the time of sealing the can is required in order to have a bubble in the can for agitation of the product. Inadequate headspace will greatly reduce the rate of heating and can create a major spoilage problem. The rate of can rotation in the retort must be high to induce adequate agitation. The consistency of the cream style corn processed in continuous agitating cookers must be adjusted and controlled within known limits by additions of starch, free of thermophilic spores.

End-Over-End Discontinuous Agitating Sterilizer

The use of an agitating sterilizer, using end-over-end agitation, makes possible the processing of semiliquid food products in larger can sizes without overcooking.   The rate of heating is increased by rotating the cans of food at a speed that will cause the headspace bubble to cross the center of the container, heating and mixing the product as it proceeds.   This unit is for a batch or semiautomatic operation and is commercially feasible only for large size containers where the increased quality of the shorter processed product and the reduction in numbers of containers warrants the increased labor and equipment cost involved is using this method of sterilization.

Water Bath Pasteurization

For acid food products that can be adequately pasteurized at temperatures of 212°F. or below and nonsterile meat items, the water bath is one of the simplest methods of heating for pasteurization. The water bath may either be a rectangular steel tank or a discarded 42-in. diam. vertical retort, the product is packed in retort crates or in racks and immersed in the bath for pasteurization.   Cooling may be carried out in the same tank used for heating or the containers may be moved from the heating tank to a cooling tank.   Heating and cooling also may be carried out in steps.   Essentially, the same procedure is followed in processing of meats, pickles, apple sauce and other acid food products.

The continuous water bath is an improvement over the batch operation and is in use by both pickle processors and fruit canners for pasteurization where higher production rates are required.   A continuous water bath pasteurizer may be as long as 100 ft. and up to 12 ft. wide.   The depth of the tank may vary from 2 to 3 ft.   A conveyor belt moves through the tank at a selected speed to provide adequate time in the bath to accomplish pasteurization.   The tank is usually divided into sections, each section heated and controlled individually.   In some installations, two conveyors (operated at different speeds) are used to convey food products through the same pasteurizing tank permitting two sizes and packs of products to be pasteurized simultaneously.

The problems of fruit and juice canners are not directly comparable to those of pickle processors since the fruit canner may also cook to soften texture, in addition to preserving, while the pickle processor is attempting to maintain as crisp texture as possible.   In the manufacture of pickle products, the jar to jar variation due to hand packing and variation in size of the product causes wide variation in rates of heating.   It has been found practical to heat pickle products to a predetermined cold-point temperature of 173° to 175°F. depending on the product and on plant conditions; however, the cold point temperature that will give the desired lethality will vary with heating medium temperature, initial temperature, and cooling conditions. Since the majority of the fresh cucumber products are packed in glass containers, a tempering zone usually precedes the rapid cooling zone which allows for the accumulation of considerable lethality, in addition to that accumulated during the heating portion of the process.

In continuous water bath pasteurizers, the jars and cans must proceed down an incline into the tank and up an incline when they come out of the tank.   Since there is considerable hazard in conveying glass containers up or down an incline, plants that pasteurize glass packed products have gone to water spray or steam pasteurizers.

Continuous Steam or Water Spray Pasteurizer

The continuous water spray pasteurizer is extensively used for pasteurizing beer and acid food products.   In this type of unit the bottles or cans are conveyed through the pasteurizer either by a walking beam or by a continuous belt conveyor.   It is common practice to have as many as six different temperature zones or sections through the pasteurizer to obtain maximum efficiency.   The sections are: first preheat, second preheat, pasteurizing zone, precool, cooling and final cooling zone.   Water spray units are designed so the water in the first preheat zone is the water that drains off the jars in the precool zone, and the water that is sprayed in the precool zone is the water that is used in the first preheat zone.   In this way a considerable amount of heat is recovered and reused and also a reduced amount of cooling water is required.   Cooling water is also recirculated.

Glass containers should not be subjected to an excessive "thermal shock"; when heating products in glass containers it is recommended that the thermal shock temperature difference be kept below 70°F. and under no condition exceed 100°F.   When cooling a hot product in a glass container, temperatures are more critical and 50°F. is a desirable maximum, and under no conditions should the temperature change exceed 70°F.

Several sections in both continuous steam and water spray pasteurizers are necessary to heat glass containers efficiently; however, metal containers may be pasteurized in the same equipment.   Through the use of sectionalized equipment, it is possible to have high temperature heating and low temperature cooling of glass containers with a minimum amount of "thermal shock" breakage. The water-spray-type unit has been very successful in the pasteurization of beer and similar products where the operation proceeds under ideal conditions. However, water-spray pasteurizers in pickle plants have been almost totally replaced by the steam heated pasteurizer. The presence of acid and salt in pickle plants causes rapid corrosion in all metal tanks and pipes and leads to early plugging of nozzles. The cooling sections of the steam-heated pickle pasteurizers operate on a principle similar to the cooling section of the total water spray system outlined above. Since they operate at a lower temperature, corrosion is not as serious a problem in the cooling sections as in the heating area.

In the continuous steam-heated pasteurizer the unit is divided into sections usually ten feet in length, each containing its own temperature control device. The sensing element for the temperature controller is located below the product conveying belt, and heat is applied both above and below the conveyor to obtain a uniform temperature. Care must be taken to design the headers with equal pressure drop or resistance so that heat will be supplied uniformly above and below the conveyor belt. The temperatures in steam-heated pasteurizers can fluctuate widely.

The steam pasteurizer is simply a tunnel that must be open at both ends with a conveyor along the bottom. The loading end of a steam pasteurizer is shown in Fig. 62. Cloth baffles are hung between each section but these are not adequate to hold the steam in the pasteurizer against strong air currents. The rate of heat transfer from the steam-air mixture to the food container is not constant in the steam pasteurizer but varies with steam temperature and steam velocity. A partially empty pasteurizer under equilibrium temperature conditions will have a much lower heat transfer rate due to the lower steam velocity, than a unit at the same temperature having a greater steam demand rate. As the pasteurizer temperature is raised, the heat transfer rate is increased. The pasteurizer case should be as tight as practical; however, ports should be located in each section for inspection purposes and to remove product if necessary (Pflug and Blaisdell 1961).

Continuous Agitating Atmospheric Cooker

The continuous agitating atmospheric cooker is widely used in the processing of fruits and fruit juices. This type of cooker is also used extensively for processing tomato products. The can conveying mechanism is identical to that of the continuous agitating pressure cooker, in that the cans travel along a spiral track around and through

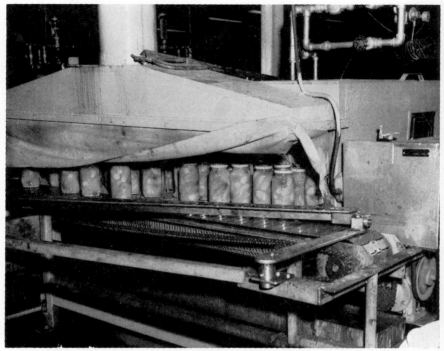

FIG. 62.   LOADING END OF CONTINUOUS STEAM HEATED PASTEURIZER

the unit.   The difference is that the shell is not pressurized, and, therefore, the heating medium is maintained at atmospheric pressure. The present models have a shell that has a rectangular top; however, the bottom is a semicircle to conform to the outside of the rotating unit, thereby reducing the amount of heating medium required. These units are used with both steam at atmospheric pressure, normally near 212°F., and as water cookers.   When they are used as water cookers, they are filled about three-fourths full of water.   In some cases they may be used with half steam and half water.   In the atmospheric cooker a rather simple mechanism instead of the pressurized valve is used to feed the cans into the unit.   The atmospheric cooker is considerably less expensive than the continuous agitating pressure cooker because of the more simple feed mechanisms and the use of an open top tank.   In general, the capacity of one of these units is about the same as a can line of about 150 to 250 cans per minute. The atmospheric cooker is usually equipped with several discharge ports so that the product need not proceed through the entire unit if its thermal requirements are low, but can be discharged after only a few rotations.

EQUIPMENT AND PROCEDURES FOR HEATING FOODS
BEFORE PLACING IN THE CONTAINER

It is much easier to pre-pasteurize or sterilize a food product that can be pumped through a heat exchanger than to heat-sterilize after it has been sealed in a container.   Under a given set of conditions the rate of heating of a product depends upon the distance the heat has to flow (rate of heat flow varies inversely with the square of the thickness) and the degree of agitation or mixing.   In general, "heat exchanger" is the name given a device designed to allow heat to flow from one fluid to another fluid as economically as possible.   In heat exchangers, the distance heat must flow is small, and the rate of fluid flow of both the heating medium and product are as high as economical pumping will permit, since short heat flow distances and high velocities produce the highest heat transfer rates.   The chief limiting factor is that the product must be of such consistency that it can be pumped through the heat exchanger.   Heat exchangers are normally classified according to the geometry of the heating surface but are sometimes classified by other special characteristics.   Common types of heat exchangers are: (1) the tubular heat exchanger (round or flattened tubes are used and the product normally flows through the tubes and the heating medium surrounds the tubes).   A typical tubular heat exchanger is shown in Fig. 63; (2) plate heat exchangers—a series of plates are built up with appropriate openings and gaskets so that the heating medium is on one side of the plate and the product is on the other side (Fig. 64). Plate heat exchangers have a great amount of surface in relation to their physical size and are now available in designs that permit heating to 250°F., using steam as the heating medium, and are of

FIG. 63.   TYPICAL TUBULAR HEAT EXCHANGER

Courtesy of APV Co., Inc.

FIG. 64. HIGH PRESSURE PLATE TYPE HEAT EXCHANGER

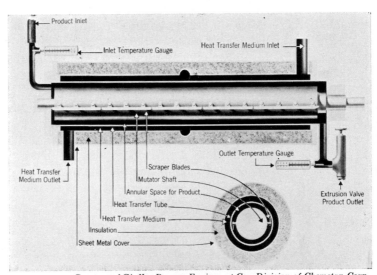

Courtesy of Girdler Process Equipment Co., Division of Chemstan Corp.

FIG. 65. SCRAPED SURFACE TYPE HEAT EXCHANGER

such construction that the food product can be used as either the heating or cooling medium; (3) scraped-surface heat exchangers (Fig. 65) are in reality large diameter tubular heat exchangers in which there is a mechanical scraping device to help agitate the product and keep the product next to the wall continuously scraped away from the wall and mixed with the remainder of the product. Scraped-surface heat exchangers have very large heat transfer coefficients. A comparison of heat transfer rates for heating food products is given in Table 78.

TABLE 78

HEAT TRANSFER COEFFICIENTS FOR FOOD PRODUCTS PROCESSED IN TYPICAL EQUIPMENT

Process	Conductance, h B.t.u./Ft.^{2}hr. °F.	Remarks
Outside film coefficients for single food containers		
Steam	620 to 860	Retorts at 220° to 250°F.[1]
Water flowing in 0.5 in. annulus parallel to container	550 to 2,120	10 to 110 g.p.m. past 300 × 408 cylinders[2]
Agitated waterbath	220 to 300	Heating and cooling 300 × 408 single containers processed in water at 60° to 180°F.[2]
Still water	7 to 24⎫	Cooling various sizes of containers[3]
Cooling in still air	2 ⎬	
Inside film coefficient for food products heated inside 1-in. diam. tubes (tubular type heat exchanger.) Water, mean temperature 175°F.		
2,000 lbs./hr.	630⎫	
4,000 lbs./hr.	1,015⎬	Values calculated[4]
6,000 lbs./hr.	1,320⎭	
Banana purée	38–230[5]	
Inside film coefficient for food products heated inside scraped surface heat exchanger[6]		
Water 400 to 1,000 lbs./hr.	1,600	500 r.p.m.
	2,050	900 r.p.m.
	3,000	1800 r.p.m.
Carrot purée 1,000 lbs./hr.	710	425 r.p.m.
	1,000	550 r.p.m.
Carrot purée 4,000 lbs./hr.	1,000	425 r.p.m.
	1,300	550 r.p.m.

[1] Merrill (1948).
[2] Blaisdell (1963).
[3] Ban (1941).
[4] Al-Arabi (1959).
[5] Charm and Merrill (1959).
[6] Harriott (1958).

Each of these three general classes of heat exchangers contains many types that vary but slightly in construction or operation. The Roswell heater is a type of tubular heat exchanger which uses a rectangular shaped annular area between two cylindrical heat transfer surfaces as the passage for the product at a high velocity and a small temperature difference between heating medium and product to achieve high heat transfer rates and low burn-on.

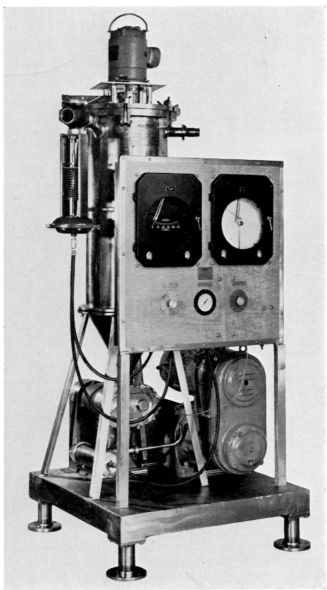

Courtesy of The W. J. Fitzpatrick Co.

FIG. 66.   DIRECT STEAM INJECTION TYPE HEATER

A second method of heating a food product is through the direct injection of live steam into or adjoining the food product, as in the Vacreater or the Fritzpatrick Calefactor. Direct injection heating units have large heating capacity for their physical size. Assuming that the product is at 150°F., and the designed temperature is 250°F., one pound of steam will heat approximately ten pounds of product; however, one pound of water would be added in the process. The advantage of this system is obvious in that the heat energy is injected directly into the product and there is merely an equilibrium to be reached which is the new temperature. The weight of steam that is added, of course, condenses to water and this is normally removed in a flash tank where the heated product, after having been held long enough to achieve sterilization, is flashed to a low pressure that will bring it back to the original temperature through the evaporation of a quantity of water approximately equal to the amount that was added to heat the product. When using direct steam injection heating the processor must take adequate precautions to guard against the addition of impurities contained in the steam. There are heat exchange units now available where purified softened, hot tap water can be converted into steam using the steam from the central boiler as the heat source. In this way the processor has direct control over the material added to the product.

The use of heat exchangers or steam injection for heating food products, has application in several types of canning which, although all do not come under the title of aseptic canning, all of them do qualify in the fact that no heat is added to the product after the product has been put in the container and sealed. In general, these processes are classified as: (1) Presterilized. Food product is heated and sterilized or pasteurized before placing in container; container not sterilized or pasteurized. Product and container sterilized or pasteurized after sealing but prior to cooling. (2) Aseptic canning. Food product heated, sterilized or pasteurized then cooled and aseptically packed in sterile containers.

Presterilized

According to Cruess (1958) tomato juice is normally heated in a closed system and flash sterilized by heating to a temperature of 240° to 250°F., and then cooling to about 210°F. The product is filled in the containers at a temperature of 205°F. or higher, the container sealed and cooled. The same general procedure is recommended for most fruit juices such as apricot, grapefruit, orange, and pineapple which are normally heated to about 190°F. in a plate type heat exchanger, filled into cans or bottles (making sure that the closing temperature is at least 175°F.) sealed, held for a few minutes and then rapidly cooled.

The equipment required in this system of canning is a heat exchanger in addition to the standard filling and sealing equipment. Can tracks can be used to obtain the few minutes of hold in an economical way. For example, a canning line producing 160 303-size cans per minute would require 150 ft. of can track from closing machine to cooler operating at about 50 f.p.m. to obtain a three-minute hold. Since can tracks can be located near the ceiling, the space requirements are small. Cold water spray coolers are usually used to cool the product in metal containers. If glass containers are used, then a holding conveyor is required which is usually part of the cooling system. To minimize thermal shock breakage, the cooler must have a tempering zone where the water temperature is about 130°F. in addition to the final cooling zone where the water temperature is 60° to 80°F. An air blast is used to dry the jars if they are to be labelled immediately. The product should be cooled to 100°F. before warehousing.

Aseptic Packing of Sterile Foods

Milk, vegetable soups and vegetable purees are heat processed by pumping through heat exchangers (either plate-type units, tubular-type units, scrap-surface-type units, or steam-injection-type heaters) until the desired sterilizing temperature is reached which may be as high as 300°F. The product then flows through a holding tube to accumulate the necessary lethality, is rapidly cooled in equipment usually similar to the heating equipment after which the product is filled under aseptic conditions into sterile containers, the container sealed, and warehoused. Since the product has been cooled prior to filling, there is no need to cool after filling and sealing.

The basic requirement in operating an aseptic packing system is that the product be heated quickly to a sterilization temperature, held until sterile, then aseptically cooled, aseptically filled into sterile containers and the containers aseptically sealed. Theoretically one surviving organism per container is all that is necessary for a total loss.

Either of the three types of heat exchangers may be used to transfer heat to the product prior to sterilization and to remove this heat after sterilization. The chief requirement for the equipment is that it be able to heat the product to 280° or 300°F. at the desired rate of production.

At the present time, the Dole system is the only aseptic canning

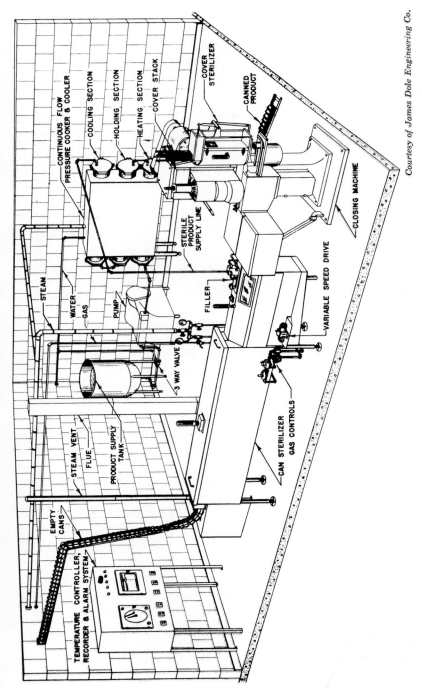

FIG. 67.   PLANT LAYOUT FOR DOLE ASEPTIC CANNING SYSTEM

Courtesy of James Dole Engineering Co.

FIG. 68. DOLE ASEPTIC CANNING UNIT

unit that is available as commercial equipment for consumer size containers. A typical plant layout is shown in Fig. 67, a photograph of the Dole unit is shown in Fig. 68. The container and cover sterilizer, filler and modified sealing machine are furnished together as the Dole system. In the Dole system, superheated steam is used to sterilize the containers and covers, to sterilize the filler and closing machine before start-up and to maintain a sterile atmosphere in the filler and closing machine during operation. Superheated steam is not nearly so efficient as saturated steam as a bactericidal agent since it is dry heat, however, if the temperature is high enough, it will adequately sterilize a clean dry surface. The advantage of superheated steam is that it is at atmospheric pressure, thereby eliminating the necessity of valving the containers into and out of the sterilizing chamber. As a result, the can and cover sterilizing apparatus are simple compared to a system that uses saturated steam under pressure. The low heat transfer rate of superheated steam makes it a good medium to maintain sterile conditions in the filler and closing machine to avoid contamination of a cold food product.

Empty cans are sterilized by conveying them through a tunnel where superheated steam is directed against the bottom of the can from below and to the interior of the can from above. The cans are carried on a cable conveyor, one against the other, and the time interval in passing through the sterilizer varies from 40 sec. to one min. The superheated steam temperature is often as high as 525° to 550°F., and the duct temperature may be as high as 490°F. The temperature of the cans is in the range of 420° to 425°F.; the covers, 410 to 415°F. Since tin starts to melt at 450°F., care must be exercised to insure that the container is not altered due to excessive temperatures.

The cover sterilizer consists of a closed box surrounding two screws that separate the covers and feeds them as needed to the cover feed mechanism of the closing machine. Superheated steam is blown between the covers as they pass down these screws to raise the temperature to a point that is adequate to produce a sterile surface. The cover sterilizing time is usually a little over one minute, but may be as high as 1.5 min. Consequently, the temperature of the cover does not have to be quite as high as that necessary to achieve a sterile can.

The filler used in the Dole system is usually of the slot type. The fill of the container is governed by the length of this slot, the relative rate of liquid flow from the filling nozzle and the speed of the can conveyor system. The cans are conveyed under the filling nozzle by a screw conveyor driven by the seaming machine which is powered through a variable speed drive. This readily allows the operator to adjust the fill. Empty cans entering the filling chamber may be cooled slightly by spraying cool, sterile water against the outside prior to filling. The flanges of the cans overlap each other to minimize product loss as the cans pass under the filling nozzle. After filling, the cans are separated by the screw and timed into the seaming machine. As the can passes into the seamer, a sterile cover is placed on the can and the cover double seamed to the can. The filled can is then discharged and usually is ready for casing, although in some instances, further cooling is necessary.

The atmosphere in the filling and sealing chambers is usually composed of superheated-steam, but flue gas from superheater burners is used in some units to dilute the superheated steam and, thereby, reduce the vacuum in the cans. An extremely high vacuum is produced if all gas in the headspace at the time of sealing is steam.

Standard types of single and multiple seaming head closing machine are modified and used in the Dole aseptic canning system.

The temperature measuring, control and alarm system is a very important part of the aseptic canning unit. Both the product sterilization system and the can and cover sterilization system are equipped with automatic controls to maintain a constant temperature.

In addition, all critical temperatures are monitored in a system that both records the temperature and sounds an alarm if the temperature at a critical point drops below the safe temperature.

The improved quality of aseptically canned food products is achieved by taking advantage of the difference in thermal destruction rates between bacteria and quality factors. Therefore, the advantage of the method lies not in the fact that aseptic canning *per se* has an advantage, but that high-temperature short-time sterilization has an advantage over low-temperature, in-container sterilization. The aseptic canning system is simply the means for using high-temperature, short-time sterilization.

An important development in the canning industry is the high-short sterilization of food products prior to packaging in bulk quantities. Food products such as tomato pulp and grape pulp, destined to be reprocessed into soups, preserves and condiments, must be preserved from the time the raw product is harvested until they are needed by the soup, preserve or condiment manufacturer. It has been customary to pack products for this market in No. 10 cans or to freeze in 30-lb. tins. Equipment and procedure have recently been developed for aseptically packing a sterile food product in 50-gal. hermetic steel drums. A photograph of this equipment is shown in Fig. 69. The equipment is designed for cyclic operation. Four

Courtesy of Thermovac, Inc.

FIG. 69. ASEPTIC DRUM FILLING AND SEALING SYSTEM

50-gal. drums are sterilized, filled and sealed per cycle. The capacity of the four drums is equivalent to about 270 No. 10 cans and represents a large production rate when measured in tons of product per hour.

Where the processor has facilities for handling and storage of larger hermetic containers, 500-gal. to tank car size, these can be used in an assembled-on-the-job aseptic canning system. The container is first fitted with the necessary sanitary fittings and valves and then tested to be sure it is tight; it is then sterilized using saturated steam. Sterile nitrogen gas is used to flush the steam and condensate from the tank through an appropriate seal, after which the sterile cool food product is admitted. When large containers are used, it is possible to have an economical operation even when sterilization, purging and filling each must be carried out as a separate operation. Savings made by reusable containers and improved quality through high-temperature, short-time sterilization, gives great promise to this procedure.

Acknowledgement—The authors acknowledge the assistance of many individuals and companies in providing material for this chapter. Special thanks go to John Blaisdell of the Food Science Department, Michigan State University, and Henry J. Bock of the Continental Can Co., Chicago, Ill., who reviewed this chapter and made many constructive suggestions.

BIBLIOGRAPHY

AL-ARABI, M. 1959. Study of existing data for heating of air and water in turbulent flow in inside tubes. ASME Paper No. 58-14-298, October.

ALSTRAD, D. V., and BENJAMIN, H. A. 1949. Thermal processing of canned foods in tin containers. V. Effect of retorting procedures on sterilization values in canned foods. Food Research *14*, 253–260.

ALSTRAND, D. V., and ECKLUND, O. F. 1952. Mechanics of heat penetration tests in canned foods. Food Technol. *6*, 185–189.

ANDERSON, E. E., ESSELEN, W. B., JR., and FELLERS, C. R. 1949. Effect of acid, salt, sugar and other food ingredients on thermal resistance of *Bacillus thermoacidurans*. Food Research *14*, 499–510.

ANDERSON, E. E., ESSELEN, W. B., JR., and HANDLEMAN, A. R. 1953. The effect of essential oils on the inhibition and thermal resistance of microorganisms in acid food products. Food Research *18*, 40–47.

BAKER, H. D., RYDER, E. A., and BAKER, N. H. 1953. Temperature Measurement in Engineering. Vol. 1. John Wiley and Sons, New York.

BALL, C. O. 1923. Thermal process time for canned foods. Bull. Natl. Research Council 7.

BALL, C. O. 1928. Mathematical solution of problems on thermal processing of canned foods. Univ. of Calif. Pub. in Public Health 1.

BALL, C. O. 1943. Short time pasteurization of milk. Ind. Eng. Chem. *35*, 71–91.

BALL, C. O. 1947. New technic speeds sterilization of canned corn. Food Inds. *21*, 307–311.

BALL, C. O., and OLSON, F. C. W. 1957. Sterilization in Food Technology. McGraw-Hill Book Co., New York.

BAN, H. 1941. Practical relations concerning cooling of cans. Jap. Soc. Sci. Fish Bull. *10*, 131–134.

BATEN, W. D., and EICHMEYER, A. H. 1958. A comparison of weather conditions at Monroe, East Lansing and South Haven, Mich. 1931–1952. Agr. Expt. Sta., Michigan State Univ., East Lansing, Mich., March.

BAUMGARTNER, J. G. 1946. Canned Foods. An Introduction to Their Microbiology. D. Van Nostrand, New York.

BELL, T. A., and ETCHELLS, J. L., 1952. Sugar and acid tolerance of spoilage yeasts from sweet-cucumber pickles. Food Technol. *6*, 468–472.

BIGELOW, W. D. 1921. The logarithmic nature of thermal death time curves. J. Infectious Diseases *29*, 528–532.

BIGELOW, W. D., BOHART, G. S., RICHARDSON, A. C., and BALL, C. O. 1920. Heat penetration in processing canned foods. Natl. Canners Assoc. Bull. *16-L*.

BLAISDELL, J. L. 1963. Natural convection of liquids in unagitated food containers. Unpublished Ph.D. dissertation, Food Sci. Dept., Michigan State Univ., East Lansing, Mich.

BLAISDELL, J. L., and ZAHRADNIK, J. W. 1959. Longitudinal temperature distribution in a scraped-surface heat exchanger. Food Technol. *13*, 659–662.

BOARD, R. W. 1953. Factors affecting the practical determination of thermal processes, a paper presented to the Third Annual Convention of the Institute of Food Technologists. Australian Regional Section, May.

BOCK, J. H. 1957. Retort installation equipment and operating procedures. Bull. Nov. Continental Can Co., Inc., Chicago, Ill.

BOCK, J. H., and NEWSOME, L. 1954. Steam requirements in canning. Address to Canning Problems Conference of the National Canners Assoc., Atlantic City, N. J., Jan. 24.

BORGES, J. M. 1953. Design and development of a multiaction pressure retort. M. S. dissertation, Horticulture Dept., Purdue Univ., Lafayette, Ind.

BORGES, J. M., and DESROSIER, N. W. 1953. New high temperature short time multiaction pressure retort. Food Eng. *26*, 54, 153–155.

BOYD, J. M., and BOCK, J. H. 1952. Vacuum in canned foods—vs. significance and the measurement. National Canners Assoc. Information Letter *1371*, 41–44.

BRENNER, S., WODICA, V. O., and DUNLOP, S. G. 1948. Effect of high temperature storage on the retention of nutrients in canned foods. Food Technol. *2*, 207–221.

BRODY, A. L., and BEDROSIAN, K. 1961. Effect of room temperature vs. refrigerated storage on quality of canned fruit and vegetable products. Food Technol. *15*, 367–370.

CAMERON, E. J., PILCHER, R. W., and CLIFCORN, L. E. 1949. Nutrient retention during canned food production. Am. J. Public Health, *39*, 756–763.

CHARM, S. E., and MERRILL, E. W. 1959. Heat transfer coefficients in straight tubes for pseudoplastic food materials in streamline flow. Food Research *24*, 319–331.

CLIFCORN, L. E., PETERSON, G. T., BOYD, J. M., and O'NEIL, J. H. 1950. A new principle for agitating in processing canned foods. Bull. *20*. Continental Can Co., Chicago, Ill.

CONLEY, W., KAAP, L., and SCHUHMANN, J. 1951. The application of end-over-end agitation to the heating and cooling of canned food products. Food Technol. *5*, 457–461.

COWELL, N. D., EVANS, H. L., HICKS, E. W., and MELLOR, J. D. Conduction errosion thermocouples used for heat penetration measurements in foods which heat by conduction. Food Technol. *13*, 425–429.

CRUESS, W. V. 1958. Commercial Fruit and Vegetable Products. 4th Edition. McGraw-Hill Book Co., New York.

CURRAN, H. R. 1935. Influence of some environmental factors upon the thermal resistance of bacterial spores. J. Infectious Diseases. 56, 373–380.

DACK, G. M. 1956. Food Poisoning. Univ. of Chicago Press, Chicago, Ill.

DAVIS, E. G., and ELLIOTT, A. G. L. 1958. Estimation of vacuum in unopened containers. Food Technol. 12, 473–478.

ECKLUND, O. F. 1949. Apparatus for measurement of the rate of heat penetration in canned food. Food Technol. 3, 231.

ERICKSON, E. J., and FABIAN, F. W. 1942. Preserving and germicidal actions of various sugars and organic acids on yeast and bacteria. Food Research 7, 68–79.

ESTY, J. R., and MEYER, K. R. 1922. The heat resistance of the spores of B. botulinus (sie.) and allied anaerobes. 11. J. Infectious Diseases 31, 650–663.

EVANS, H. L., and BOARD, P. W. 1954. Studies in canning processes. I. Effect of headspace on heat penetration in products heating by conduction. Food Technol. 8, 258–262.

FAGERSON, I. S., and ESSELEN, W. B., JR. 1950. Heat transfer in commercial glass containers during thermal processing. Food Technol. 4, 411–414.

FELICIOTTI, E., and ESSELEN, W. B., JR. 1957. Thermal destruction rates of thiamine in pureed meats and vegetables. Food Technol. 11, 77–84.

FRAZIER, W. G. 1958. Food Microbiology. McGraw-Hill Book Co., New York.

GILLESPY, T. G. 1947. The heat resistance of the spores of thermophilic bacteria. II. Thermophilic anaerobes. Ann. Rept. Fruit and Veg. Presvn. Sta., 40–54, Camden, England.

GILLESPY, P. G. 1951. Estimation of sterilizing values of processes as applied to canned food. I. Packs heating by conduction. J. Sci. Food Agr. 2, 108–125.

GORESLINE, H. E., LEINEN, N. J., and MRAK, E. M. 1953. Establishing optimum conditions for storage and handling of semi-perishable subsistance items. Office of the Quartermaster General, Washington, D. C.

HARRIOTT, P. 1958. Heat transfer in scraped-surface exchangers. School of Chemical Engineering, Dept. Publ., Cornell Univ., Ithaca, N. Y.

HICKS, E. W. 1951. On the evaluation of canning processes. Food Technol. 5, 134–142.

HICKS, E. W. 1952. Some complications of recent theoretical work on canning processes. Food Technol. 6, 175–178.

KIRATSOUS, A. S., FRANCIS, F. J., and ZAHRADNIK, J. W. 1962. Temperature profiles of thickening agents in high temperature short-time and retort processing. Food Technol. 16, 107–110.

MARTIN, W. M. 1948. Flash process, aseptic fill are used in new canning unit. Food Inds. 20, 832–834.

McCONNELL, J. E. W., FELLERS, C. R., and ESSELEN, W. B., JR. 1946. Effect of storage temperature on processed and dehydrated foods. Glass Packer.

MERRILL, D. G. 1948. Heating rates of foods in glass and other containers. Ind. Eng. Chem. 40, 2263–2269.

MORPETH, J. C. 1951. Food Manufacture. Leonard Hill, Ltd., London.

NATIONAL CANNERS ASSOC. 1955. Processes for low acid canned foods in glass containers. Natl. Canners Assoc. Bull. 30-L.

NATIONAL CANNERS ASSOC. 1959. An information bulletin on retort operation. Natl. Canners Assoc. Bull. 32-L.

NATIONAL CANNERS ASSOC. 1962. Processes for low acid canned foods in metal containers. 9th Edition. Natl. Canners Bull. 26-L.

NELSON, A. I., HU, K. H., and STEINBERG, M. P. 1956. Heat processible food films. Modern Packaging 29, 248–251.

NICHOLAS, R. C., and PFLUG, I. J. 1960. Effects of high temperature storage on the quality of fresh cucumber pickles. Glass Packer 39, No. 4, 35, 38–39, 65.

NICHOLAS, R. C., PFLUG, I. J., and COSTILOW, R. N. 1957. Effects of jar size, liquor, and product to liquor ratio on characteristics of fresh packed pickle products. Food Technol. *11*, 488–490.

OLSON, F. C. W., and STEVENS, H. P. 1939. Thermal processing of canned foods in tin containers. II. Monograms for graphic calculations of thermal processes for non-acid canned foods exhibiting straight line semi-logarithmic heating curves. Food Research *4*, 1–10.

PARCELL, J. 1930. Investigations on retorting glass containers. Canning Age *11*, 475–479.

PATASHNIK, M. 1953. A simplified procedure for thermal process evaluation. Food Technol. *7*, 1–6.

PEEPLES, M. L. 1962. Forced convection heat transfer characteristics of fluid milk products. A review. J. Dairy Sci. *45*, 293–302.

PEEPLES, M. L., GOULD, I. A., JONES, C. D., and HARPER, W. J. 1962. Forced convection heat transfer characteristics of fluid milk products. J. Dairy Sci. *45*, 303–310.

PFLUG, I. J., and ESSELEN, W. B., JR. 1954. Observations on the thermal resistance of putrefactive anaerobe No. 3679 spores in the temperature range 250° to 300°F. Food Research, *19*, 92–97.

PFLUG, I. J. 1963. Sterilization of food in flexible packages. Food Technol. (In press).

PFLUG, I. J., and BLAISDELL, J. L. 1961. The effect of velocity of steam-air mixture on the heating of glass containers. Mich. Agr. Expt. Sta. Quart. Bull. *44*, 235–244.

PFLUG, I. J., and NICHOLAS, R. C. 1961. Heating rates in glass containers as affected by heating medium and product. Mich. Agr. Expt. Sta. Quart. Bull. *44*, 153–165.

RAHN, O. 1945. Injury and death of bacteria by chemical agents. Biodynamica Monographs, Normandy, Mo.

REED, J. M., BOHRER, C. W., and CAMERON, E. J. 1951. Spore destruction rate studies on organisms of significance in the processing of canned foods. Food Research *16*, 383–408.

SCHMIDT, C. F. 1957. Thermal resistance of microorganisms. *In* Antiseptics, Disinfectants, Fungicides, and Chemical and Physical Sterilization. G. F. Reddish, Editor. 2nd Edition. Lea and Febiger, Philadelphia, Pa.

SCHMIDT, C. F., BOCK, J. H., and MOBERG, J. A. 1955. Thermal resistance determination in steam using thermal death time retorts. Food Research *20*, 606–613.

SCHULTZ, O. T., and OLSON, F. C. W. 1938. Thermal processing of canned foods in tin containers. I. Variation of heating rate with can size for products heating by convection. Food Research *3*, 647–753.

SCHULTZ, O. T., and OLSON, F. C. W. 1940. Thermal processing of canned foods in tin containers. III. Recent improvements in the general method of thermal process calculations. A special coordinate paper and methods of converting initial and retort temperatures. Food Research *5*, 339–349.

SILLIKER, J. H., GREENBERG, R. A., and SCHACK, W. R. 1958. Effect of individual curing ingredients on the shelf stability of canned comminuted meats. Food Technol. *12*, 551–554.

SOGNEFEST, P., and BENJAMIN, H. A. 1944. Heating lag in thermal death time cans and tubes. Food Research *9*, 234–236.

SOGNEFEST, P., HAYS, G. L., WHEATON, E., and BENJAMIN, H. A. 1948. Effect of pH on thermal process requirements of canned food. Food Research *13*, 400–416.

STUMBO, C. W. 1948. Bacteriological considerations relating to process evaluation. Food Technol. *2*, 116–122.

STUMBO, C. W. 1949. Further consideration relating to evaluation of thermal processes for foods. Food Technol. *3*, 126–130.

TANNER, F. W. 1944. The Microbiology of Foods. 2nd Edition.. Garrard Press, Champaign, Ill.

TOEPFER, C. T., REYNOLDS, H., GILPIN, G. L., and TAUBE, K. 1946. Home canning processes for low acid foods. U. S. Dept. Agr. Tech. Bull. *930*.

TOWNSEND, C. T., ESTY, J. R., and BASELT, J. C. 1938. Heat resistance studies on spores of putrefactive anaerobes in relation to determination of safe processes for canned foods. Food Research *3*, 323–330.

TOWNSEND, C. T., REED, J. M., McDONNELL, F. E. W., POWERS, J. J., ESSELEN, W. B., JR., SOMERS, I. I., DWYER, J. J., and BALL, C. O. 1949. Comparative heat penetration studies on jars and cans. Food Technol. *3*, 213–218.

TOWNSEND, C. T., SOMERS, I. I., LAMB, F. C., and OLSON, N. A. 1956. A laboratory manual for the canning industry. Natl. Canners Assoc., Washington, D. C.

TRESSLER, D. K., and JOSLYN, M. A. 1954. The Chemistry and Technology of Fruit and Vegetable Juice Production. Avi Publishing Co., Westport, Conn.

VAIL, G. E. 1942. The effect of processing upon nutritive value of foods. J. Am. Dietet. Assoc. *18*, 569–574.

VETTER, J. L., NELSON, A. I., and STEINBERG, M. P. 1957. Direct steam injection for high-temperature short-time sterilization of whole kernel corn. Food Technol. *11*, 271–274.

VON LOESECKE, H. W. 1949. Outlines of Food Technology. Reinhold Publishing Corp., New York.

WILBUR, P. C. 1949. Factors influencing process determination in agitation pressure cookers. Convection Issue, Information Letter, *1219*, Natl. Canners Assoc., Washington, D. C.

WILLIAMS, O. B. 1929. The heat resistance of bacterial spores. J. Infectious Diseases *44*, 421–465.

WILLIAMS, O. B. 1940. Experimental procedure for process determination for canned foods. Proc. Inst. Food Technol. *1940*, 323–327.

SUPPLEMENTAL NOTE ON ASEPTIC CANNING

In the hot-fill techniques described in this chapter, filling and closing are carried out at atmospheric pressure, limiting the process to acid foods which can be adequately sterilized in short periods at or below 212°F.

A system has been developed for filling and sealing containers in a pressurized room held at 18 p.s.i. gage, making it possible to apply high temperature, hot-fill processing to low acid foods (with pH above 4.5). In this system the food may be heated as high as 255°F. in a heat exchanger, filled and sealed in tin or glass containers at this temperature in the pressurized room, then rapidly cooled. Heat damage during in-container cooling is slight compared to heat damage to sensitive foods during in-container heating in large (No. 10) containers. The system has obvious advantages for packing sterilized, non-acid foods in large, hermetically sealed containers.

CHAPTER 12

Samuel A. Goldblith

Radiation Processing of Foods and Drugs

BRIEF HISTORICAL INTRODUCTION

The potentialities of utilizing ionizing energy for the destruction of microorganisms were recognized soon after the discovery of x-rays by Roentgen and radioactivity by Becquerel in 1895 and 1896, respectively.

However, there were but limited studies in this field in the first third of the present century (the most notable researches perhaps being those of Coolidge and Moore (1926) at the General Electric Research Laboratories using cathode rays). The discovery of the fission process and subsequent developments in nuclear energy plus the developments in high energy accelerators during World War II served as stimuli for the intensification of research in this field.

The needs for powerful radiation sources, even for research purposes, become apparent if one considers the relative dosages needed for destruction of microorganisms and the output of the accelerators and isotopic sources available prior to World War II.

Thus, as may be seen in Fig. 70, the dose requirements for radiation preservation exceed those for medical diagnostic purposes and tumor therapy by several orders of magnitude (factors of ten).

In addition, one should bear in mind the fact that accelerators producing x-rays were designed and built by physicists and electrical engineers for radiologists to be used on a noncontinuous basis, and at relatively low power outputs (in contrast with food and drug processing requirements of continuous processing, using high outputs of radiation with a high degree of reliability).

Thus, in 1946, following the above cited developments in radiation sources, research in food and drug preservation increased many-fold.

In 1946, three laboratories in the United States were engaged in this field. In 1950 through Atomic Energy Commission sponsorship and in 1953 through Department of the Army, Quartermaster Corps sponsorship, the number of laboratories and researchers in this field increased many-fold. The field has become international, with research activities in Japan, Israel and in a number of countries in Europe.

SAMUEL A. GOLDBLITH is Professor of Food Science and Executive Officer, Department of Nutrition and Food Science, Massachusetts Institute of Technology, Cambridge, Mass.

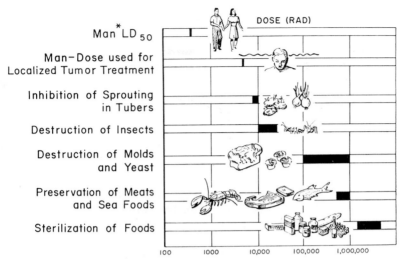

*LD$_{50}$ whole body radiation dose necessary to destroy 50% of people exposed.

FIG. 70. APPROXIMATE DOSAGES OF IONIZING RADIATIONS
REQUIRED FOR SPECIFIC EFFECTS

While this is not primarily a historical narrative, it should be pointed out that there were many persons in the United States in 1950 who felt that certainly within five years, some radiation-preserved food products would be on the commercial market. Others have, ill-advisedly, published articles indicating miraculous futures for this potential method of processing while still others have completely derided it.

As a result, in spite of the fact that a great deal of progress has been made, the over-all unfortunate publicity has, at times, been responsible for at least temporary withdrawal of financial support from the Atomic Energy Commission and the Quartermaster Corps.

At the time of writing of this chapter, this field is in a state of flux. Some $20 million has been spent. Powerful new radiation facilities are being constructed at the Quartermaster Research and Engineering Command at Natick which may have much to do with demonstrating technological feasibility of the process; the new Atomic Energy Commission program on radiation-preserved foods (particularly fish) is just getting under way and requires about twelve months more of intensive research before considered judgments may be rendered. Data relative to obtaining clearance on the first of the irradiation-processed products, bacon, are being prepared for submission to the U. S. Food and Drug Administration.

This state of flux represents progress and the present chapter can only be deemed a progress report on an unfinished and unrefined potential method of food and drug preservation. Obviously, from the last paragraph, a more definitive chapter might be written some twelve months from now, or conversely, a chapter such as this might not be written a year hence. Pasteur wrote a century ago, "It is characteristic of science and progress that they continually open new fields to our vision." It is in this spirit that the present chapter is prepared. Obviously no more than a minute fraction of the several thousand papers in this field can be cited or covered herein. It cannot, therefore, be called a literature review in this field. Instead, this chapter attempts to present important factors relating to radiation preservation of foods insofar as the sources and the products are concerned. It attempts to integrate these into a rational process, presents the problems, outlines the potential solutions and the rationale thereof and attempts to prophesy future prospects.

THE RELATIONSHIP OF REGULATORY AGENCIES

Since the Food Additives Amendment of 1958 (Public Law 85–929) to the Federal Food, Drug and Cosmetic Act of 1938 passed by the Congress of the United States specifically mentions "radiation" in the definition of the term "food additive," it is important to outline, at the outset, the procedural methods which must be followed before a radiation-treated product can be sold in interstate commerce, as these have important bearing not only with respect to radiation sources, but also in the area of products.

Under this law, anyone wishing to utilize radiation as a method of processing or for process control must file a petition with the Secretary of Health, Education and Welfare requesting the issuance of a regulation permitting the use of the method. In addition to various items relating to the nature of the additive, conditions of proposed use, labeling, etc., full reports of investigations with respect to safety of the process must be filed also.

Thus, before radiation preservation of foods can be permitted in the United States, the law with respect to Food Additives must be satisfied. To date (March, 1962) no petition for use of radiation preservation of any foodstuff has been filed with the U. S. Food and Drug Administration. However, a regulation permitting the use of ionizing radiation for inspection of foods, food packages and for controlling food processes has been issued as a result of petitions filed by various nuclear firms who manufacture such sources (Federal Register, March 2, 1961). These petitions were based on studies utilizing cobalt-60, cesium-137, strontium-90 and 300 kvp. x-ray sources. Data, demonstrating that radioactivity was not induced and that the wholesomeness of the product was not impaired, were presented with the petition and the regulation was published which permitted the use of radiation from the above cited sources for the above cited purposes with a maximum absorbed dose of 1,000 rad.[1] Thus, a precedent permitting the use of cobalt-60, strontium-90 and cesium-137 sources for bombardment of foods has been established (with respect to lack of induced radioactivity).

UNITS AND TERMS

The definitions and units of ionizing energy which are pertinent hereto are:

Roentgen (r).—That quantity of x- or gamma radiations producing one e.s.u. of charge of either sign per cc. of air under standard conditions of temperature and pressure.

Equivalents: 2.08×10^9 ion pairs/cc. of air (dry); 1.61×10^{12} ion pairs/gm. of air (dry); 5.24×10^7 mev. absorbed/gm. air (dry); 83.8 erg. absorbed/gm. air (dry).

Rad.—Quantity of ionizing radiation which results in the absorption of 100 ergs per gram of irradiated material.

Erg.—A unit of energy expended when a force of one dyne acts through a distance of one centimeter.

$$1 \text{ erg.} = 10^{-7} \text{ joules}$$

Watt.—Unit of power (P).

$$1 \text{ w.} = 10^7 \text{ ergs. per second} = 1 \text{ joule per second}$$

Joule.—Amount of work $(W) = 10^7$ ergs.

$$\frac{P}{(\text{watts})} = \frac{W \text{ (joules)}}{t \text{ (seconds)}}$$

Curie.—That quantity of radioactive isotope which results in 3.700×10^{10} disintegrations per second.

Electron Volts (ev).—Energy acquired by any charged particle carrying unit electronic charge when it falls through a potential difference of one volt (1 ev. $= 1.60207 \times 10^{-12}$ erg.).

Since the electron volt represents such a minute amount of energy, it is customary to calculate in units of million electron volts (mev.), where 10^6 ev. $= 1$ mev.

---

[1] The studies cited herein were done by the writer and associates at the Massachusetts Institute of Technology under U. S. Atomic Energy Commission sponsorship.

TYPES OF RADIATIONS USED FOR PRESERVATION OF FOODS AND DRUGS

Beta Particles.—Negatively charged particles ejected from the nucleii of radioactive atoms during their disintegration process. Identical to electrons with the single exception of origin.

Cathode Rays (or Electrons).—Streams of negatively charged electrons generated by "boiling off" the electrons from a cathode in an evacuated tube and accelerating them down the tube by applying a potential difference between the cathode and the anode.

Gamma Rays.—Short wavelength electromagnetic radiation of high energy emitted from the nucleii of radioactive atoms during their decay process.

X-rays.—Identical with gamma rays except in their origin. X-rays are produced in man-made machines by bombardment of heavy metal targets (at anode) with cathode rays.

Neutrons.—Heavy, electrically neutral, particles produced in immense quantities in nuclear piles.

DEVELOPMENT OF CONVERSION FACTORS

$$1 \text{ rad} = 100 \; \frac{\text{ergs.}}{\text{gm.}}$$

Therefore

$$10^6 \text{ rad} = 10^8 \; \frac{\text{ergs.}}{\text{gm.}} \times 1 \; \frac{\text{joule}}{10^7 \text{ ergs.}} \times 1 \; \frac{\text{w.-sec.}}{\text{joule}}$$

Therefore

$$10^6 \text{ rad} = 10 \; \frac{\text{w.-sec.}}{\text{gm.}}$$

or, expressing it another way, in order to treat 1 gm./sec. of material with a dose of 10^6 rad, 10 w. of radiation power are required. One gm./sec. is equivalent to 3,600 gm./hr. or 7.96 lbs./hr./10 w. Therefore, 1,000 w. or 1 kw. will treat 796 lbs./hr. (assuming 100 per cent efficiency of absorption of radiation), with a dose of 10^6 rad.

Power (in Terms of Accelerators)

(1) Direct Accelerators.—$P(\text{watts}) = E_{(\text{mev.})} \times I(\text{amperes}) \; (\times$ Efficiency of utilization).

(2) Indirect Accelerators.—$P_{\text{watts}} = E_{(\text{mev.})} \times I_{\text{peak}} \times$ Pulse duration $\times$ Pulse repetition rate $\times$ Efficiency of utilization.

Power (in Terms of Isotopes)

$$1 \text{ curie} = 3.7 \times 10^{10} \frac{\text{disintegrations}}{\text{second}} \times \frac{\text{Energy}}{\text{disintegration}}$$

e.g., for cobalt-60, Energy = 2.5 mev./dis.   Therefore

$$1 \text{ curie of cobalt-60} = 3.7 \times 10^{10} \frac{\text{dis.}}{\text{second}} \times \frac{2.5 \text{ mev.}}{\text{dis.}} \times$$

$$\frac{1.602 \times 10^{-6} \text{ erg.}}{\text{mev.}} \times 1 \frac{\text{joule}}{10^{7} \text{ erg.}} \times 1 \frac{\text{w.-sec}}{\text{joule}}$$

Therefore 1 curie (cobalt 60) = 14.8×10^{-3} w.

Therefore in order to obtain 1,000 w. of ionizing power from cobalt-60, one needs 10^{3} w./(14.8×10^{-3} w./curie), or 67,800 curies (assuming 100 per cent efficiency of absorption).

TABLE 79

POWER EQUIVALENTS AND OTHER CHARACTERISTICS OF VARIOUS RADIONUCLIDES

Isotope	Decay Energy mev.	Number of Curies per Kilowatt	Half Life Yrs.	Type of Radiation
Cobalt-60[1]	1.1+, 1.3+	68,000	5.3	γ
Cesium-137	0.67	310,000	33	γ
Strontium-90	2.18	156,000	19.9	β
Promethium-147	0.223	2,330,000	3.6	β

[1] Cobalt-60 produces two gammas in cascade, with a total energy per disintegration of 2.5 mev. per nucleus.   (From Arthur D. Little Inc. 1959.)

RADIATION SOURCES

General

The radiation sources for food and drug preservation may be classified as in Table 80.

TABLE 80

RADIATION SOURCES FOR FOOD AND DRUG PRESERVATION

Isotopic Sources	Machine Sources
Pile-produced isotopes	Direct accelerators
(a) cobalt-60	(a) Van de Graaff
Fission isotopes	(b) Resonant transformer
(a) mixed, e.g., fuel rods	(c) Dynamitron
(b) separated, e.g., strontium-90, cesium-137	Indirect accelerators
	(a) Linear electron accelerator

At the outset, it should be stated that a number of other sources are potentially available but are not considered to any extent herein for the reasons cited below.   These other sources are: (a) nuclear reactors and reactor loops; (*b*) fuel rods; (*c*) fission products gas reactors; (*d*) betatrons and other circular accelerators; and (*e*) x-ray machines.

Reactors and reactor loops produce gamma rays in which there are some neutrons. Considering the Food Additives Amendment of 1958, the extensive shielding required to filter out the neutrons (which can cause induced radioactivity) also reduces the gamma ray intensity to such an extent as to make these radiation sources extremely expensive. Fuel rods contain some delayed neutrons which can also cause some induced radioactivity.

In 1956, as a result of the interest of the Army Quartermaster Corps, a Fission Product Reactor, utilizing as the radiation sources the short half-lived isotopes of xenon and krypton (gases) which are produced as by-products of nuclear fission, has been considered and preliminary designs made. There is uncertainty in the calculated gamma power of the gas system and, as a result, an experimental program would be needed to obtain an accurate figure. To date, this has not been undertaken and, as a result, all the cost data which have been published are based on assumptions as yet unproved experimentally.

Since a gaseous-fission product irradiator is associated with a fluid-fueled reactor, such experimental work may be 5–10 years away even if a decision were made to undertake such experimental work.

The betatron and other indirect (nonlinear) accelerators are capable of high energy levels, but do not produce many electrons and therefore have relatively low electron beam power. Consequently, these are of but little value as radiation sources.

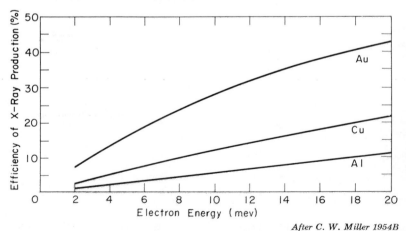

After C. W. Miller 1954B

FIG. 71. THE EFFICIENCY OF X-RAY PRODUCTION FOR VARIOUS TARGET MATERIALS AND ELECTRON ENERGIES

X-rays are indeed of interest, but the conversion of the primary electron beam to x-rays is inefficient and consequently is not considered herein, other than to point out that the conversion efficiency of cathode rays to x-rays increases with the atomic number of the target and with the electron beam energy (Fig. 71).

It is interesting, however, to compare the half-value of thickness for x-rays (and gamma rays) and comparable energy electrons in material of unit density, bearing in mind the potential problem of induced radioactivity, the thickness of conventional packages and the need to penetrate into the center of the foodstuffs in order to sterilize (Fig. 72). The induced radioactivity problem will be discussed further herein.

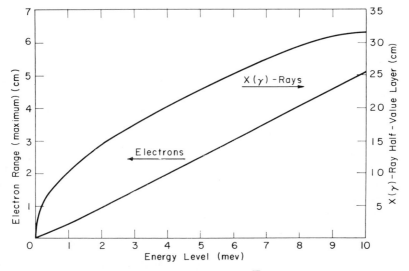

FIG. 72. MAXIMUM RANGE OF ELECTRON AND
X(γ)-RAY HALF-VALUE LAYERS IN WATER

Electron values based on Feather Equation; X(γ)-ray values based
on data from Fano (1953).

In general, it is considered that x-ray sources are inefficient and therefore prohibitive in cost in comparison with other sources.

Efficiency of Utilization of Radiations in Matter

The total amount of radiation needed in respect to any given process is dependent on: (a) the dose needed to achieve a given result; (b) the efficiency of utilization of the radiation beam; and (c) the reliability of operation of the entire system.

The dose needed for specific problems is discussed later herein in

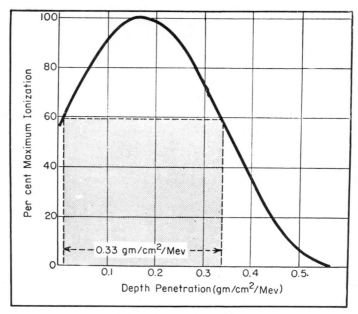

FIG. 73.   IONIZATION INTENSITY VS. PENETRATION FOR SINGLE
IRRADIATION FROM ONE SIDE

more detail.   Reliability is a factor which is important in determining
the over-all cost of any process inasmuch as it is one of the deter-
minants for (in the case of machine sources) the total capital cost of
the number of spare machines needed as standbys as well as those
needed for the process and may be an important factor in the over-all
cost of the process, particularly in respect to processes involving
microbicidal effects wherein the *minimum dose* delivered to and absorbed by every minute quantity of the product is the factor governing
total dose needed rather than the *average dose* (as in the case of chemical processing).

    Efficiency of utilization refers to the ratio of the amount of
radiation absorbed by the product at the cited dose level to the total
quantity of ionizing energy available and being emitted from a given
radiation source.

    Efficiency of Utilization of Cathode Ray Beams.—The pene-
tration of cathode ray beams in matter is presented in Fig. 73.   The
maximum range is finite and expressed by the typical Feather Equation:

$$R_{max} = \frac{0.542E - 0.133}{P}$$

where:

R_{max} = the maximum range in unit density material (cm.)
E = the energy (mev.) of the electron beam ($E > 0.8$ mev.)
P = the density of the absorber (gm./cm.³)

By "crossfiring," or exposure from both sides, the "tailings" of the ionization in depth curve may be utilized, thus increasing the efficiency of utilization in depth.

Goldblith and Proctor (1952) present in detail the aspects of efficiency of utilization and the necessity of selection of proper energy level to avoid inefficiency due to overdosing the innermost layers of

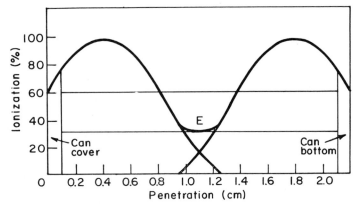

FIG. 74. CROSS FIRING THROUGH AN ALUMINUM SARDINE CAN USING 2.75 MEV ELECTRONS

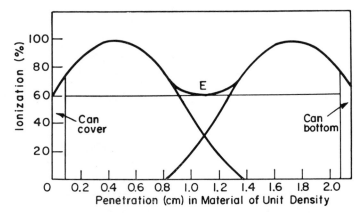

FIG. 75. CROSS FIRING THROUGH AN ALUMINUM SARDINE CAN USING 2.50 MEV ELECTRONS

the product should too high an energy level beam be used or overdosing the outermost (top and bottom) layers of the product should too low an energy level beam be used.

This is illustrated in Figs. 74 and 75 taken from Goldblith and Proctor (1952).

Consideration must also be given to the efficiency utilization of the beam in the lateral aspects also—e.g., how much of the over-all beam area is not continually utilized by product surface area.

In the case of cathode ray beams, the efficiency of utilization in depth increases with higher energy beams.   This is apparent if one examines Fig. 76 which shows what a higher relative entrance does for the higher energy electron beams.

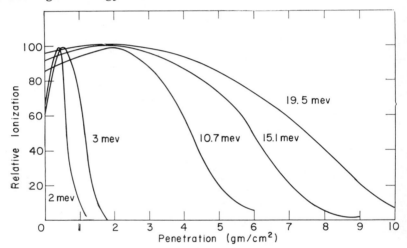

Fig. 76.   Depth Dose Curves for Electron
Beams of Different Energy Levels

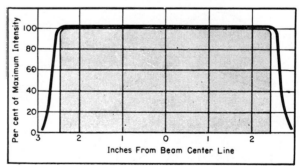

From Foster et al. (1953)

Fig. 77.   Distribution of Intensity Across a 5-in.
Container with a Scanned Beam

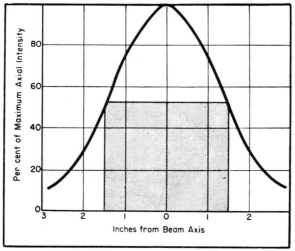

From Foster et al. (1953)

FIG. 78. OPTIMUM DISTRIBUTION OF INTENSITY ACROSS A 3-IN.
CONTAINER WITH AN UNSCANNED BEAM

In the case of lateral efficiency of utilization, beam scanning has been found to markedly increase the beam utilization (Figs. 77 and 78).

In general, over-all beam utilization efficiencies over 50 per cent and up to 80 per cent are possible, dependent on the geometry of the product and the nature of the beam.

Since conventional metal containers also absorb an appreciable portion of the total beam, consideration must be given to the geometry and physical characteristics of the container (e.g., with cylindrical containers there is a great deal of void space between containers). It is for this reason that flexible films have been suggested in place of rigid steel containers and aluminum has been suggested in place of steel. Suffice it to say that, *a priori*, the container must still be one with optimal functional characteristics in protecting the product.

Efficiency of Utilization of Gamma Ray Beams.—Since gamma rays are absorbed exponentially (Table 81), and since the conventional sources are sufficiently thick so that there is considerable self-absorption, the efficiency of utilization by the product is smaller than in the case of cathode rays. Not only can there be overdose problems in the case of thick samples, as occurs with cathode ray beams with relatively thin samples, but there is also the problem of utilizing the entire gamma ray beam. Manowitz *et al.* (1956, 1957) have studied this in detail in a conceptual design study as have others earlier.

TABLE 81

ABSORPTION IN MATTER

Comparison of electrons (beta particles) and x-rays (gamma rays)

Type of Radiation	Symbol	Mass, gm.	Charge, esu.	Absorption in Matter	Absorption Formulas
Electrons, beta particles	ϵ^-, β^-	9.106×10^{-28}	-4.083×10^{10}	Finite	$R_{max} = \dfrac{0.542E-0.133}{P}$
X-Rays, gamma rays	$X - \gamma$	0	0	Exponential	$I/I_0 = \rho - \mu_e x$

R_{max} = maximum range. E = energy, in mev. P = density. μ_e = linear absorption coefficient. μ_m = mass absorption coefficient = μ_e/P.

These articles are particularly useful inasmuch as they form the basis for the multicurie (over 10^6 curies) cobalt-60 source of the Quartermaster Corps installed in Natick, Mass.

Earlier studies by the Vitro Corp. under Atomic Energy Commission sponsorship have shown the methods of calculation of efficiency of utilization for various types of sources, including hollow cylinders and solid rods.

Isotopic Sources

Cobalt-60.—There are a number of publications which compare the various radiation sources that have been proposed for food and drug preservation.

One of the best of these is a report by Beeley (1956, 1958) of the North American Aviation Co. which was done as part of the Quartermaster effort in 1956.

This is a report of a study which compares the various known radiation sources of sufficient size to be of interest in large-scale radiation processing.

This study did not include cobalt-60 as a potential irradiation source. Concurrently, however, it became known that cobalt-60, in megacurie amounts, could be produced relatively cheaply in power or production reactors.

Manowitz et al. (1956) presented a preliminary design study on a megacurie cobalt-60 source. This study plus subsequent ones by Manowitz and his group, particularly the one by Manowitz et al. (1957), has served as a basis for the large megacurie sources prepared for the Quartermaster Research and Engineering Command in Natick.

At the time of this writing several multikilocurie sources are in use. One, at this institution, an underwater 32,000 curie source designed by the Brookhaven National Laboratory, is being used. A second, of over 1 megacurie, also designed by the Brookhaven Group, was installed in April–June, 1962 at the Quartermaster Research and Engineering Command at Natick, Mass.

For details as to efficiency, dwelltime, etc., the reader is referred to the above cited articles as well as to a report by Arthur D. Little (1959) which compares the various radiation sources as well as discusses and describes the potential of cobalt-60 as a source for intense beams of ionizing energy.

Cobalt-60 has a relatively great amount of ionizing power per atom, yielding approximately 2.5 mev. per disintegration (in comparison to cesium-137 with an average gamma energy of 0.67 mev./nucleus disintegrating). In addition, its energy level of 1.1+ and 1.3+ mev. offer greater penetration. For these reasons, there is less loss of cobalt-60 in self-absorption within the radiation source and greater possible efficiency of utilization.

Cesium-137.—This is the most important and potential gamma emitter from the fission products. Its relatively long half-life of over 33 years makes its replacement problem of less magnitude than with cobalt-60. However, its lower energy per nucleus (0.67 mev. for cesium vs. 2.5 mev. for cobalt), its poorer penetrability (0.67 mev. for cesium vs. 1.1+ and 1.3+ mev. for cobalt) plus the fact that the production facilities in the United States, at the present, for the separation of cesium-137 from spent nuclear fuels amount to only about 200,000 curies per year, make this isotope not of any immediate practical significance. (The comparative figures in Table 79 indicate 200,000 curies equivalent to approximately two-thirds of a kilowatt of gamma power, at 100 per cent efficiency of utilization.)

Strontium-90.—This is the single most important beta-emitter of the fission by-products. It could potentially be an important source of radiation power where but little penetration is needed, as in surface treatment of foods.

However, the cost of separation of the strontium-90 is relatively expensive and until such costs are reduced markedly and larger amounts of strontium-90 made available, it is difficult to see how this isotope can compete with electron accelerators for some time.

Machine Sources

In general, machine sources consist of (a) a source of electrons, (b) a means of accelerating the electrons either directly by creating a potential difference between the cathode (source of the electrons) and the anode, or indirectly via radio-frequency energy as in the linear electron accelerator, (c) a means of increasing the lateral efficiency of utilization by such means as scanning, etc.

In the main, the different types of machine sources differ mainly in the manner in which the voltage or potential difference is obtained.

Van de Graaff Accelerator.—This electrostatic accelerator, first proposed by Van de Graaff *et al.* (1933) has been refined and developed greatly since that time by Drs. Van de Graaff, Trump and their associates at M.I.T. and at the High Voltage Engineering Corp.

This machine develops the accelerating voltage by carrying electrostatic charges to an insulated high-voltage terminal on a rapidly moving belt. Cathode rays, or streams of electrons are accelerated through an evacuated tube between the cathode which is located at the high voltage terminal and the anode at the lower end of the accelerator.

The entire voltage supply is directly insulated by gas under pressure.

In general, the Van de Graaff accelerator is considered a relatively low energy accelerator, up to 4 mev. (in comparison with the linear electron accelerator), of fairly high power (from 250 to 4,000 w.). It produces a mono-energetic beam with a high degree of precision.

The characteristics of the electron beam from a Van de Graaff and its operation for processing purposes were first described by Trump and Van de Graaff (1948) and more recently in brochures of the High Voltage Engineering Co. of Burlington, Mass., the manufacturers of this type of source.

Resonant Transformer.—This radiation source is an a-c machine which develops its voltage by a transformer which has a secondary or high voltage circuit tuned to resonance (180 cycles) and which eliminates the need for an iron core, thus making it a more compact unit.

This equipment, described by Knowlton *et al.* (1953), was first developed by Charlton and Westendorp (Charlton *et al.* 1939, Charlton and Westendorp 1944).

This type of unit, being an a-c source, is not mono-energetic and thus the energy levels specified are "peak." Units from 1 to 3.5 mev. and with power outputs up to 26,000 w. are available.

Dynamitron.—One of the more recent high energy sources of electrons, the Dynamitron, is a compact constant potential unit which convert slow voltage a-c power to high voltage d-c power by means of a cascaded rectifier system driven in parallel from a radio-frequency oscillator.

Units at 1 mev. and 15 kw. output have been built and units up to 3.0 mev. and 30 kw. electron beam output are now available. It is based on the patent of Cleland (1959) and has been described by Cleland and Morganstern (1960). This type of accelerator has been said to offer means of reducing costs of radiation for processing to approximately one-eighth the costs cited by the Arthur D. Little report (1959). This may become an important commercial source, providing the reliability aspects of the source are maintained.

The Linear Electron Accelerator.—Until recent years, this accelerator has been considered to be a relatively high energy, low power radiation source. Developments in radio-frequency sources and in design over the past seven years have made possible linear electron accelerators of more than 20 kw in electron beam power and up to 24 mev. in energy.

A linear accelerator is a means of increasing the energy of a particle of x-electron volts, traveling in a straight line path, to an energy many times x-electron volts, but without the use of a potential difference greater than x-volts. This type of accelerator was proposed by Sloan and Lawrence (1931). Newbery (1949) presents a brief historical introduction to the state of development of the linear electron accelerator as well as other indirect accelerators.

In actual practice, the radio-frequency linear accelerator imparts energy to electrons by setting up highly localized alternating or traveling fields along an evacuated straight-line accelerating path and subjecting suitably timed bunches of electrons to the accelerating action of these fields (Dewey *et al.* 1954; Miller 1954A,B).

The advantage of the indirect accelerator over the direct one, e.g., the resonant transformer or the Van de Graaff, lies mainly in the fact that in the orthodox accelerator, the full accelerating voltage must be applied between the cathode and anode. Thus to achieve high energies, relatively large and expensive machines must be made in order to have adequate insulation for the desired energy level.

The successful development of high power linear electron accelerators is due mainly to the development, during and after World War II, of microwave techniques and high power radio-frequency generators.

By use of the linear accelerator techniques, the waveguide or that portion of the accelerator in which the electrons are injected and accelerated is relatively small (e.g., 8 mev. in a 1 meter tube). Thus, the volume of equipment that must be in a shielded area is relatively small, although the accessory radio-frequency generators, etc., may require considerable unshielded space.

The early linear electron accelerators (lineacs) were essentially high-energy, low-power machines. Developments in the early 1950's of microwave power supplies of high power improved techniques of increasing both the pulse duration as well as the pulse repetition rate,

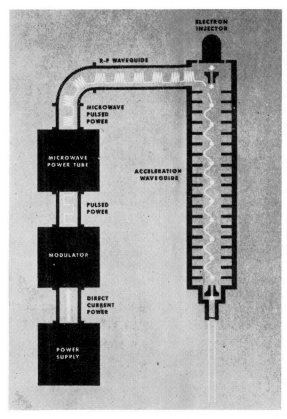

FIG. 79. LINEAR ACCEL-
ERATOR

*From "The Microwave Linear Ac-
celerator," HVEC (1961)*

Principle of operation. The
basic microwave linear electron accelerator system is
shown schematically. It
consists of:

Power Supply, providing
high-voltage dc power to
the *Modulator,* which converts the dc to high-peak
pulses which drive the
Power Source, a high-power
amplifier tube (magnetron,
klystron, or amplitron).
Pulses of microwave fre-
quency power from the
tube are coupled to the *Acceleration Waveguide,* which
is designed to propagate a
traveling microwave field.
Electrons are injected into
this field by the *Electron
Injector,* a heated cathode
with associated pulsing,
focusing, and pre-accelera-
tion components.

The system is equipped
with a *Vacuum System,*
which maintains the elec-
tron injector and acceleration wave-guide under the
proper vacuum conditions, and a *Control Console,* center for all operating and
servicing controls.

Electrons are emitted from the injector at moderate energies The injector
system operates at pulse repetition rates up to several thousand pulses per second,
with pulse lengths of a few microseconds. Injector systems bunch the electrons
so that they are injected into the waveguide in the proper phase relationship with
the microwave power. The accelerating section consists of disc-loaded cylindrical waveguides. The accelerator may comprise only one such section or several
in series, depending on desired electron energy. To obtain very high energies
the electrons will always be successively accelerated in multiple accelerating
sections.

Microwave frequency power is fed from the amplifiers to the waveguide at the
beginning of each section. Electrons are injected only into the initial section.
The electrons gain energy by absorbing energy from the microwave fields as they
travel through the accelerator. The synchronization of power tubes and electron injector is accomplished by means of trigger pulses originating from a single
master timing oscillator. These trigger pulses are precisely adjustable to provide the proper sequence.

In operation, electrons will be bunched about a narrow phase compared to the
microwave cycle, and the power into each accelerating section will be coherent.
When the electron beam passes from one accelerating section to another, however, it is necessary that the proper phase relationship between the bunched
electrons and the microwave power in the new section be achieved. This is accomplished by remotely operated phase shifters for each section.

A good vacuum is required to prevent electrical break-down in the accelerating waveguide and to prevent poisoning of the cathodes in the electron injector.
Energy, current, pulse characteristics, vacuum, cooling and protective interlocks
are all monitored and controlled remotely from the central control console,

plus development of better synchronization of power tubes and electron injectors have made it possible to achieve high energy-high power sources.

The principle of operation and schematic outline of a linear accelerator are presented in Fig. 79.

The importance of these factors becomes apparent in the consideration of the equation below:

$$\begin{array}{c}\text{Power} \qquad\qquad \text{current} \quad \text{beam} \quad \text{pulse} \\ \text{output} = \text{energy} \times I_{\text{peak}} \times \text{length} \times \text{pulse frequency} \\ \text{(mev.)} \quad \text{(amp.)} \quad \text{(sec.} \times 10^{-6}) \quad \text{(no. of pulses/sec.)}\end{array}$$

The earlier accelerators operated at the so-called S-band frequency (2,855 megacycles). With the power supplies, operating at this wavelength, higher energies are available for a given length of acceleration tube. More recent developments with L-band (1,300 mc.) power supplies allow for considerably longer pulse lengths and higher peak currents. This capability is a result of the large amount of stored radio-frequency energy in the L-band accelerator guide, an inherent advantage of the lower frequency.

The High Voltage Engineering Co. and its subsidiary, The Applied Radiation Corp., in a recent brochure (1961) on the microwave linear accelerator, show some interesting figures which indicate beam power outputs of 40 kw. and greater at high (greater than 25 mev.) energy levels. (Of course, it is realized that such high energy levels may induce radioactivity.)

The following brief table indicates the means of achieving these potentially high power outputs:

TABLE 82

MEANS OF ACHIEVING HIGH POWER FROM LINEAR ACCELERATORS

Pulse repetition rate	1–800
Pulse length (max)	30 μsec.
Pulse intensity (I_{peak})	1 ampere or greater
Conversion efficiency of microwave power: electron beam power	50–75%

From High Voltage Engineering Corp., 1961.

Some interesting characteristics of lineacs already built (or being built) are presented in Table 83.

The detail in which the discussion on the lineac is presented is indicative of the importance attached by the writer to this particular type of accelerator for processing of the future wherein moderate penetration and high beam power outputs are needed.

TABLE 83

PHYSICAL PERFORMANCE DATA OF "LINEACS" IN USE OR IN CONSTRUCTION

Location	Nominal Energy, mev.	Maximum Energy, mev.	I_{peak} ma	Beam Pulse Length μsec.	Pulse Repetition Rate, p.p.s.	Frequency S = 2855 mc. L = 1300 mc.	Maximum Beam Power, kw.
Ethicon, Inc.	5	6	200	5	800	S	3.75
Ethicon, Inc.	6	9	300	4.4	720	S	6
HVEC, Midwest Irrad. Center	8	12	200	1–10	15–180	S	3
Phillips Petrol Co., Oklahoma	6		220	12	15–360	S	4
Osaka Isotope Center, Japan	8.5	15	300	0.1–5.5	10–500	S	7.75
General Atomic Div. of Gen. Dynamics	30.	40.		0.01–4.5	10–720	L	12
Rensselaer Poly. Inst.	35	77	800	0.1–4.5	7.5–720	L	48
Natl. Bur. Stds.	100	130	242	0.1–6.	7.5–720	L	40
Q.M.C. Res. & Eng. Com'd., Natick, Mass.	24	30	400	5.5	45–360	S	18

Taken mainly from High Voltage Engineering Corp., 1961.

There is no question but what the limitations on energy level of electrons will be imposed not by accelerator design limitations but rather by consideration of the problem of induced radioactivity.

The accelerators described in Table 83 above are not necessarily those which the writer feels are optimal in design or in choice of manufacturer; they are merely presented herein as being representative of the important types of lineacs.

Comparison of Sources

There are several ways which have been suggested whereby various radiation sources may be compared. A comparison based on the consideration of cost per kilowatt of ionizing power does not tell the complete story, although this is certainly an important consideration. In the last analysis, each particular application must be evaluated with all factors being considered. Since prices of equipment such as electron source change (as do prices of isotopes) price quotations as of this time are not necessarily meaningful except as generalized guides. Moreover, multiple unit purchases of machines also result in reduced prices.

In general, the cost of electrons is much cheaper than the cost of gamma rays. However, since electrons are accelerated by machines which may have some degree of inherent instability and may have periodic breakdown, certain additional machines may be needed as "spares" dependent on the performance of the equipment. For certain products, penetration may be needed which exceeds the energy level at which measurable induced radioactivity occurs and thus electrons are not able to be used at all for these products, and gamma rays would, of necessity, be needed.

The following factors are important in the consideration of electron accelerators insofar as cost of processing is concerned:

Capital costs are determined by: (1) energy level needed for effective penetration and optimal efficiency of utilization of the beam; (2) total ionizing power requirements for the process; (3) reliability of the equipment; (4) integration of (1) (2) and (3) above, to give the resultant total numbers and characteristics of machines needed; (5) conveyor costs and auxiliary equipment; (6) building and shielding costs.

Operating costs are determined by: (1) maintenance costs; (2) labor costs; (3) power costs; (4) replacement costs of components (chiefly electron tubes).

In the case of isotopes, the following factors are important:

Capital costs are determined by: (1) cost of the curiage needed of the selected isotope; (2) shielding and building costs; (3) conveyor and instrumentation costs.

Operating costs are determined by: (1) maintenance costs; (2) labor costs; (3) power costs; (4) replacement costs for isotopes.

Much more meaningful over-all cost data are available with respect to electron accelerators today than with isotopes.

On the assumption of 100 per cent efficiency of utilization and all other factors being equal (neither of which assumptions are valid in actual practice) capital costs of isotopic sources which must be met in order to be competitive are presented in Table 84.

TABLE 84

THEORETICAL CAPITAL COST COMPARISONS

Assume Electron Power Costs per Kilowatt of	Cost of Cobalt per Curie Should Be[1]	Cost of Cesium-137 per Curie Should Be[2]
$10,000.	$0.147	$0.032
20,000.	0.294	0.064
40,000.	0.598	0.128

[1] Based on 68,000 curies per kw.
[2] Based on 310,000 curies per kw.

It should again be re-emphasized, however, that capital cost considerations alone are not sufficient. For certain products and packages isotopic sources may be needed for effective penetration. Moreover, operating costs, etc., enter into the calculation as do replacement costs for isotopes as well as for accelerator components. Within the past ten years, the cost of cobalt-60 has been reduced from about $5.00/curie to less than $2.00/curie. It is to be expected that further and large cost reductions will be effected in the near future with production of multi-megacurie sources.

Approximate costs for processing today using electrons appear to be in the neighborhood of 0.5 to 1.5¢ per megarad-lb. dependent on the particular accelerator chosen (Arthur D. Little, Inc. 1959; Stockman and Bauman 1957; Ranftl 1956, 1957; Huber and Heid, 1956). Insufficient data are available on isotopic sources to permit reasonable "guesstimates" at this time.

DOSIMETRY OF INTENSE BEAMS OF IONIZING ENERGY

General

Accurate dosimetric systems for intense beams of ionizing energy are basic to the development of any radiation preservation process. This is true not only in order to ascertain the exact quantity of radiation being absorbed by the sample being exposed, but also is necessary in order to estimate total ionizing energy requirements for a process, for assurance of reproducibility of experimental data between laboratories, for dose distribution measurements in large packages and for relationship of the basic radiation parameters of energy, current, scan, etc., to the dose of radiation absorbed in the food package.

Certain basic considerations are needed. When one is considering chemical effects of ionizing energy, one usually specifies the *average dose* received by a sample. When one is dealing with microbicidal effects, while *average dose* may be specified, the more important specification re dose is the *minimum* dose received by any small integral part of the sample. With both gamma rays (in the case of relatively large containers) and with electrons, non-uniform distribution of energy (i.e., dose) makes the specification of average, minimum, or maximum dose very important.

With respect to cathode rays or electrons, this was first pointed out by Trump *et al.* (1950).

For intense beams of high energy radiation, the ideal dosimetric system should have the characteristics outlined in Table 85.

Obviously, no single system will have all the above characteristics and, in practice, combination of systems may be needed.

Types of Dosimetric Systems

Primary.—There are two general types of dosimeters, primary and secondary (actinometers). The primary dosimeters (or standards) are based on the total dose equivalent of the radiation beam in terms of *ionizing* energy and in terms of *thermal* energy. Thus, in the former case, ionization chambers are used and in the latter, calorimeters. Both of these techniques, i.e., ionization and calorimetry,

TABLE 85

PERFORMANCE CRITERIA OF DOSIMETRIC SYSTEMS FOR INTENSE BEAMS
OF IONIZING ENERGY

Characteristic	Requirement
Dose range	10^4–10^7 rad
Dose rate	Independent to 5×10^8 rad/min.
Energy	Independent from 0.3 to 3 mev (α)
	from 0.5 to 12 mev (β^-)
Precision	General $\pm 5.0\%$, sometimes as low as $\pm 2.0\%$ needed
Inertness	Chemically and biologically
Stability	To heat, light and temperature, pre- and post-irradiation
Temperature	Independent ($20°$–$170°$F.)
Convenience	In simplicity of preparation
	In simplicity of measurement
	Low in cost

are important basic tools for exact measurement of beams of ionizing energy and are necessary as primary standards. Both, however, are not suitable for routine work, are complicated methods requiring highly skilled personnel, are time consuming, expensive and are not readily adapted to routine use.

The development of primary dosimeters and the problems associated therewith have been considered by numerous authors. Hine and Brownell (1956) in their book offer a rather complete consideration of these, particularly in Chapter 4 by J. W. Boag.

More recent developments in primary standards have been outlined in detail by Schuler (1958), Hart et al. (1958) and Taimuty et al. (1958A,B). Suffice it to say that accurate primary dosimeters are now available to serve as standard calibration sources for high energy, intense beams of ionizing radiations.

Secondary.—Secondary dosimeters or actinometers, which must be calibrated against a primary standard, may be classified in several ways, such as solid state, liquid state, etc., or chemical, biological and other.

The more important actinometers are the oxidation of ferrous ions to ferric, a reaction first studied by Fricke and Morse (1929). Although this has a restricted total dose range (less than 40,000 rad) it is acknowledged as an accurate and precise secondary standard.

The reduction of ceric to cerous ions based on the work of Hardwick (1952) is a most useful dosimeter in the megaroentgen region. More recent studies on ceric dosimetry by Harlan and Hart (1959) indicate accurate measurements of dose may be made with this dosimeter up to at least 10^8 rad.

Aqueous solutions of dyes, which change color due to radiation exposure, have also been proposed as dosimeters and offer promise (Goldblith *et al.* 1952).

Among the solid state dosimeters are colored cellophane studies by Henley (1954), polyvinyl chloride films by Henley and Miller (1951), silver-phosphate glass by Schulman *et al.* (1955) and Davison *et al.* (1956), photographic films by Nitka (1959), cobalt glass by Kreidl and Blair (1956, 1960), and luminescence degradation by Schulman *et al.* (1957) and by Attix (1959).

The above are by no means all of the actinometers that have been suggested or studied, but represent the more important ones.

A number of papers have been published on the comparison of many of these sources. Taimuty and his associates (1958A) at the Stanford Research Institute have recently completed a comparative study on the various secondary dosimetric systems.

Comparison of the various systems have been made by Taimuty *et al.* (1958A), Hart *et al.* (1958) and in a symposium published in Nucleonics in October, 1959 (Kreidl *et al.* 1959). A summary of the experimental findings on comparative dosimetric systems taken from Taimuty *et al.* (1958A) is presented in Tables 86 and 87.

Based on Taimuty's studies, an ad hoc committee of the National

TABLE 86

CHARACTERISTICS OF AQUEOUS SOLUTION AND LUMINESCENT DOSIMETERS[11]

Dosimeter	Dose Range, rads $\times 10^{-6}$	Dose Rate,[1] rads/sec	Precision, %	Post-Irradiation Stability[1]	Convenience
Fricke	0.004–0.04[2]	2 × 10⁶ (ave.)[3] 10¹⁰ (peak)	±1	Stable	B
Ceric	0.05–100	2 × 10⁶ (ave.) 2 × 10⁸ (peak)	±4[4]	Stable	B
Ferrous sulfate-Cupric sulfate	0.1–10	200	. . .	25%	C
Methylene blue	0.01–10	10⁵	±6	1%	C[5]
Anthracene	0.3–200	4 × 10⁵	±10[7]	Stable	A
Naphthalene[8]	0.1–200[8]	4 × 10⁵	±10[7]	Stable[9]	C[9]
Bibenzyl[10]	0.2–4	200	±10[7]	Stable	A
Acetylsalicylic acid (aspirin)	0.2–4	200	±10[7]	Stable	A

[1] See text for comments.
[2] Air-saturated solutions; upper limit is 2 × 10⁵ rads for oxygen-saturated solutions.
[3] Limited by local oxygen depletion; high dose rates require extremely short exposures of high solution stirring rates.
[4] Using solutions made up of once-distilled water and reagent grade chemicals (12).
[5] Concentration-dependent, G = 0.4 at 3 × 10⁻⁵ molar, G = 0.9 at 6 × 10⁻²M.
[6] Luminescence degradation measured with λ 3650 excitation.
[7] Preliminary value, should be improved considerably with further development.
[8] Luminescence degradation measured with λ 2537 excitation, range 3 × 10⁵–10⁸ rads; radiophotoluminescence measured with λ 3650 excitation, range 10⁵–10⁷ rads.
[9] Stable luminescence effect, poor mechanical stability due to rapid sublimation rate.
[10] Radiophotoluminescence measured with λ 3650 excitation.
[11] From: Taimuty *et al.* (1958A).

TABLE 87

CHARACTERISTICS OF GLASS AND MISCELLANEOUS DOSIMETERS[9]

Dosimeter	Dose Range, rads $\times 10^{-6}$	Dose Rate,[1] rads/sec	Precision, %	Post-Irradiation Stability[1]	Convenience[1]
Cobalt[2] F-0450	0.01–2	200[3]	±2	10–14%[4]	B[5]
Cobalt[2] F-0621	0.01–2	10^6[4]	±2	1–2%[4]	A
Silver phosphate	0.01–2	10^5[3]	±2	8–19%[4]	B[5]
Manganese[6] (No. 9762)		3×10^4[3]	±3	4–6%[4]	B[5]
Microscope slides	0.01–2	10^4[3]	±5	16–30%[4]	B[5]
Nitrous oxide	0.01–3×10^3	200	±5	Stable	D
Cyclohexane	0.01–130[7]	200	±6	Stable	D
Chlorinated hydrocarbons	0.01–1	200	5–10	Stable	C
Cellophane[8]	0.5–15	10^5	5–10	Stable	B

[1] See text for comments.
[2] Manufactured by Bausch and Lomb Optical Company.
[3] Fading during irradiation produces pseudo rate dependence.
[4] Dependent on dose and wavelength.
[5] Fading correction necessary.
[6] Manufactured by Corning Glass Company.
[7] Reduced yield observed at higher doses.
[8] Type 300-MSC blue manufactured by E. I. Dupont de Nemours.
[9] From: Taimuty et al. (1958A).

Research Council Advisory Board on Quartermaster Research recommended three secondary standards for use with their radiation sources. These are: (a) the Fricke ferrous-ferric dosimeter; (b) the ceric-cerous dosimeter; (c) cobalt-F-0621 glass slides.

In addition to the above, development of a "go-no go" or "yes or no" dosimeter has been undertaken by the Quartermaster Corps in order to indicate simply whether or not a sample has been exposed to a radiation beam. These are in the form of tapes which depend on changes of color in dyes in the tapes, and in the development of liquid plastics which will gel on irradiation.

Thus, secondary dosimetric systems are available now for processing work, with the accuracy needed, provided careful selection is made with respect to intended application, geometry, total dose, etc. One item of particular importance is the care that must be given to the standardization of each batch of a secondary dosimeter against a primary standard such as an ionization chamber or a calorimeter. This will then take care of such problems as impurities in dyestuffs or in chemicals, etc.

With good laboratory standardization and procedures, with careful manipulation, clean glassware and careful attention to the various other aspects of any chemical or physico-chemical procedure, routine secondary dosimetry can be accurate, precise and indicative of the actual dose to which the food sample has been exposed.

Monitoring devices.—Electronic monitoring devices are particularly of importance with machine sources of radiation. With isotopic sources, once the source is calibrated, and with the exception of such factors as variations in geometry, distance from the source, etc., the dose received by a product can be based on calculations made as a result of accurate measurements done at an earlier date. "Go-no go" type dosimeters can be used to reassure that the samples have been exposed to the radiation beam.

With machine sources, however, since certain degrees of instability may exist in the performance of the machines, continuous monitoring of those parameters which determine the total dose given to all the product is necessary. At the present time, monitoring of the following characteristics of the electron beam is needed: (a) total beam current; (b) energy level; (c) scan width; (d) scan uniformity; (e) in the case of linear accelerators: pulse repetition rate, pulse length and peak current.

Electrical monitoring as a continuous production system needs to ascertain whether the dose delivered to every point of all the packages being treated is within the specified limits.

Such a system of electrical monitoring has not yet been developed and only by careful evaluation of the performance of the monitoring devices designed for the Quartermaster Corps Natick accelerator can one then be in a position to set up further specifications for the type of electron beam monitoring needed, and the relationship between these parameters and absorbed dose.

It should be re-emphasized that these measurements must be of the beam itself. Control panel measurements, e.g., of voltage via generating voltmeter readings, are not sufficient. To the point of providing information of this type, the Quartermaster accelerator now under construction in Natick will be of immense value.

WHOLESOMENESS

Introduction

The intensive Quartermaster and Surgeon General research program, begun in 1953, has resulted in the development of a great deal of valuable information in the wholesomeness aspects of food preservation by ionizing energy.

Wholesomeness of irradiated foods may be considered under the following categories: (a) effect of the radiation treatment on the nutritive value of food; (b) consideration of the possible production of toxic substances in the foods by irradiation; (c) consideration of the possible production of carcinogenic substances by the radiation treatment; (*d*) possible induction of radioactivity in the radiation treated food.

Nutrient Aspects

A great deal of data have been developed on the effect of ionizing energy on the nutritive components of foods. These studies, beginning with the early work of Proctor and Goldblith (1948) through more recent studies under the auspices of the office of Surgeon General of the Department of the Army and of the Atomic Energy Commission, have shown the following:

(*a*) The effects of ionizing energy on nutrients are due to the indirect action of the radiations via the solvent medium, water.

(*b*) Therefore, the effects are greater in the more dilute solutions of pure nutrients in contrast with the effects on nutrients *in situ* or in foods, wherein the effects are relatively small.

(*c*) The effects of ionizing energy on nutrients in foods parallel, in degree, those effects observed with other methods of food processing, with respect to comparative radiosensitivity of the particular nutrients.

The above is summarized in the review papers of Kraybill (1958) and by Johnson *et al.* (1958).

Thus, it may be concluded that the effects of ionizing energy on the nutrients in foods is no greater than those observed with other methods of processing. From a practical dietary standpoint, however, consideration of the amount of destruction of nutrients should be taken into account.

Toxicity

A tremendous amount of work has been done on the effect of ionizing energy on the possible induction of toxic products in irradiated foods as a result of the concentrated program of the Department of the Army. To date, no manifestations of toxicity have been observed in the many foods subjected to: (*a*) several-fold increase in degree of radiation exposure above that needed for sterilization; (*b*) two-year feeding tests to more than one species of animal, including reproduction, lactation and pathological studies.

While all of the data are not complete at the time of this writing, suffice it to say that thus far, there is no evidence of the induction of any toxicity as a result of the radiation treatment. All of the abnormalities observed thus far have been shown to be due entirely to destruction of nutrients in the irradiated foods fed to animals or to genetic anomalies in the test animals.

Carcinogenicity

Detailed studies on the potential conversion of the sterols normally present in foods into carcinogenic compounds have shown no indication at all of the production of carcinogenic substances.

Induced Radioactivity

This aspect of wholesomeness is of importance particularly with reference to the Food Additives Amendment of 1958 as pointed out earlier herein.

The induction of radioactivity is a function of the following: (a) the type of radiation; (b) the energy level of the incident radiation; (c) the dose applied to the food; (d) the per cent isotopic abundance of the elements; (e) the half-life of the radioactive nuclide produced.

The extensive report by Glass and Smith (1960) summarizes the probability of induction of radioactivity by high energy electrons. Skaggs et al. (1948) point out the probability of a direct electron disintegration being only 1/400th of that with an equal number of photons. Usually a neutron is ejected from the nucleus. Bremsstrahlung or secondary x-ray production which occurs when electrons react nuclei of the food elements should also be considered as responsible for inducing the radioactivity and Glass and Smith (1960) take this into account in their calculated theoretical quantity of radioactivity produced.

The probability of a (γ, n) reaction with subsequent induction of radioactivity is dependent on the energy level of the incident radiation being above the threshold level for a particular photoneutron reaction. For instance for beryllium (Be^9) the γ, n threshold is 1.65 mev., and for deuterium (D^2) the γ, n threshold is 2.23 mev. However, since the per cent isotopic abundance of each is relatively small, the probability of neutron production and thus induction of radioactivity in foods due to these elements is negligible. The amount of radioactivity induced is a direct function of the total dose of the incident electron beam. Herschman (1956) has developed a simple relationship which illustrates this:

$$Q \angle 30 \ DEn/T$$

where:

Q = the activity in micro-micro curies
E = the beam energy in mev
D = the dose in mega-rep
n = the amount of material (parent element) present per gram
    of food
T = the half-life in years of the isotope formed

Glass and Smith (1960) point out that, based on these data, the Herschman expression overestimates the induced radioactivity by a factor of 2 to 10 due to Herschman's taking into account only the gross aspects of the interaction process.

For the purpose of this discussion, since the γ,p reaction is only about half as probable as the γ,n reaction for the light elements, only the γ,n reactions will be considered. Table 88 lists these reactions, nuclides formed, threshold energies, etc.

TABLE 88

SOME OF THE CHARACTERISTICS OF POTENTIALLY IMPORTANT AND PROBABLE REACTIONS LEADING TO INDUCED RADIOACTIVITY IN FOODS

Nuclide Parent (Daughter)	Isotopic Abundance, %	α-n Threshold, mev.	Half-life of Radioactivity Produced		
			α,n	α,p	n,α
$C^{12}(C^{11})$	98.9	18.7	20.5 min.	Stable	Stable
$N^{14}(N^{13})$	99.6	10.8	10.0 min.	Stable	Stable
$O^{16}(O^{15})$	99.8	15.6	2.1 min.	Stable	Stable
$Na^{23}(Na^{22})$	100	12 mev.	2.58 yr.	Stable	15.06 hr.
$P^{31}(P^{32})$	100	12.4	2.55 min.	Stable	14.2 d.
$S^{34}(P^{33})$	4.2	10.9(?)	...	24 d.	...
$Cl^{33}(S^{35})$	?	?	...	87 d.(α, pn)	...
$Mn^{55}(Mn^{54})$	100	10.0	291 d.	Stable	...
$Fe^{56}(Fe^{55})$	91.7	11.2	2.94 yr.	Stable	Stable
$Zn^{66}(Zn^{65})$	27.8	11.2	245 d.	Stable	Stable
$Rb^{85}(Rb^{84})$	?	?	33 d.	...	...
$O^{127}I(I^{126})$	100	9.3	13.3 d.	Stable	25.0 min.

Taken from miscellaneous sources including Glass and Smith (1960) and Van Patter and Whaling (1954).

Table 89 presents data on some of the important long-lived activity produced by 24 mev. electrons in beef. These data are based on the work done by the Stanford Research Institute under Department of the Army sponsorship. Comparisons with the Maximum Permissable Concentrations (M.P.C.) of the National Bureau of Standards (N.B.S.) Handbook 69 are also presented.

In order to have a picture of the relative importance of these values in the over-all picture of man's exposure to radiation, comparative data in a qualitative form are presented in Table 90.

Consideration of the above results in the following conclusions, with respect to radioactivity induced at energy levels of 24 mev.:

(a) Some relatively small amounts of long-lived activities are induced in foods.

(b) Concentrations of these activities are dependent on the material being irradiated and the dose used.

(c) Concentrations of these long-lived nuclides (Na^{22}, P^{33}, Rb^{84}) are less than the concentration of the nuclides normally present in foods, e.g., K^{40}, C^{14} and in the same range as that due to fallout.

TABLE 89

TABLE 89

SOME OF THE IMPORTANT LONG-LIVED ACTIVITY PRODUCED IN BEEF IRRADIATED BY 24 MEV. ELECTRONS[1]

| Isotope | Half-life | Detection Code | Amount (Immediately After Irradiation) | | M.P.C. μcuries/ml. | Ratio |
			d.p.m./lb.	μcuries/gm.		
(1)	(2)	(3)	(4)	(5)	(6)	(6)/(5)
Na^{22}	2.58 y	AFLT	260	2.6×10^{-7}	4×10^{-4}	1.5×10^3
P^{32}	14 d	A	170	1.7×10^{-7}	2×10^{-4}	830
		I	65	6.5×10^{-8}		
P^{33}	24 d	I	600	6.0×10^{-7}	3×10^{-5}	50
S^{35}	87 d	I	4.5	4.5×10^{-9}	6×10^{-4}	1.3×10^5
Mn^{54}	291 d	I	0.6	6.1×10^{-10}	1×10^{-3}	1.6×10^6
Fe^{55}	2.9 y	I	17.	1.7×10^{-8}	8×10^{-3}	4.7×10^5
Zn^{65}	245 d	AF	12.	1.2×10^{-8}	1.0×10^{-3}	8.3×10^4
Rb^{84}	33 d	L	52.	5.2×10^{-8}	3.0×10^{-5}	590
I^{126}	13.3 d	AFT	3.9	3.9×10^{-9}	2.0×10^{-5}	5.1×10^3

Detection code: A = detected in concentrated (to 10%) aqueous solutions of food elements; F = detected in food enriched in food elements; L = detected in enriched foods; I = calculated by empirical equation but not measured directly; T = calculated by theoretical analysis; D = detectable in foods without enrichment or concentration; C = chemical separation and concentration of a food element; E = enrichment (up to a maximum of 10%) permits detection; μcuries/gm. = $10^{-9} \times$ d.p.m./lb. M.P.C. (maximum permissible concentrations) are from N.B.S. Handbook 69, 1959 (revision of Handbook No. 52)).
[1] From Glass and Smith, 1960 (and assumes dose of 5 megarads delivered to the food).

TABLE 90

SOURCES OF RADIOACTIVITIES IN FOODS[1]

| Concentration | | | Man-made | |
d.p.m./lb.	μc/gm.	Natural	Fallout	Sterilization[2]
10^3	10^{-6}	K^{40}, C^{14}	...	...
10^2	10^{-7}	...	Sr^{89}	Na^{22}, p^{33}, P^{32}, Rb^{84}
10	10^{-8}	H^3	Sr^{90}	Zn^{65}, I^{126}, Fe^{55}
1	10^{-9}	Ra^{226}	...	...

[1] From Glass and Smith (1960).
[2] 24 mev. electrons, dose 5 megarad.

(d) These values of induced radioactivity are far less than the MPC values of the National Bureau of Standards.

(e) Some short-lived induced radioactivities from C^{11}, N^{13} and O^{15} contribute to a maximum level around irradiated packages of several roentgens per hour, immediately following irradiation. This reaches background level after about 5 hr., thus posing no problem.

At energy levels below 5 mev., no measurable quantity of radioactivity which may be detected by present means is induced in foods.

At levels of approximately 7 to 20+ mev., little is known relative to the possibility of inducing measurable amounts of radioactivity other than from calculations.

Mayneord et al. (1949) found measurable quantities of radioactivity induced by 17 mev. x-rays. Actually, however, in this "grey" zone above 7 mev. and below about 20 mev. very little experimental data are available on the degree of radioactivity induced in different foods. This is an important energy area with respect to practical applications of ionizing energy in food preservation and the penetration needed for conventional packages. Studies on measurement of radioactivity are necessary with different foodstuffs exposed to intense beams of ionizing energy at energy levels between 7 and 20 mev.

In addition, realistic legislation must be considered which takes into account an experimental truth—namely that there is no "zero" radioactivity level. Therefore, as our methods of counting and equipment became more sophisticated, what may have been zero by today's methods and instrumentation may not be zero tomorrow. Realistic legislation based upon MPC values, coupled with an uncommon amount of common sense, will be needed in the evaluation of experimental data obtained at the energy levels between 7 and 20 mev.

Meanwhile, from the earlier cited regulation using cobalt-60 and other isotopes as process control devices (Federal Register 1961), it would appear that cobalt-60 sources and electrons below 5 mev. and certainly below 2.3 mev. would be permitted by the U. S. Food and Drug Administration. Again, however, it should be re-emphasized that a petition must be filed in order to obtain a regulation permitting the use of ionizing energy for food preservation in the United States. At the time of writing this chapter, such a petition is being prepared for "clearance of irradiated bacon" by the Department of the Army.

THE EFFECT OF DOSE RATE AND TYPE OF RADIATION

Theoretical analysis as well as experimental studies indicate that for high energy electrons, gamma rays and x-rays, there should be no difference in degree or type of biological effect for equal doses of energy absorbed.

Goldblith *et al.* (1953) studied this with bacteria and found no differences in destruction rate with either cobalt-60 gamma rays, 2 mev. electrons or 2 mev. x-rays.

Taimuty (1957) made more extensive studies and included chemical as well as microbiological effects using a cobalt-60 source as well as a 6–9 mev. linear electron accelerator and obtained no difference in the type nor degree of effect for equal energy absorption.

RADIOLOGICAL SAFETY

Of primary concern to man, with respect to any potential uses of ionizing energy, is man's own welfare.

There have been a number of articles, books and reports which deal with this problem and its solution. The fact that the LD_{50} of man is about 400 roentgens and the LD_{50} of the organisms which man is attempting to destroy is several orders of magnitude greater is one of the *a priori* reasons for the relatively great importance attached to radiological safety.

The National Bureau of Standards Handbook No. 69 (1959) cited earlier plus a number of other useful N.B.S. handbooks have been developed to ease the solution of the problems relating to radiological safety and health for the worker in the field.   Such references as the excellent text by Price *et al.* (1957), the paper by Fano (1953) and the Radiological Health Handbook of the Public Health Service (1960) all serve a useful function in this respect.

In particular, however, when one is dealing with electron accelerators, the following are some of the important factors concerning radiological safety:

(*a*)   Development of adequate interlock systems to prevent the equipment from being turned on while someone is in the irradiation vault.

(*b*)   Calculation of sufficient shielding for the quantity and quality of the secondary x-rays produced (minimum wavelength of which, and therefore maximum penetration, may be determined by the Compton Effect equation).

(*c*)   Reduction of the volume of the irradiation chamber to a practical minimum in order to assure minimum volume of shielding and therefore minimum cost.

(*d*)   Checkout of all ports and vents to be assured of no stray scattered electrons escaping.

(*e*)   Running the equipment with a fully integrated survey system which can automatically shut down the accelerator should, for some reason, the level of radiation exceed the designated level at the point where men are working.

Articles such as that by Levin (1954) are useful in this regard as are the brochures of the accelerator manufacturers and of the design sections of the Atomic Energy Commission and, in particular, of the Brookhaven National Laboratory who have designed the large cobalt-60 sources in this country.

CHEMICAL, PHYSICAL AND BIOLOGICAL CHANGES BROUGHT ABOUT BY IONIZING RADIATIONS

Ionizing energy can bring about different kinds of effects dependent upon the nature of the material being subjected to irradiation and upon the dose used.

In a material as complex as food, prediction of the kind and degree of effect is almost impossible. It is still necessary to consider each particular food material as a separate entity.

Studies in radiation chemistry and in radiation biology have shown that vitamins, amino acids, enzymes and the like are destroyed, by and large, indirectly by the interaction of these compounds with the free radicals and activated molecules produced when the ionizing radiations bombard the solvent medium, water. Large molecules and microorganisms such as molds, yeasts and bacteria, are destroyed mainly by direct hits of the radiations at or near a sensitive center of the organism.

The various methods of distinguishing between direct and indirect action have been thoroughly covered by the excellent work of Lea (1947) and reviewed more recently by Goldblith (1959).

In essence, therefore, bacteria, molds and yeasts are destroyed largely though direct hits of ionizing particles or rays, at or near a sensitive center (although indirect effects are also important) whereas color changes, flavor changes, nutrient destruction and texture changes occur predominantly because of indirect action as a result of the free-radicals and activated molecules produced by the radiations in the medium. The free-radicals are both oxidative and reducing (hydroxyl, hydroperoxyl, etc., vs. hydrogen). Thus a reducible molecule in the substrate being irradiated will be reduced, whereas an oxidizable molecule will be oxidized. In a material so complex as food, however, as mentioned earlier, prediction is almost impossible and the lack of space herein prevents a complete coverage of this. The reader is referred to a number of excellent references on the subject including the following: Proctor and Goldblith (1951A,B; 1952A,B), Proctor and O'Meara (1951), Corson et al. (1951), Hannan (1955), Hannan and Coleby (1957) which are not inclusively complete by any means. Suffice it to say, however, that the above-cited articles illustrate the side-reactions, most of which are undesirable, which can and do occur and which should be circumvented. A number of means of circumventing these changes has been suggested varying from the most basic, e.g., isolation and identification of the molecular changes which occur on irradiation as illustrated in the work of Wick et al. (1961A) to the more applied Edisonian type of approaches which will be discussed in the next section.

At this point, it might be well to consider again the relative dose levels needed to achieve specific reactions and effects. This is illustrated in Fig. 70 (p. 329).

A number of studies have been made which illustrate the fact that, while most of the microorganisms are destroyed largely by direct action, indirect effects are also important in the destruction of most species.   This has been studied in detail by Hollaender *et al.* (1951) and reviewed by Goldblith (1959).   Figs. 80, 81 and 82 from Goldblith (1959) illustrate the importance of indirect effect as influenced by the medium and atmosphere.

An additional and important factor relating to the microbial effects of ionizing energy is the complementary effect of thermal and ionizing energy (Morgan and Reed 1954; Kempe 1955; Kan *et al.* 1957). This sensitization of bacterial spores by ionizing energy to subsequent thermal treatment, while important from the point of view of reducing the thermal requirements of the process, apparently does not obviate appreciably the need for thermal inactivation of enzymes in foodstuffs (Farkas and Goldblith 1962; Baker and Goldblith 1961).

PREVENTION OR OBVIATING THE UNDESIRABLE SIDE REACTIONS INDUCED BY IONIZING RADIATIONS

Obviously that method of radiation treatment of foods which will maximize the direct effects of the radiation (in order to destroy the microorganisms responsible for spoilage) and yet will minimize the indirect effects which cause undesirable side reactions is the ultimate of methods that might be developed and would certainly be the method of choice.

To this end, the following approaches have been suggested towards the minimization of the undesirable side reactions and the development of the most acceptable radiation preservation process:

(1)   Irradiation in the Frozen State
(2)   Irradiation in a Vacuum or Inert Atmosphere
(3)   Addition of Free Radical Scavengers
(4)   Distillation at Low Temperatures
(5)   Reduction of Moisture Content during Irradiation (Concurrent Radiation-Distillation)
(6)   Reduction of the Dose of Ionizing Energy required by (*a*) reducing the initial microbial load;   (*b*) addition of microbial sensitizing agents;   (*c*) complementary action of ionizing and other types of energy such as thermal energy.

Bierman, *et al.* (1956) point out the magnitude of this problem in the case of milk, wherein the off-flavor recognition threshold is as low as approximately 10,000 rad whereas the sterilization is several orders of magnitude higher.   Recognition should also be given to the possibility that, in any suggested method, the degree

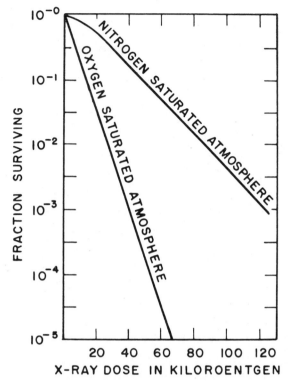

FIG. 80. COMPARATIVE SENSITIVITY OF *Escherichia coli*
IRRADIATED IN OXYGEN-SATURATED AND
NITROGEN-SATURATED MEDIA

to which a decrease in the indirect effect reduced off-flavor reactions
may more than be offset by also increasing the sterilizing dose needed.

Irradiation in the Frozen State

This method exerts its beneficial effects, insofar as reduction of
undesirable side reactions is concerned, by immobilization of the
free-radicals, thus reducing the indirect effect of the radiation considerably. Whether the indirect effect is completely prevented by
reduction of the temperature is not completely known at the present
time. However, the fact remains that while freezing a sample of
food reduces the degree of undesirable side-reactions, or conversely,
increases the off-flavor recognition-threshold dose level, freezing alone
is not sufficient to completely reduce these reactions to the extent
necessary for complete acceptability for all foods sterilized by this
means.

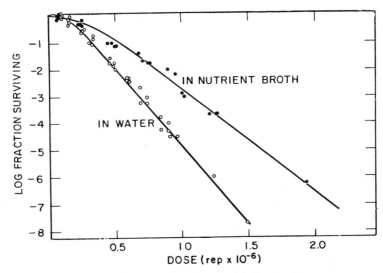

FIG. 81.   LETHAL EFFECTS OF COBALT-60 GAMMA RADIATION ON
SPORES OF *Bacillus stearothermophilus*

Irradiation in a Vacuum or Inert Atmosphere

The efficacy of this method, suggested first for foods by Huber
et al. (1953), is based on the reduction in the numbers of oxidative free
radicals which may be formed.   Both x-(γ—)-rays and β-(ρe$^-$) rays
have similar effects on biological materials.   Both react with water to
form a water ion and eject an orbital electron:

$$H_2O \xrightarrow{h\nu} H_2O^+ + e^-$$

The ejected electron may have enough energy to repeat the above
process or may, instead, be captured to form a negative water ion:

$$e^- + H_2O \rightarrow H^2O^-$$

The positive and negative water ions dissociate as follows:

$$H_2O^+ \rightarrow H^+ + OH*$$
$$H_2O^- \rightarrow OH^- + H*$$

The H˙ may react with oxygen to form an oxidizing radical such
as HO_2˙, viz:

$$H* + O_2 \rightarrow HO_2* \text{ or,}$$
$$H_2 + O_2 \rightarrow H_2O_2.$$

While the above reactions are not complete they illustrate the

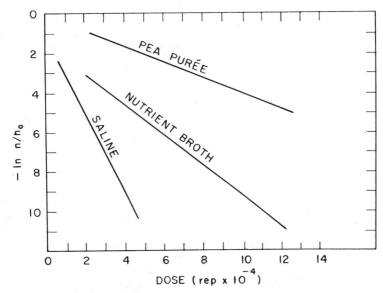

FIG. 82. EFFECTS OF GAMMA RAYS ON *Escherichia coli*
SUSPENDED IN THREE DIFFERENT MEDIA

types of oxidation and reduction reactions induced by the reaction of ionizing energy with water.

Obviously inert atmospheres or nitrogen stripping will reduce the oxidative effects and thus result in improved products from the organoptic point of view.   Again, however, this technique while more applicable, from a practical standpoint, to liquid foods than to solid foods, thus far has not proven to be the complete answer for all products at sterilization dose levels.   In addition, the work of Huber *et al.* (1953), Hollaender *et al.* (1951)   and others have shown that microorganisms are far more sensitive in the presence of oxygen than in its absence, thus providing a difficult and paradoxical situation.

Addition of Free Radical Scavengers

The addition of free-radical scavengers, such as sodium ascorbate, was first suggested by Proctor and Goldblith (1952B) and Proctor *et al.* (1952).   This method is predicated on the fact that some compounds such as ascorbic acid, its derivatives and analogues, are more competitive for the free radicals produced by the radiation than the flavor molecules, thus protecting the flavor molecules.

In addition to the problem in finding the almost perfect free-radical acceptor which will not only be more competitive for the free radicals than the molecules being protected, there are the additional *a priori* considerations that the scavengers must be nontoxic, must not contribute, in themselves, undesirable flavors and must not appreciably increase the dosages needed for the sterilization process. Suffice it to say that, while the above-cited sodium ascorbate is efficacious to a considerable degree, the perfect free radical scavenger has yet to be found. Obviously, the compound must also be mixed thoroughly with the foodstuff, thus offering an additional limitation of this technique being usable for only liquid or well-mascerated or disintegrated foods.

Concurrent Radiation-Distillation

The concurrent radiation distillation technique, described by Wertheim *et al.* (1957), is based on the premise that there are certain volatile precursors to irradiation off-flavor and that the development of the compounds responsible for the off-flavor proceeds via a chain reaction. The concurrent radiation distillation technique removes these volatile off-flavor precursor compounds before they are allowed to react to produce off-flavors in the liquid food.

Obviously, this technique has several limitations. First, it assumes that all irradiation off-flavor precursors are volatile. Secondly, it is limited to liquid foods. Thirdly, with radiation sources of relatively low dose rates, e.g., the 1000-curie cobalt-60 source in which the original work was done by Wertheim *et al.* (1957), recycling is necessary, thus in effect making it practically impossible to achieve a sterile product.

Wertheim *et al.* (1959) proceeded to develop this technique for electron sources wherein recycling would be done as with the gamma ray sources. Later, Saravacos *et al.* (1961) developed a small unit which would allow for complete sterilization in one pass under the electron beam with the product to be aseptically packaged.

All in all, while this technique does reduce the off-flavor intensity of irradiated milk appreciably, it does not remove all the radiation-induced off-flavor components and it is not a commercially practical method.

Its main use has been as an excellent fundamental tool for the isolation and separation of radiation-induced off-flavors in liquid foodstuffs as shown by Wick *et al.* (1961A,B).

Reduction of Moisture Content

Lowering of moisture content reduces the numbers of free radicals. Thus, the degree of off-flavor should be less in a product irradiated in the dry state than in the "wet" state. Bierman *et al.* (1956) have shown dry skim milk to have a recognition difference threshold five times higher than that of fluid skim milk (106,000 rep *vs.* 20,000 rep).

In general, it may be stated that dried foods have higher off-flavor recognition threshold doses than their wet counterparts. On the other hand, since the indirect action of the radiation energy is minimized through reduction of the amount of solvent and since bacteria are destroyed to some extent by indirect action also, the sterilization dose required may also be higher.

Reduction of Dose Requirements

By Reducing the Initial Bacteriological Load.—Based on consideration of the target theory, reduction of the initial bacteriological load will cause some reduction in dose requirements for a given degree of sterilization. This fact, which is similar to that observed with thermal energy, has been discussed by Goldblith (1959), Proctor and Goldblith (1952B) and others.

The rate of destruction of organisms by ionizing energy, assuming strictly target-theory one-hit phenomenon, follows a first order reaction, viz.:

$$N/N_0 = e^{-D/D_0},$$

where N is the number of organisms surviving a dose D;

D_0 is the slope of the survival curve (also known as the 37 per cent dose, or that dose which results in 63 per cent kill or 37 per cent survival);

N_0 is the initial number of organisms present.

Thus, an order of magnitude difference in the initial microbial load will result in only relatively few per cent difference in dose requirement. However, in accordance with good food plant sanitation practices, any means of reducing the initial load should be followed and will result in a better product. It should be recognized, however, that the reduction in dose requirements brought about by this means is relatively small.

Addition of Microbial Sensitizing Agents.—Compounds, which are nontoxic and which may increase the sensitivity of microbes to ionizing energy, are well worth considering as a means of reducing the radiation dose requirements. *A priori*, these compounds must not only be nontoxic, but also must not contribute off-flavors or off-odors to the food.

Shehata (1961) studied the potentialities of one such compound, namely Vitamin K_5, which looks promising. This work, however, is in its early stages and much more needs to be done. The compounds must also be specific for a number of species of organisms, and most particularly, the pathogenic spoilage organisms such as *Clostridium botulinum*. A number of other workers have studied the possibility of combining radiation and antibiotics as a means of reducing the dose requirements. With the antibiotics, however, in accordance with the administrative practice of the Food Additives Amendment of 1958 by the U. S. Food and Drug Administration, there must be no antibiotic left in the foodstuff before consumption in order for approval to be given for its use. This places an additional requirement on the use of this class of materials in combination with ionizing energy, thus rendering the process impractical at the present time.

Complementary Action of Thermal Energy and Ionizing Energy.—Work by Morgan and Reed (1954), Kempe (1955), Kan *et al.* (1957) and others has shown that substerilizing doses of ionizing energy can reduce the quantity of thermal energy needed to sterilize foodstuffs.

This kind of complementary action has great practical potential, especially for a number of meat products which are packaged in containers too large to allow for complete sterilization of the entire contents of the package inasmuch as the time-temperature needed to sterilize the center of the package would cause over-heating of the outside layers of the product.

Examples of the destruction rates which occur in complementary action are presented in Fig. 83.

Not only is this of potential practical significance in reducing the thermal energy requirements for sterilization, but it may be looked at from the opposite point of view in using thermal energy to reduce the ionizing energy requirements.

THE EFFECTS OF IONIZING ENERGY ON ENZYMES

Enzymes are affected, by and large, indirectly via the free radicals formed in the solvent. Thus, dilute solutions of enzymes are relatively radiosensitive, whereas more concentrated solutions are more resistant and enzymes *in situ*, in foods, are relatively very resistant—a dose of ten times that needed to sterilize raw milk being insufficient to completely destroy the phosphatase content of the milk (Proctor and Goldblith (1951B).

The practical findings of a number of workers who have found tyrosine crystals in radiation-sterilized meats after storage at 72°–100°F. for several months also confirm the fact that enzymes *in situ* are relatively radiation resistant.

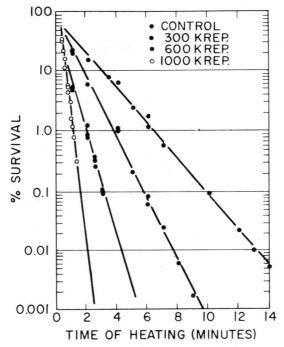

FIG. 83. EFFECT OF TIME OF HEATING AT 90°C. ON *Bacillus cereus* SPORES THAT HAVE BEEN PREVIOUSLY TREATED BY 3×10^5, 6×10^5 AND 1×10^6 REP OF GAMMA RADIATION FROM A COBALT-60 SOURCE

This points out the need to have some additional means, other than ionizing energy, in order to inactivate the enzyme systems in foods. The best known enzyme inhibitor is, of course, heat. Findings by Baker and Goldblith (1961) with peroxidase in peas show that there is no complementary effect of ionizing and thermal energy for enzymes as in the case of bacteria. Thus, irradiation doses in the sterilizing region do not markedly reduce the thermal energy requirements for enzyme inactivation, nor does the relatively small amount of heat needed to inhibit enzymes markedly affect the doses needed for sterilization.

Enzymes must be inhibited in foods to be radiation processed. By and large relatively small amounts of heat are still the best method that is available at the present time.

RADIATION—PROSPECTS

In the light of known science and technology, what are the prospects for radiation-preservation of foods? What types of foods? Of what will the processes consist?　Will radiation replace existing methods of preservation?

These are all cogent questions—but questions that need answers. The answers presented herein are, for the most part, pertinent mainly to the United States.　It should be recognized, however, that there may be other and different uses for various countries.

A priori, it is felt by the author that the basis of any proposed uses for ionizing energy in the food field must be premised on careful consideration primarily to the wholesomeness aspects.

It is for this reason that it is felt that there will be more immediate prospects for radiation-"preserved" foods (dose levels under 10^6 rad) than for radiation-sterilized foods.

The undesirable side-reactions as well as any possible effects on wholesomeness attributes are reduced by decreasing the dosages.

The present program of the U. S. Atomic Energy Commission is based on this premise.　Encouraging results have already been obtained in the author's laboratories using radiation-preserved fish[2] and other seafoods.　Not only are the dose levels less than with sterilization, but also the costs of the process are lessened by the lower dose (Brownell and Purohit 1956).

Similarly, results on the preservation of meat (in contrast to sterilization) are also encouraging.

There may indeed be similar preservation potentials with certain species of fruits which are now being studied at the University of California under Atomic Energy Commission contract.

Of economic potential, and technological feasibility as well, is the potential use of ionizing energy in conjunction with thermal energy, the one complementing the other.

With respect to other low dose applications, destruction of *Salmonellae* species in dried eggs is technologically feasible.　So too is the use of ionizing energy for the destruction of trichinae in pork and insects in grain and flour.

In the case of trichinae, there are equally efficacious methods of dealing with the problem, whereas in the case of insect destruction, prevention of reinfestation is still an important and paramount problem.　It is for these reasons that the writer does not feel that radiation will be used for these latter purposes.

In the case of radiation-sterilized products, however, certain ration items such as bacon are felt by the military not to be adversely affected by sterilizing doses of ionizing energy.　In addition, the whole-

---

[2] Fish treated by ~400,000 rad of ionizing energy and held at 32°–33°F. for upwards of two weeks.

someness studies on this and a few other products are well under way and soon definitive information should be available.

At the time of writing this paper, large-scale pilot plant-production studies on several million pounds of potatoes are being conducted in Canada. The irradiation dose level of 10,000 rad being used is sufficient to inhibit sprouting of the potatoes and all look with interest at the results of the Canadian large-scale tests.

In the light of what is now known, and with due scientific conservatism and yet realistic optimism, one can, it is believed, realistically expect some uses of ionizing energy in the food field in the next decade. Just as frozen foods did not replace canned foods, but rather freezing complemented canning and many of the successful freezers were and are successful canners, so radiation processing will not replace canning or freezing. Instead, it too will find its own place among our known preservation methods, complementing but not supplanting present methods and thus offering an additional means of continuing man's combat against the forces of nature which destroy his food supply.

BIBLIOGRAPHY

ANON. 1961. Sources of Radiation used for Inspection of Food, For Inspection of Packaged Food and For Controlling Food Processing. Regulation Published in Federal Register, March 2, (21 CFR part 121).

ATTIX, F. H. 1959. High level dosimetry by luminescence degradation. Nucleonics 17, No. 4, 142–148.

BAKER, R. W., and GOLDBLITH, S. A. 1961. The complementary effects of thermal energy and ionizing energy on peroxidase activity in green beans. Food Science 26, 91–94.

BEELEY, R. J. 1956. Logistic and Economic Feasibility Study on Radiation Sterilization of Foods. Final Report to U.S. Army Quartermaster Corps on Contract No. DA 19-129-QM-491 for period June 23, 1955 to August 28, 1956.

BEELEY, R. J. 1958. Radiation processing of foods. Nuclear Science and Engineering 3, 660–693.

BIERMAN, G. W., PROCTOR, B. E., and GOLDBLITH, S. A. 1956. Radiation preservation of milk and milk products. II. Off-flavors in milk and cream induced by ionizing radiations as judged by organoleptic tests. J. Dairy Sci. 39, No. 4, 379–390.

BROWNELL, L. E., and PUROHIT, S. N. 1956. Combining gamma radiation, refrigeration. Refrigerating Eng. 64, No. 6, 39–50.

BURRILL, E. A. 1957. Ionizing radiations—A new chemical engineering tool. Chem. Eng. 64, 235–241.

CHARLTON, E. E., and WESTENDORP, W. F. 1944. Two Million Volt Mobile X-Ray Unit. Proc. First National Electronics Conference.

CHARLTON, E. E., WESTENDORP, W. F., DEMPSTER, L. E., and HOTALING, G. 1939. A new million volt x-ray unit. J. Appl. Phys. 10, 374–385.

CLELAND, M. R. 1959. Voltage Multiplication Apparatus. U. S. Pat. 2,875,394.

CLELAND, M. R., and MORGANSTERN, K. H. 1960. 1. Dynamitron—A high power electron accelerator. Nucleonics 18, No. 8, 52–53.

COOLIDGE, W. D., and MOORE, C. N. 1926. Some experiments with high voltage cathode rays outside of the generating tube. J. Franklin Inst. 202, 722–735.

CORSON, M., GOLDBLITH, S. A., PROCTOR, B. E., HOGNESS, J. R., and LANGHORN, W. H. 1951. The effect of supervoltage cathode rays on p-aminobenzoic acid and anthranilic acid labeled with C^{14}. Arch. Biochem. Biophys. *33*, No. 2, 263–269.

DAVISON, S., GOLDBLITH, S. A., and PROCTOR, B. E. 1956. Glass dosimetry. Nucleonics *14*, No. 1, 34–39.

DESROSIER, N. W., and ROSENSTOCK, H. M. 1960. Radiation Technology in Food, Agriculture and Biology. Avi Publishing Co., Westport, Conn.

DEWEY, D. R. II, NYGARD, J. C., and KELLIKER, M. G. 1954. Electron linear accelerators for radiation processing. Nucleonics *12*, No. 12, 40–41.

FANO, U. 1953. Gamma-ray attention. Nucleonics *11*, No. 8, 8–12.

FARKAS, D. F., and GOLDBLITH, S. A. 1962. Studies on the kinetics of lipoxidase inactivation using thermal and ionizing energy. J. Food Sci. 27, 262–276.

FOSTER, F. L., DEWEY, D. R. II, and GALE, A. J. 1953. Van de Graaff accelerators for sterilization use. Nucleonics *11*, No. 10, 14–17.

FRICKE, H., and MORSE, S. 1929. The action of x-rays on $FeSO_4$ solutions. Phil. Mag. *7*, 129.

GLASS, R. A., and SMITH, H. D. 1959. Radioactive Isomer Production in Foods by Gamma Rays and X-Rays. Final report to Army Quartermaster Corps on Contract DA 19-129-QM-1511 for the period November 26, 1959 to August 31, 1960.

GLASS, R. A., and SMITH, H. D. 1960. Radioactivities Produced in Foods by High Energy Electrons. Summary Technical Report of the Stanford Research Institute with the Department of the Army, Contract DA 19-129-QM-1100, No. 10, S-572. (period Jan. 5, 1958 to Dec. 1, 1959).

GOLDBLITH, S. A. 1959. Direct and Indirect Effects of Radiation. Proc. Inter. Conf. on the Preservation of Foods by Ionizing Energy, 91–102. (July 27–30).

GOLDBLITH, S. A., and PROCTOR, B. E. 1952. Evaluation of food sterilization efficiency. Nucleonics *10*, No. 9, 28–29.

GOLDBLITH, S. A., and PROCTOR B. E. 1954. Relative events of cathode rays and gamma radiation. Nucleonics *12*, No. 2, 32–35.

GOLDBLITH, S. A., PROCTOR, B. E., DAVISON, S., KAN, B., BATES, C. J., OBERLE, E. M., KAREL, M., and LANG, D. A. 1953. Relative bactericidal efficiencies of three types of high-energy ionizing radiations. Food Research *18*, 659–677.

GOLDBLITH, S. A., PROCTOR, B. E., and HAMMERLE, O. A. 1952. Evaluation of food irradiation procedures. Quantitative measurements utilizing high energy cathode rays. Ind. Eng. Chem. *44*, 310–314.

HANNAN, R. S. 1955. Scientific and Technological Problems Involved in Using Ionizing Radiations for the Preservation of Food. Dept. of Scientific and Industrial Research Food Investigation Special Report No. 61. Her Majesty's Stationery Office, London.

HANNAN, R. S. 1957. Radiation preservation of foods. J. Royal Society of Health *77*, 457–465.

HANNAN, R. S., and COLEBY, B. 1957. The food scientist looks at radiation. Nuclear Power *2*, No. 8, 1–5.

HARDWICK, T. J. 1952. The reduction of ceric sulfate solutions by ionizing radiations. Can. J. Chem. *30*, 23–38.

HARLAN, J. T., and HART, E. J. 1959. Ceric dosimetry: Accurate measurements at 10^8 rads. Nucleonics *17*, No. 8, 102, 107–111.

HART, E. J., KOCH, H. W., PETREE, B., SCHULMAN, J. H., TAIMUTY, S. I., and WYCKOFF, H. O. 1958. Measurement systems for high level dosimetry. Presented at the Second United Nations Conference on the Peaceful Uses of Atomic Energy. Paper A, Conf. 15/P/1927, U.S.A.

HENLEY, E. J. 1954. Gamma-ray dosimetry with cellophane-dye systems. Nucleonics *12*, No. 9, 62–63.

HENLEY, E. J., and MILLER, A. 1951. Gamma-ray dosimetry with polyvinyl-chloride films. Nucleonics 9, No. 6, 62–66.

HERSCHMAN, A. 1956. An estimate of the maximum induced radioactivity caused by electron irradiation of foods. Rept. 1 of Project No. 7-84-01-002 to QM. Food and Container Institute for Sept. 17, to Oct. 31.

HIGH VOLTAGE ENGINEERING CORPORATION. 1961. The microwave linear accelerator. A brochure of the High Voltage Engineering Corporation, Burlington, Mass.

HINE, G. J., and BROWNELL, G. L. 1956. Radiation Dosimetry. Academic Press, Inc., New York.

HOLLAENDER, A., STAPLETON, G. E., and MARTIN, F. L. 1951. X-ray sensitivity of E. coli as modified by oxygen tension. Nature 167, 103–104.

HUBER, W., BRASCH, A., and WALY, A. 1953. Effect of processing conditions on organoleptic changes in foodstuffs sterilized with high intensity electrons. Food Technol. 7, 109–115.

HUBER, W., and HEID, J. L. 1956. Ionizing radiations in food products manufacture. Western Canner and Packer 6, No. 9, 25–28, 33–37.

JOHNSON, B. C., METTA, V. C., and TSIEN, W. S. 1958. The Effect of Irradiation Sterilization on the Nutritive Value of the Protein and Energy Components of Foods. Second United Nation Inter. Conf. on the Peaceful Uses of Atomic Energy. A. Conf. 15/P/799.

KAN, B., GOLDBLITH, S. A., and PROCTOR, B. E. 1957. Complementary effects of heat and ionizing radiation. Food Research 22, 509–518.

KEMPE, L. L. 1955. Combined effect of heat and radiation in food sterilization. Applied Microbiol. 3, 346–352.

KNOWLTON, J. A., MAHN, G. R., and RANFTL, J. W. 1953. The resonant transformer: A source of high energy electrons. Nucleonics 11, No. 11, 64–66.

KRAYBILL, H. F. 1958. Nutritional and biochemical aspects of foods preserved by ionizing radiation. J. Home Econ. 50, 695–700.

KREIDL et al. 1959. Measuring large radiation doses. (A series of papers by Kreidl, Blair, Nitka, Attix, Artandi, Chandler, Taimuty, Scholl and Harmer.) Nucleonics 17, No. 10, 57–76.

KREIDL, N. J., and BLAIR, G. E. 1956. Recent developments in glass dosimetry. Nucleonics 14, No. 3, 82–83.

KREIDL, N. J., and BLAIR, G. E. 1960. A system of megaroentgen glass dosimetry. Nucleonics 18, No. 1, 56–60.

LAUGHLIN, J. S., OVADIA, J., BEATTIE, J. W., HENDERSON, W. J., HARVEY, R. A., and HAAS, L. L. 1953. Some physical aspects of electron beam therapy. Radiology 60, No. 2, 165–184.

LEA, D. E. 1947. Actions of Radiation on Living Cells. Macmillan Co., New York.

LEVIN, S. 1954. Radiological safety in cathode-ray sterilization. Nucleonics 12, No. 6, 54–57.

LITTLE, ARTHUR D., INC. 1959. Radiation: A Tool for Industry-(A Survey of Current Technology.) A report prepared for The Emerson Radio Phonograph Corporation (CEM Group) under Contract AT (49-10)-1485 with the Office of Isotopes Development of the U.S.A.E.C. and for the General Electric Co., Hanford Atomic Products Operation under Contract W-31-109-Eng-52 to the Div. of Production of the U.S.A.E.C.

MANOWITZ, B., KUHL, O. A., and GALANTER, L. 1957. A Megacurie Cobalt-60 Food Irradiator. Second Nuclear Engineering and Science Conference, March 11–14, Philadelphia, Pa. Paper No. 57-NESC-86.

MANOWITZ, B., METZ, D. J., and BRETTON, R. H. 1956. Design study of a megacurie source. Science 124 (3226), 814–817.

MAYNEORD, W. V., MARTIN, J. H., and LAYNE, D. A.   1949.   Production of radioactivity in animal tissues by high energy x-rays.   Nature (London) *164*, 728.

MILLER, C. W.   1954A.   An 8-mev linear accelerator for x-ray therapy.   Proc. Institution of Electrical Engineers *101* part 1, No. 130, 207–222.

MILLER, C. W.   1954B.   Industrial radiography and the linear accelerator. J. Brit. Inst. of Radio. Engineers *14*, No. 8, 361–375.

MORGAN, B. H., and REED, J. M.   1954.   Resistance of bacterial spores to gamma irradiation.   Food Research *19*, 357–366.

NATIONAL BUREAU OF STANDARDS.   1959.   Maximum permissible body burdens and maximum permissible concentrations of radionuclides in air and in water for occupational exposure.   Handbook 69, National Bureau of Standards. (Recommendation of the National Committee on Radiation Protection.)

NEWBERY, G. R.   1949.   The microwave linear electron accelerator.   Brit. J. Radiol. *22*, No. 260, 473–486.

NITKA, H. F.   1959.   Photographic methods (in symposium on dosimetry). Nucleonics *17*, No. 10, 58–59.

PRICE, B. T., HORTON, C. C., and SPINNEY, K. T.   1957.   Radiation Shielding. Pergamon Press, New York.

PROCTOR, B. E., and GOLDBLITH, S. A.   1948.   Effect of high-voltage x-rays and cathode rays on vitamins (niacin).   Nucleonics *3*, No. 2, 32–43.

PROCTOR, B. E., and GOLDBLITH, S. A.   1951A.   Electromagnetic radiation fundamentals and their application in food technology.   Advances in Food Research *3*, 119–196.

PROCTOR, B. E., and GOLDBLITH, S. A.   1951B.   Food processing with ionizing radiations.   Food Technol. *5*, 376–380.

PROCTOR, B. E., and GOLDBLITH, S. A.   1952A.   A Critical Evaluation of the Literature Pertaining to the Application of Ionizing Radiations to the Food and Pharmaceutical Fields.   Report No. NYO 3337, Jan. 1, to the U.S.A.E.C., Contract AT(30-1)-1164.

PROCTOR, B. E., and GOLDBLITH, S. A.   1952B.   Prevention of side effects in sterilization of foods and drugs by ionizing radiations.   Nucleonics *10*, No. 4, 64–65.

PROCTOR, B. E., GOLDBLITH, S. A., BATES, C. J., and HAMMERLE, O. A.   1952. Biochemical prevention of flavor and chemical changes in foods and tissues sterilized by ionizing radiations.   Food Technol. *6*, 237–242.

PROCTOR, B. E., and O'MEARA, J. P.   1951.   Effect of high-voltage cathode rays on ascorbic acid—*in vitro* and *in situ* experiments.   Ind. Eng. Chem. *43*, 718–721.

PUBLIC HEALTH SERVICE.   1960.   Radiological Health Handbook.   (Compiled and Edited by the Division of Radiological Health).   U. S. Dept. of Health, Education and Welfare, Washington, D. C.

RANFTL, J. W.   1956.   Sterilization by radiation.   Presented at Fall Meeting of Amer. Drug Manufacturers Assoc., Production and Engineering Section, Oct. 19, Boston, Mass.

RANFTL, J. W.   1957.   Economics of electron beam irradiation.   Presented at the Second Industrial Nuclear Technology Conference, May 16, Chicago, Ill.

SARAVACOS, G. D., HOFF, J. E., GOLDBLITH, S. A., and WICK, E. L.   1961. Radiation preservation of milk and milk products.   XII.   Radiation sterilization of milk in a rotary-disc apparatus.   J. Food Tech. *15*, No. 5, 239–241.

SCHULER, R. H.   1958.   Absolute dosimetry of irradiations with charged particles.   Paper No. A/Conf. 15/P/761.   Presented at the Second United Nations International Conf. on the Peaceful Uses of Atomic Energy.

SCHULMAN, J. H., ETZEL, H. W., and ALLARD, J. C. 1957. Application of luminescence changes in organic solids to dosimetry. J. Appl. Phys. *28*, No. 7, 792-795.

SCHULMAN, J. H., KLICK, C. C., and RABIN, H. 1955. Measuring high doses by absorption changes in glass. Nucleonics *13*, No. 2, 30–33.

SHEHATA, A. M. EL-TABEY. 1961. Effect of combined action of ionizing radiation and chemical preservatives on microorganisms. 1. Vitamin K_5 as a sensitizing agent. Rad. Res. *15*, No. 1, 78–85.

SKAGGS, L., LAUGHLIN, J. S., HANSON, A. O., and ORLIN, J. J. 1948. The electro-disintegration of Cu^{63}, Ag^{107} and Ag^{109}. Phys. Rev. *73*, No. 4, 420.

SLOAN, D. H., and LAWRENCE, E. O. 1931. The production of heavy high speed ions without the use of high voltages. Phys. Rev. *38*, No. 11, 2021–2032.

STOCKMAN, C. H., and BAUMAN, R. G. 1957. Machines give cheaper radiation. Chem. Eng. News *35*, No. 31, 16–21.

TAIMUTY, S. I. 1957. A Comparative Study of the Effects of High and Low Intensity Radiation in Food Sterilization. Report No. 9, (Termination, dated Sept. 17, 1957) Contract DA 19-129-QM-429. With the Department of the Army, Quartermaster Corps, for the period June 1, 1955 to August 31, 1957.

TAIMUTY, S. I., GLASS, R. A., and DEAVER, B. S. 1958A. High level dosimetry of gamma and electron beam sources. Presented at the Second United Nations International Conference on the Peaceful Uses of Atomic Energy. Paper A/Conf. 15/P/2014, U.S.A.

TAIMUTY, S. I., TOWLE, L. H., DEAVER, B. S., and PETERSON, D. D. 1958B. Obtaining a system of dosimetry. Progress and Final Reports on Contract No. DA 19-129-QM-766, with the U. S. Army Quartermaster Corps.

TRUMP, J. G., and VAN DE GRAAFF, R. J. 1948. Irradiation of biological materials by high energy roentgen rays and cathode rays. J. Appl. Phys. *19*, No. 7, 599–604.

TRUMP, J. G., WRIGHT, K. A., and CLARKE, A. M. 1950. Distribution of ionization in materials irradiated by two and three million-volt cathode rays. J. Appl. Phys. *21*, No. 4, 345–348.

VAN DE GRAAFF, R. J., COMPTON, K. T., and VAN ATTA, L. C. 1933. Electrostatic production of high voltages for nuclear investigation. Phys. Rev. *43*, 149–157.

VAN PATTER, D. M., and WHALING, W. 1954. Nuclear disintegration energies. Rev. Mod. Phys. *26*, No. 4, 402–443.

WERTHEIM, J. H., ROYCHOUDHURY, R. N., HOFF, J., GOLDBLITH, S. A., and PROCTOR, B. E. 1957. Irradiation preservation of milk and milk products. J. Agr. Food Chem. *5*, No. 12, 944–950.

WERTHEIM, J. H., HOFF, J. E., SARAVACOS, G. D., PROCTOR, B. E., and GOLDBLITH, S. A. 1959. Radiation preservation of milk and milk products VII. Radiation-distillation apparatus for using high energy electrons. Food Tech. *13*, 94.

WICK, E. L., HOFF, J. E., GOLDBLITH, S. A., and PROCTOR, B. E. 1961A. The application of radiation-distillation to the production and isolation of components of beef irradiation flavor. J. Food Sci. *26*, No. 3, 258–260.

WICK, E. L., TEI YAMANISHI, WERTHEIMER, L. C., HOFF, J. E., PROCTOR, B. E., and GOLDBLITH, S. A. 1961B. An investigation of some volatile components of irradiated beef. J. Agr. Food Chem. *9*, No. 4, 289–293.

CHAPTER 13

Carl S. Pederson | Processing by Fermentation

INTRODUCTION

The preparation and preservation of foods by fermentation processes are dependent upon the production by certain microorganisms of chemical substances inhibitive to the growth of undesirable microorganisms. The simplest example of such action is the inhibition of toxin-producing bacteria by the lactic acid produced in many fermented foods. Although fermentation is one of the most ancient methods of food preservation, it is still one of the least understood. Even in many food processing plants where fermentation is an essential step in processing of the food the operators are unaware of the role of the microorganisms involved. Since microorganisms were unknown for many centuries, obviously no one attributed the typical changes involved in various food products to microscopic forms of life. With the plentiful supplies of canned and frozen foods, many refrigerated foods, and various packaged foods available to this nation today, it is difficult to realize that approximately 90 per cent of the world's population is still dependent upon naturally dried foods such as cereals and fermented foods for their food.

From the dawn of human existence to our present complex social structure, man has always been concerned with means of preserving food. The laws of nature require that when an animal or plant dies, its organic material must be decomposed to make available again in the soil the elements for further use in new life. If this were not possible, elements necessary for life would soon be combined in complex forms which could not be utilized. This would eventually lead to the disappearance of all living forms from this earth. Nature has provided for the decomposition of every organic substance produced in nature. Prevention of any form of decomposition is, therefore, contrary to the forces of nature.

ROLE OF MICROORGANISMS

The primary role which microorganisms play is of a catabolic rather than metabolic nature. They decompose organic components of

---

CARL S. PEDERSON is Professor, Bacteriology, Food Science and Technology Department, New York State Agricultural Experiment Station, Cornell University, Geneva, N. Y.

foods to obtain energy for their growth. The processes are complex but ultimately the organic components are reduced to their elements to become part of the soil. Many types of microorganisms have evolved, each of which may have some specific role in this destructive process. The decomposition of many organic substances may involve a series of distinct changes brought about by various microorganisms. Each type has adapted itself to the environmental conditions in which it must exist.

Industrial fermentation is the conversion of a labile constituent (carbohydrate) by controlled biochemical decomposition into more stable substances capable of preventing or inhibiting microbial activity (ethyl alcohol, lactic acid, acetic acid, propionic acid, etc.). During this conversion the stability of the final product is increased both by removal of the relatively unstable constituent and its conversion into a substance that, in sufficient concentration, is a preservative. Products of fermentation can be used to preserve other foods.

Unlike preservation by freezing in which minimum alteration in the raw material qualities occurs, in preservation by fermentation there is the greatest change in character of the raw material. Fermentation processes, however, must be conducted under controlled conditions since natural uncontrolled fermentation ultimately leads to stabilization of carbohydrates by conversion into carbon dioxide and water.

One large group of bacteria which play an important role in this process consists of those bacteria that produce lactic acid. They carry on essential metabolic biological processes without oxygen by means of a complex series of intramolecular oxidations and reductions. Since they cannot utilize oxygen, the changes they accomplish do not decompose the matrix to basic components: carbon dioxide, water, simple nitrates and sulfates. Rather, the most commonly recognized end-product of their metabolism is lactic acid derived from sugar. They also produce other products from sugar and alter other food components.

It is this ability to convert carbohydrates to lactic acid, acetic acid, alcohol and carbon dioxide which has made this group so important to mankind in the preservation of edible and nutritive qualities in food. There is little caloric change in the conversion of carbohydrates to lactic acid. The bacteria, therefore, may be accused of an inefficient use of their energy source. This inefficiency, however, is fortuitous to mankind as it provides us with fermented food which can be utilized.

Early man has observed that many fermented food products in various stages of fermentation were not only edible and nutritious but in some cases more appetizing than the original substance. Although man knew nothing about the causes of such changes, he observed many of the environmental conditions most suitable for altering the food in the most desirable manner. Today we have considerable knowledge in regard to the nature of the biological changes and their optimal environmental conditions.

Practically every civilization has developed some type of acid food product as well as some type of alcoholic drink. Each has also observed a souring of alcoholic drinks and has used the soured products, or "vinegar," to flavor and preserve other types of foods. Every civilization that has domesticated animals has utilized the milk from such animals in the forms of soured milk, butter, and cheese. It is not at all surprising that there are over 400 names for varieties of cheese recognized in the world today. Among the products, alcoholic, acetic and lactic in nature, we have examples of the three primary methods of food preservation brought about by microorganisms: (1) yeast fermentation, resulting in the production of alcohol; (2) bacterial fermentation of alcohol to the acetic acid of vinegar; and (3) bacterial fermentation of carbohydrates to lactic acid and other byproducts. Although we are more aware of the alcoholic fermentations, the lactic fermentations are economically more important in feeding the populations of the world and, therefore, will be emphasized in this section.

The preservation of foods by lactic fermentation depends upon the production of lactic acid as a major end product of the activity of a number of types of lactic acid bacteria. The lactic acid inhibits the growth of other types of bacteria, particularly those which may cause illness if ingested. The foods involved may be classed in four categories: milk products, vegetable products, cereal products and meat products. These encompass a large variety of food products, such as soured milks, butters, cheeses, pickles, sauerkraut, olives, breads, sausages and many other foods (Table 91).

LACTIC ACID FERMENTATIONS

When considered separately, each fermentation seems to be complex and unrelated; however, when grouped by classes of food products and considered in the light of their environment, a great similarity is found among these fermentations. The lactic acid bacteria are carbohydrate fermenting. The species have adapted themselves to

TABLE 91

SOME INDUSTRIAL FERMENTATIONS IN FOOD INDUSTRIES

(I) Lactic acid bacteria
   (A) Vegetables and fruits
      (1) Cucumbers → dill pickles, sour pickles, salt stock
      (2) Olives → green olives, ripe olives
      (3) Cabbage → sauerkraut
      (4) Turnips → sauerrüben
      (5) Lettuce → lettuce kraut
      (6) Mixed vegetables, turnips, radish, cabbage → Paw Tsay
      (7) Mixed vegetables in Chinese cabbage → Kimchi
      (8) Vegetables and milk → Tarhana
      (9) Vegetables and rice → Sajur asin
      (10) Dough and milk → Kishk
      (11) Coffee cherries → coffee beans
      (12) Vanilla beans → Vanilla
      (13) Taro → poi
   (B) Meats → sausages such as salami, Thuringer, summer, pork roll,
            Lebanon bologna, cervelet
   (C) Dairy products
      (1) Sour cream
      (2) Sour milk drinks—acidophilus, yoghurt, cultured buttermilk,
            bulgarian, skyr, gioddu, leban, dadhi, taette,
            mazun
      (3) Butter—sour cream butter, cultured butter, ghee
      (4) Cheese—unripened → cottage, pot, schmierkase, cream
            whey → mysost, primost, ricotta, schottengsied.
            ripened → Cheddar, American, Edam, Gouda, Che-
            shire, provolone
(II) Lactic acid bacteria with other microorganisms
   (A) Dairy products
      (a) With other bacteria
         (1) Propionic acid bacteria—Emmenthaler, Swiss, Samso,
            Gruyére cheeses
         (2) Surface ripening bacteria—Limburger, brick, Trappist,
            Münster, Port de Salut
      (b) With yeasts—kefir, kumiss or kumys
      (c) With molds—Roquefort, Camembert, Brie, hand, Gorgonzola,
         Stilton, Blue
   (B) Vegetable products
      (a) With yeasts—Nukamiso pickles
      (b) With mold—tempeh, soya sauce
(III) Acetic acid bacteria—wine, cider, malt, honey, or any alcoholic and
     sugary or starchy products may be converted to vinegar
(IV) Yeasts
   Malt → beer, ale, porter, stout, bock, Pilsner
   Fruit → wine, vermouth
   Wines → brandy
   Molasses → rum
   Grain mash → whiskey
   Rice → saké, sonti
   Agave → pulque
   Bread doughs → bread
(V) Yeasts with lactic acid bacteria
   Cereal products → sour dough bread, sour dough pancakes, rye bread
   Ginger plant → ginger beer
   Beans → vermicelli
(VI) Yeasts with acetic acid bacteria
   Cacao beans
   Citron
(VII) Mold and other organisms
   Soybeans—miso, chiang, su fu, tamari sauce, soy sauce
   Fish and rice-lao, chao.

the environment to carry on their metabolic processes without using free oxygen. The organisms involved are included among species of four genera, *Streptococcus*, *Leuconostoc*, *Pediococcus* and *Lactobacillus*. All of these genera are included in the family *Lactobacteriaceae*. They have many characteristics in common. They are ordinarily considered sugar fermenters and it was generally assumed that they brought about little change in the other food components. All are relatively fastidious in their growth requirements, requiring certain proteins, vitamins, minerals and lipids even though their primary activity is apparently directed toward carbohydrates. Some of the essential vitamins can be replaced by certain fatty acids. Their requirements tend to group the various species, regardless of genera, by types which will ferment certain classes of food products.

The coccus forms include two homofermentative genera, *Streptococcus* and *Pediococcus*, and the heterofermentative genus, *Leuconostoc*. By the present system of classification all of the rod forms, both homofermentative and heterofermentative, are included in the single genus, *Lactobacillus*. The homofermenters convert carbohydrates primarily to lactic acid, while the heterofermenters convert carbohydrates to lactic and acetic acids, ethyl alcohol and carbon dioxide. Those of the second group also produce mannitol from fructose and may produce dextran from sucrose. Their complex metabolic changes, involving proteins, lipids, vitamins and other nutrients, have not been elucidated.

The various species among the genera often grow in a food product in a definite sequence, in the order of their increasing ability to form acids. The sequence is typical for each type of food product. In milk products containing lactose as the primary sugar, the typical sequence is *Streptococcus lactis* or *Streptococcus cremoris*, followed by *Lactobacillus casei* and then *Lactobacillus bulgaricus*. In vegetable products containing sucrose as the primary sugar, the typical sequence is more likely *Leuconostoc mesenteroides*, *Lactobacillus brevis*, *Pediococcus cerevisiae* and *Lactobacillus plantarum*. The essential nutrients involved in these sequences are not yet well defined. Because of environmental factors, the natural sequences of growth among cereal products and meat products particularly have not yet been elucidated. Knowledge of the effects of the physical and chemical environment necessary for growth of the various species of bacteria, yeasts, and molds is essential to the establishment of ideal conditions to insure that the metabolic changes that occur are those most desirable for the food product. This must begin with an understanding of the natural relationships among the various organisms.

Species of Lactic Acid Bacteria

There have been numerous attempts to arrange the species of bacteria in natural systems of classification. The necessity for applying names to species or kinds of bacteria is self-evident. It is highly desirable that the name applied to an organism by one person should be understood by others. It is further desirable that as far as practical, all individuals use the same name for the same kind of organisms. Thus some method of classification of the bacteria is essential if the names are to be rendered accessible and identification of unknown forms is to be made. It is important that all microorganisms of similar characteristics be grouped together. A species of bacteria is assumed to be one kind of organism. No rule can be laid down as to how much difference must exist between two cultures before one is justified in regarding them as distinct species. Groups of related species are included in a genus. Thus, when the name *Streptococcus lactis* is used, *lactis* is the specific name applied to all strains of bacteria with similar characters, and *Streptococcus* is the generic name to include all of the lactic acid producing coccus forms somewhat related to the specific species *S. lactis*. A Family in taxonomy is a group of related genera. An Order is a group of related families, and a Class is a group of related orders. Thus, in the seventh edition of Bergey's "Manual of Determinative Bacteriology" in the class *Schizomycetes* there are 13 orders including 47 families and 193 genera. However, when the subject of preservation of food by fermentation is discussed, we are confined almost entirely to bacteria in one family, *Lactobacillaceae*, which includes the species in four genera, namely *Streptococcus*, *Leuconostoc*, *Pediococcus* and *Lactobacillus*. To be more complete, the propionic acid producers of the genus *Propionibacterium*, and the acetic acid producers, genus *Acetobacter* should be included. Other species may be involved in certain food products. In addition, a number of species of yeasts and molds are involved in some fermentations. These will be discussed in the individual sections in which they are involved.

In order to have a more clear understanding of the relationship among these bacteria, a part of the keys from the Seventh Edition of Bergey's Manual (1957) is presented with comments, particularly as to occurrence.

Division I. Schizophyta Cohn 1875 (Fission plants).
Class II—Schizomycetes, von Naegeli 1857 (Fission fungi, bacteria).
Order IV. Eubacteriales Buchanan, 1917 (The true bacteria).
Eu.bac.te.ri.a' les; Greek prefer *eu* meaning true; Greek *bacterium* a small rod; *ales* ending denoting order.

Simple undifferentiated, rigid cells which are either spherical or straight rods. There are nonmotile as well as motile species. All of the species in certain families are definitely Gram-negative, in other families the majority of species are Gram-positive. Reproduction is by transverse fission.

Family X. *Lactobacillaceae.* Winslow *et al.* (1917).

Lac.to.ba.cil.la' ce.ae. Latin *lac, lactis* milk; Latin *bacillus*, a little rod; *aceae* denotes family ending.

Long or short rods or cocci which divide like rods in one plane only, producing chains, occasionally tetrads; filamentous as well as so-called false branching forms sometimes occur. Usually nonmotile but may be motile. Gram-positive. Pigment production rare; a few species produce a yellow, orange, red or rusty brown pigment. Gelatin liquefaction rare. Surface growth on all media is poor or absent. Carbohydrates are essential for good development; they are fermented to lactic acid, sometimes with volatile acid, alcohol and carbon dioxide as by products. Nitrites not produced from nitrates, but among the strict anaerobes there are a few species that are known to reduce nitrates. Microaerophilic to anaerobic, found regularly in mouth and intestinal tract of man and other animals, in food and dairy products, and in fermenting vegetable juices.

Tribe I. *Streptococceae.* Trevisan 1889.

Cocci occurring singly, in pairs and in chains (rarely tetrads).

Genus II. *Streptococcus* Rosenbach 1884.

Strep.to.coc'cus. Greek *streptus* pliant; Greek *coccus* a grain, berry.

These species are of great economic importance in the dairy industry. Certain strains are employed as starter cultures in preparing cheeses and cultured milk drinks. Some strains are capable of fermenting citric acid when incorporated with a fermentable sugar with production of carbon dioxide, acetic acid and diacetyl. Normally they produce dextro lactic acid from sugars; they acidify and curdle milk.

Species 14. *Streptococcus thermophilus.* This is the species employed as a starter for Swiss cheese.

Species 16. *Streptococcus faecalis.* This species is easily distinguished from other *Streptococcus* species by their wide temperature limits for growth, their salt tolerance and their ability to initiate growth at pH 9.6. They are found in the intestines of humans and warm blooded animals and sometimes in fermenting dairy and vegetable products.

Species 18. *Streptococcus lactis.* This species is commonly found in milk and other dairy products but it probably has a plant origin.

Species 19. *Streptococcus cremoris.* A species closely related to *Streptococcus lactis.* Also used in commercial dairy starters.

Genus III. *Pediococcus* Balcke 1884.

Pe.di.o.coc' cus Greek *medium* a plane; Greek *coccus* a berry, sphere.

These are saprophytic organisms found in fermenting vegetables, mashes, beer and wort. They occur as cocci singly, in pairs, as tetrads, and occasionally in short chains. They produce inactive lactic acid and in larger quantities than streptococci. Although some strains will grow in milk, they ordinarily do not find it a good medium and seldom produce enough acid to curdle the milk.

Species I. *Pediococcus cerevisiae.* Widely distributed in fermenting materials such as beer, sauerkraut and pickles.

Species II. *Pediococcus acidolactici.* Found in mash and unhopped wort.

Genus IV. *Leuconostoc* van Tieghem emend Hucker and Pederson.

Leu.co.nos' toc. Greek *leucus* clear, light; Latin *Nostoc* algal generic name.

These are saprophytic organisms found in milk, plant juices including those from sugar cane, vegetables and fruits. The cells are normally spherical and may occur singly, in pairs, or in short chains. In sucrose solutions many strains grow with a characteristic slime formation by which they may be characterized. Generally acid, lactic and acetic, is produced as well as alcohol and carbon dioxide. Fructose is sometimes reduced to mannitol. The lactic acid is levorotatory. They do not grow well if at all in milk and seldom curdle it. Of the three species, *L. mesenteroides* is most often found among fermenting vegetables and fruit products while *L. citrovorum* is most often found in milk and dairy products.

Species I. *Leuconostoc mesenteroides.* Most active of the genus. Encountered in fermenting vegetable materials and meat products. Isolated from slimy sugar solutions.

Species II. *Leuconostoc dextranicum.* Found in plant materials and in milk products.

Species III. *Leuconostoc citrovorum.* Isolated from dairy products.

Tribe II. *Lactobacilleae* Winslow *et al.* 1920.

Straight or curved rods, usually occurring singly, or in chains, sometimes in filaments; false branching may occur. Non-motile—non-spore forming. Gram positive—microaerophilic.

Genus I. *Lactobacillus* Beijerinck 1901.

Lac.to.ba.cil'lus. Latin *lactis* milk. Latin *bacillus*, a small rod.

These are saprophytic organisms. Species 1, 2, 3, 4, 5, 6 and 8 are primarily associated with milk products. The other species are associated with fruit, vegetable and cereal products. There are numerous other specific names applied to organisms similar in character to those listed. Many of these may be recognized as distinct species on the basis of further study. Many of these specific names will be discussed in the various sections dealing with the food product.

Homofermentative, producing lactic acid as major growth product.

Species 1. *Lactobacillus caucasicus* isolated from kefir and from cheese.

2. *Lactobacillus lactis* isolated from cheese and sour milk.

3. *Lactobacillus helveticus* isolated from cheese and sour milk.

4. *Lactobacillus acidophilus* isolated from feces of milk fed infants.

5. *Lactobacillus bulgaricus* from milk products at high temperature.

6. *Lactobacillus thermophilus* from pasteurized milk.

7. *Lactobacillus delbrueckii* from sour mash and fermenting vegetables.

8. *Lactobacillus casei* from milk and cheese.

9. *Lactobacillus leichmannii* from dairy and plant products.

10. *Lactobacillus plantarum* widely distributed in fermenting plant and animal products.

Heterofermentative, producing lactic acid, acetic acid, alcohol and carbon dioxide from glucose; mannitol from fructose, occasionally dextran from sucrose.

11. *Lactobacillus pastorianus* from sour beer and distilling yeast.
12. *Lactobacillus buchneri* from fermenting vegetable material.
13. *Lactobacillus brevis* widely distributed in plant and animal products.
14. *Lactobacillus fermenti* widely distributed in plant and animal products.

Family XI. *Propionibacteriaceae* Delwiche.

Pro.pi.on.i.bac.te.ri.a′ce.ae Latin *Propionibacterium* the type genus; *aceae* denotes a family.

Genus I. *Propionibacterium* Orla-Jensen 1909.

Produce propionic and acetic acids and carbon dioxide. Nonmotile, non-spore forming, Gram-positive bacteria which occur as rods, diphtheroid rods which resemble streptococci and occasionally as club shaped and branching rods. They ferment lactic acids, carbohydrates and polyhydroxy alcohols with production of propionic and acetic acid, and carbon dioxide.

Species: Eleven species are listed. All are associated with dairy products but particularly cheese. A few strains have been isolated from other sources, soils, ensilage.

Order I. *Pseudomonadales* Orla-Jensen.

Family IV. *Pseudomonadaceae* Winslow *et al.*

Pseu.do.mo.na.da′ ce.eae

Genus III. *Acetobacter* Beijerinck.

A.ce.to.bac′ter. Latin *acetum*, vinegar; *bacter*, a rod or staff.

Oxidize various organic compounds to organic acids. Widely distributed in nature where they are particularly abundant in plant materials undergoing alcoholic fermentations. They are of importance for their role in the production of vinegar.

Species I. *Acetobacter aceti* from vinegar.

Species 1–7, from many fruits and vegetables, beverages, beer, grain mashes and similar products.

ENVIRONMENTAL FACTORS

To insure that the metabolic and physical changes which occur are those most desirable for the food product, a knowledge of the effects of the physical and chemical environment necessary for growth of the various species of bacteria, yeasts and molds is essential. The temperature of fermentation, the salt concentration, oxygen supply and freedom from or degree of contamination are some of the controlling factors of great importance. The specific conditions will in large part govern the course of fermentation. The effects of the various environmental factors may be more readily illustrated with the different vegetable fermentations. The same factors, however, have a pronounced effect in preparation of many other fermented foods, particularly the many cheese products.

Vegetable Fermentations

From the meager information available it seems that the Chinese may have been the first to preserve vegetables by fermentation processes. The present day "Yen Tsai," meaning vegetables preserved in brine, has been prepared from mixtures of the various vegetables available since ancient times. Turnips, radishes, cabbage and other vegetables were used in these preparations with little regard for proportions. Salt, if available, was added. Little is known about the bacteriology and chemistry of these predecessors of sauerkraut, but much can be assumed from present knowledge of fermented cabbage. The first description of the preparation of sauerkraut as it is known today is in the publication, "A Treatise on Scurvy," by Lind in 1792. However there are and were a number of variations, some of which will be mentioned later. Little was known in regard to the nature of these fermentations until relatively recently. The influence of environmental factors are at least partly elucidated today. A fermentation in which $2^1/_4$ per cent salt is added to the finely shredded cabbage, held at about 65°F., will be accomplished by growth of a sequence of bacterial types beginning with the heterofermenting coccus *Leuconostoc mesenteroides*, followed by the heterofermentative rod, *Lactobacillus brevis*, and the homofermentative rod, *Lactobacillus plantarum*. *Pediococcus cerevisiae* is often found, usually in limited numbers. Lactic acid, acetic acid, ethyl alcohol and carbon dioxide are the primary products of fermentation. The carbon dioxide tends to flush out free entrapped oxygen and thus protect ascorbic acid against oxidation. The alcohol combines with acids to form esters. Lactic acid and acetic acid occur in proportions of about 4 to 1. Even when only partially fermented, reducing sugars may be entirely absent. They are converted early during the fermentation to mannitol and dextrans. These may be present in variable quantities in the fully fermented product. The proteins are altered somewhat and there may be some change in sulfur components. Lipids are partially hydrolyzed to yield free fatty acids. Among these lipids, the phospholipids may yield choline which combines with the acids to form the esters, acetyl and lactyl choline. The final result is a product that has a typical distinctive mellow fermented acidic flavor with little of the typical sulfur-like cabbage character. However, if certain conditions are changed, the fermentation is altered and the resultant sauerkraut may be quite different. Salt concentration, temperature of fermentation, oxygen supply and the bacteriological sanitary condition are the environmental factors that have been shown to be most important in attaining an excellent product. Excess salt will partially or entirely inhibit the heterofermentative bacteria, and favor the more salt tolerant species, *Streptococcus faecalis*, *Pediococcus cerevisiae* and *Lactobacillus plantarum*. Since salt is not distributed uniformly, all three of these species will be found in some part of a vat of kraut. All are homofermentative species. Thus in such a fermentation lactic acid is produced in relatively larger proportions. Since carbon dioxide, ethyl alcohol and acetic acid are present in lesser quantities, the protective influence of carbon dioxide is reduced and the ester-like flavor due to alcohol and acid is reduced. Since lactic acid has a higher dissociation constant than acetic acid, a lower pH value is obtained even though less total acid is present. The resulting kraut is inferior in quality. If the salt content is considerably higher than three per cent, heterofermentation may be entirely inhibited, and yeast growth, particularly pink yeasts, is favored. On the other hand, when the salt content is too low, enzyme activity is not inhibited to the same degree and softening may occur. Furthermore, less brine is formed and it may be insufficient to cover the solid shreds for the first several hours or a day. Air entrapped in the shredded cabbage will favor yeast growth.

High temperatures of 80° to 90°F. may have a similar effect upon a fermentation but the cause is somewhat different. The higher temperatures are more favorable to the growth of the various homofermentative than to the heterofermentative species. These species, therefore, play a greater role, particularly in the early stages of fermentation and produce lower proportionate amounts of carbon dioxide, ethyl alcohol and acetic acid, as well as mannitol and dextran. In addition, there appears to be a more rapid alteration of certain sulfur compounds which in cabbage, have a reducing effect and tend to aid in retaining the natural color. Raised temperatures also increase the rate of enzyme action and may cause softening of texture.

In a similar manner bacteriological cleanliness is very important in such fermentations. Since the complete fermentation is the result of growth of a sequence of bacterial species, the species surviving on the inside of the walls of a tank are the high acid, homofermentative type. If not removed they tend to serve as a mass inoculum or starter for the next filling of the tank, resulting in a predominating homofermentation. Such mass inocula have often been the cause of inferior areas of kraut adjacent to the side of the kraut vats. Common practice therefore among better packers is to coat the inside walls of a tank with hot paraffin to penetrate into the pores of the wood. This facilitates removal of bacteria from a previous fermentation as well as slime molds which develop after the tank is emptied. The principle of mass inoculation is essential in other types of food fermentation, as will be subsequently discussed.

Today most kraut packers cover the kraut in vats or tanks with some type of plastic cover, filling the cover with water or weak salt brine to serve as a weight. This weight should be sufficient to keep the brine level up to the level of the solids to exclude air. Mold and yeast growth, so common on the surface of kraut packed before the use of plastic covers, often causes marked changes in the character of the product. However, it must be realized that consumers were at one time so accustomed to the character produced by such secondary fermentations, that they expected these strong flavors and softer texture, and felt that the product was improperly cured if the kraut was mild-flavored and more acid. This type of secondary fermentation has been utilized in many other fermented foods to impart characteristics desired by many consumers. Cheeses such as Roquefort and Limburger, fermented beans, such as tempeh and sauces such as soy sauce are in this category. Incidentally, it is interesting that in preparing fermented foods, the Chinese in some areas, use a type of container with a moat around the top so that a water seal may be used. This is effective in excluding air and controlling mold and yeast growth.

Many other leafy and root vegetables, when cut up, will ferment in a manner very similar to cabbage and yield quite satisfactory fermented foods. However, the character of the products is quite different from sauerkraut and in general they are not so acceptable. For example, turnips ferment well, but because of their high sulfur content and strong flavor yield a product which is too highly flavored for many people. Radishes also have this characteristic but, in addition, do not have sufficient sugar to yield a good acid product. Since beets contain considerable sucrose, a large amount of dextran is produced by the leuconostoc. The fermented product is usually viscous or slimy. Sliced green beans ferment well but because of their higher buffer content they show slow change in pH values. Green tomatoes when sliced will ferment but due to their acidity the leuconostoc stage of the fermentation may be partially inhibited.

In some countries in Europe, the whole heads of cabbage are fermented in a salt brine similar to methods used in pickling cucumbers. In this method unless a higher concentration of salt is used than customary in making conventional sauerkraut, the center of the heads of cabbage will soften in texture. The penetration of salt brine and acid into the head occurs apparently at such a level that a final salt concentration of about $3^1/_2$ per cent is necessary. Since there is initially a much higher concentration of salt in the brine, the fermentation rate is retarded and the relative effect of the heterofermentative species is lessened. Many vegetables other than cucumbers, such as cauliflower, onions, green tomatoes and beans are preserved in brine. Problems are varied in character. Cauliflower in low salt concentration brine will be fermented by leuconostoc, with a slimy dextran fermentation. Therefore they are often packed in a high concentration brine of 15 per cent salt or more. Salt brine penetrates into the small onions primarily through the vascular system. Poor penetration will result in softening of the inner part of the onions. Green tomatoes have a somewhat impervious skin and are quite acid. Thus in salt brines they tend to shrivel and sometimes the locule areas collapse almost entirely. Fermentation is relatively slow. Uncut green beans in salt brine ferment rapidly but because of their high buffer content due to high protein and mineral content, the pH changes are relatively slow. Sometimes due to the slow change in pH, a faulty fermentation may occur. Brussels sprouts will ferment in salt brine, but the fermented sprouts are uneven in texture and do not have the characteristic mellow, acidic flavor of sauerkraut. All of these products are fermented by the lactic acid bacteria. The relative influence of each species will depend in large part upon environmental conditions.

Cucumbers and olives lend themselves to a brine fermentation because of their relatively low acidity and their content of ample amounts of sugar and other nutritional substances. The fermented products have a pleasing characteristic of texture, flavor and color not found in many of the other fermented foods. Dill pickles and salt or acid pickles are fermented in relatively low brine concentrations, sometimes as low as five per cent salt. On the other hand, cucumbers for salt stock are packed in 20°, 30°, or 40° brines and even as high as 60°. The brines are usually held at this salt concentration by addition of more salt at intervals as the cucumbers absorb the salt. A few packers allow the concentration of salt in the brine to decrease without addition of more salt, at least until the early stages of fermentation and curing are complete. Needless to say the type of fermentation will be affected by the salt concentration more than by any other single factor. The fermentation of dill pickles and low salt acid pickles similar to the fermentation of sauerkraut, is carried on by the same sequence of lactic acid bacteria, i.e., *Leuconostoc mesenteroides, Lactobacillus brevis, Lactobacillus plantarum* and *Pediococcus cerevisiae*. The typical mellow, acidic character of these types of pickles to which Europeans are so accustomed, cannot be duplicated by preparation from fresh cucumbers or from salt stock. In fermentation for salt stock, small cucumbers which absorb salt readily and produce brine readily, will exhibit a sequential bacterial flora during fermentation. An acidity of about 1 to 1.2 per cent acid may be produced within a week or two. As the size and maturity of the cucumber is increased the relative absorption rate decreases. Penetration to the locule or seed area of the cucumber may be very slow. The problems of curing these cucumbers are thus increased. With large mature stock bloating may become a very serious problem and the fermented cucumbers may be suitable only for cut pickles or relish. As the salt concentration is increased in the brine, the role of the heterofermenters, *Leuconostoc mesenteroides* and *Lactobacillus brevis* decreases. In high salt concentration brines, fermentation may be entirely due to *Pediococcus cerevisiae* and *Lactobacillus plantarum*, and the fermentation product may consist primarily of lactic acid. In a similar way, at higher fermentation temperatures the relative influence of the homofermentative species is increased. The two great problems of the pickle industry, softening of salt stock on the one hand, and bloating on the other hand, are closely associated with salt concentration and fermentation temperatures. Penetration of salt is affected by variety, size and maturity. These are reflections of the permeability of the skin, the passage of brine through the vascular system and apparently the type of fermentation. Although less bloating occurs in low salt concentrations, at higher fermentation temperatures softening may become the more serious problem.

The fermentation of the different types of olives presents an interesting contrast in necessary environmental conditions conducive to producing the most desirable products. The dark brown color of ripe olives requires an exposure to air to induce oxidation of certain constituents and development of the desirable color. In contrast, the desirable, typical olive green color of the fermented green olive is impaired by contact with air.

It has been known for years that the several varieties of olives behave differently in processing. Differences among varieties and sizes are very important. The optimum salt concentration in the brine varies with varieties. This concentration will affect the bacterial flora as well as the amounts and relative proportions of fermentation end products. In low salt concentration brines, such as three per cent, one could expect growth and fermentation by a sequence of the bacterial species, *Leuconostoc mesenteroides*, *Lactobacillus brevis*, *Pediococcus cerevisiae* and *Lactobacillus plantarum*. With an increasing concentration of salt in the brine, the relative influence of the heterofermenting species will be lessened. Therefore in the high concentration of eight per cent salt, sometimes used, one would expect the fermentation to be carried on primarily by the more salt tolerant homofermenters. A slower fermentation would occur than in the lower concentrations of brine. Since lactic acid would be the primary acid former, the pH would be lowered more rapidly and therefore less acid would be produced.

Some of the observations on salting and the necessity of preliminary lye treatment have been known for centuries. The Romans valued the unripe fruit steeped in brine; pickled olives have been found among the buried ruins of Pompeii. Even then they were used to enhance the flavor of wine. However, little is known in regard to the methods used for their preservation.

The fresh green olives after harvesting are placed in a $1^1/_4$ to 2 per cent sodium hydroxide, lye, solution to destroy the bitter glucosides. The lye which is allowed to penetrate about $^2/_3$ to $^3/_4$ of the way to the pits, must be leached out with water before the olives are placed in barrels, covered with salt brine, and allowed to ferment. Naturally much of the soluble carbohydrates and other soluble constituents are leached out by this preprocessing. The amount of carbohydrate, buffering substances and nutrients remaining in the olives for bacterial growth and the concentration of salt in the brine are factors of great importance in fermentation. Naturally the acidity is less than that produced in cucumber pickle fermentations. The acidity in a good fermentation will rarely exceed 0.8 per cent.

Ripe olives are ordinarily started by soaking the olives in a series of lye solutions, $^1/_2$ to 2.0 per cent sodium hydroxide. This not only fixes the color but hydrolyzes the bitter glucoside. After each lye treatment, fresh water is added, and the olives are stirred and aerated so as to produce a uniform and intense color. After leaching out the excess lye, sometimes with addition of acid, the olives are covered with dilute salt solutions followed by canning. They may be canned before any fermentation occurs.

Several other methods are used for processing olives. Problems of spoilage are great, undoubtedly due in part to the necessity of lye treatment and the slower rate and lower acidity attained than with other fermented vegetable products.

The practice of storing vegetables as fermented products antedates recorded history. Methods of fermentation of the vegetables in the Orient vary considerably. Any vegetable or mixture of vegetables available in excess of immediate needs may be preserved. The Chinese "Yen Tsai" or "paw tsay" have their counterparts in other areas. "Kimchi" produced in Korea is prepared by first wilting Chinese cabbage in salt brine for several hours then pulling back the individual leaves and filling with a raw vegetable mixture, sometimes containing fish, between the leaves. After tying the leaves together again, the heads are packed in salt brine for fermentation. A rice and vegetable mixture "Sajur Asin" is prepared by fermentation in Indonesia and the fermented product, "Tarhana" containing vegetables is produced in Turkey.

Actually so little bacteriological and chemical study has been conducted with these products that little can be said about the most ideal environmental conditions, but it can be assumed that the conditions are similar to those for our own vegetable products.

Preservation of Meat Products

The freezing and icing of meats and fish for preservation have been practiced for centuries in Northern Europe and Asia. They also practiced salt preservation and desiccation. Salt curing of meats was well established in the time of Homer. It may have been practiced in the salt deserts of Asia since salt was not plentiful with the Greeks and Romans. Jews, Egyptians, Romans and Greeks inherited methods from each other.

Although various species of bacteria including the lactic acid bacteria are involved in the curing of meats, it is in the sausage industry where the lactic acid bacteria play the most important role in the curing and imparting of characteristic flavors to meat products. Like many other fermented foods, the origin of sausages can be traced to an obscure antiquity. They may have originated with the Ancient Babylonians or Chaldeans but certainly they were prepared by the Greeks and Romans. In fact, the Romans at the time of the Caesars were well acquainted with methods of preparing dry sausages of the salami type. These might be considered the forerunners of the many dry and semi-dry cured sausages prepared today, such as cervelet, salami, Thuringer, summer sausage, Genoa pepperoni, mortadella capicolla, Essex, Lebanon bologna, Goteborg and others.

The pleasant, tangy flavor of such sausages is brought about by fermentation by various lactic acid bacteria. Originally, before knowledge of the role of microorganisms in curing meat products, bacteria were accidentally introduced from the surroundings existing in a sausage preparation room. Bacteriological examination at a later date revealed the presence of several types of lactic acid bacteria. A method of controlled inoculation by strains of species of *Leuconostoc* and *Lactobacillus* was patented in 1940.

Several species of such starters yielded superior and constant results.

This might indicate that under uncontrolled conditions the growth of a sequence of bacterial types similar to those observed in vegetable fermentation were responsible for the pleasant tangy flavor. Recently a strain of *Pediococcus cerevisiae* has been found to yield superior sausage and still later another strain of this species has imparted an improved better character. As in the case of starters for milk products and wines, possibly it is no longer sufficient to designate only the species but rather a strain of a species as yielding the best results. *Micrococcus aurantiacus* has been used as a starter because of its ability to reduce nitrates to nitrites in curing. Most sausage formulations include added nitrites.

Experience with attempts to duplicate the characteristic flavor of Lebanon bologna which originated with the Pennsylvania Dutch may be cited as a case of effects of mass inoculation. This bologna could not be prepared in any plant except that in which it originated until it was found that certain strains of *Lactobacillus* were responsible for the flavor. When they were introduced in pure culture it was possible to duplicate the product in other plants.

Even though today bacterial flora are controlled to a large extent by mass inoculation, either by pure cultures or from the surroundings, other environmental conditions play an important role in preparation of the many types of sausage. The amount of salt added, the spice formulation, and carbohydrate added, as well as the specific temperature, are effective in controlling the rate of growth and fermentation. The final acidity attained at pH 4.0 to 5.5 is much lower than that attained in the many fermented vegetable products. Although the problem of contamination is increased, the important pathogens cannot develop in the semidry, salty foods.

Although the biologically produced lactic acid is effective in lowering the pH, it is doubtful if this alone is responsible for the stability of the sausages. Among the fatty acids, some of which are produced during fermentation, acetic acid has been most commonly used as a preservative. Propionic acid, an effective preservative in certain bakery products, and other lower molecular weight fatty acids, i.e., butyric, caproic, caprylic and capric, are effective inhibitors of microbial growth. Possibly others, lauric, myristic, oleic and linoleic acids which are bacteriostatic may be equally effective.

Bread Making

The Egyptians are credited with noting that leavening of bread dough yielded a lighter and more edible bread, and about 2600 B.C. they carried the art of bread baking to high perfection. Remains of cakes made with coarsely ground grain have been found in the Swiss lake-dwellings dating back to the stone age. Ovens for baking were found in the court yards of the Chaldeans. Biblical passages referring to the use of unleavened bread, would indicate that a leavened bread was also prepared. The seeding of the dough with air borne yeasts was undoubtedly accidental. The propagation of the fermentation system by carrying over some of the dough from one day's baking to the next and the methods of control were undoubtedly the basis of the bread bakers' art of that day. The art was carried on throughout the centuries. The knowledge of the fundamental principles involved originated with the work of Pasteur and the subsequent discoveries in the field of bacteriology.

The light, airy characteristic of our present day bread is primarily due to a yeast fermentation. Pure yeast cultures were not available until recently and still are not available in many areas of the world, where baking is dependent upon carrying part of the dough from one baking to the next in order to introduce the yeast. The rye and black breads of Europe and Asia depend upon this method. Today it is a well known fact that such doughs carried, in addition to the yeast, a variable amount of lactic acid bacteria. The organisms, *Lactobacillus brevis* (*Bacterium panis fermentatae*), *Lactobacillus delbrueckii*, *Lactobacillus plantarum* and others acidified the bread dough producing conditions unfavorable to the growth of detrimental organisms that may result in ropy bread, red bread and similar undesirable conditions. The control of these fermentations was and still is an art in many areas of the world. Production of the sour dough breads prepared in this country is dependent upon control of yeast and bacteria.

There are many in the industry today who feel that with present methods, certain lactic acid bacteria impart a desirable flavor to bread. Strains of leuconostoc and lactobacilli have been reported as improving flavor. In some rural areas today, bread doughs, but more often pancake doughs, are still carried over from day to day to propagate the yeast culture.

Fermented Milks, Sour Cream, Butter and Cheese

Foods prepared from milk illustrate a great variety of products as a result of different environmental conditions. The 400 to 500 names applied to cheeses included in about 18 types, and the various milk drinks, sour creams and butters are the results of accidental contamination and various conditions encountered in the many areas of the world. Although milk may possibly be fermented by a sequence of bacterial types, it seldom does, because of the differing conditions to which it is subjected.   Obviously one would not expect the same organisms to develop in the hot desert as in the cool climate of the Swiss Alps or the Saeters of Norway.   Furthermore a hot and dry climate will result in more rapid drying than would be experienced in a cool moist climate.

Milk has been subjected to many modifications throughout history. Souring of fresh milk was the simplest method of preserving the product for a period of time.   The accidental contamination from the containers used, from the air and from the body usually resulted in a soured product which was safe and nutritious.   Undoubtedly both cheese and butter were first accidentally prepared.

It is not known when animals were first domesticated to become servants of man or when milk and milk products were first used.   This came to pass long before man had advanced far enough to leave permanent records.   It is known that the cow and other domesticated animals have served man thoughout the ages as beasts of burden and as sources of food, and in some cases objects of worship and sacrificial offerings.   The ancient Egyptians left records of their interest in dairying in their writings and carvings.   Remains of milk, butter, and cheese have been found dating from about 3,000 B.C.   Ruins in the temple in Ur in Mesopotamia, said to date back to 3,000 B.C., depict the act of milking.   Records from India dating back to 2,000 B.C. indicate people were then raising cattle.   The Bible makes frequent reference to the use of milk (Deut. 32, 14, "Butter of kine, and milk of sheep).

Consumption of milk products that have undergone extensive changes as a result of the growth of microorganisms is common in all countries of the world in which milk is available.   They ordinarily have high food value and also appear to have certain therapeutic properties in correcting certain intestinal disorders.   In late years there has been a steady increase in consumption of fermented milk in the United States and in some localities fermented milks make up a considerable percentage of the total milk sales.   At present cultured buttermilk and yoghurt appear to be most popular.   However, several years ago, beneficial results ascribed to the use of acidophilus milk served to stimulate interest in fermented milks.

The familiar fermented milks are the results of acid fermentations in which the sugar (lactose) of milk is converted to lactic acid and other growth products.   There are two main types of fermentation.   The most important are the acid fermentations in which lactic acid is the main end product with only traces of other products such as acetic acid and carbon dioxide.   In the second type, acid and gas formation occur in various milk drinks.   This is a more complex fermentation, in which at least two types of bacteria and yeasts play the important roles. Contaminating organisms are often present and may influence the chemical changes that take place.

Although the consumption of sour milk drinks undoubtedly began shortly after man obtained milk from domesticated animals, it was probably realized that some preparations were more appetizing than others. Attempts were therefore undoubtedly made at an early date to simulate the conditions conducive to development of the most desirable drinks. Climatic conditions and use of certain containers obviously played an important role.

The consumption of sour milk drinks has continued through the centuries. Interest, stimulated by the work of Metchnikoff and physicians caused many others to become interested in this possible use for therapeutic values.

The best known of the sour milk preparations are yoghurt, acidophilus milk and cultured buttermilk. However, there are many preparations which may be similar. "Yogurt" of Turkey, "Gioddu" of Sardinia, "Dadhi" of India, "Leben" of Egypt, "Taette" of Scandinavia, "Mazun" of Armenia, and "Kesselo Mleko" of the Balkans are generally highly acid, curdled milks containing little or no alcohol and carbon dioxide. On the other hand, "kefir" and "kumiss" are limpid, mildly acid milks with a distinctly alcoholic character. These products are fairly constant when prepared in the various areas of the world. Considering the chances of contamination, it is not at all surprising that there is some variation.

In order to understand the preparation of various fermented milks, one must obtain a concept of differences existing among the microorganisms involved in the preparation of these products. Milk is an ideal medium for growth of a certain group of lactic acid bacteria, but oddly enough is a poor medium for growth of others in the same genera.

The milk-fermenting, lactic acid bacteria may be arranged in order of the amount of acid they are able to produce. This arrangement is important since each species and each strain within a species has a limited acid tolerance. When this acidity is attained, the organisms slowly die. When an organism is growing in the presence of a higher acid producing species, the lower acid producing bacteria die quickly when the acidity has exceeded the tolerance of the species. Among the true lactic acid producers involved in these fermentations, the lowest acid producers are the cocci, *Streptococcus lactis* and closely allied types, such as *Streptococcus cremoris*. These species are of great economic importance in the entire dairy industry. Strains of these are used in many commercial starters for cheese, as well as in cultured milk drinks. *Streptococcus faecalis*, a species more tolerant to the adverse growth conditions, and one which produces a slightly higher acidity, is frequently found in milk and may be confused with these forementioned species.   The rod forms in order of their approximate acid production are *Lactobacillus acidophilus*, *Lactobacillus casei*, *Lactobacillus lactis*, *Lactobacillus helveticus* and *Lactobacillus bulgaricus*.   There is confusion in regard to the identity of these species.   This is, in part, due to variability of strains and overlapping of characteristics, as well as a certain degree of change in characteristics with change in environment. For example, there is some evidence to indicate that *Lactobacillus acidophilus*, so important in acidophilus therapy, is a variant of *Lactobacillus casei* changed by its continued growth in the unfavorable environment of the intestinal canal.   Or one may state that *Lactobacillus casei* may be considered the variant which has become accustomed to the more favorable environment of milk.   Regardless of these considerations, the variations produced in different milk drinks are attributable in part to the different degrees of acidity produced. There are a great number of specific names applied to various milk producing strains but, in general, they are now ordinarily considered as synonymous with one or another of the above named species.

Although the fermentation of milk may be carried out by a more or less typical sequence of growth of certain lactic acid bacteria, the effects of environments are so pronounced that this seldom occurs.

For centuries such environmental conditions have influenced the types of fermented milks used in the various areas of the world.   However, the "Taette myelk" produced in sections of Norway and the high acid "yoghurt" of Bulgaria are essentially the same in that they are homofermentative lactic acid fermentations.   They differ primarily in the degree of acidity and thus the firmness of the curd.   The two milk drinks, "kefir" and "kumiss," differ from the other types in that they are fermentations brought about by a mixed flora of homofermentative lactic acid bacteria and yeasts.   In some instances sporeforming bacteria are present.   The yeasts as well as the homofermentative lactic acid bacteria ordinarily do not utilize lactose and must therefore depend upon the homofermentative lactics to hydrolyze the lactose and make glucose and galactose available.   The effervescent drink produced is quite different from the usual soured milk drink.   In the "kefir" fermentation, the bacteria, yeast and curdled milk form typical irregularly shaped grains which settle.   These when transferred to fresh milk are the inoculum to carry on the typical fermentation.   As prepared under native conditions in Europe and Asia undoubtedly certain contaminations with other organisms occur.

Today much of the buttermilk, yoghurt, bulgaricus, acidophilus and other milk drinks, the various types of cheese, and the butters are prepared with pure culture starter.   The use of this type of mass inoculation could be said to have originated with the ancients by their continued re-use of certain containers such as unglazed porous bowls and skin bags and pouches.   For centuries in Europe the practice of saving a pail of whey or buttermilk from one day's cheese making or butter churning to add to the next day's milk or cream was very common.   If the new product did not develop the desired flavor, common practice was to visit a neighboring operation to obtain a pail of whey or buttermilk.   Creameries in Denmark and Holland added buttermilk to fresh cream to hasten its souring as far back as 1860.   About 1890 pure culture starters, usually *Streptococcus lactis* were prepared with skim milk, previously heated to 180° to 190°F. and subsequently cooled to 70°F.

A starter can be any selected pure culture of a desirable organism capable of producing a flavor desired in a fermented milk, butter or cheese.   Cultures of *Streptococcus lactis, S. cremoris, S. thermophilus, Leuconostoc citrovorum, L. dextranicum, Lactobacillus bulgaricus, L. casei, L. helveticus, Propionibacterium shermanii* and others are used for specific purposes.   Sometimes a mixture of pure cultures are prepared, such as *Streptococcus lactis* and *Leuconostoc citrovorum*.   The latter is capable of utilizing citric acid, sometimes added to the milk to convert it to diacetyl.   Such·a starter mixture establishes conditions favorable for the conversion of acetylmethylcarbinol to diacetyl.   Diacetyl has been considered as a most important flavor ingredient of butter.   Certain lactones are also considered important flavor-forming substances.   Sweet cream butter is a relatively recent innovation.   In the past, most of the cream to be used for butter making was soured by lactic acid bacteria.   The development of certain characteristic flavors in butter is a result of this growth.   The production of lactic acid in the cream aids in inhibiting growth of microorganisms responsible for many of the defects in butter quality.

Sour cream for butter making is now ordinarily neutralized to about one-fourth of one per cent lactic acid by use of calcium carbonate, sodium bicarbonate or other neutralizers before it is pasteurized.   A starter is then added and the cream is allowed to ripen overnight.   Sweet cream may be made into butter immediately after pasteurization or the pasteurized cream may be treated with a starter to ripen the cream.

A clarified butter is made in various areas of Asia and Europe.   India's "Ghi" or "Ghee" was made from either cows' milk or buffalo milk.   It was often aged for years in order to develop characteristic rancid flavor.   It was also used as a medicinal agent., This may have been the butter referred to in the Hindu Veda written 3,500 years ago.

Sour cream is a favorite milk product among people of Europe.   It is used not only as a spread for butter but also for salad dressing, for creaming cheese and blending with soups.   The rich, creamy, soured and curdled product is also eaten as a pudding.   The typical Devonshire cheese can be classified as a sour cream.

Cheese, made from the milk from many different species of animals, was possibly the earliest form of dairy manufacture.   In general, cheese consists of much of the essential food nutrients of milk which can be collected into a curd.   This is done by souring with or without the addition of rennet.   The use of rennet may be traced to the ancient peoples who used skins and stomachs of animals as containers for milk.   The fermentation by microorganisms and the curdling due in part to the rennet in the stomach occurred naturally.   For centuries cheese making throughout the world was an art that was carried on through rule of thumb methods.   It is not at all surprising that there are 400 to 500 different names applied to cheeses of different types in the world today.   These might be grouped into relatively few types. They are most frequently classified on the basis of hardness but there is an overlapping in any classification.

The simplest cheese to make is ordinary cottage, pot cheese, or schmierkäse.   The milk is pasteurized, cooled to about 70°F. a lactic starter is added and rennet also may be added.   The milk is held until it curdles into a firm but not hard curd.   It is then heated to attain a definite firmness, the whey is drained off, it is washed with water ending with a very cold water, then drained and salted.   The curd resembles popped corn.   These cheeses are not ripened.

Cream cheese and American-made Neufchâtel cheese are variations. Cream cheese is a soft, unripened cheese usually containing more cream, but differs from cottage cheese in that the curd is stirred and heated to 115° to 125° to give a smooth creamy texture.

The whey from such cheese is frequently concentrated by boiling to one-fourth its original volume.   The albuminoids are skimmed off and then cooled with continuous stirring to prevent formation of large lactose crystals.   The sweet brown cheese is frequently mixed with cream, buttermilk, sugar or even spices to impart desirable characteristics.   Ricotta, Mysost, Primost, Schottengsied and many others are soft cheeses of this type.

Several types of soft cheeses are started in a manner somewhat similar to cottage cheese but the curd is placed in forms or molds and allowed to continue to drain until fairly solid. The cheeses are then removed from the molds and allowed to ripen by mold, yeast, and bacteria present on their surface or the microorganisms applied to the surface. The enzymes released by these organisms penetrate into the cheese causing a further curing and usually a softening of the curd. Camembert is the best known of this type although Bel Paese, Brie, Hand, Cooked and French Neufchâtel are also of this general type. For Camembert cheese the lactic acid starter is added and the milk is warmed to about 85°F. After the curd is set, the whey drained and the curd placed in hoops, it is allowed to stand about two days. The cheeses are removed from the hoops, placed in curing rooms at about 55°F. with a high humidity of 85 to 90 per cent. The secondary fermentation due primarily to the mold, *Penicillium camemberti*, produces a white, soft, felt-like surface growth. Slime producing bacteria sometimes grow on the surface. The surface of cheeses may take on a yellow to russet red color but the interior is creamy in texture and color. Others of the types mentioned above are variations produced by varied conditions.

Limburger, Trappist and Port du Salut are semisoft cheeses which depend upon a surface fermentation for a partial digestion of the curd. Limburger is prefermented at 85° to 95°F. with a lactic starter. After the curd is drained, it is placed into forms for making individual cheeses. These, when removed, are dry salted or immersed in salt brines and then placed on shelves in high humidity rooms. Yeasts and the bacterium *Bacterium linens* develop on the surface. The enzymes produce a semisoft cheese with a characteristic strong odor.

Brick and Münster cheeses are made in a similar manner but with less surface fermentation. The cheeses have less of the pungent odor of Limburger but are not as sharp as Cheddar.

Roquefort, Gorgonzola, Bleu cheese, Blue, Stilton and others are sharp highly flavored cheeses characterized by the blue veined growth of *Penicillium roquefortii*. The drained curds are dry salted over a period of a week, punched with holes to allow the mold to penetrate and then placed in racks to cure. The pure mold culture inhibits the growth of other molds and slime forming bacteria.

Cheddar is the best known of the hard type cheeses which include Edam, Gouda, Caciocavallo, Provolone, Cheshire, American and many others. The name Cheddar comes from the method of matting the curd. The pasteurized milk is cooled to 85° to 90°F.; sufficient starter is added to develop acidity at desired rate, and rennet is added. The curd is cut and stirred while draining the whey. When the whey is drained it is allowed to collect and then matted or cheddared. The curd is put through a curd mill, salted and transferred to cloth lined hoops and pressed. The cheeses after removal from the hoops are dipped in paraffin and cured at 40° to 50°F. for two months or more, even as long as a year. The cheese, white to yellow in color, somewhat smooth but neither rubbery nor granular in texture, with no holes, varies in strength of flavor depending upon its age.

Cheeses of somewhat the same texture but which are characterized by holes throughout include Swiss or Emmenthaler, Samso, and Gruyère. Swiss cheeses are large hard cheeses characterized by eyes or holes and the pleasing nut-like sweet flavor. Swiss cheese is fermented at somewhat higher temperatures. The starters always contain *Propionibacterium shermanii*, the eye former and usually *Streptococcus thermophilus* and either *Lactobacillus bulgaricus* or *L. lactis*. The propionic acid bacteria are responsible for flavor and eyes.

The very hard cheeses, Parmesan, Romano, Pecorina, Sapsago and others are used primarily for grating. Parmesan is fermented at 90° to 100°F. with a *Streptococcus thermophilus* starter. Draining of whey is continued over a longer period of time than for other cheese types and after salting the cheeses are dried for a week or more before placing in a curing room. There they are held for a year or more. They are cleaned and rubbed with oil at frequent intervals. Later they are coated with lamp black and burnt umber.

There are any number of variations of these cheeses obtained by flavoring, spicing, and processing. Essentially the differences obtained among these cheeses are due to methods of handling. All are fermented first by lactic acid bacteria, usually added as a starter. Temperature influences the rate of fermentation. Some undergo continued or a second fermentation.

In reviewing the methods of preparation of the many types of cheeses produced throughout the world one must conclude that almost all are the natural products of environment. Salt concentration, temperature, humidity, degree of exposure to air, and the effects of mass inoculation from equipment are some of the more important of these environmental factors. It may be said that if some of these products were introduced today as new products they would be unacceptable. However during decades of use in which their safety has been demonstrated, they have become standard articles of our diet.

Other Products

Today many other food products are fermented in identical ways, are just as nutritious and could be equally appetizing if we would accustom people to their use.

Starchy products such as those prepared from the corms of the taro root are fermented to yield considerable quantities of food for certain peoples. "Poi" produced in Hawaii undergoes a fermentation by microorganisms similar to those which cause vegetable fermentations. The usual soil and water borne organisms are present in the ground mass of the corms but the lactic acid bacteria control the fermentation. "Kishk" is prepared in Syria by adding sour milk to flour to make a dough. "Tarhana" produced in Turkey contains vegetables. Other fermented foods are prepared from starchy foods but little is known in regard to their biological changes. "Manoic" fermented in plantain leaves is consumed in tropical Africa.

The separation of the seeds of many fruits from the matrix by lactic fermentation methods has been practiced for years. Seeds, such as those of tomato, for example, are enveloped in a pectinous coating which tends to cause the seed matrix to mat in drying. When fermented, the pectinous coating is dissolved and separation is relatively simple. Incidentally, the acid condition produced is apparently effective in destroying or inhibiting development of some plant pathogens. The red coffee cherries each contain two beans surrounded by a hard coating with a pectinous layer. In order to dry the hard coating so that it can be readily removed, the outer slimy layers are subjected to a sweating or a fermentation process. It is not known whether the character of the fermentation affects the flavor of the coffee. Vanilla beans are fermented in a somewhat similar manner. In the process of fermentation and subsequent curing, glucosides are hydrolyzed. The vanillin and other flavor substances often crystallize on the surface of the bean as white or slightly yellow needle-like crystals. Cacao or cocoa beans are covered with a pectinous pulp when removed from the pods. The beans, gathered in piles for curing, are often covered with leaves to aid in keeping the mass moist. Little is known in regard to the organisms responsible for the changes that occur. but it would seem to be a mixture of lactics, soil bacteria and yeasts.

Acidification by lactic fermentation precedes the more obvious fermentations that follow in the manufacture of products such as soy bean sauce and "tempeh." Fermentation of a rice and vegetable mixture is commonly practiced in the Orient in products such as "Sajur Asin" of Indonesia.

Many vegetables are preserved in brine; cauliflower, whole head cabbage, turnips, peppers, tomatoes, okra and others. Similarly many other vegetables when suitably prepared by slicing and salting will ferment by bacterial processes similar to those of sauerkraut. Among these is the common animal food, silage. Although ordinarily prepared from corn, other forage crops are used singly or in combination to prepare silage.

In many areas of the world, and particularly in the Orient, many food items are prepared by fermentation. However since so little is known of the nature of the microbiological changes, these will not be discussed. Chinese preserved eggs, Natto, Nukamiso pickles, Tamari sauce, soy bean sauce and Miso are a few. However many of these are produced under so many variable conditions that it would be difficult to describe any standard method.

SPOILAGE TYPES OF LACTIC ACID FERMENTATIONS

It has been established that the growth of lactic acid bacteria in foods with subsequent production of lactic acid and other inhibitory agents controls the development of harmful microorganisms. There are a large number of food products in which growth of these lactic organisms causes typical biochemical changes. The changes, however, are not considered desirable and therefore the food product is considered spoiled. The best known of this class is ordinary sour milk. The rusty color of cheese is a defect caused by the abnormal growth of certain lactic acid bacteria. The original isolation of the heterofermentative lactic acid bacterium *Leuconostoc mesenteroides*, was obtained from sugar mills. The slimy dextran produced by the leuconostoc from sugar not only reduced the sugar content but also interfered with normal factory operations.

The organism which caused souring of beer was one of the first lactic acid bacteria described. Other species are now known to sour beer on occasion. Similarly the lower acid wines are subjected at all times to growth of the lactic acid bacteria. Since these wines are acid, the lactic acid bacteria do not grow well and the strains that develop are abnormal. Molasses, although often used in fermentation industries as a source of sugar for chemical by-products, also is undesirably spoiled at times by the lactics. Tomato products of many types furnish an excellent medium for growth of various lactic acid bacteria. Canned tomatoes, juice, catsup, pork and beans with tomato sauce, and other sauces containing tomato, such as Tabasco sauce, have at some time supported an undesirable fermentation. Similar fermentations have been observed in numerous foods during preparation for preservation. Canned vegetables and fruit products are often spoiled by one or another of the various species of this group of microorganisms. The product could be consumed without ill effects if there were assurance that no other organisms had grown in the food. The can, however, is usually swelled and therefore the product never reaches the market. In the normal fermentation of vegetables of many types, changes may occur which are considered undesirable. Sauerkraut and pickle brines are sometimes slimy and stringy, a condition caused by the prolonged growth of leuconostocs. The condition usually clears itself in later stages of fermentation. High sugar vegetables such as beets, may produce so much dextran during early fermentation that the sliminess is not cleared in later stages. In products such as sauerkraut, a disturbance of the normal sequential development of the different species results in an inferior product. Spoilage of salad dressings, slime formation, excessive souring and green discoloration of sausage and ham souring are other spoilage conditions caused by lactic acid bacteria.

Although consumption of such foods will not cause illness, "spoiled" products represent serious losses and so must be avoided. Each type of spoilage represents a different problem. Growth of atypical strains of normal fermenting organisms, contamination of yeast fermentations, disturbance of the sequential growth and contamination of processing lines, present different problems and no single method can be prescribed for avoiding difficulty.

Appreciation of the importance of microbiological cleanliness and avoiding accumulations of contaminating substances are the first requisites. Continuous operation of processing lines tends to cause an accumulation of food exudates, juices and discrete particles. Growth of organisms in these "slimes" serves as a continuous source of inoculation for products passing through the lines. It is important to learn how often it is necessary to shut down, clean up and sanitize all equipment which serves as a source of contamination. Plant personnel cannot be expected to comprehend the small size or rapid growth of spoilage organisms. An adequately controlled sanitation program is the only insurance against costly losses. Operators of sugar mills years ago discovered the economic necessity of sanitary control. The canning and freezing industries went through similar periods of learning the hard way. Mold control was a must for large scale meat packing operations. Each industry has had to discover its problems and methods of surmounting them.

THE VINEGAR FERMENTATION

The manufacture of vinegar is of such ancient origin that even the oldest available literature records only details of methods and appliances employed. Vinegar, as its name implies, was first made from wine. It is mentioned in the Old Testament. Pliny relates that Cleopatra, to gain a wager, dissolved pearls in vinegar which she drank. Hippocrates used vinegar as a medicine. An account of the methods used in making vinegar was given in 1616 by Oliver de Serres. No radical improvement was made for two hundred years.

Although vinegar was first made from wine, cider vinegar is more commonly known today. It may be prepared from almost any watery substance which contains sufficient sugar and other nutrients to provide an alcoholic fermentation followed by an acetic fermentation. Malt vinegar, most common today, was prepared in England from ale or beer which had soured. At one time the term "alegar" was used. Juices prepared from apples, grapes, peaches, pears, persimmons, berries, oranges, watermelons, honey, maple syrup, grains and molasses have been used in the preparation of vinegar.

Vinegar is essentially a dilute solution of acetic acid made by a fermentation process. Sugars are first fermented by yeasts to an alcoholic liquor, which is then converted to vinegar by acetic acid bacteria. The French or Orleans process is the method which has been used for many years for oxidizing alcohol to acetic acid. The fermented cider or wine is placed in barrels with sufficient surface exposed to allow the vinegar bacteria, which are aerobic, to grow on the surface of the liquid. If sufficient surface area is exposed, the rate of acid production may be very rapid, particularly after a good bacterial film, the "Mother of Vinegar" is formed on the surface. Vinegar may be withdrawn at almost any time after production and more alcoholic juice then added. This is the method used on farms or small manufacturing plants. Frequently, however, the containers are filled so full that little surface is exposed and fermentation is very slow.

The "quick process" might be said to have originated with Boerhave, a Dutch chemist. About 1732 he observed that if hard cider was run slowly over pomace, vinegar was obtained in a few days. In 1823, Schüzenbach provided ventilating holes near the bottom of a large vat in which the cider stock was distributed over loose material to provide maximum exposure to air. This development was very important to the industry. The apparatus was designated "the generator" and the process called "quick process," "generator process" or "German process." A number of variations have been effected over a period of years, particularly in type of equipment, method of introducing air, and type of loose material over which the hard cider or other liquor may trickle. Wood shavings, coke, corncobs and other materials are used. Several hundred patents have been granted for variations of the basic process.

Microbiologically, the process is initiated by a simple alcoholic fermentation in which sugar is converted to alcohol and carbon dioxide by strains of yeast, particularly *Saccharomyces ellipsoideus*. This part of the fermentation may be carried out under relatively low oxygen tension. The second fermentation, the acetic fermentation, is an oxidation process in which the alcohol is converted to acetic acid by the vinegar bacteria *Acetobacter aceti* (*Bacterium aceti*). This oxidative fermentation may be carried out by strains of other species of bacteria.

Vinegar is widely used as a flavoring medium, but even more as a preservative. When vinegar is added, in general the pH of the food product is lowered sufficiently so that many other types of microorganisms, and particularly spore forming bacteria, cannot grow in the food product. Since the fruits contain other organic acids such as malic, tartaric, citric and others the effectiveness of the acetic acid as a preservative is augmented by the fruit acids. In the preparation of some food products, citric or other organic acids are now used instead of vinegar.

Vinegar has a distinct volatile flavor desirable in many food products. In the opinion of many, other organic acids and even other types of vinegar can not therefore be substituted for cider vinegar. Today certain people use cider vinegar as a medicine as Hippocrates used it centuries ago.

CONDITIONS GOVERNING GROWTH

A knowledge of the physical and chemical environment necessary for the various species of bacteria, yeasts and molds is essential to establish ideal conditions for growth and to insure that the metabolic changes which take place are those most desirable for the food product.

Although bacteria, yeasts and molds are said to be ubiquitous, still heavy inocula of them are often desirable in order to insure that they dominate the particular fermentation. Pure culture inoculation is employed in the preparation of many food products. In others, because of the complicated nature of the fermentations, sometimes involving a sequence of growth of several species, pure culture inoculations proved to be unsuccessful. For centuries, however, the introduction of proper organisms was dependent upon chance inoculation. In some cases, experience had shown that most satisfactory results were obtained when products were packed in certain vessels or rooms. The inoculation of milk and vegetables accomplished by the organisms in the pores of the early unglazed pottery vessels, the success attained by early Roman butchers in preparations of sausages in certain rooms, the complete contact of cheese such as Limburger, accomplished by turning at intervals the individual cheese on the shelves upon which they ripened, and the introduction into cheese such as Roquefort and Camembert of the proper mold culture present in certain areas are examples of practical ancient inoculating methods.

Since the lactic acid bacteria obtain their energy primarily by fermentation of sugar, sugar is essential in most media. Many of the strains can utilize not only some of the simple mono and di-saccharides, but also some of the more complex polysaccharides, dextrins, starches and glucosides, such as amygdalin, salicin and others. Although these may seem to be simple requirements, the metabolism of the group however is complex. This fastidious group requires certain proteins, minerals, vitamins and even lipids for optimum activity. By contrast to the lactics, some of the other bacteria as well as yeasts and molds seem to thrive on the metabolic residues of lactic fermentation, while others appear to require very simple nutritive substances.

Oxygen in an amount equal to that present in the air is actually toxic to some of the lactic acid bacteria. Low oxygen tension is the more desirable condition for the majority of strains, not only because they do not require oxygen, but also because the lactics have a better opportunity to dominate the more aerobic types of organisms in such a low oxygen environment.

Temperature, salt and acidity are controlling factors of great importance. In each case, the specific conditions will in part govern the fermentation. In vegetable fermentations, the lower temperatures and lower salt concentrations will favor the growth of the heterofermentative leuconostocs over the homofermentative streptococci, pediococci and lactobacilli which are favored by the higher ranges of temperature and are more tolerant to salt. Since each of the types has a maximum acidity range, a sequence of growth of the streptococci, leuconostoc, pediococci and lactobacilli may occur in order. The approximate order will be governed by the maximum acidity produced by each species of these genera. Some of the early studies on milk fermentations, cheese making and vegetable fermentations demonstrated this type of growth sequence. However, in certain cases, the rapid growth or the abnormally high level of acids produced by one species of such organisms in a sequence may delay or even entirely inhibit the growth of the next in such a sequence. The growth in some of the complex fermentations is dependent upon the symbiotic relationship existing between or among different species of microorganisms. The milk drink, kefir, in which yeasts, and homofermentative and heterofermentative lactic acid bacteria bring about the fermentation, is apparently dependent upon such a relationship. The heterofermentative bacterial species as well as the yeasts are unable to utilize the lactose until it has been hydrolyzed by the homofermenters. The desirable character imparted by the combination of acetic acid, ethyl alcohol, carbon dioxide and lactic acid is a result of the growth of the hetero-fermenting bacteria and yeast. In addition it seems that the formation of the kefir grains used as starters is dependent upon the agglomeration of all three types.

CHEMICAL CHANGES IN FERMENTED FOODS

Fermentations not only aid in the preservation of food but they also impart certain distinctive characteristics which appeal to the consumer. In general, these characteristics can be attained only through the complex changes produced during fermentation. The mellowed effect produced in many fermented foods is difficult to analyze and has not been artificially duplicated. While the changes known to occur among the carbohydrates are complex, a knowledge of the nature of the changes in the proteins, lipids, vitamins and other essentials of fermentation are wholly inadequate.

The complex metabolic pathway followed by some of our standard cultures when using glucose is amply described in a number of text books on microbial physiology. These internal oxidations and reductions conducted by the microbial cell, known as the Embden-Meyer-

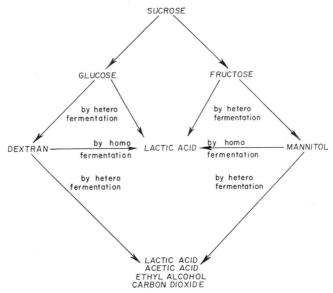

FIG. 84. END PRODUCTS OF FERMENTATIONS
OF VARIOUS CARBOHYDRATES

hof-Parmas pathway of glycolysis are very complex.   However, when complicated by a growth sequence of several types of microorganisms using sucrose as the primary energy source, the pathway becomes even more complex.   In simplified form, Fig. 84 illustrates the increased complexity showing only the major metabolic end products.

In fermentations involving sucrose, therefore, one will find lactic acid, acetic acid, ethyl alcohol, carbon dioxide, mannitol and dextran as major metabolic end products.   The relative amounts of each will be governed in large part by the environmental conditions favorable to the different bacterial species.

The most marked changes in milk occur in the protein fractions resulting in the typical curdling, the first step in cheese making.   The lipids in some instances are quite completely hydrolyzed.   Some of the fatty acids are effective preservative agents in themselves, and undoubtedly are in part responsible for the better preservative action of certain well aged fermented cheeses.   The laxative properties of certain fermented foods have been ascribed to acetyl choline and lactylcholine, which are formed when the acetic and lactic acids produced from sugar combine with the choline which is formed possibly by the metabolic hydrolysis of the lecithin.   One could continue the discussion of the numerous metabolic changes known to occur in fermented foods.   Suffice it to say that fermentation results in some marked changes in the character of foods that can not be duplicated by known ordinary processing methods.

BIBLIOGRAPHY

BREED, R. S., MURRAY, E. G. D., and SMITH, N. R.   1957.   Bergey's Manual of Determinative Bacteriology.   7th Edition.   The Williams and Wilkins Co., Baltimore, Md.

FRAZIER, W. C.   1958.   Food Microbiology.   McGraw-Hill Book Co., New York.

JENSEN, L. B.   1954.   Microbiology of Meats.   3rd Edition.   Garrard Press, Champaign, Ill.

OGINSKY, E. L., and UMBREIT, W. W.   1959.   An Introduction to Bacterial Physiology.   2nd Edition.   W. H. Freeman and Co., San Francisco, Calif.

PEDERSON, C. S.   1960.   Sauerkraut.   Advances in Food Research 10, 223–291.

RAHN, O.   1945.   Microbes of Merit.   Jacques Cattell Press, Lancaster, Pa.

SANDERS, G. P.   1953.   Cheese Varieties and Descriptions.   Agr. Handbook 54. U. S. Dept. Agr., Washington, D. C.

UNDERKOFLER, L. A., and HICKEY, R. J.   1954.   Industrial Fermentations. Vols. I and II.   The Chemical Publishing Co., New York.

CHAPTER 14

Samuel A. Matz | # Baking

INTRODUCTION

The purpose of this chapter is to acquaint those readers who are not specialists in baking technology with some of the most important processing techniques, equipment and special ingredients used in bakeries. Because of the limitations of space and the complexity of the subject, detailed instructions for manufacturing specific bakery products could not be included. Interested readers can obtain a thorough introduction to such matters by consulting such texts as Bakery Technology and Engineering (Matz 1960), Baking Science and Technology (Pyler 1952), and The Chemistry and Technology of Cereals as Food and Feed (Matz 1959).

Although bakery products are exceedingly diverse so far as their appearance and taste are concerned, they can be divided into four major groups based on the source of the leavening action. Because foods in each of the four categories possess many characteristics in common, and since the processing methods and equipment used in their manufacture are usually somewhat similar, discussion and consideration of these subjects are simplified by such a classification. The system of classification to be used in this chapter is given below:

Class 1.—Yeast leavened foods, comprised of products which depend upon the generation of carbon dioxide by fermenting yeast. Bread is the most common example of this class.

Class 2.—Chemically leavened products, including those items deriving their leavening gas from the reaction of sodium bicarbonate with some acidic substance. Layer cakes, baking powder biscuits, and cake doughnuts fall in this category.

Class 3.—Air leavened foods. This class is composed of products which are leavened by air bubbles enfolded or injected into the batter (or some part of it) during one stage of the mixing process. Angel food cake typifies these products.

Class 4.—Unleavened bakery products.—A group consisting of foods not included in the preceding classes. Pie crusts are the predominant commercial item of this group. Although these foods are described as "unleavened" because there is no intentional addition of

SAMUEL A. MATZ is Vice President, Research and Development, Robert A. Johnston Company, Milwaukee, Wis.

a leavening agent, some expansion may occur during baking as the result of increased water vapor pressure and the evolution of dissolved gases.

SPECIAL INGREDIENTS OF BAKING

Eggs, milk, salt, shortening, water and sugars are ingredients commonly used in bakery products, but they are also of importance in many other compounded foods and in the latter applications have been discussed elsewhere in this volume. In some cases, there are special requirements for these ingredients when they are to be used in certain bakery products. For these specifications, the reader is advised to consult a more specialized text.

On the other hand, flour and leavening agents are ingredients which are responsible for the characteristic appearance, texture and flavor of most bakery products and they will be discussed in some detail in the following sections. To these raw materials may be added some specially compounded mixtures, such as yeast foods and dough improvers, which do not have any applications outside the baking industry.

Flour

Wheat flour is unique among cereal flours in that, when mixed with water in the correct proportions, its protein component will form an elastic network which is capable of holding gas and which will set to a rather firm spongy structure when heated in the oven. It is this behavior which makes possible the production of bread as we know it.

In order to secure batter and doughs which will handle satisfactorily and yield finished products of good eating quality, the proper flour must be used. Suitability of a flour for a particular purpose is governed primarily by the variety of wheat from which it was milled, the protein content of the flour, and the milling conditions.

For the purposes of this discussion, wheats may be divided into soft and hard, with the latter group subdivided into winter and spring wheats. Hard wheats are indispensable for the production of flour intended for use in bakery foods of low density, such as ordinary white bread. Flours made from hard wheats can yield doughs which are elastic, have excellent gas-holding properties, and respond well to the usual bake-shop processing techniques. Spring wheats often yield flours which are somewhat "stronger" than those obtained from winter wheats.

Flours from soft wheats are used for cakes, cookies, pie crusts and other products when a high specific volume is not essential and a tender texture is desired.   They are also usually whiter in color and blander in flavor than flours from winter wheats.

Purpose of Milling.—The purpose of milling is to separate the wheat endosperm (the source of flour) from the germ and the bran layers, and to reduce the endosperm chunks to a fine powder.   In conventional milling processes this is accomplished by passing the wheat kernels and their products through a series of pairs of rolls and sieves.   The initial sets of rolls break open the seed coat and strip out the friable endosperm.   Subsequent sets of rolls grind the products

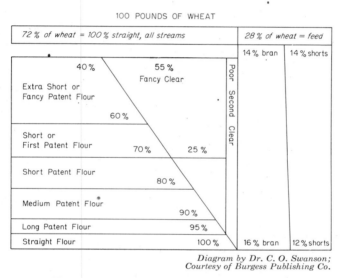

Diagram by Dr. C. O. Swanson;
Courtesy of Burgess Publishing Co.

FIG. 85.   RELATIONSHIP OF FLOUR GRADES
TO EXTRACTION PERCENTAGES

finer, or perform other essential functions such as flattening the germ (which facilitates its separation from the endosperm).   At each stage, stacks of screens each having a different mesh size separate the ground material into several streams.   These streams may be further processed by grinding, they may be drawn off for feed, or they may be combined to yield flours of different qualities.

By selecting the proper streams, the miller can furnish flours of widely varying quality from the same wheat blend.   Of course, the inherent quality of the wheat places an upper limit on the excellence of flour which can be obtained from it.   Ordinarily, about 70 per cent of the wheat kernel emerges as flour of some sort.   Usually the first endosperm fractions obtained from the wheat kernel, constituting perhaps 50 to 90 per cent of the total flours, are combined to make a so-called "patent" flour. The remaining flour would then be called a "clear" flour, and is considered to be of inferior quality because it is of darker color and usually exhibits poorer baking performance. If all of the flour streams are combined to make only one product, the latter is called a "straight" flour. Figure 85 demonstrates some of these relationships.

Quality Tests for Flour.—The complex nature of flour and the many kinds of products in which it is used make it impossible to prescribe a simple chemical or physical test for overall quality. The most successful tests have been based upon the comparison of baked products made from the experimental flour and a control sample. In most cases, the conditions presumed to exist during commercial processing are duplicated in the test, so far as feasible. Nearly all specifications for flours intended to be used in bakery products include some test of this type. Many such tests are based on the "standard" bread baking and cake baking tests of the American Association of Cereal Chemists (Anon. 1957). Test baking procedures for cookies, crackers, biscuits, and several other products have also been published.

Of the chemical tests for flour quality, protein, ash and moisture determinations are in widest use. The moisture content has the obvious value of indicating the amount of an inactive substance—or diluent—which is present, and, in addition, flour containing more than about 14.5 per cent moisture does not store well. The protein content (actually a Kjeldahl determination of total nitrogen is the most common test) is closely related to the baking performance of the flour. High protein content is desirable for bread flours while cakes, cookies, and pie crusts require flours of relatively low protein content.

The ash content is an indirect indication of the protein quality of the flour. Patent flours have lower ash contents than straight or clear flours from the same wheat. Much of the higher ash content of the latter two flours results from the inclusion of a larger amount of the bran and adjacent layers which also contribute higher percentages of nongluten protein. Higher ash content is almost always associated with darker color in the flour and this effect carries over into the baked product. Fat, fiber, starch, reducing sugars and amylase activity are other chemical determinations sometimes applied to flours.

Many empirical physical tests have been developed for estimating flour quality. Several of these measure the resistance of doughs to some type of mixing action. The Brabender farinograph, illustrated in Fig. 86, is probably the best known of this type. Other devices determine the resistance of dough pieces to stretching or tearing, etc.

It is often difficult to establish the relationship of values obtained with these machines to the baking quality of a flour.

The color of flour is an important quality factor and may be measured subjectively in the Pekar test, which requires the comparison of smooth wetted surfaces of the unknown and control flours, or it may be determined electronically by a reflectance colorimeter. The importance of particle size in flour behavior has only recently been recog-

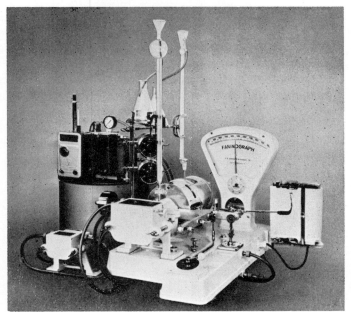

Courtesy of C. W. Brabender Instruments, Inc.

FIG. 86.   THE BRABENDER FARINOGRAPH

nized. Generally, the fragments of flour are too small to be accurately classified by sieves, and more accurate methods must be used. Microscopic measurements are precise but very tedious. Techniques involving determination of sedimentation rates and resistance to permeation by streams of gases have been developed and are described in the literature.

When the rate of viscosity increase in heated aqueous suspensions of flour is followed, valuable information about the gelatinization characteristics of the starch can be derived. These data can in turn be used to predict some aspects of the performance of the flour in certain baked products. Consequently, some specifications for cake, pie and pastry flour include requirements for minimum or maximum viscosity development under standardized conditions. By including a time variable, the rate of action of the starch digesting enzymes can be estimated. This is a factor of importance in the fermentation of bread doughs.

Leavening Agents

Yeast.—Bakers' yeast is composed of the living cells of *Saccharomyces cerevisiae*. There may be a small amount of diluent included in some brands to improve their dispersibility in water, but most of the weight of a fresh block of yeast is composed of active cells.

Bakers' yeast may be purchased in the compressed form as cakes of 1 oz., 2 oz., 1 lb., and 5 lbs. or as active dry yeast in the form of small granules. Compressed yeast contains about 70 per cent water and must be stored at refrigerator temperatures while active dry yeast con-

Photo by Dr. H. J. Peppler

Fig. 87.   Blish-Sandstedt Pressuremeters
in Water Bath

tains approximately eight per cent water and can be kept at higher temperatures if necessary. Compressed yeast can be used simply by mixing it into a dough along with the other ingredients but active dry yeast must first be rehydrated. The temperature of the rehydration water is very critical and the yeast will be completely inactivated if the water is too hot or too cold. Automatic devices for rehydrating yeast under optimum conditions have been made available by some manufacturers of the product.

Yeast performs its leavening function by fermenting carbohydrates such as glucose, fructose, maltose and sucrose. It can not use lactose, the predominant carbohydrate of milk. The principal products of fermentation are ethanol and carbon dioxide, the latter being the leavening gas.   Ethanol is important in the aroma of baking bread, a fact which is not always recognized.   There are various other products of the yeast's activity which flavor the baked product and change the dough's physical properties.

Quality tests for yeasts include baking techniques similar in principle to those used for estimating flour quality, and gas production measurements.   Some rather complex instruments have been devised for determining the amount of carbon dioxide given off by yeast which has been mixed in a dough of standard formulation.   In this country, the simple Blish-Sandstedt pressuremeters (shown in Fig. 87) are widely used.   They consist of a cylindrical brass bowl coupled to a removable head which bears a pressure-relief valve and an anaeroid gage or mercury manometer-type of pressure sensing device.   Such pressuremeters are maintained in constant temperature baths during the measuring period.

Chemical tests are not of value in determining the activity of baker's yeast.

Chemical Leavening Agents.—Layers cakes, cookies, biscuits and many other bakery products are leavened by carbon dioxide originating from added sodium bicarbonate (baking soda).   When soda is added alone it tends to make the dough alkaline, leading to flavor deterioration and discoloration, and the carbon dioxide is released very slowly.   Addition of an acid along with the soda promotes a vigorous evolution of gas and keeps the dough pH near neutrality.

The rate of gas release from solution controls the size of the bubbles in the dough and consequently influences the grain, volume and texture of the finished product.   Much research has been devoted to developing leavening acids which will maintain the rate of gas release within the desired range.   Acids such as acetic (as from vinegar) or lactic (as from sour milk) usually act much too fast.   The most successful compounds have been cream of tartar (potassium acid tartrate), sodium aluminum sulfate (alum), sodium acid pyrophosphate, and various forms of calcium phosphate.   The chemical formulas of these compounds do not adequately define their function in doughs. Small amounts of additives included during manufacture can have a profound effect on the rate of reaction of the compound.   Granule size and form also have important modifying actions.   For example, companies specializing in leavening acids usually offer several types of sodium acid pyrophosphate.   Although the chemical formulas of the main constituent are the same and analysis will reveal only variations in the trace elements, the slowest reacting member of the sodium acid pyrophosphate series will cause an initial rate of gas evolution many times slower than the rate promoted by the fastest reacting member.

Most bakers use baking powder instead of measuring soda and leavening acids into the dough in separate additions. This substance is a mixture of soda and acid in correct proportions plus diluents which simplify measuring and improve stability. The end products of baking powder reaction are carbon dioxide and harmless salts having more or less bland flavors. Baking powders from all reliable firms have about the same amount of "available carbon dioxide" and differ, if at all, in the speed of reaction. Most commercial baking powders are of the double-action type, i.e., they give off a small amount of the available carbon dioxide during the mixing and make-up stages and then remain relatively quiescent until the temperature begins to rise after the batter is placed in the oven. This type of action ensures that excessive loss of leavening gas will not occur if the baker finds it necessary to leave the batter in an unbaked condition for long periods.

Quality testing of baking powders involves a bake test made under actual conditions of use. It is difficult to predict commercial performance from the results of standardized laboratory tests because one of the attributes of a good baking powder is its lack of sensitivity to changes in conditions. There is a common laboratory technique for determining available carbon dioxide which involves measurement of the volume of gas released from baking powder which has been treated with a strong acid. This test gives no indication of the speed of reaction of the baking powder when it is mixed into a dough or batter.

Special Minor Ingredients

There are a few kinds of specialized compositions which can be added to a dough in small amounts in order to modify its properties. These include enzymes, yeast foods and dough improvers. Enzymes which have been recommended for addition to doughs are proteases, which act on the gluten to alter dough extensibility, amylases, which digest some of the starch so as to supply fermentable carbohydrates to the yeast, and lipoxidases, which whiten the dough by destroying flour pigments and perhaps affect the flavor.

Yeast foods are usually composed of ammonium salts, phosphates, and sulfates. These yeast nutrients presumably encourage yeast growth and may indirectly accelerate gas production. If the water supply is unusually soft, the salts in yeast foods may have a direct beneficial effect on the physical properties of the dough.

Oxidizing agents can be very effective in improving the handling characteristics of dough and the specific volume and texture (indirectly) of the finished products. The most common oxidizer is potassium bromate, but potassium iodate and calcium peroxide are also used to some extent. These substances exert their effect on the mechanical properties of dough by causing the formation of additional cross-bonds between gluten molecules.

Not all flours benefit from the addition of oxidizers. Well-aged flour, or flour which has been treated with optimum quantities of oxidizers at the mill, may not show any beneficial results from the addition of dough improvers and may, in fact, give doughs and bread of inferior quality when supplemented in this manner. Flours which react best to supplementation are likely to be long extraction, freshly milled flours from wheats of generally good baking quality. Short extraction flours from poor varieties of wheat may not be improved at all by the addition of oxidizers.

THE SPECIAL EQUIPMENT OF BAKING

Much of the equipment used in preparing bakery foods is highly specialized, often having been developed especially for some particular task which was formerly performed by hand. This is true partly because some of the processing steps in bakery work are not closely analogous to any other operation in the food field, but in other cases (e.g., mixers), special equipment is necessary because the materials being handled possess unusual characteristics and respond poorly to the machines used for less sensitive foods.

Materials Handling Equipment

Many bakeries, including those of moderate size, have found that bulk handling of flour is more economical, convenient, and sanitary than the century-old steps of bag transfer and dumping. Most large flour mills are now equipped to ship flour in bulk trailers or freight cars. The bakery must install a number of receiving bins and a pneumatic conveying system. The conveying system may be of the positive pressure or negative pressure type. The former is easier to engineer and is probably less expensive but it may be more hazardous since a break in the conveyor will result in ejection of large amounts of explosive flour dust into the atmosphere.

For batch mixing, the flour charge is usually weighed in a scaling mechanism located immediately above the mixer bowl. A "loss-in-weight" procedure based on measurements at the bin is also possible. It is advisable, but not essential, to have some sort of sifting device in the delivery end of the system.

Bulk shortening installations are fairly common. These are based, of course, on storing and conveying fat in the melted state.   For some bakery products, a plastic fat must be added to the mixer in order to obtain the desired texture and appearance in the finished product. This can be accomplished by running the liquid fat through a chilling unit, such as a Votator, and extruding the solidified fat directly into the mixer bowl.   Many excellent liquid metering devices are available for measuring liquid shortening.

Bulk sugar is used by some bakeries.   Although granular sugar can be handled by pneumatic conveying, it is more common to use and store sugar syrups.   Cane sugar syrups, some special syrups and many different kinds of corn syrups can be delivered in bulk.   Generally, the economics of these systems are favorable only for the larger plants. Most preparation techniques can be adapted to allow the use of liquid sugars although problems may be encountered if there is a critical "creaming" step in the process.

Mixers

In many food manufacturing processes, mixing is a step conducted merely to assure a uniform distribution of the separate ingredients

Courtesy of Baker Perkins, Inc.

Fig. 88.   Horizontal Dough Mixers Showing Bulk Flour Weighing System and a Dough Trough Being Elevated

Courtesy of Baker Perkins, Inc.

FIG. 89. VERTICAL OR PLANETARY BATCH
MIXER FOR DOUGHS AND BATTERS

throughout the mass of the finished item. This function is also important in the mixing of doughs and batters, but here two other purposes are evident. These are the incorporation of minute bubbles of air to serve as foci for the evolution of carbon dioxide and the "development" of the gluten. The latter function is critical in the preparation of bread doughs and the like but is of no significance in mixing layer cake batters, pie doughs, etc.

Nearly all bread doughs (batch process) made in this country are mixed in equipment similar to that shown in Fig. 88. These horizontal dough mixers are very effective in developing the gluten because the essentially unidirectional action of the agitator bars rapidly orients and aligns the protein fibrils. The agitator is composed of three cylindrical members, 2, 3 or 4 in. in diameter, disposed parallel to the long axis of the bowl. The mixer arms are mounted on two spiders connected to a powered shaft which passes axially through the mixer. In some cases, a swing bar replaces one or more of the fixed arms. Other less common designs are also available for the agitators.

FIG. 90. THE MORTON "WHISK"
WITH FLOUR HOPPER ATTACHED

The mixer bowl may have a smooth interior or it can be provided with baffles or stationary bars mounted parallel to the agitator shaft. Since a great deal of heat is generated during high speed mixing, the bowls of horizontal mixers are jacketed so that cooling can be accomplished by circulation of ethylene glycol or by direct expansion of a refrigerant gas.

Two mixing speeds are usually available. High speed (about 70 r.p.m.) is used for dough development while low speed (about 35 r.p.m.) is used primarily for the initial incorporation of water. To open the mixing chamber, the bowl is rotated through about 90 degrees by the power unit. Horizontal dough mixers are available in

capacities of about 1,000 lbs. to about 2,000 lbs. from seven different manufacturers in the United States. Laboratory size units or
larger mixers can be obtained on special order.

Batch mixing of batters is accomplished with equipment such as
that shown in Fig. 89. These vertical planetary mixers have bowl
capacities of up to 340 qt. Various agitator designs are available.
For example, wire whips are used for egg white foams, batter beaters
for the usual layer cake mixes, and pastry cutters for pie doughs.
Provision is usually made for three different beater speeds.

There are specialized mixers which can be mentioned only briefly
here. The Artofex mixer, of European design, combines two agitators
traveling through intersecting elliptical paths and a constant revolving
bowl to give an action resembling that of hand kneading. These de-

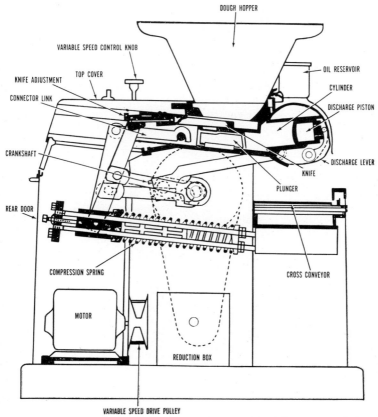

Courtesy of U. S. Department of Defense

FIG. 91. DIAGRAM OF A DOUGH DIVIDER

vices have attained some popularity with pie manufacturers and are also used for some specialty breads. The Oakes continuous mixer can give high yields of certain types of cake batters. The Morton "Whisk" (see Fig. 90) permits batters to be mixed in a pressurized chamber. This is very beneficial to the volume of air leavened products such as angel food cakes.

Dough Forming Equipment

Dough Dividers.—At some stage in the processing, and frequently immediately after mixing, it is necessary to divide a large mass of dough into pieces corresponding to single units of the finished product. The machines which perform this function operate on a volume displacement system rather than on a weight basis. The dough is rammed into a chamber having adjustable volume and the measured piece is then severed from the main body.

Fig. 91 illustrates the principal operating elements of a typical dough divider. The dough flows from the hopper into the underlying compression chamber. At the start of the cycle, a knife moves horizontally to cut off a piece of dough near the hopper bottom. Next, the ram or piston moves forward pressing the severed dough piece into

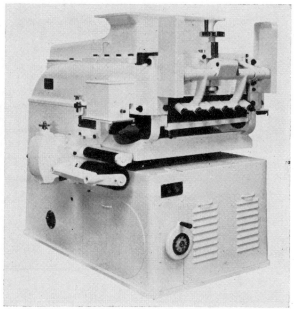

Courtesy of Baker Perkins, Inc.

FIG. 92.   SIX-POCKET DOUGH DIVIDER
WITH VARIABLE SPEED DRIVE

a chamber contained in a rotatable cylinder.   At the end of the ram stroke, the cylinder turns, cutting off the excess dough, and, finally, the discharge lever ejects the measured dough piece.   In the return cycle, the emptied cylinder is turned back so that the cavities face the compression chamber, and the knife and compression piston withdraw, allowing more dough to be drawn into the chamber by gravity and suction.

Commercial models (see Fig. 92) have from 2 to 8 pockets in the cylinder and operate at speeds up to 25 strokes per minute.   Scaling range is from 6 to 36 oz.   Motors with ratings of up to $7^1/_2$ h.p. are used.   The volume of the pockets which scale the dough pieces can be adjusted by changes of the piston depth.

Anything which affects the dough density will change the weight of the scaled pieces.   Since the dough continues to ferment in the hopper, with the gas production contributing to a lower density, a slight decrease in scale weight can be expected as each batch of dough is processed, with a rise in weight as a new batch starts to flow into the compression chamber.   If the batches are small enough and divider operation is rapid enough, the changes in piece weight will probably be within limits that can be tolerated.   If the divider has to be shut down for an appreciable length of time while there is dough in the hopper, a considerable error in scaling weight must be expected.

Rounders.—When the dough piece leaves the divider, it is irregular in shape with sticky cut surfaces from which the gas can readily diffuse.   The gluten structure is disoriented and so not in a condition suitable for molding.   It is the function of the rounder to close these cut surfaces, giving the dough piece a smooth and dry exterior, to make a relatively thick and continuous skin around the dough piece, to re-orient the gluten fibrils, and to form the dough into a ball for easier handling in the subsequent processing steps.   It performs these functions by rolling the well-floured dough piece around the surface of a drum or cone while moving it upward or downward along this surface by means of a spiral track.   As a result of this action, the surface is dried by an even distribution of dusting flour as well as by the dehydration occurring because of its exposure to the air, the gas cells near the surface of the ball are collapsed forming a thick layer which inhibits the diffusion of gases from the dough, and the dough piece assumes an approximately spherical shape.

Rounders may be conveniently classified as bowl-, drum- or umbrella-type.   The conical or bowl variety consists of a rotatable cone-shaped bowl around the interior of which is placed a stationary spiral track or "race."   Figure 93 schematically illustrates such a device.

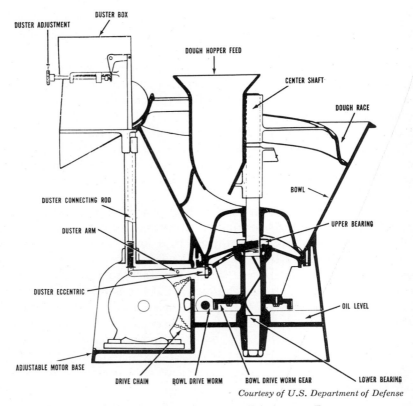

DUSTER BOX
DUSTER ADJUSTMENT
DOUGH HOPPER FEED
CENTER SHAFT
DOUGH RACE
DUSTER CONNECTING ROD
BOWL
DUSTER ARM
UPPER BEARING
DUSTER ECCENTRIC
OIL LEVEL
ADJUSTABLE MOTOR BASE
DRIVE CHAIN   BOWL DRIVE WORM   BOWL DRIVE WORM GEAR   LOWER BEARING

Courtesy of U.S. Department of Defense

FIG. 93. SCHEMATIC DIAGRAM OF A BOWL-TYPE ROUNDER

From the conveyor leading from the divider the dough pieces fall into the feed hopper of the rounder and then drop to the bottom of the rotating bowl. The pieces are tumbled and rolled along the dough race until they emerge from the top of the bowl and fall onto the belt leading to the intermediate proofer.

A second popular type of rounder is the so-called umbrella or inverted cone variety. These machines differ from the preceding type in that the dough piece is carried along the outside surface of a cone which has its apex facing upward. Figure 94 shows such a rounder.

The third type of rounder is the drum rounder. This machine differs from the bowl and umbrella styles in that the cone segment has very little slope to its sides, i.e., the sides are almost vertical. The dough piece enters near the bottom of the drum and rolls upward.

In addition to their form, rounding machines may vary in the texture or composition of the rotating surface, in the means provided for adjusting the relationship of the dough race to the drum or cone, in the method of applying dusting flour, etc. The rotating surface is usually corrugated vertically or horizontally, but the design and the size of the ribs vary considerably from one manufacturer to another. The surface may be waxed or it may be coated with a plastic such as Teflon to reduce sticking. Frequently, a device to shunt aside over-size dough pieces (doubles) is fixed to the exit chute.

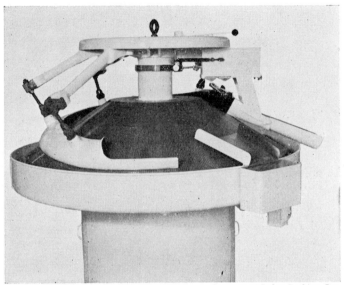

Courtesy of Baker Perkins, Inc.

FIG. 94. UMBRELLA-TYPE LOAF ROUNDER

Fermentation Rooms and Proofing Equipment.—In all conventional processing methods for yeast-leavened products, there are one or more rest stages during which the dough is allowed to ferment so as to accumulate carbon dioxide and flavoring constituents. In the usual bread-making procedure there are three or four of these steps: the fermentation, which occurs shortly after the dough leaves the mixer; the intermediate proof which takes place after the dough has been divided and rounded; and the pan proof during which the shaped and panned dough pieces are allowed to accumulate gas just prior to being placed in the oven. In most plants, the fermentation stage is divided into two sections separated by a remix step.

It is highly desirable that the doughs be held under conditions of controlled temperature and humidity during these steps, since the

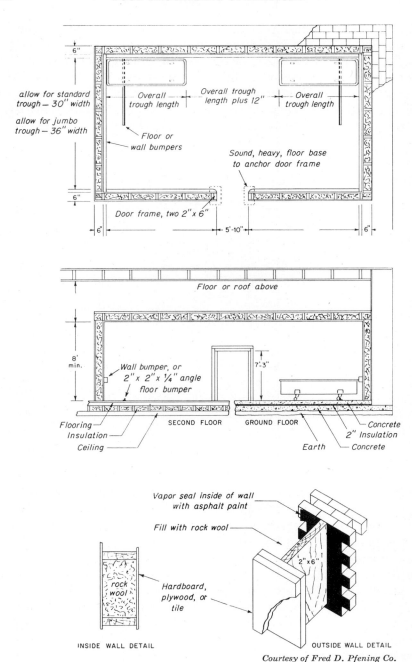

FIG. 95. CONSTRUCTION DETAILS OF A FERMENTATION ROOM

rate (and, to some extent, the quality) of the fermentation is strongly dependent upon the temperature, and the handling properties of the dough surface depend upon the extent to which drying occurs. Therefore, all modern bakeries have fermentation rooms and intermediate proofing cabinets with controlled atmospheres for storing the dough during the rest periods.

A fermentation room is essentially a well-insulated box provided with means for humidifying and warming the inclosed air. Figure 95 indicates construction principles of a fermentation room.

When fermenting dough is transferred in bulk, dough troughs on casters are used as the containers. When shaped pieces are proofed, they are placed on trays, the trays are placed on racks, and the racks are wheeled into the proof room. In some plants, racks or troughs may be moved in and through the holding room by powered arrangements of one sort or another. Air conditioning systems for fermentation

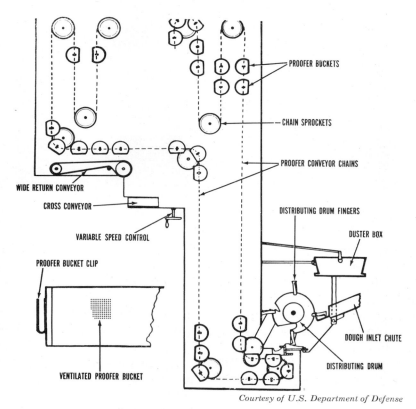

PROOFER BUCKETS

CHAIN SPROCKETS

PROOFER CONVEYOR CHAINS

WIDE RETURN CONVEYOR

CROSS CONVEYOR

DISTRIBUTING DRUM FINGERS

DUSTER BOX

VARIABLE SPEED CONTROL

PROOFER BUCKET CLIP

DOUGH INLET CHUTE

DISTRIBUTING DRUM

VENTILATED PROOFER BUCKET

Courtesy of U.S. Department of Defense

FIG. 96. DIAGRAM OF A TRAY-TYPE INTERMEDIATE
PROOFER SHOWING LOADING MECHANISM

rooms should be capable of maintaining a dry bulk temperature of 80°F., plus or minus one degree, and a relative humidity of 76 per cent, plus or minus one per cent, regardless of the temperature and relative humidity of the surrounding atmosphere.

In the manufacture of bread, there is a specialized piece of machinery called the intermediate proofer which receives the dough pieces as they come from.the rounder. Gas is generated as the dough pieces are carried through the intermediate proofer and the dough "relaxes" so that it is in better condition for molding. No large capacity (over 3,000 lbs./hr.) intermediate proofers are available with

Courtesy of Baker Perkins, Inc.

FIG. 97. OVERHEAD PROOFER SHOWN WITH
DIVIDER AND MOLDER

air conditioning equipment built in. The humidity and temperature of the inclosed space are controlled to some extent by the dough pieces themselves, and the dough is not very sensitive to changes in these factors during this stage in its processing.

Most intermediate proofers used at the present time are the overhead type in which the principal part of the cabinet is raised several feet above the floor. When overhead space is not adequate, one of the floor-level models can be installed. Intermediate proofers may be conveniently classified as belt-types and tray-types, the latter variety having many subtypes. Belt proofers consist essentially of endless belts running in a closed cabinet. The dough pieces are carried forward to the end of the cabinet, then dropped down on the next lower belt traveling in the opposite direction, and so on until they reach the exit conveyor. Figure 96 illustrates the principles of operation of such a machine.

Tray-type conveyors include those proofers which have segmented conveyors of any design. The dough pieces may be moved in metal pans, troughs or buckets, wooden trays or canvas loops. Fig. 96 illustrates schematically an overhead tray-type proofer which has perforated metal troughs or tubes in which the dough pieces are carried. This diagram also shows details of the loading mechanism, a vital part of the intermediate proofer. The loading mechanism receives the dough pieces which come along the conveyor belt in single file and arranges them in rows in the receptacle of the intermediate proofer. The proofer trays may contain spaces for 2 to 8 dough pieces placed across the tray. Figure 97 shows an intermediate proofer with related equipment.

Dough Molding and Shaping Equipment.—In the bread-making plant, the molder receives pieces of dough from the intermediate proofer and shapes them into cylinders (loaves) ready to be placed in the pans. There are several types of molders, but all have four functions in common: sheeting, curling, rolling and sealing. Some writers consider the last two as one function, since they are performed simultaneously. Figure 98 is a schematic diagram of a simple type of molder in which these operations are illustrated.

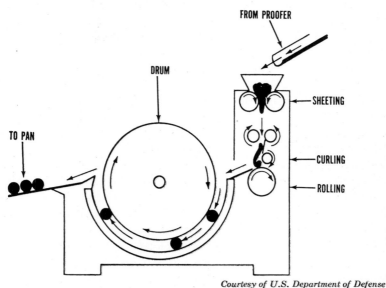

Courtesy of U.S. Department of Defense

FIG. 98. DIAGRAM OF A SIMPLE DRUM MOLDER

The dough as it comes from the intermediate proofer is a flattened spheroid. The first operation of the molder is to flatten this spheroid still more to form a thick sheet which can be properly manipulated in the later stages of molder operation. This effect is usually achieved by two or more (usually three) consecutive pairs of rollers, each succeeding pair being set closer together than the ones which preceded it. The first pair of rolls, called the head rolls, exerts only a relatively slight pressure on the dough piece. The second set of rolls, the center rolls, operate at an intermediate pressure. The last set, which may be called either the sheeting rolls or the lower rolls, exerts the maximum pressure on the dough sheet. The gradual reduction in thickness caused by this multiple roller system minimizes the punishment received by the dough, so that tearing and similar problems are reduced.

After the dough has been sheeted out, it is curled up into a loose cylinder. This operation is conventionally performed by a special set of rolls, but it may also be done by a pair of canvas belts. The lower conveyor moves the dough piece forward until the upper curling belt or mat engages the front end of the piece, brings it back, and curls it up into a loose cylinder. A more advanced development substitutes a short length of woven metal mat or linked metal bars for the upper curling belt.

The layers in the cylinder of dough are not tightly adherent when it leaves the curling section. The next function of the molder is to seal the dough piece so that it will not unroll when it expands in the oven. In this step, the cylinder of dough is also lengthened so that its axial dimension is somewhat greater than the length of the pan. Entrapped air is expelled from between the spirals in this operation. The conventional molder achieves the desired results by rolling the dough cylinder between a large drum surfaced with canvas and a semicircular compression "board" having a smooth surface. Clearance between the drum and the board is gradually reduced along the route of dough travel so that the piece is continuously compressed.

Many modifications in the basic steps have been made in an attempt to improve the uniformity and texture of the finished product. The cross-grain molder curls the dough sheet at right angles to its direction of travel through the sheeter rolls. The reverse-sheeting molder was devised to curl the sheet of dough so that the wet end of the piece would be folded into the center of the load. The dough piece is turned over or reversed between the second or third set of rolls, thus placing the original trailing end in the leading position. Fig. 99 is a diagram of a molder-panner which includes these operations. Another type of

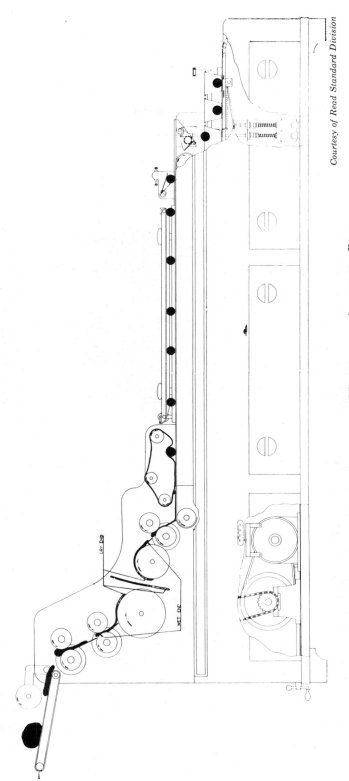

FIG. 99. A REVERSE-SHEETING MOLDER AND AUTOMATIC PANNER

molder, developed primarily to give loaves with more uniform cell structure, twists the dough pieces after they have been rolled into cylinders.

In general, the operations involved in shaping and forming sweet goods have not been mechanized as completely as those required for making bread loaves. However, mechanical benches such as the one illustrated in Fig. 100 can automatically sheet sweet doughs, apply liquid and solid flavoring agents, roll the sheet into an endless helical tube, seal the edge and cut off segments of the desired size.

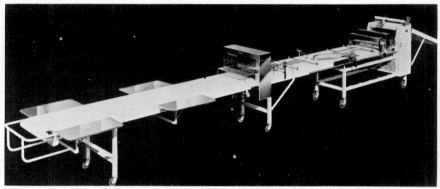

Courtesy of Moline, Inc.

FIG. 100. A MECHANICAL BENCH FOR SWEET GOODS PRODUCTION

Cookies are usually formed by a die-forming procedure or an extrusion technique. The latter may be a complex process such as that used in making fig bars, in which an endless casing of dough is extruded around a center extrusion of fig jam; or it may be a simple procedure such as those used in making deposited or drop type cookies, of which vanilla wafers, chocolate chip, oatmeal and coconut bars are representative. The principle is the same in each case—pressure is applied to a reservoir of dough to force strands of it through an orifice which may be circular or fancy in shape. The dough strand is cut into cookie size pieces by slicing devices reciprocating across the orifice, or, as in the case of fig bars, by slicing discs rolled across the lines of baked cookies as they emerge from the band oven.

Cookies produced on rotary molders include sandwich types and all of those having embossed designs. A steel cylinder whose surface is covered by engraved pockets rotates past the opening of a hopper filled with cookie dough. The pockets fill with dough, which is sheared off from the main mass as the cylinder completes its resolution, and the dough pieces are ejected on to a conveyor belt leading to the band oven.

Continuous Bread Making Processes

The conventional bread-making process was regarded as difficult to mechanize because of the problems involved in handling and holding large quantities of dough which could not be pumped or otherwise transferred in a continuous manner. In recent years, continuous processing has been achieved by mixing the dough just prior to depositing it in the pans. The fermentation flavor is obtained, not by holding large masses of dough for long times at controlled temperatures and humidities, but by fermenting liquid concentrates which can be pumped directly into the mixer.

There are at least three continuous bread-making processes in use today. These plants are made by Baker Perkins, American Machine and Foundry, and the Baker Process Division of Wallace and Tiernan. The Baker Process Do-Maker requires a "broth" which is a blend of yeast, sugar, milk, salt, yeast food, vitamins and mold inhibitor in water. This mixture is fermented in large tanks for 2 to $2\frac{1}{2}$ hr. before being transferred through a transfer tank, constant

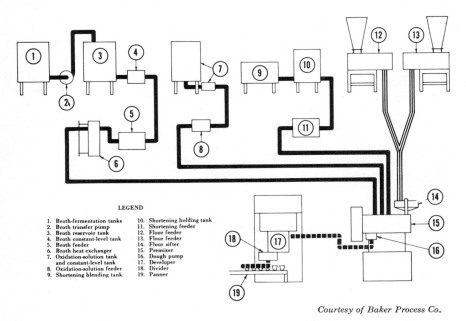

LEGEND

1. Broth-fermentation tanks
2. Broth transfer pump
3. Broth reservoir tank
4. Broth constant-level tank
5. Broth feeder
6. Broth heat exchanger
7. Oxidation-solution tank and constant-level tank
8. Oxidation-solution feeder
9. Shortening blending tank
10. Shortening holding tank
11. Shortening feeder
12. Flour feeder
13. Flour feeder
14. Flour sifter
15. Premixer
16. Dough pump
17. Developer
18. Divider
19. Panner

Courtesy of Baker Process Co.

Fig. 101. Flow Sheet of the Do-maker Process

level tank and heat exchanger (the latter reduces the temperature which has risen due to fermentation) to the premixer.   In the premix unit, liquid shortening, flour and oxidant are mixed with the broth to yield a homogeneous slurry.   The developer then turns the slurry into a dough or batter which is extruded in pieces of the desired shape and size.   Baking pans receive the dough and are conveyed to the proof. After the dough increases in size by a predetermined amount, the pans are sent to the oven and the dough baked in a conventional manner. The flowsheet in Fig. 101 summarizes these steps.

The other two continuous processes differ in significant details from the operation described above and each of the three has certain advantages and disadvantages which cannot be discussed here because of space limitations.

Ovens

Early types of bakery ovens were essentially chambers of brick or stone which were heated by building fires in them.   Technical refinements over the years have been directed mostly toward improving the temperature control and minimizing the labor required to get the products into and out of the oven.   Modern ovens suitable for quantity production can be classified as reel ovens, single-lap ovens, double-lap ovens and traveling-hearth ovens.   In small capacity plants or for special purposes, peel ovens or rotary-hearth ovens are still used.

The reel oven consists essentially of a series of shelves each suspended between arms radially disposed from powered axles located in the approximate center of the sides of the oven.   The arms are slowly rotated during the baking cycle so that the shelves describe a cylindrical path.   Rotation of the product means that top-to-bottom differences in temperature will not cause product irregularities.   Pans can be placed on the shelves as the latter pass a narrow opening in the front of the oven.   Baked loaves are removed through the same opening.   The reel oven is not suited for production of more than about 1,000 to 2,000 lbs. of bread per hour.

Single-lap and double-lap ovens also use traveling trays, but, unlike the reel oven, they use a system of chains, sprockets and curved tracks to move the trays back and forth within the chamber.   As a result of these design features, they have more capacity per unit area of floor space than the reel ovens have.   The single lap oven has two horizontal arrays of pans while the double-lap oven has four horizontal runs.   While the single lap oven has two pairs of sprockets like any ordinary conveyor, the double-lap has five pairs of sprockets, two of which are used to carry a vertical or inclined run of trays.   Double-

Courtesy of Baker Perkins, Inc.

FIG. 102. A DIRECT GAS-FIRED TUNNEL OVEN

lap ovens have been designed to bake as much as 10,000 lbs. of bread per hour.

Tunnel ovens (traveling hearth ovens) are the most satisfactory type for high capacity plants and are the only kind suitable for continuous processing systems. The hearth is a band of solid steel or steel mesh which carries the pans through a long heating chamber open at both ends (see Fig. 102). The product is loaded on the band at one end and taken off at the same level from the other end. Temperature can be varied in different sections of the tunnel to give a flexibility not attainable in any other type of oven.

THE REACTIONS OF BAKING

Many of the techniques applied in the bakery are unlike those of any other technology. For this reason it is important to consider them here even though limitations of space preclude a detailed discussion of all of the specialized processes. There will be no attempt to include sample formulations or "how-to" instructions for performing specific operations.

Mixing

The major objective of all mixing processes is, of course, the affecting of a uniform distribution of the separate ingredients. Bakery mixing also has the special purpose of introducing into the dough or batter bubbles of air which not only leaven the product to some extent but serve as foci for the evolution of leavening gas from dissolved carbon dioxide. In addition, dough mixing has the very important function of developing the gluten so that the vesicle walls will possess maximum elasticity.

The order in which ingredients are added to the mixer may be critical, especially in batter processing. Generally, however, sugar, salt, vitamins, yeast foods, mineral supplements, malt and milk can be added to doughs or batters in any sequence. They are sometimes dissolved in the water, but the water used for dispersing the yeast

Photo by Dr. H. H. Schopmeyer

FIG. 103. A WELL-DEVELOPED BREAD DOUGH

should not contain any of these ingredients. It is considered desirable to add shortening last when mixing doughs since the lubricating effect of the fat may interfere with the early stages of gluten development. The initial step in some cake preparation methods is a "creaming" process in which a fluffy mass is formed by beating the shortening and sugar. The air bubbles which are incorporated during creaming have a beneficial effect on the grain of the cake.

Bread doughs are mixed either by the sponge dough method or by the straight dough method. The latter is the simpler process, all of the ingredients being added at the start of the line. The sponge dough mixing requires two separate additions of ingredients interrupted by a lengthy fermentation period. All of the yeast, the yeast nutrients, the malt, 50 to 75 per cent of the flour, and enough water to yield a moderately stiff dough are mixed together in the first stage.   This "sponge," as it is called, is fermented for a few hours (e.g., 3 to 4) and then is mixed with milk, salt, sugar, shortening and the remainder of the flour and water.

A very important function of the mixer in bread processing is the development of the dough.   Development, in this special sense, can be defined as the use of the mixer to yield a dough having satisfactory handling properties and capable of being processed into a finished product of good quality.   If a dough has not been developed properly, it will be difficult or impossible to handle by ordinary means during subsequent processing steps and will yield a product of inferior quality regardless of the corrective measures which may be applied.

Macroscopically, development is accompanied by an increase in extensibility of the dough, a decrease in the apparent wetness and stickiness, and other changes.   When well developed, the dough can be stretched manually into a thin film, as shown in Fig. 103.   On the molecular basis, development appears to be due to increases in the orderly orientation of the gluten molecules, in the number of intermolecular bonds, and in the degree of hydration of the proteins.   Oxidation may also play a part.   If mixing is carried beyond the optimum stage, the dough starts to break down, eventually becoming sticky and "short."

Development must be carefully avoided in the mixing of batters for cakes and the like.   Increasing the elasticity of the gluten network in such mixtures leads to defects in the texture of the finished product, especially to toughness.   Pie doughs are also harmed by development and the ideal mixing treatment for these products is the minimum action necessary to give a coherent mass.

Leavening

The gas primarily responsible for the volume increase in chemically- or yeast-leavened baked goods is carbon dioxide, although steam, air and ethanol may also contribute to the expansion.   Carbon dioxide may originate from added sodium bicarbonate or from the action of yeast on fermentable sugars.   In either case, it is originally present in the aqueous phase of the dough as an equilibrium mixture of carbonate ion, bicarbonate ion and dissolved carbon dioxide.   If the source of the gas is the added bicarbonate, the amount which goes over into the gaseous phase is determined by the pH, the temperature, the concentration of the bicarbonate, and some other poorly understood factors.

When yeast is present, the situation is considerably more complex. The potential supply of gas is then limited by the amount of fermentable sugars, but these compounds may be, and usually are, replenished continually by amylolytic enzymes acting on the starch of the dough. The rate at which the sugars are supplied may not be fast enough to permit optimum yeast activity. The rate at which the yeast uses available carbohydrates depends upon the temperature, the pH, the concentration of certain co-factors, the osmolality of the aqueous phase, the concentration of specific inhibitors, the condition of the yeast cells, and the ratio of yeast to sugar, as well as other conditions. Few of these factors are subject to change at will, and practical control of yeast action is obtained by varying the temperature and the concentration of sugars.

In chemically-leavened doughs and batters, all of the soda is dissolved soon after it is mixed with the other components. Control of the rate of gas evolution by varying the solubility of the soda has been found to be impractical, and leavener manufacturers have resorted to manipulating the speed with which acid is released into the aqueous phase. In some cases, the solubility of the leavening acid determines the rate at which it reacts with bicarbonate. Sodium acid pyrophosphate, a common leavening acid, is hydrolyzed to give the more effective orthophosphate. The rate of this hydrolysis is determined by the activity of enzymes in the dough, the pH, etc.

Not all of the gas given off by the yeast or chemical leavening systems is retained within the dough. Carbon dioxide is constantly diffusing through the vesicle walls and much of it is ultimately lost to the atmosphere. The stretching, cutting, compression, and twisting undergone during processing drives out considerable quantities of the gas. The amount of carbon dioxide retained at the time the dough goes into the oven is the useful amount and is affected by the composition of the dough (including the quality of the flour proteins) and the severity of the treatment accorded the dough pieces.

Baking

Some of the important over-all phenomena occurring in the oven are expansion, coagulation of proteins, gelatinization of starches and evaporation of water. Expansion occurs not only as the result of increases in the volume of gases already present in the vesicles, but as the consequence of further evolution of carbon dioxide, the increased vapor pressure of water and the volatilization of ethanol-water azeotropes.

Coagulation of protein and gelatinization of starch alter the characteristics of the vesicle walls causing them to become more permeable to carbon dioxide. The protein becomes less elastic, retarding expansion of the loaf. There is not enough water in the dough to permit complete gelatinization of the starch, and as a result the carbohydrate remains in a state of incomplete hydration. The crumb of the baked bread is thus dry and elastic rather than sticky and gummy.

Loss of water is continuous during the baking period but is much more rapid during the last few minutes. The dehydration, in combination with protein denaturation and starch gelatinization, fixes or sets the crumb so that it does not collapse when cooled. However, some shrinkage always occurs in the later stages of baking and after removal from the oven because the structure is not strong enough to withstand completely the forces exerted on it.

A layer of collapsed and thickened cells, i.e., a crust, surrounds the dough piece even before it is placed in the oven. This film becomes more elastic as it is heated and exposed to the atmosphere of steam in the oven, permitting the desired expansion to take place. Ultimately, however, denaturation and dehydration take place and limit further expansion. Since the crust is heated much more efficiently than the interior of the loaf, it sets before expansion of the interior ceases. This results in formation of the "break and shred," areas along the sides of the loaf where the first crust has broken and separated, allowing the exposure of under layers which then form a secondary crust of somewhat different appearance.

Nonenzymatic browning and perhaps caramelization of the outer layers of dough are responsible for the color of the crust and for some of the odor and taste of bread. It is important that radiant energy be properly balanced with the thermal energy transferred by convection and conduction to prevent burning of the crust (or inadequate coloration) before the interior has completely baked.

BIBLIOGRAPHY

ABBOTT, J. A. 1953. Continuous mixing. Food Eng. *25*, No. 8, 64–65, 134.

ANON. 1947. American Standard Safety Code for Bakery Equipment. American Standards Assoc., New York.

ANON. 1957. Cereal Laboratory Methods. 6th Edition. Am. Assoc. of Cereal Chemists, St. Paul, Minn.

ANON. 1958. Automated coffee cake operation. Baking Ind. *110*, (Dec. 27), 28.

AUTHIER, D. K. 1961. Continuous mix bread production—production problems. Proc. Am. Soc. Bakery Engrs. 177–181.

BAKER, J. C., and MIZE, M. D. 1946. Gas occlusion during dough mixing. Cereal Chem. *23*, 39–51.

BOHRINGER, R. 1952. Quality of bread as affected by underproof and overproof. Proc. Am. Soc. Bakery Engrs. *1952*, 88–92.

BRUNETTI, C. 1956. How automation applies to the bread industry. Baking Ind. *105*, No. 3, 51–54.

HUNTER, C. L. 1949. Conventional moldings vs. loose curl cross-molding. Proc. Am. Soc. Bakery Engrs. *1949*, 91–93.

JOHNSON, J. A., and MILLER, B. S. 1957. Pre-ferments, their role in bread-making. Baker's Dig. *31*, No. 3, 29–35, 76–77.

KELLY, K. M. 1961. Cake batter mixing—continuous—batch. Proc. Am. Soc. Bakery Engrs. *1961*, 260–264.

KOLLMAN, W. C. 1961. Some engineering and economic aspects of bulk systems. Proc. Am. Soc. Bakery Engrs. *1961*, 199–207.

MASELLI, J. A. 1958. Brew processes: the general history. Bakers Weekly *168*, No. 6, 30–32.

MATZ, S. A. 1959. The Chemistry and Technology of Cereals as Food and Feed. Avi Publishing Co., Westport, Conn.

MATZ, S. A. 1960. Bakery Technology and Engineering. Avi Publishing Co., Westport, Conn.

MATZ, S. A. 1962. Food Texture. Avi Publishing Co., Westport, Conn.

PYLER, E. J. 1952. Baking Science and Technology. Siebel Publishing Co., Chicago, Ill.

SCHIEB, W. S. 1961. Equipment—its job—efficient operation. Proc. Am. Soc. Bakery Engrs. *1961*, 60–66.

WAGNER, J. 1955. Automatic equipment—its operation for profit. Proc. Am. Soc. Bakery Engrs. *1955*, 144–150.

CHAPTER 15

J. T. R. Nickerson and
M. Karel

Preservation of Food by Freezing

INTRODUCTION

The first commercial use of frozen foods in the United States occurred about 1854, when frozen herring, shipped from the Maritime Provinces of Canada during winter months, were used both for fish bait and for human food (Goode 1887).

When artificial freezing of foods was applied to fish, ice and salt mixtures were used to provide temperatures required for freezing and storage (Stevenson 1900). Freezing of fish by mechanical refrigeration began in 1892 (Anderson 1953).

Prior to 1920, food freezing in the United States grew slowly for such commodities as fish, poultry, eggs and fruit. The industry earned a bad reputation because of such practices as (1) freezing products which were spoiled or about to spoil, and (2) defrosting frozen products and selling them as fresh. This situation eventually prompted the passage of State laws requiring display of signs in the retail store indicating that the food had been frozen, if it was sold in the defrosted state.

Quick freezing of foods (fish) was started around 1920 (Birdseye and Fitzgerald 1932) and about 1924, Clarence Birdseye entered the field and eventually applied quick freezing methods to fish, fruits, vegetables, meats and poultry (Birdseye 1935). Birdseye advocated freezing only of foods in first class condition and promoted careful handling, adequate packaging and quick freezing of foods as well as low temperature storage after freezing. It was soon learned that enzymes must be inactivated to prevent off-flavor development in vegetables during frozen storage (Joslyn and Marsh 1933).

Since the advent of quick freezing as a method of food preservation, there has been a considerable increase in the quantity and variety of frozen foods. Trends in freezing preservation as a method of food processing are shown in Table 92A. The production of frozen foods has steadily increased in volume since 1940. The greatest increase has taken place in recent years. Specialty products and concentrated orange juice (in terms of the single strength product) have increased in greater proportion than have other commodities. There is also indication that

J. T. R. NICKERSON is Professor, Department of Nutrition and Food Science, Massachusetts Institute of Technology, and M. KAREL is Associate Professor, Department of Nutrition and Food Science, Massachusetts Institute of Technology, Cambridge, Mass.

specialty products will continue to increase for some time to come. These specialties include meat, fish and poultry dinners, meat pies, nationality foods, fruit pies, bakery products, entrees, soups, seafood specialties, cream pies, breaded precooked poultry, vegetables with sauces and miscellaneous products.

For comparison with Table 92A, similar data on the quantities of foods preserved by canning are shown in Table 92B. It is believed that the freezing of foods will grow in volume to eventually take its place along with canning, as an approximately equal factor in the field of food preservation.

TABLE 92A

APPROXIMATE AMOUNTS FROZEN
(Thousands of Pounds)

Year	Concentrated Orange Juice	Fruits and Berries	Vegetables	Eggs	Meat	Poultry	Seafoods	Specialty Products	Total
1940[1]	...	170,000	83,000	190,000	499,000	168,000	196,000	...	1,306,000
1946[1]	2,234[4]	523,000	453,000	392,000	430,000	356,000	280,000	...	2,436,234
1955[1,2]	770,000	660,000	1,140,000	...	250,000	575,000	520,000	340,000	4,255,000
1957[3]	627,000	671,000	1,367,000	...	343,000	530,000	541,000	530,000	4,609,000
1960[3]	869,000	697,000	1,959,000	...	330,000	2,330,000	506,000	826,000	7,517,000

[1] Figures taken from Tressler and Evers (1957).
[2] Figures taken from Quick Frozen Foods (Anon. 1960–1961).
[3] Figures taken from Quick Frozen Foods (Anon. 1961–1962).
[4] In terms of single strength juice.

RAW MATERIALS FOR FREEZING

Essentially all fruits (prepared as such or as juices), vegetables, meat, poultry and eggs which are preserved in this country by freezing are grown or produced in continental United States. Fish may be harvested in waters off continental United States or may be taken from the ocean off Alaska or Canada. Some of the frozen marine products consumed in the United States are prepared and frozen in Alaska, Canada, Iceland or other countries and much of the raw-product fish material used in this country for the production of frozen fish sticks or frozen breaded fish portions is actually filleted and frozen in Canada or Iceland (Anon. 1962A).

In arranging for raw vegetable products to be processed in freezing plants, the freezer usually contracts with farmers to provide the commodity. This planning and regulation of crops usually involves the services of personnel trained in the agricultural sciences. Technical advice is given to growers concerning varieties, or the seed may be provided by the freezer. Fertilizers may likewise be specified or provided. In some cases, pesticides or fungicides are specified as well as dates and quantities for application. The freezer, through a field crew, will specify

TABLE 92B

APPROXIMATE AMOUNTS CANNED

(Millions of standard cases[1] and millions of pounds[1])

Year	Fruits		Vegetables		Juices		Specialties		Milk		Fish		Meat		Total	
	Cases	Lbs.	Cases	Lbs.	Cases	Lbs.	Cases	Lbs.	Cases	Lbs.	Cases	Lbs.	Cases	Lbs.	Cases	Lbs.
1940	49	2205	133	3990	55	1650	79	2370	58	2523	19	598.5	12	440	405	13776.5
1946	83	3735	201	6030	105	3150	102	3060	74	3219	21	661.5	30	1350	616	21205.5
1955	92	4140	197	5910	99	2970	128	3840	60	2610	26	819	33	1485	635	21774
1957	91	4095	209	6270	104	3120	132	3960	58	2523	31	976.5	37	1665	662	22609.5
1960	104	4680	217	6510	108	3240	136	4080	51	2218.5	35	1102.5	39	1755	690	23586

Figures and conversion factors provided by the National Canners Association, Washington, D. C. (1962).

when a particular area should be planted, and when the product should be harvested.

Planting is oftentimes carried out according to a schedule which arranges for the seeding, on a specified day, of sufficient acreage to provide raw materials for one day's operation. After the first planting is made a certain number of heat units (degree-hours above a base temperature below which the product will not grow) must accumulate before the next planting can be made. The number of units between plantings will be approximately that number which will accumulate per 24-hr. day during the harvest season (Seaton and Huffington 1954).

If the processor grows his own vegetables, he still has to consider and carry out the described practices in order to assure an adequate supply of freshly harvested vegetables.

Harvesting of vegetables may be done by hand as in the case of asparagus, pole beans and certain others, or by machine as is done with bush beans, peas and sweet corn. Some products may be placed in lug boxes or hoppers and brought to the plant on trucks. Others, such as unhusked corn, are carried on side enclosed trucks without small unit containers. Peas and lima beans are harvested by mowing the vines and passing them through the viner. The pea or bean seeds are released when the pod is split by impact from rotating paddles. They are separated through screens and collected in hoppers which are trucked to the processing plant in bulk or in palletized lug boxes handled by fork trucks.

Freezers specify varieties of fruit in contracting for annual crops. For perennial fruits, contracts are made with growers who produce varieties desired for freezing.

Peaches, apples, raspberries and strawberries are picked by hand; blueberries are usually harvested with hand rakes but may be picked by hand, and cherries are stripped from the tree or picked by hand. Larger fruits are brought to the plant in baskets or boxes. Apples are usually cooled and stored prior to processing for freezing. Cherries are handled in boxes. Blueberries, strawberries and raspberries are placed in hallocks (holding about one pound) which are stacked in crates.

Stems are removed from the larger fruits at the time of picking and hulls are usually removed from berries at the time of picking, although some strawberries are not hulled when picked.

Citrus fruits which are to be processed as juice concentrates are picked by hand and delivered in bulk in open-top trucks.

Eggs are delivered in crates holding 24 dozen. The individual eggs are held on cardboard liners shaped as to fit the contour of the shells. Prior to processing eggs are held in storage at optimum temperature near 32°F. and at a relative humidity of 85 to 92 per cent (depending on the rate of air circulation) (Romanoff and Romanoff 1949). If the frozen product is to be of the best quality, eggs should not be held in storage for more than a few weeks even though the conditions may be optimum.

Poultry may be purchased from farmers or raised by the freezer. Poultry raising has undergone many innovations in recent years. Today, the eggs of selected breeds are hatched in incubators. The poults are raised under controlled conditions of temperature in houses where adequate food and water are always available. At the required size, live birds are placed in crates and brought to dressing plants for slaughter. Some operators raise poultry in houses with dirt floors covered with shavings. Once the flock has been removed, a bulldozer is brought in to remove the soiled shavings, the house is thoroughly disinfected and the floor covered with clean shavings in readiness for the next group of chicks.

The killing and plucking of chickens is usually carried out adjacent to the room where evisceration is performed. However, there are still some operations in which slaughtering and plucking operations are located some distance from the freezing plant, the birds being delivered for further processing in the "New York dressed" state (Stewart and Lowe 1948).

Meat is usually frozen by processors who also sell fresh, cut or uncut meat. In such cases, the slaughtering, dressing and cooling of animal carcasses is the regular process in which the company participates. Cattle, hogs, lambs etc., are brought to the plant on the hoof, slaughtered, dressed, inspected by veterinarians, cooled and held at temperatures near 32°F. and relative humidities near 85 to 90 per cent prior to processing for freezing. Carcasses of beef are held for several days, to allow the meat to pass through rigor and undergo "tenderization" prior to cutting for freezing (Wiesman 1947).

Fish in the unprocessed state may be handled in several ways prior to freezing (Tressler and Lemon 1951). A considerable quantity of ocean perch is processed and frozen in this country. Ocean perch are caught in otter trawls and moved into hold pens through manholes in the deck, first using a layer of ice, then a layer of fish, another layer of ice, another layer of fish, and so on. Due to the distances which must be traveled from fishing grounds, these fish may have been held iced ten days when landed in port. The fish are delivered to the processing plant in the uneviscerated state after separating from ice.

Haddock are caught much in the same manner as ocean perch. However, on the boat the fish must first be eviscerated and washed and may be gilled prior to placing in hold pens. Much of the frozen haddock consumed in the United States is processed and frozen in Canada or Iceland. Since these countries are closer to the banks where the fish are caught, haddock may be held on ice for shorter periods of time than is ocean perch. This, however, is not necessarily true.

Frozen cod consumed in this country is also mostly produced in Canada or Iceland. A considerable portion of the cod frozen in Canada is caught near the shore with hand lines or line trawls and brought to the plant eviscerated, without ice. The fish is in good condition when landed because it has been out of water for a comparatively short period and ambient temperatures under which it will have been held will not be high enough to cause rapid spoilage. Some cod is caught and handled as described for haddock.

Frozen halibut, consumed in the United States, is mostly shipped in from Alaska or Canada, and there is some processing of this product in the State of Washington. This fish is caught with long lines or line trawls. It is eviscerated, gilled and placed in hold pens with layers of ice and fish alternately until the pen is filled. The poke or belly cavity of large fish is also iced. Halibut will have been held on ice from 3 to 10 days when landed. This fish holds up well under these conditions.

Small flounders, of which there are a number of species, are caught and handled aboard boats in much the same manner as ocean perch.

The chief crustacean products preserved by freezing are shrimp and king crabs. Shrimp are principally caught in the Gulf of Mexico using otter trawls. Boats handling shrimp, however, are smaller and use smaller trawls than for ocean perch. The shrimp are emptied onto the deck, and are culled and headed. The tails are placed in the holds in ice. Shrimp may be held in this condition aboard the boat up to ten days or more (Fieger 1950). Unless well iced, they are subject to rapid deterioration due to the growth of bacteria. Shrimp are brought to the freezing plants as tails with shell on.

Some quantities of ocean scallops or sea scallops are frozen. Only the adductor muscle of this specimen is eaten. The bivalve is taken in a metal dredge and emptied onto the deck of the boat. The product is culled and the adductor muscle is removed, and is washed and placed in cloth or plastic bags. The bagged product is refrigerated in ice until landed in port, one to several days after harvesting.

Other fishery products, frozen in comparatively small quantities, will not be described here.

PREPARATION FOR FREEZING

No detailed description of the preparation of foods for purposes of freezing can be given in a single chapter. This subject will, therefore, be treated in a somewhat general sense.

Vegetables

Vegetables are brought to the processing plant in the whole or cut or vined state. Some products such as peas or beans may be size graded prior to further treatment. Corn may be judged for maturity organoleptically, on the basis of moisture content, or the refractive index of the kernel "milk" may be used as a criterion of maturity. Some vegetables are selected to include a general maturity range but are not graded specifically.

Some vegetables are dry cleaned prior to washing. Peas and lima beans are passed through a fanning mill. Broccoli is sorted and trimmed by hand or the butt end may be removed with a rotating knife, then the spears may be split with a hand knife to portions of suitable size. The base of the brussels sprout is trimmed off by machine. Corn must be husked before it can be washed. This is done in a machine which cuts off the stalk attachment and removes the husk as the ear passes over rubber rollers. Spinach is dry cleaned by passing it through rotating reels; dirt, stones, and other detritus passing through the spaces in the reel to the outside.

Prior to washing cauliflower, the base of the cluster and the leaves are trimmed off with a hand knife, the core is cut out and the individual flowerettes are broken off. The flowerettes are then passed through a cylindrical rod cleaner to remove detritus.

Peas and lima beans are washed in flotation-type, water-filled machines which pass them over stone traps in such a manner that dense materials sink to the bottom and are removed. The products pass over the top and are separated from water by means of a reel. Special washers may be used for peas in which case the product is passed through a mineral oil-detergent-water emulsion. When treated in this manner and passed into water, sound peas sink and are separated; thistle buds, nightshade berries, skins and other foreign material float and are separated at the top. Sprays of water are then used to clean the sound peas.

Reel-type washers with forced sprays may be used to wash some products prior to blanching. Soaker-type washers with agitating sprays may be used for broccoli, brussels sprouts and cauliflower flowerettes. Carrots usually receive both spray and soaker-type washings. Green beans are not washed before blanching. Spinach is washed in moving water in tanks fitted with a drum which immerses the product as it moves along. It is then passed through a wet reel where it is further washed with water sprays, then passed over a wire-mesh belt for drainage, inspection and removal of foreign material.

Other operations which must be carried out before the products are blanched include snap beans—snipping by machine, cross-cutting or

TABLE 93

BLANCHING TIMES FOR VEGETABLES TO BE FROZEN[1]

Product	Heating Medium	Blanching Time
Asparagus	Live steam	$3^1/_2$ to 5 min. depending upon stalk diameter
Broccoli	Live steam	$3^1/_2$ min.
Brussels sprouts	Live steam	5 to 6 min.
Carrots	Water at 210°F.	2 to 3 min.
Cauliflower	Live steam	4 to 5 min.
Corn on the cob	Live steam	6 to 11 min.
Cut corn	Live steam	3 min.
Lima beans (Fordhook)	Live steam	3 to 4 min.
Lima beans (baby)	Water at 210°F.	$2^1/_2$ min.
Peas (green)	Water at 210° to 212°F.	50 to 60 sec.
	Live steam	2 to 3 min.
Snap beans (crosscut)	Live steam or water at 210°F.	2 to 4 min.
Snap beans (frenched)	Live steam	2 to 4 min.
Spinach	Live steam	2 to 3 min.

[1] Tressler and Evers (1957); Joslyn (1961).

Frenching, also by machine; carrots—steam peeling, spray washing, trimming and dicing; cut corn—cutting the kernels from the cob by machine, if the product is to be blanched in this form (usually the case).

All vegetables, except onions, must be blanched prior to freezing, to inactivate enzymes which would otherwise cause the development of off-flavors during frozen storage. Blanching is carried out in hot water or in steam. In water blanching the product is conducted through water at 190° to 210°F. In steam blanching the product is carried on a belt (usually wire mesh) through a hooded section into which live steam is injected. The time and temperatures are regulated in such a manner that the enzymes which could cause off-flavor development are inactivated (see Table 93). Tests for catalase or peroxidase (Joslyn 1949) are used to determine the adequacy of blanching. It is considered by some workers in the field that a negative peroxidase test is a better indication of the adequacy of blanching than a negative catalase test (Joslyn 1946A).

After blanching, vegetables are quickly cooled at least to 70°F. This may be done by emptying the product from the blancher into a flume of running water which serves to cool the product and convey to the next operation. In some cases, blanched products are emptied into a perforated or rod-type cylindrical reel fitted with forced water sprays or into a funnel-shaped tank, with a stream of cold water.

Corn is blanched on the cob or as cut kernels as it passes along on a hooded, wire-mesh belt. The cut product must be cooled on the belt with atomized water sprays but corn on the cob may be cooled in a tank of slowly moving water.

After blanching and cooling, lima beans are passed through a quality grader or separator containing nearly saturated brine (sodium chloride solution). The less mature beans float and can be removed from the surface while the wrinkled, over-mature beans sink and are removed from an outlet near the bottom of the separation tank. Over-mature beans are discarded. Beans which float will become the frozen product and these must be washed to remove salt. This is done by fluming in water or by passing through a rod-reel fitted with water sprays.

Whole kernel (cut) corn is cleaned before packaging to remove silk and husk particles. This may be done in a quality separator containing water instead of brine. In this case, corn kernels are removed at the bottom outlet, silk and foreign material floating off at the top.

Peas are passed through a quality separator or grader as are lima beans. However, the density of the brine solution used to separate over-mature peas is lower than that used for lima beans. The more desirable (less mature) peas float and are removed at the top, the more mature peas sink and are removed at the bottom outlet. Separated peas are washed to remove brine.

All vegetables are passed over inspection belts prior to packaging. Here small pieces of product, weeds, and other unwanted materials are removed by hand. Asparagus, French-cut green beans, broccoli, brussels sprouts and cauliflower may also be size graded at this time.

After blanching and cooling, and prior to packaging, spinach must be pressed and drained to remove water picked up during processing. This is done by passing the product over a wire-mesh belt fitted with a weighted roller which rides on the spinach as it passes by. Packages are filled by hand.

Lima beans, cross-cut string beans, cut corn and peas are filled into packages by automatic volumetric fillers. A certain proportion of the filled packages are check weighed.

Carrots are often loose frozen as individual cubes prior to packaging. This permits use in mixtures with peas. After freezing they are packed "in bulk" in polyethylene bags and metal containers and stored at temperatures near 0°F. until mixed with other vegetables and packaged in retail or institutional size containers. Volumetric fillers may be used for placing the mixed, frozen products in packages.

Fruits

Apples are not packed in retail packages. Frozen apple slices or sections are used for bakery products. Apples are peeled and cored by machine, then passed over a belt where trimming is done by hand. They are then sliced by machine, passed over a vibrating screen to remove small pieces and then over an inspection belt.

Prior to freezing, apples are treated to prevent browning due to enzyme action during freezing and storage. This is usually accomplished by sulfiting (dipping for one minute in a solution containing 0.2 to 0.25 per cent of available sulfur dioxide at pH 2.8 to 3.0). The apples are allowed to stand for at least eight hours in a refrigerated room prior to freezing to allow the sulfur dioxide to penetrate, otherwise browning will occur in the interior.

Blanching-and-cooling, or soaking in solutions containing salt, sugar and/or ascorbic acid are also used to retard browning in frozen apples. Soaking may be combined with vacuum treatment to promote penetration of the slices.

Blanching may cause apple slices to become soft. Ascorbic acid-sugar-vacuum treatment is not always suitable. Calcium salts are sometimes added to solutions for firming apple slices.

Apple slices to be frozen are usually packed in enameled, slip-cover cans holding 30 to 50 lbs. of product. The filled containers are placed in cold rooms or tunnels at temperatures below 0°F. for freezing.

Blueberries preserved by freezing are generally used for bakery products although the cultivated blueberry may be frozen for consumers. Wild berries, harvested by raking, must be cleaned by fanning to remove leaves, etc. They are then size graded, washed and flumed to remove heavy detritus. The dewatered berries are spread on trays and frozen in air blast tunnels. After freezing, the clusters are broken apart and berries are passed through a destemming reel, inspected as they are carried on a belt to remove unripe berries and other unwanted materials before packing in enameled, slip-cover cans holding 20 lbs.

Red, sour cherries make up the bulk of the frozen cherry pack used in the bakery trade. At the packing plant, the fruit is soaked in tanks of ice water to which some calcium chloride may be added to firm the fruit. After soaking, the fruit is passed over a belt-type size grader which separates undersize fruit. Cherries are then passed over an inspection belt where foreign material and defective fruit are removed by hand. The fruit is then pitted by passing it through a machine which punches out the pit. Cherries are packed with sugar in 30- to 50-lb. enameled, slip-cover cans or in 50-gal. barrels. Usually a mixture of 3 parts of fruit plus 1 of sucrose (by weight) is used but 4 parts plus 1 mixtures are sometimes packed. Sugar is added and mixed as the fruit is placed in the container. The mixture is sharp frozen at 0°F. or below in tunnels or in rooms where there is air movement.

Grape purées are frozen for jelly and jam manufacture. The fruit is stemmed, washed and usually heated to 150°F. and passed through a finisher to eliminate seeds and skins. The pulp is packed in 50-gal.

barrels or 50-lb. enameled, slip-cover cans and frozen as has been described for cherries.

Peaches are mostly frozen in large-sized containers although there is some retail trade for this product. Ripe yellow freestone peaches are selected for freezing. The fruit is immersed in a lye solution (6 to 8 per cent) at 140°F. for about one minute, removed and subjected to forced water sprays which remove the skin. The peaches are then halved and pitted, then trimmed and defective fruit trimmed or removed by hand. Halves are then turned cup side down and sliced by machine.

Retail peach packs are filled into containers by hand and 60 per cent sucrose syrup is added by machine. In packing sliced peaches in cans holding 30 lbs. of product, 24 lbs. of peaches and 6 lbs. of 50° or 60° Brix syrup are combined. A depressor may be used to hold slices under the syrup.

A syrup containing about 0.2 per cent of l-ascorbic or d-iso ascorbic acid has been found helpful in retarding enzymatic browning of peaches during frozen storage and defrosting for use.

Red raspberries to be frozen are washed in flume washers agitated by sprays of water. They are then passed over inspection belts where green fruit and other undesirable materials are picked out. Retail packs are filled into cartons by hand and covered with 40 to 50 per cent syrup.

Some red raspberries are packed in 30- to 50-lb. tins or in barrels for jam and jelly production. Berries may be mixed with sugar (usually 3 parts of fruit plus 1 of sugar) before filling, or sugar may be added as the berries are filled in barrels. Freezing is carried out as in the case of cherries.

Both bulk and retail packaged strawberries are frozen. The berries are usually hulled when picked but in some sections of the country berries are capped in the packing plant by machine. Capped berries are washed in agitated water flumes, then inspected to remove green and spoiled fruit. The product may be packed in 30-lb. tins, barrels or in retail-sized cartons, whole or sliced by machine and mixed with 1 part of sugar for each 4 of fruit. Large cans or barrels are filled simultaneously with fruit and sugar (3 parts of fruit to 1 of sugar). Freezing is carried out as in the case of cherries but barrels may be rolled or agitated daily to mix the ingredients during freezing; which requires several days.

Concentrated Fruit Juices

Orange concentrate is by far the largest among frozen fruit juice concentrates. Grapefruit juice, lemon and tangerine juice may also be concentrated and frozen as well as grapefruit-orange juice mixtures, lemonade and the juice of some other fruits.

On arrival at the plant, oranges are inspected to remove undesirable fruit. The juice of a representative sample is checked. In Florida, the Brix may not be less than 11.0° Brix, and the Brix-acid ratio may not be less than 12 to 1 nor more than 18 to 1. In California and Arizona the Brix-acid ratio may not be less than 11 to 1 nor more than 17 to 1.

Oranges, accumulated in baffled bins, are scrubbed with detergent and rinsed with chlorinated water before juicing in automatic equipment of several designs. The original procedure for preparing frozen concentrate was to separate strained and pulpy juice by gravity, then concentrate the strained juice to 58° Brix at temperatures below 80°F. in low temperature evaporators, then cut back to 42° Brix with the chilled pulpy fraction containing intact juice sacs. The blend was slush frozen in cylindrical, scraped surface freezers, filled and vapor-vacuum (or nitrogen) closed in cans which were hardened in a freezer tunnel before casing. Leached and second-pressed juices may be used in beverage bases.

To increase the yield of frozen concentrate, "pulp washing" has come into general use. Pulpy juice from the extractors is pressed through finishers. The pulpy fraction is reverse-washed and re-pressed 4 to 6 times, and the extract (at 4° to 7° Brix) is combined with the strained juice which is flash heated to 165°F. and cooled to inactivate pectic enzymes extracted from the pulp. Eighty per cent of the juice is concentrated to 58° Brix and recombined with the chilled 20 per cent cut-back fraction to reduce the Brix to 42°.

Processors are continuously testing modifications. In one, designed to increase the quality of flavoring volatiles in the product, cut-back juice is freeze-concentrated. To avoid entrainment losses, solids entrained in the ice fraction are combined with juice going to the evaporator. This makes it possible to use a higher percentage of cut-back juice. In another variation, high density concentrates are flavored with orange oil instead of cut-back juice to effect savings in container, shipping and storage costs. This has focused attention on producing high density concentrates of lower viscosity. This, and the desire to retard deposits in evaporators, has led to use of super centrifuges to separate heavy suspended solids from strained juice before evaporation.

In a modification of the freezing technique, the cooled containers of concentrate are passed through an agitating, continuous freezer containing refrigerated alcohol, or a similar heat transfer liquid medium which remains liquid at the required temperatures.

Eggs

When received at the breaking and freezing plant, eggs are promptly cooled and held at 32°F. until processed. Dirty eggs are separated and washed before breaking. Clean eggs are conveyed to the breaking room and broken by machine or hand. In hand operations, each person breaking eggs is provided with several cups, a breaking knife, rack and tray and a spoon. Eggs are struck against a knife. The contents are placed in a cup, until each cup contains three eggs. Remaining egg white may be removed from shells by suction. When filled, the contents of each cup is smelled and, if good, is emptied into a pail. When a spoiled or musty egg is found, the contents of the cup is discarded and the cup is washed and sterilized before reuse. The broken eggs in the pails are placed in a churn for mixing, then screened or centrifuged to separate chelaza and shell fragments. Mixed eggs are chilled below 35°F. in a heat exchanger, filled in 30-lb. cans and sharp frozen.

Yolks and whites may be separated at the time of breaking and packed separately. To retard undesirable changes during frozen storage 10 per cent of sucrose, 5 to 10 per cent of salt or 7.5 per cent of glycerin may be mixed with whole eggs or yolks prior to freezing.

Poultry

Poultry for freezing is suspended by the feet on an overhead conveyor, is killed and bled, then scalded and picked, and the pin feathers are singed by a circular flame. Feet are removed and the birds re-suspended by the hocks and the head. The birds are then slit above the vent and below the neck. A cut is made around the vent and the viscera are pulled out for inspection by a veterinarian, who discards diseased birds. The liver, gizzard and heart are separated, inspected, washed and handled separately. The head is cut off, and the neck severed. The crop, gullet and windpipe, lungs and kidneys are removed and discarded with the viscera.

After thorough washing, the dressed birds are approximately sized and the body heat is removed by immersion in tanks of crushed ice, which may contain an added antibiotic.

From this point, there are many methods of handling. Birds may be cut up before freezing. They may be de-boned and frozen. Or the whole eviscerated bird may be shrink-wrapped in transparent film and transferred to the sharp freezer.

Meat

The preparation of meat for freezing is essentially the same as cutting for retail sales. Loins, ribs or round sections of beef, pork loins or lamb racks, loins or legs are cut into steaks, chops, roasts or legs and into other portions for cooking. These portions are placed in cartons or over-wrapped by hand in preparation for freezing.

Fish

Most of the frozen fish used in this country is filleted by machine although this can be done by hand. Fillet yields will vary with the species and size of the fish and may be as high as 55 per cent (with mackerel) or less than 30 per cent (with ocean perch). Oftentimes the fillets are skinned by machine or by hand prior to freezing.

After skinning, fillets are trimmed by hand and then may be candled to detect parasites which, if present, must be cut out. Fillets are next washed with water sprays although they may be carried on a belt through a 3 to 5 per cent brine solution for this purpose. After washing, the product should be thoroughly drained. The fillets are hand packed in cartons for retail sale or may be packed in several layers in cartons holding 10 lbs. or more. Cod, haddock, ocean perch and flounder are mainly packed as fillets; haddock, and especially cod are also sold as fish blocks (layers of fillets).

Frozen fish blocks are sawed, or sawed and sheared into fishstick-sized portions, are then battered, breaded, deep-fat fried, cooled, packed into cartons by hand and refrozen. Fried sticks may also be frozen prior to packaging and packaged automatically by special machines.

A considerable portion of frozen fish blocks are now sawed into four-ounce portions, battered, breaded and packed by hand into cartons holding several pounds, for the restaurant and institution trade.

Halibut, some salmon and whiting are frozen in the round, eviscerated state. Whiting are placed in pans and frozen as blocks; halibut and salmon are frozen as individual fish. The fish or pans of fish are placed on expansion pipes in cold rooms for freezing. After freezing, the fish or blocks are dipped in or sprayed with cold water to glaze surfaces with ice before storing.

Some salmon and considerable amounts of halibut are now being packed as steaks. The frozen fish is cut into steaks with band saws and the product is packaged by hand.

Shrimp are packaged in small cartons for retail or in larger cartons for the institutional trade as tails with shell on, as tails with shell on but with the sand vein removed, or as de-shelled, de-veined shrimp. The product is frozen in the carton as a block, then glazed by spraying with cold water. The de-shelled, de-veined product may be frozen on trays and then immersed in cold water to glaze individual portions prior to packaging by hand.

FREEZING METHODS AND EQUIPMENT

The freezing of foods involves the removal of heat from the food in order to achieve the following two effects: (1) crystallization as ice of most of the water present in the food; (2) lowering the temperature of the food to the desired level.

It is generally considered that the quality of frozen foods improves with increasing rate of cooling during the freezing operation, and that the lower the temperature to which the food is brought the more desirable the product. The reasons which are commonly cited for the above effects are: (1) rapid cooling results in the formation of a large number of very small uniformly distributed ice crystals and minimum damage to the tissues; (2) diffusion of soluble components is minimized by shortening the interval between onset of crystallization and maximum solidification of the system; (3) chemical and biological reactions are minimized by decreasing the temperature rapidly to a level at which the reaction rates become insignificant.

While there are some exceptions to the above principles (Joslyn 1961; Goldblith *et al.* 1963), their general validity is well established.

The rate of cooling may be most generally expressed as a function of two variables, namely the driving force and the sum of resistances to heat transfer.

$$\text{Rate of cooling} = \frac{\text{Driving force}}{\text{Sum of resistances to heat transfer}}$$

The driving force is simply the temperature difference between the product and the cooling medium. The resistances depend on the specific situation and depend on such factors as air velocity, thickness of product, geometry of the system, and composition of the product.

In order to increase cooling, one must do one or both of the following: (1) keep the temperature of the cooling medium as low as possible, or (2) minimize resistance to heat transfer. The specific methods used to decrease resistances depend on the freezing process.

There are three basic freezing processes in commercial use: (1) direct immersion of product in a cooling liquid medium; (2) indirect contact with the cooling liquid; (3) immersion in a rapidly moving stream of cold air.

The direct immersion methods may be applied either to the loose product, or to the package containing the product. The immersion medium, in turn, may be either a heat-exchange fluid cooled by indirect contact with a refrigerant, or a compressed gas such as liquid nitrogen or nitrous oxide in which case the cooling is achieved by evaporation of the immersion liquid itself.

The advantages of immersion freezing include: (1) good contact and, therefore, low resistance to heat transfer; (2) exclusion of atmospheric oxygen, eliminating oxidative changes during freezing.

The main disadvantages are the need to prevent contamination of the medium which is to come in contact with food, and the limitation of cooling media to edible materials which do not result in undesirable changes in the product. Immersion media used most commonly are solutions of sucrose, glycerol, and of sodium chloride.

These disadvantages may be overcome by immersing the food after packaging, which prevents direct contact between the food and the cooling fluid. Unfortunately, this procedure also increases the resistance to heat transfer, and is in general only efficient when the package is either a very tightly fitting plastic film (shrinkable packages for poultry) or a well-filled metallic container.

Considerable attention is now being paid to the use of compressed, liquefied N_2 or NO_2 for the freezing of foods. These media offer the advantages listed below (Anon. 1961A): (1) since the boiling point of these gases is very low ($-127.2°F.$ for NO_2, and $-320.4°F.$ for N_2) the driving force for heat transfer is large; (2) good contact with the food keeps resistance to heat transfer low; (3) since the cooling action is obtained by evaporation of the medium, there is no need for a primary refrigerant to cool this medium, and possibilities of food contamination are minimized; (4) very low product temperatures may be attained rapidly, and the quality of the food is claimed to be superior to that attained by conventional freezing methods; (5) the speed of the freezing operation allows the integration of this step with other operations in a rapid continuous, or semicontinuous, process; and (6) since no large installation and amortization expenses are required, the method is suitable for plant operations in which freezing is done only occasionally, rather than on a year-round basis.

The major disadvantages of the process are economic. According to a recent survey, the cost of freezing with liquid nitrogen is approximately 6 cents per lb. food, which is considerably higher than costs for conventional freezing (Anon. 1962A). The cost may be lowered by recovery and recompression of the evaporated nitrogen, but this approach requires additional equipment and therefore to a large extent negates some of the advantages of the process.

Indirect freezing involves contacting the food, or a package containing the food, with a surface cooled by the refrigerant, or by a heat exchange fluid, which itself is cooled by indirect contact with the refrigerant. The freezing methods may involve contact with a single cooling platen, or may involve contact from two sides in multiplate equipment. In the latter case, pressure may be applied to the plates to assure good contact with the product.

From the point of view of operation, the equipment may be of the batch type, semicontinuous or continuous. Some typical methods in each category are discussed below (see Tressler and Evers 1957).

The Birdseye multiplate freezer is typical of batch-type, double-contact freezers. It contains a number of superimposed hollow plates, movable by a hydraulic system to allow freezing by double-contact under pressure. The refrigerant or precooled brine is circulated through the hollow plates. In operation, the product, usually prepackaged in flat packages, is placed between the plates, the hydraulic system actuated to bring the plates in intimate contact with the product, and the insulated cabinets containing the plates closed for the period required to lower the product temperature to the desired level. Freezing times vary from one to several hours. Excessive pressure on the product is prevented by the simple expedient of placing spacer sticks of desired heights between each pair of plates. Simple materials handling tools, such as suitably proportioned trays, and lift trucks, may be used in loading and unloading the freezers.

The Amerio freezer is a modification of the simple batch freezer allowing a continuous operation by the use of a number of stations, which are automatically unloaded at the rear and loaded at the front, after the completion of the freezing cycle. The unit thus provides semicontinuous operation, and eliminates manual loading and unloading.

The Patterson continuous plate freezer is an example of a straight line high speed automatic freezer. The packages are fed into the 25-ft. long freezing section on belts which place the packages in front of the eight levels of plates. The packages are pushed into the eight levels, and the plates closed to provide close contact. The packages are intermittently advanced through the freezer, by an arrangement which assures that at every opening of the plates the packages are advanced one row. The unloading and casing of the packages is also automatic, and the unit operates at high speeds.

The indirect contact methods discussed above are applicable to the freezing of relatively flat solid food pieces or to packages containing either solids or liquids. For freezing of juices, purées and other liquid or semisolid foods other methods may also be employed. These methods are based on partially freezing material to a "slush"-like product in a continuous heat exchange apparatus, through which the slush is moved in a relatively thin layer by a screw or a set of scraping blades. The "Votator Slush Freezer" which may be used for freezing of ice cream, juices and similar products is typical of this type of equipment. The partially frozen food is filled into containers and the final freezing step or "hardening" is performed in an air-blast tunnel.

Efficient freezing may also be achieved by exposing the food, or packages containing it, to precooled air. The speed of freezing in this method depends greatly on the velocity of air moving past the food, since the resistance to heat transfer is a very strong function of air velocity. Rapidly flowing air may allow the removal of ten times more heat per unit time and area than air transferring heat by natural convection.

The use of still air freezing is practiced commercially to some extent, and it was one of the earliest methods of freezing. Introduced in 1861, and termed "sharp freezing," it is based on the simple procedure of placing food in rooms maintained at temperatures of $-10°$ to $-20°$F., with only gentle air agitation provided by circulating fans, or by natural convection.

In contrast to this slow freezing procedure, modern air-blast freezing equipment may operate at temperatures as low as $-80°$F., and the air velocities used may exceed hurricane wind speeds. More typical are temperatures of $-20°$ to $-50°$F. and air velocities of 2,000 to 3,000 ft. per min. The design of blast freezers varies in geometry, method of product throughput, and operating characteristics. A recently reported system used in Cincinnati includes a 60 ft. long and 17 ft. wide freezing tunnel, operating at $-50°$F., and capable of processing up to 60,000 lbs. of food per day (Anon. 1962B). Blast-freezing is an efficient rapid freezing method, readily adaptable to continuous operation at high rates of throughput. The main disadvantage arises from the fact that rapidly moving air not only facilitates heat transfer but also improves mass transfer. As a result water is removed from the food and moved to the freezing coils. This may result in undesirable desiccation, and also in need for frequent defrosting. The problem is largely avoided when blast-freezing packaged foods.

An interesting modification of the air-blast freezing principle is fluidized-bed freezing. In this method of freezing, the product is gently fed onto a fluidizing tray enclosed in an insulated section of the freezer. Refrigerated air rises through the orifices of the tray, and suspends the food particles or pieces. The particles are frozen while carried in a stream of air through the freezing zone and then dropped onto the discharge hopper.

The advantages of this method of freezing include: (1) continuous operation is achieved without the need for elaborate mechanical devices to move the product through the freezing zone; (2) the individual pieces or particles are suspended in the cold air, and the resulting good heat transfer characteristics assure rapid and uniform freezing.

The limitations of the process are primarily due to its applicability to a relatively small number of food products which can be efficiently fluidized by air. It has been applied to the freezing of peas, cut corn, diced carrots, and several kinds of berries.

The equipment has been developed in Sweden by Helsingborg Fryshus, and has recently been applied to freezing of peas in the United States. In the U. S. installation at Whiteford Packing Co., Whiteford, Md., it has been used to process peas at the rate of over 5,000 lbs. per hr. Freezing is accomplished in 6 to 8 min., indicating the rapidity of the cooling rate (Trauberman 1962).

PACKAGING OF FROZEN FOODS

The most important factors controlling the quality of frozen foods during their distribution and storage are temperature and method of packaging. The functional properties of the package must therefore receive the same degree of attention as the variables in preparation and freezing of the foods.

The important requirements for packaging of frozen foods include (Karel 1956; Heiss 1956).

Mechanical Strength

In order to protect the food, the package must maintain its mechanical integrity. The problems arising in frozen food distribution, which affect this requirement, are the low temperatures of storage, and the possibility of moisture condensation on the package. The important mechanical properties of the package are therefore: good tear and burst strength at low temperatures, and high "wet strength" (tensile strength under conditions in which the material is saturated with water).

Flexibility

The package for frozen foods is often subjected to stresses because of the expansion of the product, and changes in moisture content of the package. Furthermore, as will be discussed in detail later, it is often necessary to minimize the amount of headspace in the package so the package must conform closely to the shape of the product.

Liquid-Tightness

The package for frozen foods must be capable of preventing passage of liquids. This is particularly important for products which are normally thawed within the package.

Low Water-Vapor Permeability

Since the prevention of desiccation is one of the major functions of the package, water vapor permeability is of particular importance. The transfer of water vapor through packages may occur by means of one or both of the following mechanisms: (A) diffusion through pores, crevices and other imperfections in the package; (B) activated diffusion through the packaging material. In each case, the necessary condition for the transfer of moisture is the existence of a difference in partial pressure of water between the outside and the inside of the package. This difference exists by virtue of one of the following conditions: (A) the inside of the package is at the same temperature as the surrounding atmosphere, but the relative humidities inside and outside of the package are different; (B) there exists a temperature difference between the package contents and the surrounding atmosphere.

Water vapor transfer by activated diffusion decreases very rapidly with temperature (Barrer 1951), and at frozen storage temperatures the amount transferred through intact packages is small. On the other hand, movement of water vapor through pores and imperfections in packaging material is not significantly lowered at low temperatures and is the main source of difficulties in preventing desiccation of frozen foods. It is, therefore, particularly important to pay attention to pinhole resistance and porosity of packaging materials, and to measure the actual resistance to water vapor transfer on completed, normally handled packages, rather than on flat sheets under laboratory conditions.

Shelor and Woodroof (1954) determined the moisture losses of ground beef after one year's storage in 17 different types of packages. The losses ranged from 0.07 to 3.88 per cent. How much significance this amount of water loss will have on consumer acceptance of the product is debatable. Kaess (1943) determined the maximum acceptable moisture losses for several frozen fruits and vegetables, and found that the loss of one per cent moisture may result in an unacceptable appearance of the product. Desiccation is also an important quality defect in commercial frozen marine products (Anon. 1961B).

Low Permeability to Other Gases and Vapors

Of particular importance among gases and vapors, other than water, which may diffuse through packages, are oxygen and various volatile compounds which are constituents of flavors and odors. Low oxygen permeability may not be necessary for packaging of all frozen foods maintained at low temperatures. Certain frozen foods, however, such as poultry, salmon and other fat-containing foods, do undergo oxidative rancidity, and limitation of oxygen supply would be beneficial to improved quality (Winter and Hustrulid 1951).

Of equal importance is the permeability to flavor and odors. Many of such compounds have relatively high vapor pressures, even at low temperatures, and can migrate rapidly through the packaging materials (Kiermeier 1943; Karel et al. 1957). Losses of flavor, as well as pick-up of undesirable odors from outside the package, may be the consequence of such migration.

Additional Requirements

Specific application to frozen foods may require other specific properties of the package. Many food products undergo deterioration which are catalyzed by light. In such cases, transmission of light through the package may be an important consideration. Among changes sensitive to light are: loss or discoloration of pigments, such as chlorophyll of vegetables, myoglobin of red meats and astacene of crustaceans and salmon; oxidative rancidity and destruction of vitamins. Light sensitivity does not necessarily eliminate the possibility of transparent packaging. Exclusion of ultraviolet light by the transparent package may often be sufficient to prevent the changes, without the need for exclusion of visible light. Recent studies (Shepherd 1959) have shown that transparent packaging does not impair the color of frozen peas, in spite of the dependence of this color on a light-sensitive pigment.

Another consideration is the possible migration of package components into the food. Such components may have pharmacological significance, and impair the safety of food, or they may impart to the food undesirable taste or odor. Because of the nature of the freezing process, and the low temperatures of storage, the safety hazard from packaging migrants is inherently low. The Food and Drug regulations (Federal Register 1962) therefore require only extraction tests at relatively mild conditions for materials used for frozen food packaging. Most commonly used packaging materials meet requirements of these tests.

A more rigorous examination of the extractability of the packaging material is required, however, for packages of the "boil-in-bag" type, in which case it is intended that the consumer will cook or otherwise heat the frozen product in the original package. Recent studies (Karel and Wogan 1963) show that under conditions of elevated temperature significant migration of package components may take place, especially when the food products contain substantial amounts of fat.

Containers in Common Use

The containers used for packaging of frozen foods vary greatly in shape, style and type of material used. (Shelor and Woodroof 1954) surveyed the frozen food containers in common use in the early 1950's. They found that the containers most commonly used included the following: (1) tin cans, primarily for packaging of frozen juices, certain fruits, meats, and soups; (2) waxed paper cans, tumblers and tubs; (3) rectangular paper cartons, of several styles and sizes; (4) plastic bags, made of polyethylene, Saran-type films and rubber hydrochloride, and used primarily for packaging of poultry and irregular cuts of meat; and (5) aluminum foil wraps or dishes. Many of the paper containers were used in combination with liners or overwraps. Moisture-proof cellophanes and various grades of glassine and waxed paper were the most commonly used materials for the overwraps and liners.

In more recent years, there have been some new developments, adding importance to other types of containers. The most important of these developments are: (1) the packaging of frozen orange juice concentrates in aluminum cans, which may have applications to other products; (2) ever-increasing use of aluminum trays and dishes for various varieties of precooked frozen foods; (3) development of "boil-in-bag" frozen foods, which must be packaged in materials withstanding boiling temperatures (combinations of Mylar-polyester film with other materials, and the "Scotchpak" heat-sealable polyester film have been the materials used most frequently for this application); (4) use of composite cans, utilizing a paraffin impregnated fiberboard wall and light-weight tin plate ends; (5) heat-sealable waxed cartons requiring no liners or overwraps; and (6) increased application of rigid plastic containers made of high-impact polystyrene with polyethylene covers, for the packaging of ice cream, and other types of frozen foods.

CHANGES IN FROZEN FOODS

While changes occurring in frozen foods are usually considered to be those taking place during storage, at least some types of deterioration may also occur during freezing or defrosting. It has been found (Anon. 1960) for instance that in some methods of pallet freezing of strawberries as much as 200 per cent of the high quality life (equivalent to two years' storage at 0°F., as determined by color and flavor changes) may be lost.

Storage time and temperature inadequacy are probably most important today as causes of deterioration of frozen foods since, at least for retail products, fast freezing methods are generally applied. Table 239 gives the approximate time of high quality storage life for some foods at various temperatures. However, in bulk frozen products both the rate of freezing and the rate of defrosting may be very important factors, since changes involving the growth of microorganisms, as well as chemical changes, may take place when large masses of materials are frozen or defrosted.

In a personal communication, Tressler (1964) calls attention to the fact that the handling of fish prior to freezing is of great importance and that within his observation, many species of fish refrigerated quickly and handled rapidly under sanitary conditions and suitably packaged and frozen may be stored at 0°F. for periods as long as twelve months without appreciable deterioration.

Types of Changes Occurring in Frozen Foods

Many different kinds of changes may take place in frozen foods. They may be generally described as physical, physico-chemical, chemical, enzymatic or due to the growth of microorganisms.

Desiccation of frozen foods is a kind of physical change which takes place during frozen storage when packaging is not sufficiently moisture-vapor proof or the ice covering employed in glazing is not adequate or has sublimed. Dehydration is accelerated under conditions in which the

TABLE 94

APPROXIMATE NUMBER OF MONTHS OF HIGH QUALITY STORAGE LIFE

	Storage Temperature		
Product[1]	0°F.	10°F.	20°F.
Orange juice (heated)	27	10	4
Peaches	12	<2	0.2
Strawberries	12	2.4	10 days
Cauliflower	12	2.4	10 days
Green beans	11–12	3	1
Green peas	11–12	3	1
Spinach	6–7	<3	$^3/_4$
Raw chicken (adequately packaged)	27	$15^1/_2$	<8
Fried chicken	<3	<30 days	<0.6
Turkey pies or dinners	>30	$9^1/_2$	$2^1/_2$
Beef (raw)	13–14	5	<2
Pork (raw)	10	<4	<1.5
Lean fish (raw)	3	$<2^1/_4$	<1.5
Fat fish (raw)	2	$1^1/_2$	0.8

[1] (Anon. 1960).

temperature differential between the cooling medium and storage air is great. In such a situation, moisture from the air tends to accumulate on cooling surfaces as ice, lowering the relative humidity of the air in the storage room and promoting evaporation of moisture from stored frozen foods.

Dehydration of frozen foods accelerates some types of chemical and physico-chemical changes (Nutting et al. 1960). Moreover, dehydration may cause a frozen food product to become unsightly even when relatively small amounts of moisture have been lost. In frozen poultry, for instance, moisture losses, difficult to detect by weighing, may cause "pock marking" to occur due to dehydration of the area around feather follicles. This causes the fowl to have a mottled or speckled appearance. Dried-out portions of almost any food in the frozen state can be distinguished by eye if there has been a significant loss of moisture. For unknown reasons, desiccation of frozen foods greatly accelerates undesirable changes in proteins. Oxidation of fats is also accelerated by desiccation of frozen foods.

With some types of food packaging and holding conditions, or both, protection against moisture loss is so inadequate that there may be sufficient loss of weight, prior to consumption, to cause the product to weigh less than the declared weight (Anon. 1961C).

Cavity ice formation is a special type of dehydration in which moisture from the air in the package crystallizes out on the walls of the package. This particular phenomenon occurs when the package is not entirely filled or when there are voids in the product within the package. Cavity ice formation is accelerated by variations in the temperature at which the product is held.

The formation of cavity ice results in dehydration of the product, since the moisture which is frozen out as ice comes from the product itself. As in the case of any other type of dehydration of frozen products, this type of desiccation may accelerate physico-chemical or chemical changes in the product.

Crystallization is a physical change which may take place in some frozen food products causing an undesirable texture or consistency. Certain types of dairy products, especially ice cream or concentrated cream or milk, may develop a condition called "sandiness" during frozen storage. In this case, lactose separates out as crystals which do not redissolve at the temperature at which the product is eaten. This type of crystallization can be obviated by pretreatment of the milk or cream with lactase.

In some sweetened citrus juices, sugar crystals may develop during long storage. Crystals formed in this manner do not redissolve soon after defrosting.

It has long been recognized that in slow freezing or during frozen storage at comparatively high temperatures, large ice crystals may build up especially in the intercellular spaces of frozen foods. In the past, this observation has been used to explain some of the adverse effects of such conditions of freezing or holding, as compared with fast freezing and low temperature storage, on the basis of cell rupture which provides for leakage of cellular fluids as drip. It is not considered that the rupture of cells and the freezing out of ice into intercellular spaces is an adequate explanation for drip or other changes taking place in frozen foods, hence no further discussion of ice crystal formation in frozen foods will be undertaken.

Volatilization of low-temperature-boiling flavor components may be a factor causing loss of quality in some frozen foods. The extent of such changes is largely unknown since the particular compounds responsible for the typical flavor of most foods are unknown. However, it is conceivable that in foods such as fruits, in which flavor components might consist, at least in part, of esters, there may be some loss of these compounds by evaporation during frozen storage.

The breaking of emulsions or syneresis of gels during defrosting after freezing and storage probably has greater importance as a cause of loss of quality in foods which have been frozen than is generally considered to be the case. Some such phenomenon occurs when high moisture, pectin containing fruits such as tomatoes and some vegetables are frozen. The structure collapses and cellular fluids separate as drip upon defrosting.

Breaking and curdling of emulsions or weeping (syneresis) of gels is a definite problem in foods made up as white sauces or containing thickened gravies. Certain starches (Hansen et al. 1951) have been found to be less subject to this type of change when used as thickeners. Also the Western Regional Research Laboratory group (Hansen et al. 1957) has found that white sauces and gravies are most prone to curdling, weeping and other changes under frozen storage conditions in which there is a fluctuation of temperature, resulting in repeated fractional crystallization and irreversible dehydration of insoluble and colloidal constituents.

Protein denaturation, a general term applied to changes in proteins, resulting in a closer aggregation of protein molecules and a lessening of water holding capacity, is one of the major changes occurring in foods. Some meats and especially some fish and crustacean products are subject to protein changes of this type during freezing and storage. This causes a separation of cellular fluids as drip during defrosting, a toughening of tissues, a loss of succulence or some combination of these organoleptic changes.

The reason for protein changes of this type during frozen storage (Ironside and Love 1958) may be due to localized concentration of salts throughout the flesh resulting in the salting out of proteins. Fish flesh which has undergone this type of deterioration, when defrosted, has the appearance of a salted, undried product of the same kind.

As might be expected, oxidation of chemical components is one of the major changes occurring during freezing and storage, resulting in deterioration of color, loss of flavor and in some cases in development of off-flavors. All such changes in frozen foods are not known but some of them have been characterized.

Oxidation of ascorbic acid is one of the chemical changes which has been used to detect deterioration in the quality of frozen foods, since this particular reaction is comparatively easy to measure. The change in this case involves the oxidation of ascorbic acid (*a*) to dehydro ascorbic acid (*b*) and then to 2-3 diketo gulonic acid (*c*).

It is well known that autoxidation of the fats of frozen foods may take place during storage. Fish, crustaceans and some mollusks are especially subject to this type of change but the fats of meat, particularly those which have been cooked, may also be oxidized during frozen storage and the fat of meat which has been salted undergoes an accelerated oxidation under such conditions of holding. Oxidation of fats, if carried far enough, results in one of the several off-flavors which is characterized by the term "rancidity." The compounds causing off-flavors in rancid fats are mixtures of saturated and unsaturated aldehydes and ketones.

The first steps in the chain of oxidation of fatty acids resulting in hydroperoxide formation may be illustrated by a consideration of linoleic acid.

$$-CH=CH-CH_2-CH-CH-$$

$$\downarrow$$

$$-CH=CH-\overset{*}{CH}-CH=CH-$$

$$\downarrow \quad + \quad O_2$$

$$-CH=CH-\underset{\underset{O^*}{\overset{|}{O}}}{CH}-CH=CH-$$

$$+ \ (H) \Big\downarrow$$

$$-CH=CH-\underset{\underset{OH}{\overset{|}{O}}}{CH}-CH=CH-$$

Oxidation of fats may cause changes of color in foods, especially in those foods containing carotenoid pigments in which case peroxides formed in the fat oxidize the unsaturated carotenoids causing a shift in the absorption peak towards the ultraviolet end of the spectrum. This usually results in a lessening of the red or pink color and an intensifying of yellow or, in some cases, in an entire destruction of pigment, causing bleaching.

There may be some oxidation of anthocyanins, the coloring components of strawberries, raspberries and certain other fruits during freezing and frozen storage resulting in a lessening of the intensity of color. Also there may be leaching of these pigments into the syrup in which fruits are packed.

Chlorophyll A, the main color component of green vegetables, may be converted to pheophytin A during frozen storage, resulting in a yellow-green color which can be distinguished from the typical green color by eye or by colorimeter techniques (Dietrich *et al.* 1959).

Enzymes may cause various changes in foods during frozen storage. Uncooked crustacean products such as whole lobsters (in the shell) will undergo a proteolysis causing the meat to change in texture and become crumbly (short meated) after cooking.

Vegetables which are not blanched or not adequately blanched take on off-flavors during frozen storage (Joslyn 1946B). Some authors (Lee 1954; Lee and Wagenknecht 1951) have shown evidence that this is due to lipoxidase which catalyzes the oxidation of the small amount of fat present. There is no absolute proof that this is the cause of off-flavors in frozen foods in which enzymes are not inactivated although enzyme action of some type would appear to be involved.

Polyphenol oxidases, in the presence of oxygen, form quinones from phenols. These quinones polymerize to form dark colored compounds causing discoloration of some fruits and vegetables. Both phenolases and phenols are present in most varieties of peaches and apples and if poly-phenolase enzymes are not inactivated by the addition of sulfur dioxide, or by heating, or if some material is not added or some method of packing is not used which will keep phenols in the reduced state, discoloration will occur during freezing storage.

The growth of microorganisms in foods at temperatures below the freezing point of water depends upon the water activity of the product at the particular temperature involved. At temperatures at which a considerable amount of water is frozen out as ice, the growth of micro-organisms is exceedingly slow and the lag period may extend over a period of weeks or even months. Mold growth on turkey pies held at 20°F. has been found to involve a lag period of more than six months and bacterial growth on fish held at 23°F. a lag period of 50 weeks (Elliott and Michener 1960). It is obvious that the long lag periods required for the growth of microorganisms at temperatures considerably below 32°F. would preclude any great amount of deterioration due to microbial growth in commercial frozen foods. Commercial products held under such conditions of time and temperature as to allow microbial spoilage to take place would have been grossly mishandled.

It is well known that bacteria may be killed during freezing and that during frozen storage the surviving cells die off slowly (Van Eseltine et al. 1948; Miller 1955). However, foods after freezing and storage are not free from viable bacteria and are, therefore, subject to fast spoilage when defrosted and held at temperatures suitable for the growth of these organisms.

There is some controversy as to whether fast freezing is more destruc-tive to microorganisms in foods than is slow freezing (Haines 1937–1938; Mazur et al. 1957), but it is generally considered that bacterial cells survive better at the lower storage temperatures (McFarlane 1940; Sulzbacher 1950). The destructive effect of freezing and of frozen storage on bacteria will depend upon the type and pH of the food, etc., as well as on the type of microorganisms present. Survivals of more than 100 per cent to less than 3 per cent of the organisms originally present have been reported (Hucker et al. 1952; Miller and Winter 1951). It is well known that bacteria of the spore forming and coccal types survive freezing and frozen storage better than vegetative rod types and it is interesting to note that the Pseudomonads, which grow fastest at condi-tions of low temperature in unfrozen media, are among those most easily destroyed by freezing.

Bacteria causing food poisoning do not grow under conditions of freez-ing. It has been shown that enterotoxic staphylococci will not grow at temperatures below 50°F., and that Salmonella bacteria will not grow at temperatures below 40°F. While *Clostridium botulinum* type A and type B will not grow or form toxins at temperatures below 50°F. (Prescott and Geer 1936), type E Botulinum has been found to grow and produce toxin at temperatures as low as 38°F. However, in this case the organism was grown in a special medium and a comparatively long period of time at this temperature was required for growth and toxin production (Schmidt *et al.* 1961).

No outbreaks of botulism due to the consumption of frozen foods have been reported. There have been instances in which foods which had been frozen have been involved in Staphylococcal poisoning or in Salmonellosis (Dack 1956). However, in most instances of this kind, the food involved had been mishandled prior to or after freezing. There is no doubt that while freezing temperatures are maintained, pathogenic bacteria will not grow in foods. As in the case of any method of food preservation, if foods are mishandled prior or subsequent to freezing, public health problems may arise. Even considering mishandling, the public health record of frozen foods has been good.

Time-Temperature Tolerance of Frozen Foods

In recent years the Western Utilization Research and Development Division, Agricultural Research Service, U. S. Department of Agriculture, has carried out a number of investigations on changes taking place in frozen vegetables, fruit, fish and poultry products during storage. Among the various accomplishments of this group was the evaluation of time-temperature deteriorative effects on certain foods, especially on strawberries.

The effects on deterioration during storage of packaging, temperature variations, etc., were reported (Hansen *et al.* 1957; Van Arsdel and Guadagni 1959). Tests which were used included: organoleptic comparison, reduced and oxidized ascorbic acid, chlorophyll and pheophytin content. Variations in raw materials and processing made it possible to apply objective tests only to strawberries to determine the extent of quality changes occurring during storage of the frozen product.

It was shown that for strawberries, oxidation of ascorbic acid to dehydro ascorbic and 2-3 diketo gulonic acids would amount to a certain percentage during harvesting, processing and freezing. The quantity oxidized thereafter would depend on the time-temperature history during storage. The relative rates of loss or oxidation of ascorbic acid at various frozen storage temperatures was determined and from this a graph could be constructed upon which the time-temperature history could be determined in terms of oxidation of ascorbic acid. An arbitrary scale could then be used to integrate the extent of change. Changes occurring in a product during transportation and distribution could then be plotted as shown in Fig. 104, based upon findings of Van Arsdel and Guadagni (1959). Values shown in this figure are not those specifically found by the government investigators but were selected as typical for the purpose of illustration.

If a record of temperatures encountered in transit and storage is known, one can plot the relative rate of change as a function of the time the product was in distribution channels. This plot is shown at the right of Fig. 104. The area under the graph would then represent the integrated effects of the variable rate of change, or the effect of change which has taken place during the time of distribution. This procedure is analogous to the calculation of lethality values used in thermal processing.

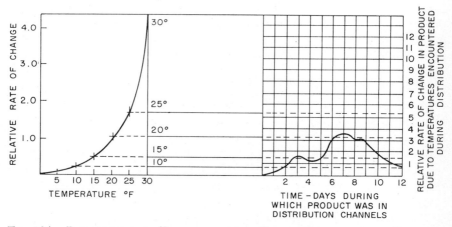

FIG. 104. RELATIONSHIP OF DETERIORATION IN FROZEN PERISHABLES TO TIME AND TEMPERATURE OF EXPOSURE TO ADVERSE CONDITIONS

Since it was found that for frozen strawberries, ten days at 20°F. resulted in a detectable change in quality as determined by color and flavor, this was considered to be the end of high quality life of the product. Ten days at 20°F. is equivalent to 30 squares under the curve. In recording the time-temperature history of strawberries, therefore, the particular area under the curve could be related to time at 20°F. or to time at any other temperature of holding.

If the relative rate of deterioration at different storage temperatures is known, the time-temperature history of any frozen food may be evaluated, as has been illustrated for strawberries. However, if the proportionate amount of change in the criterion of quality (oxidation of ascorbic acid, conversion of chlorophyll to pheophytin, deterioration of color or flavor) taking place during harvesting, processing and freezing is not relatively constant, the amount of change occurring during storage, transportation and/or retail holding cannot be determined by quality evaluation of samples of which the time-temperature history is unknown.

Rate of Deterioration in Various Foods During Frozen Storage

Some foods or food products are relatively stable at freezer storage temperatures; others deteriorate at a comparatively fast rate even when held at temperatures as low as 0°F. Some foods which are relatively stable at 0°F. may deteriorate very quickly at higher temperatures of frozen storage.

The approximate high quality storage life of a number of products is given in Table 94.

The increase in rate of deterioration of a number of frozen foods with increasing storage temperature appears to be logarithmic. That is, if the logarithm of the time required for a definite degree of deterioration is plotted against storage temperature on a rectangular scale, a straight line will result.

For strawberries, there appears to be a ten-fold increase in the rate of deterioration for about 13°F. increase in temperature above 0°F. (Anon. 1960). It has been found for lean fish (Love 1962) that there is about a seven-fold increase in the rate of deterioration for 18°F. increase in temperature above 0°F. It should be noted, however, that at 0°F. the over-all rate of deterioration is much greater for fish than for most other foods.

Tests to Determine Extent of Change in Frozen Foods

In testing frozen foods for quality, properly conducted organoleptic tests of the "difference type" appear suitable for determining whether or not a food has lost quality. When exact quantitative measurements of the extent of quality deterioration are required, organoleptic tests are far from desirable. However, for some products, no other method of evaluation is available.

Tests to determine chlorophyll degradation, based on measurement of the relative amounts of chlorophyll and pheophytin (Van Arsdel and Guadagni 1959), have been found to be suitable for determinations of the extent of changes in green vegetables. Due to variations in processing conditions such tests cannot be used to determine the actual cause of quality loss (prefreezing, freezing, storage, etc.).

Several tests (Schultz et al. 1962) are available to determine peroxides or hydroperoxides in fats. Many others, such as the 2 thiobarbituric acid value, have been proposed for following oxidation of fats. Such methods may or may not be suitable for following the rancidification of fats in a particular food. None of such tests are suitable for evaluating the quality of fats in a food having an unknown history.

The determination of reduced ascorbic acid, dehydro ascorbic acid and 2–3, diketo gulonic acid contents of certain frozen fruits or vegetables is apparently an excellent method of judging the quality of these products (Guadagni *et al.* 1957; Tressler and Evers 1957). Only in the case of strawberries can these tests be used to judge the probable cause of deterioration.

Tests for soluble color components have been found to be suitable indexes to quality in frozen cauliflower (Dietrich *et al.* 1962). The *cause* of deterioration (processing, freezing rate, storage temperature-time effect) cannot be determined in this manner.

Transfer of soluble components (sugars, colors) has been found to be a good index of loss of quality in syrup packed fruits. Like most tests such methods will not differentiate between deterioration which occurs prior to or during freezing or during frozen storage.

Reflectance measurements for color, made with suitable instruments (Dietrich *et al.* 1962) have been found to give good results in indexes of quality of some frozen fruits and vegetables. Also the soluble solids content of fruits packed in syrup may provide a satisfactory index of quality.

The cell fragility method (Love and Mackay 1962) shows promise as a test to determine protein changes occurring in certain marine products during frozen storage. This test may be suitable for evaluating the time-temperature history of such products.

FUTURE OF FROZEN FOODS

Work at the Western Regional Laboratory and elsewhere reveals that not all frozen foods are stable when held at temperatures above 0°F. and that some foods are relatively unstable at this temperature (Anon. 1960).

Representatives of the trucking industry in 1960 stated that only 35 to 40 per cent of refrigerated trucks were equipped to hold a temperature of 0°F. during transportation, and disclosed that frozen foods are in transit from 1 to 7 days with an average of 3 days.

Little is known about temperatures and times of holding frozen foods in retail display cases. Casual observation indicates that deterioration during retail display may be greater than that which occurs during transportation.

It is evident that if the frozen food industry is to assume and maintain its rightful place as a major method of food preservation, the industry as a whole must insist on improvements including subzero storage temperatures at all times for most products; —20°F. storage temperatures for products especially subject to change; transportation temperatures not above 0°F.; the elimination of the holding of frozen products on loading or unloading platforms for more time than the few minutes required to move them in or out of storage rooms; closed retail holding cases which load at the top and dispense at the bottom; display case temperatures not above 0°F. for most products, not above −20°F. for products especially subject to change.

Various segments of the frozen food industry know what should be done to bring about an improvement of the quality of frozen foods as they reach the consumers. Effort will be necessary to attain these objectives.

BIBLIOGRAPHY

ANDERSON, O. A. 1953. Refrigeration in America. A History of a New Technique and Its Impact. Princeton University Press, Princeton, N. J.

ANON. 1960. Trucking industry problems in frozen food handling. United States Department of Agriculture Conference on Frozen Food Quality, pp. 64–66. Albany, Calif.

ANON. 1960–1961. Frozen foods almanac. Quick Frozen Foods 23, No. 3, 141–172.

ANON. 1961A. The use of liquefied gases for the freezing and shipping of foods. Bull. ADE 895, Air Reduction Co., Madison, Wis.

ANON. 1961B. Fisheries of the United States (A preliminary review). C.F.S. No. 2900, U. S. Dept. of the Interior, Division of Resource Development.

ANON. 1961C. The record on shrimp. Consumer Rept. 26, No. 9, 506–510.

ANON. 1961–1962. Frozen foods almanac. Quick Frozen Foods 24, No. 4, 133–164.

ANON. 1962A. Advances in processing methods. Food Eng. 34, No. 2, 37–52.

ANON. 1962B. Blast-freezes at −50°F. Food Eng. 34, No. 3, 85.

BARRER, M. 1951. Diffusion in and Through Solids. Cambridge University Press, Cambridge, England.

BIRDSEYE, C. 1935. Progress in quick freezing in the United States. Ice and Refrig. 89, No. 1, 129–231.

BIRDSEYE, C., and FITZGERALD, G. A. 1932. History and present importance of quick freezing. Ind. Eng. Chem. 24, 676–678.

DACK, G. M. 1956. Food Poisoning. University of Chicago Press, Chicago, Ill.

DIETRICH, W. C., NUTTING, M. D., OLSON, R. L., LINDQUIST, F. E., BOGGS, M. M., BOHART, G. S., NEWMAN, H. J., and MORRIS, H. J. 1959. Time-temperature tolerance of frozen foods. XVI. Quality retention of frozen snap beans in retail packages. Food Technol. 13, 136–145.

DIETRICH, W. C., NUTTING, M. D., BOGGS, M. M., and WEINSTEIN, N. E. 1962. Time-temperature tolerance of frozen foods. XXIV. Quality changes in cauliflower. Food Technol. 16, No. 10, 123–130.

ELIOTT, R. P., and MICHENER, H. D. 1960. Review of the microbiology of frozen food. U. S. Dept. of Agriculture, Western Utilization Res. and Dev. Div., Albany, Calif.

FEDERAL REGISTER. 1962. Resinous and polymeric coatings. Amendment published in the Federal Register, Feb. 10, 1962, Paragraph 121.2514.

FIEGER, E. A. 1950. Problems in handling fresh and frozen shrimp. Food Technol. *4*, 409–411.

GOLDBLITH, S. A., KAREL, M., and LUSK, G. 1963. Freeze dehydration of foods. Food Technol. *17*, 139–144, 258–260, 263–264.

GOODE, G. B. 1887. The fisheries and fisheries industries of the United States. U. S. Commission of Fish and Fisheries I., Section V., 439–458.

GUADAGNI, D. G., NIMMO, C. C., and JANSEN, E. F. 1957. Time-temperature tolerance of frozen foods. VI. Retail packages of frozen strawberries. Food Technol. *11*, 389–397.

HAINES, R. B. 1937–1938. The effect of freezing on bacteria. Proc. Royal Soc. London B *124*, 451–463.

HANSEN, H. L., CAMPBELL, A., and LINEWEAVER, H. 1951. Preparation of stable frozen sauces and gravies. Food Technol. *5*, 432–440.

HANSEN, H. L., FLETCHER, L. R., and CAMPBELL, A. A. 1957. The time-temperature tolerance of frozen foods. V. Texture stability of thickened precooked frozen foods as influenced by composition and storage conditions. Food Technol. *11*, 339–343.

HEISS, R. 1956. Packaging of quick frozen foods. Verpackungs-Rundschau *8*, 61–64.

HUCKER, G. J., BROOKS, R. F., and EMERY, A. J. 1952. The source of bacteria in processing and their significance in frozen vegetables. Food Technol. *6*, 147–155.

IRONSIDE, J. I. M., and LOVE, R. M. 1958. Studies on the protein denaturation of frozen fish. I. Biological factors influencing the amounts of soluble and insoluble protein present in the muscle of North Sea cod. J. Sci. Food Agr. *9*, 597–617.

JOSLYN, M. A. 1946A. Enzyme activity-index of quality in frozen vegetables. Food Indus. *18*, 108–114, 238–239.

JOSLYN, M. A. 1946B. Industry needs field servicemen and technologists. Quick Frozen Foods *8*, No. 8, 71–72, 126.

JOSLYN, M. A. 1949. Enzyme activity in frozen vegetable tissue. Advan. Enzymol. *9*, 613–652.

JOSLYN, M. A. 1961. The freezing preservation of vegetables. Econ. Botany *15*, 347–375.

JOSLYN, M. A., and MARSH, G. L. 1933. Changes occurring during freezing, storage and thawing of fruits and vegetables. Calif. Agr. Expt. Sta. Bull. *551*.

KAESS, G. 1943. Qualification investigation of packaging and packaging materials for durability and preservation of frozen foods. Der Papier Fabr. *6*, 203–215.

KAREL, M. 1956. Protective packaging of frozen foods. Quick Frozen Foods *19*, No. 1, 201–203.

KAREL, M., PROCTOR, B. E., and CORNELL, A. 1957. Flavor permeability in food packaging and its evaluation. Food Technol. *11*, 141–145.

KAREL, M., and WOGAN, G. N. 1963. Migration of substances from flexible container for heat-processed foods. M.I.T. Report on U. S. Q. M. C. Contract DA-19-129-QM-2080, March 31, 1963.

KIERMEIER, F. 1943. Determination of aroma permeability of packaging material. Chem. Tech. *16*, 204–206.

LEE, F. A. 1954. Chemical changes taking place in the crude lipids during the storage of frozen raw vegetables. Food Research *19*, 515–520.

LEE, F. A., and WAGENKNECHT, A. C. 1951. On the development of off-flavor during the storage of frozen raw peas. Food Research *16*, 239–244.

LOVE, R. M. 1962. Protein denaturation in frozen fish. VI. Cold storage studies on cod using the cell fragility method. J. Sci. Food Agr. *13*, 269–278.

LOVE, R. M., and MACKAY, E. M. 1962. Protein denaturation in frozen fish. V. Development of the cell fragility method for measuring cold-storage changes in the muscle. J. Sci. Food Agr. *13*, 200–212.

MAZUR, P., RHIAN, M. A., and MAHLANDT, B. G. 1957. Survival of *Pasteurella tularensis* in sugar solutions after cooling and warming at sub-zero temperatures. J. Bacteriol. *73*, 394–397.

McFARLANE, V. H. 1940. Behavior of microorganism at sub-freezing temperatures. II. Distribution and survival of microorganisms in frozen cider, frozen syrup-packed raspberries and frozen brine packed peas. Food Research *5*, 59–68.

MILLER, W. A. 1955. Effect of freezing ground pork and subsequent storing above 32°F. upon the bacterial flora. Food Technol. *9*, 332–334.

MILLER, C., and WINTER, A. R. 1951. Pasteurized frozen whole egg and yolk for mayonnaise production. Food Research *16*, 43–49.

NATIONAL CANNERS ASSOCIATION, Washington, D. C. 1962. Personal Communication.

NUTTING, MARVEL-DARE, DIETRICH, W. C., and OLSON, R. L. 1960. Moisture loss from packages of frozen vegetables. Food Technol. *14*, 367–368.

PRESCOTT, S. C., and GEER, L. P. 1936. Observations on food poisoning organisms under refrigeration conditions. Refrig. Eng. *32*, 211–212, 282–283.

ROMANOFF, A. L., and ROMANOFF, A. J. 1949. The Avian Egg. John Wiley and Sons, New York.

SCHMIDT, C. F., LECHOWICH, R. V., and FOLINAZZO, J. F. 1961. Growth and toxin production by Type E *Clostridium botulinum* below 40°F. J. Food Sci. *26*, 626–630.

SCHULTZ, H. W., DAY, E. A., and SINNHUBER, R. O. (Editors). 1962. Symposium on Foods: Lipids and their Oxidation. Avi Publishing Co., Westport, Conn.

SEATON, H. L., and HUFFINGTON, J. M. 1954. Raw Product Quality Control. Research Division, Continental Can Co., Inc.

SHELOR, E., and WOODROOF, J. G. 1954. Frozen food containers. Food Technol. *8*, 490–497.

SHEPHERD, A. D. 1959. Effect of illumination on color of frozen peas packaged in a transparent film. Food Technol. *13*, 539–540.

STEVENSON, C. H. 1900. Freezing and storing fish. Ice and Refrig. *18*, No. 2, 99–103.

STEWART, G. F., and LOWE, B. 1948. Producing and maintaining quality in frozen eviscerated poultry. Frozen Food Ind. *4*, No. 5, 8–9, 29.

SULZBACHER, W. L. 1950. Survival of microorganisms in frozen meat. Food Technol. *4*, 396–390.

TARR, H. L. A.   1947.   Preservation of quality of edible fish products.   Fisheries Res. Bd. of Canada, Pacific Coast Stations, Progress Rept. *17*, 15–20.

TRAUBERMAN, L.   1962.   Simple fluidizing freezer cuts costs, guards quality. Food Eng. *34*, No. 8, 46–49.

TRESSLER, D. K.   1964.   Personal communication.   Westport, Conn.

TRESSLER, D. K., and EVERS, C. F.   1957.   The Freezing Preservation of Foods. Vol. I.   Avi Publishing Co., Westport, Conn.

TRESSLER, D. K., and LEMON, J. M.   1951.   Marine Products of Commerce. 2nd Edition.   Reinhold Publishing Co., New York.

VAN ARSDEL, W. B., and GUADAGNI, D. G.   1959.   Time-temperature tolerance of frozen foods.   XV.   Methods of using temperature histories to estimate changes in frozen food quality.   Food Technol. *13*, 14–19.

VAN ESELTINE, W. P., NELLIS, L. F., LEE, F. A., and HUCKER, G. J.   1948. Effect of rate of freezing on bacterial content of frozen vegetables.   Food Research *13*, 271–280.

WIESMAN, C. K.   1947.   Factors influencing quality of frozen meat.   Ice and Refrig. *112*, No. 4, 21–24.

WINTER, J. D., and HUSTRULID, A.   1951.   Flavor factors in frozen-food wraps. Modern Packaging *24*, No. 9, 133–184.

CHAPTER 16

Bernard Feinberg | **Concentration by Evaporation**

INTRODUCTION

Water is the predominant ingredient in most food materials and exceeds 85 per cent in milk and in fruit and vegetable juices. This water content can frequently be advantageously reduced, to lower container, storage and shipping costs, or to achieve other desirable results in food processing.

For liquid foods, fractional crystallization and evaporation are the commonest methods for reducing the water content. Partial freezing in winter weather is the traditional method for concentrating hard cider to produce applejack. More recently, beer and vinegar have been concentrated by continuous processes involving fractional crystallization of ice. There is some application of fractional crystallization to citrus juices, but for practical reasons, single and multiple effect vacuum pans with or without ester recovery devices are most widely used for reducing the water content of liquid foods. In this chapter, we are principally concerned with the equipment and methods used in the food industry to concentrate liquid foods by evaporation of a portion of the water.

Evaporation of sugar or salt solutions prior to crystallization; boiling of sugar syrups for caramelization and other changes essential to candy making; concentration of milk, fruit and vegetable juices are but a few applications of evaporative concentration.

In 1960, food processors in the United States produced over 85,000,000 gal. of orange juice concentrate, 250,000,000 gal. of condensed milk and 36,000,000 gal. of tomato paste. Jam and jelly preservers today use millions of gallons of concentrated apple juice, strawberry juice and grape juice. Packers of nectar use millions of gallons of apricot, peach and pear concentrates. "Pancake Houses" use an increasing volume of syrups made from concentrated fruit pulps and juices. Poultry feeders use concentrated buttermilk; ice cream manufacturers use many types of fruit concentrates in special ice cream flavors. The housewife finds frozen concentrated lemonade a welcome alternative to squeezing lemons and dissolving sugar in ice water. One manufacturer now offers a concentrated cooking and flavoring "wine" from which the alcohol has been distilled and the product concentrated eight-fold. California, with less

BERNARD FEINBERG was formerly Technical Director of Fair View Packing Co., Hollister, Calif., is now at U. S. Department of Agriculture Western Regional Research Laboratory, Albany, Calif.

TABLE 95

SPECIFIC GRAVITY AND SOLIDS RELATIONSHIP OF TOMATO PULP AND COMMERCIAL TOMATO CONCENTRATES

Total Solids, %	Specific Gravity at 68°F.	Dry Tomato Solids per Gallon at 68°F., lbs.
6.0 Tomato pulp	1.025	0.51
10.8 ⎫	1.045	0.94
12.0 ⎪	1.050	1.05
14.2 ⎬ Tomato purée	1.060	1.25
16.5 ⎭	1.070	1.47
25.0 ⎫	1.107	2.31
26.0 ⎪	1.112	2.41
28.0 ⎬ Tomato paste	1.120	2.61
30.0 ⎪	1.129	2.82
32.0 ⎭	1.138	3.03

With permission: From "A Laboratory Manual for the Canning Industry." 1956. Second Edition. National Canners Association, Washington, D. C.

TABLE 96

PROPERTIES OF SATURATED STEAM: PRESSURES[1]

Pressure			Pressure		
Absolute, lb. per sq. in.	Absolute, in. Hg	Temp., °F.	Absolute, lb. per sq. in.	Absolute, in. Hg	Temp., °F.
5	10.2	162.2	11	22.4	197.7
6	12.2	170.1	12	24.4	202.0
7	14.2	176.8	13	26.4	205.9
8	16.3	182.9	14	28.5	209.6
9	18.3	188.3	14.7	29.9	212.0
10	20.4	193.2			

Approx. Gage, lb. per sq. in.					
15	0	213.0	100	85	327.8
20	5	228.0	105	90	331.4
25	10	240.1	110	95	334.8
30	15	250.3	115	100	338.1
35	20	259.3	120	105	341.2
40	25	267.2	125	110	344.3
45	30	274.4	130	115	347.3
50	35	281.0	135	120	350.2
55	40	287.1	140	125	353.0
60	45	292.7	145	130	355.8
65	50	298.0	150	135	358.4
70	55	302.9	160	145	363.5
75	60	307.6	170	155	368.4
80	65	312.0	180	165	373.1
85	70	316.2	190	175	377.5
90	75	320.3	200	185	381.8
95	80	324.1	215	200	387.9

[1] Abstracted by permission from "Thermodynamic Properties of Steam" by J. H. Keenan and F. G. Keyes published by John Wiley & Sons, Inc.

than ten per cent of our population, produces more than half the tomatoes processed in the United States. Much of this production is shipped to Eastern population centers in the form of concentrated tomato products.

Table 95 compares the solids content of concentrated tomato purée with that of single strength pulp.

It is frequently necessary to compare equivalent volumes of tomato products. The above table and the following formula (from NCA Lab. Manual) may be used for this purpose as follows:

$$\frac{\text{Volume of Product A}}{\text{Volume of Product B}} = \frac{\text{Pounds of Tomato Solids per Gallon of B}}{\text{Pounds of Tomato Solids per Gallon of A}}$$

Example.—How many gallons of 1.045 tomato purée can be made from one gallon 30 per cent tomato paste?

$$\frac{\text{X gal. of 1.045 purée}}{\text{1 gal. of 30\% paste}} = \frac{\text{2.82 lbs. of tomato solids/gal.}}{\text{0.94 lbs. of tomato solids/gal.}}$$

1 gal. of 30 per cent tomato paste is equivalent to 3 gal. of 1.045 sp. gr. purée.

One important tomato product shipped from California to New York is tomato pulp concentrated to a solids content of 10.8 per cent and commonly sold in Number 10 cans as "1.045 specific gravity Tomato Purée." A tomato processor who packs 300,000 cases of 1.045 purée for shipment to New York might note from Table 95 that 300,000 cases of purée are equivalent to 100,000 cases of 30 per cent tomato paste. The comparative costs of packing and shipping these two products may be calculated as follows:

Miscellaneous Costs	One Case, 1.045 Purée		One Case 30% Tomato Paste	
Cans, 6 at $0.12		$0.72		$0.72
Cases, 1 at $0.10		0.10		0.10
Warehousing & labels at $0.10/case		0.10		0.10
Freight California to New York at $1.90/100 lbs.	(44 lbs.)	0.84	(50 lbs.)	0.95
Total per case		$1.76		$1.87
or, for				
300,000 cases purée			$528,000	
100,000 cases of 30 per cent paste			$187,000	
Possible savings in containers and freight			$343,000	

Such savings may be counterbalanced by consumer preference for low-density concentrates, by increased overhead and other costs resulting from lowered volume production, by large capital investment necessary for production of high-density concentrates, by limitations of steam, water, know-how and by other considerations.

It is not necessary to concentrate to high densities to effect substantial reductions in weight and volume. If 1,000 gal. of tomato pulp at 94 per cent water (6 per cent solids) are reduced to 500 gal. by boiling off 500 gal. of water, the remaining "concentrate" is still 88 per cent water (12 per cent solids).

SOLAR EVAPORATION

Most liquid foods are concentrated by heating with steam. One exception is "solar evaporation" of salt brines which has been practiced

Courtesy of Leslie Salt Co.

FIG. 105.   SOLAR EVAPORATION OF OCEAN WATER IN PRODUCING SALT

since early history. Today, over 1,000,000 tons of salt are produced each year in southern San Francisco Bay by essentially the same methods practiced by the California Indians, using more than 40,000 acres of lagoons exposed to sun and wind to evaporate 37,000,000 tons of water a year from sea water. Figure 105 illustrates a solar evaporation installation for the manufacture of salt.

Evaporators are frequently evaluated in terms of pounds of water evaporated per hour from each square foot of heating surface. The average evaporation rate in the system described above is about one-tenth of an ounce of water per hour per square foot of lagoon. Such a leisurely rate does not meet the needs of processing perishable foods where large quantities of water must be quickly boiled away and evaporation rates of 125 lbs. per hr. per sq. ft. are common.

EVAPORATORS

High capacity evaporative concentrators for liquid foods consist of heat exchangers to supply latent heat of evaporation, and vapor separators for removing the vapor from the residual liquid. Several types of heat exchangers may be used. In the "direct" type, a flame under a kettle supplies heat which is transferred by conduction through the kettle wall. Sugar maple sap is commonly concentrated at boiling temperature up to 240°F. in mild steel open pans over an open fire.

Still another type of direct fired atmospheric evaporator uses an inverted burner, supplied with gas and oxygen under pressure, submerged beneath the surface of the liquid, commonly rising in a conical receptacle and overflowing the edges. Such equipment may be selected for concentrating a liquid prone to deposit heat-retarding "scale" on heat exchange surfaces.

At the other extreme, heat-sensitive orange juice is concentrated in stainless steel at reduced pressure which permits rapid boiling at temperatures as low as 50°F. Latent heat of evaporation is supplied by condensing water vapor, ammonia, or other compressed refrigerant.

Between the maple syrup "boiler" and the juice "evaporator," food processors may select a great variety of equipment suited to specific needs and products, balancing equipment and operating costs against quality factors and production rates.

Parker (1963) discusses the factors which must be considered before selecting an evaporator and tells how to write up the evaporator specification. A specific example is given for a theoretical plant where 4,380 lbs. 12° Brix apple juice per hr. is to be converted to 760 lbs. 70° Brix apple juice concentrate. He also discusses the many factors to be considered in selecting the evaporator vendor.

In the chapter on steam, readers will find definitions of such terms as latent heat of evaporation, sensible heat, thermal units, etc. Understanding of these terms is essential to understanding evaporation.

Evaporators use specialized heat-exchangers designed for specific applications. They are usually indirect, involving a heat exchange medium which transfers latent or sensible heat from the heating medium to the solution to be concentrated.

In the concentration of solutions by evaporation, the liquid to be concentrated continuously flows across a heat exchange surface which separates it from the heating medium. The heating medium may range from high pressure steam at 365°F. to ammonia vapor at 60°F. The heating surface is usually a metal wall in the form of a tube plate or kettle wall. "Thermo-siphon," or natural circulation, is circulation of the product resulting from reduction in the specific gravity of the solution on heating and from pressure generated by vapor evolved at the heat exchange surface. Natural circulation evaporators are usually inexpensive but are difficult to use for concentration of viscous solutions such as 30 per cent tomato paste. For such products, a circulating pump is used to insure high velocity across the heating surface. Such systems are called "forced circulation" evaporators.

Open Kettles

These are the simplest and cheapest natural circulation evaporators. They are simply big pots open to the atmosphere. In one type, the heating steam is condensed in an exterior jacket covering the curved bottom and about half way up the cylindrical wall. While these are in common use for heating and "cooking" they have insufficient heating area to rapidly boil off large volumes of water. Another type of open kettle has a stationary spiral coil of heavy three-inch copper or stainless steel tubing suspended in a horizontal plane a few inches from the bottom of the kettle. These units provide a relatively large heating surface and are inexpensive. In the tomato industry they are primarily used for preconcentrating and in the manufacture of low density products such as purée, tomato sauce and catsup. Some processors believe that the concentration of crushed tomatoes by boiling above 212°F. prior to the screening of seeds and skin results in a desirable increase in viscosity. Horizontal heater coils are subject to "burn-on" and require frequent cleaning. They are unsuitable for viscous tomato products such as tomato paste or for heat-sensitive fruit pulps and juices.

Another type of open kettle uses a revolving coil. Here the steam coil revolves as a horizontal shaft, resulting in turbulence that improves heat transfer and decreases the rate of fouling or "burn-on." One manufacturer of such a coil specifies evaporation of 1500 gal. of water per hour from tomato pulp entering at 180°F. with a coil of 85 sq. ft. heating surface using 100 p.s.i.g. steam as the heating system. Figure 106 shows this equipment.

Shell-and-Tube Heat Exchangers

These are frequently found in processing plants as preheaters before evaporation, or after-heaters for heating the product to filling temperatures. They are also components of many evaporators. Such heat exchangers are essentially a cylindrical shell of large diameter which houses a number of parallel tubes called the "tube bundle." They are constructed so that the product flows inside the tubes while heat is supplied

Courtesy of Langsenkamp Co.

Fig. 106. Atmospheric Evaporation with Rotating Steam Coil

by a high temperature liquid, by condensing water vapor, or by other heating medium on the outside of the tubes. The heat exchanger is called "single-pass" if the product flows through all the tubes in the same direction and "multiple-pass" if the product goes one way through some of the tubes and returns through the others. Most shell-and-tube heat exchangers used in evaporators are single-pass.

Shell-and-tube heat exchangers may be used at atmospheric or at reduced pressure. If they are used as atmospheric evaporators the product will have a boiling point in excess of 212°F. Steam pressure in excess of 40 p.s.i.g. is commonly employed to provide adequate temperature differential for efficient heat transfer. (See Heat Transfer Formula, p. 495).

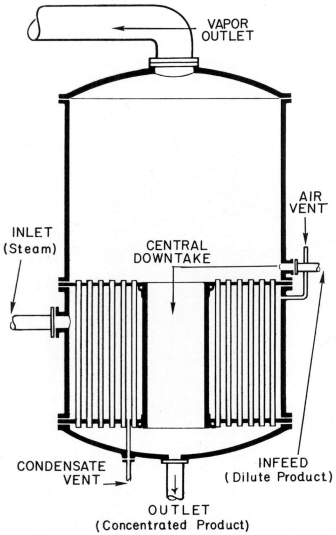

VAPOR OUTLET

AIR VENT

INLET (Steam)

CENTRAL DOWNTAKE

CONDENSATE VENT

INFEED (Dilute Product)

OUTLET (Concentrated Product)

Courtesy of Chicago Bridge and Iron Works

FIG. 107. DIAGRAM SHOWING DESIGN OF CALANDRIA EVAPORATOR

This high temperature may lead to "burn-on" or the formation of a vapor barrier between the product and the heating wall, unless the product is pumped through the tubes at high velocity with resulting turbulence.

An evaporator frequently found in the food industry is the "internal calandria" vacuum pan (see Fig. 107). This is a shell-and-tube, steam chest heat exchanger with a ring of short vertical tubes and a large central downtake. The vapor separator and heat exchanger are assembled as one unit. The product circulates by convection, rising through the steam-jacketed tubes and returning through the central "downtake." Such evaporators are relatively inexpensive and trouble-free but are difficult to use with products of high viscosity or poor heat transfer. They customarily are designed to use steam pressures a few pounds above or below that of the atmosphere.

Flash Evaporators

Brown *et al.* (1951) described the advantages of heating of fluid foods rapidly by direct steam injection. In a pilot plant, temperatures up to 300°F. could be obtained in a 0.5 sec. or less. This technique can be used to effect pasteurization, sterilization, enzyme inactivation, and/or removing odors from juices, milk, etc. It has also proved useful in commercial installations for separating and concentrating fruit "essences" and for evaporation.

At least 15 commercial evaporation systems using direct steam injection are in operation in the United States (Morgan *et al.* 1959). In this method of evaporation (Fig. 108), the product is preheated in a conventional heat exchanger to about 210°F., and pumped through a vertical or diagonal tube where clean "culinary" steam is tangentially injected to superheat the liquid to the desired temperature (250° to 300°F.). The superheated liquid is released into a down-flow, single-pass heat exchanger where it quickly flashes into a mixture of vapor and liquid. The high velocity minimizes fouling. The mixture of vapor and concentrated product is fed to a separator where entrained product is separated from the vapor. The vapor may be vented, condensed, or used as a heating medium for a vacuum evaporator. The exit vapors from such a separator are usually under 2 to 5 lbs. pressure. Such systems are in commercial use for grape juice, apple juice and tomato concentrate (Nowlin and Henwood 1954; O'Connell 1954).

Another type of flash evaporator is commercially known as the Thermally Accelerated Short-Time Evaporator (TASTE). This equipment is used by several concentrators of citrus products. Direct steam injection heating is not used in this system. Instead, the initial feed is preheated to approximately 195°F. in a conventional heat exchanger and flashed through a series of down-flow, single-pass evaporators with progressively higher vacuums. A four-effect, five-stage evaporator of this type having a capacity of 40,000 lbs./hr. evaporation is in use in Florida for concentration of orange juice (Anon. 1963).

Rising-Film Evaporators

Evaporators are sometimes classified as long-tube and short-tube. The internal calandria vacuum pan, illustrated in Fig. 107 (p. 482), is a typical short-tube evaporator. The product flow in a long-tube evapor-

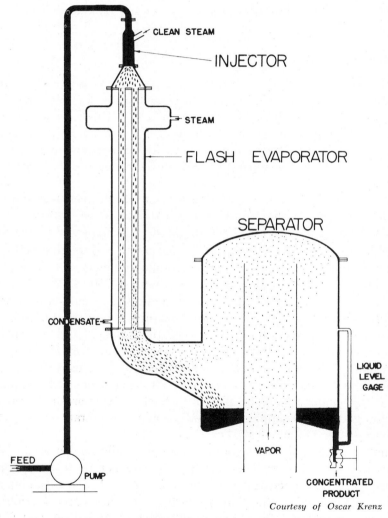

Courtesy of Oscar Krenz

Fig. 108.   Diagram Showing Operation of Flash Evaporator

ator may be horizontal or vertical. In a rising-film evaporator, the dilute liquid is fed into the chamber below the lower sheet and rises in the tube. As steam is admitted to the chest the liquid reaches the boiling point and bubbles of vapor are formed in the column of liquid. As the bubbles rise they expand and push the liquid ahead with increasing velocity. The turbulent mixture of vapor and liquid exits from the tubes into a vapor separator, as shown in Fig. 109.

Falling-Film Evaporators

In a down-flow or falling-film evaporator the dilute liquid is introduced to the chamber above the upper tube sheet and flows as a thin film down the inner surface of the tubes. Only a small amount of product is in the

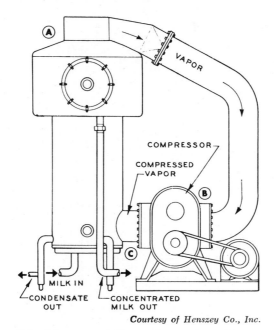

Courtesy of Henszey Co., Inc.

Fig. 109. Mechanical Vapor Compression Evaporator Condensing the Compressed Vapor While Evaporating Additional Water from the Product

tube, compared with the column of liquid in the rising film evaporator. The concentrated product is usually recirculated in such evaporators. Hydrostatic head loss found in rising-film evaporators is absent in down-flow evaporators. They are frequently used for the concentration of citrus juices.

Plate Type Evaporators

The plate type or AVP evaporator, developed in England, is a single-pass evaporator using specially modified stainless steel plates as heat exchange surfaces.   There are more than 100 installations throughout the world concentrating orange juice, apple juice, grape juice, ice cream mix, milk, etc.   Pilot plant tests have been claimed to produce high quality tomato paste of 40 per cent solids.   In a Florida orange juice concentrate installation, described by Lawler (1960), a 12,500 lbs. per hr., double-

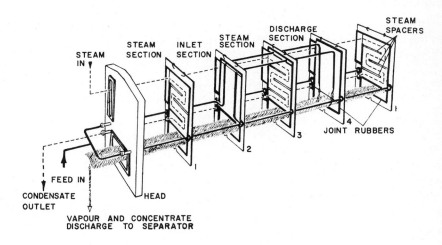

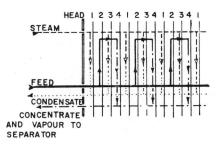

From Tressler and Joslyn's Fruit and Vegetable Juice Processing Technology

FIG. 110.   DIAGRAMMATIC ARRANGEMENT OF PLATES FOR ONE COMPLETE FEED PASS

This action occurs simultaneously within each group of plates as shown.

effect, plate evaporator and auxiliaries were installed in an 18 x 27 ft. room with a 9 ft. ceiling.   This is considerably more compact than conventional vacuum evaporators.   One of the advantages claimed for this method of evaporation is the small amount of product in the system at any one time.   In the orange juice concentrator described above, there is less than five gallons of product in each effect at any one time.   The system may be described as a rising and falling film evaporator with liquid fed from the bottom, rising and descending through alternate plates (see Fig. 110).

Thin-Film, Centrifugal Evaporators

In these devices, the liquid to be evaporated flows down the heated wall of a cylinder or truncated cone. A thin film is mechanically induced by rapidly rotating vanes which both agitate and spread the film. Heat for evaporation is transferred through the jacketed cylinder wall. Different manufacturers use terms such as "agitated film," "swept surface," "wiped film," etc., to describe their models. The liquid/vapor mixture produced during heating may be separated in an adjoining vapor separator or an integral separator contained in the evaporator.

Low holding time, short retention time, and maintenance of all liquid as a film on the heating surface make thin film or mechanically induced film evaporators ideal for concentration of materials which are either heat-sensitive or viscous, or both (Dedert and Moore 1963). Harper (1960) obtained concentrates of apricot, peach and pear pulp of about 60 per cent solids using a "wiped film" evaporator. Qualitative comparisons between the feed material and samples of products reconstituted to the original concentration showed no apparent differences in color or taste.

Since thin-film evaporators can be used at high operating temperatures without heat damage, it is frequently possible to "hot-fill" the concentrate at temperatures of 185°F. or higher directly from the evaporator without the use of an after-heater. Fig. 111 illustrates the principle of this equipment.

Vapor Separation

Evaporation produces a mixture of vapors and concentrated liquid which must be separated rapidly and thoroughly. Heid and Casten (1961) described factors influencing the design of vapor separators which are essentially cylinders and "cyclones" of appropriate design to effect the elimination of entrained liquid from the vapor. They may operate under pressure or vacuum. Separated vapors are frequently used as a heating medium for an additional effect in another evaporator.

VACUUM EVAPORATION

The rate of evaporation is directly related to the amount of heat which can be transferred from the heating medium (steam, hot water, ammonia vapors, etc.) to the liquid being evaporated. This is usually expressed in B.t.u. per sq. ft., of heating surface per hr. The rate of heat transfer is dependent, not on the temperature of the heating medium, but on the *difference* in temperature between the heating medium and the boiling liquid. If water with a boiling point of 212°F. at atmospheric pressure is heated in an open steam-jacketed kettle using steam at 212°F. as a heating medium there will be no difference in temperature; no heat transfer; no evaporation. To obtain a temperature difference the temperature of the

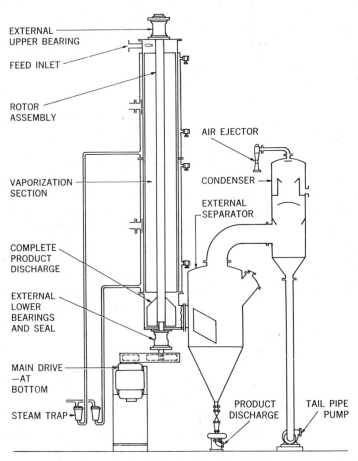

EXTERNAL
UPPER BEARING

FEED INLET

ROTOR
ASSEMBLY

AIR EJECTOR

VAPORIZATION
SECTION

CONDENSER

EXTERNAL
SEPARATOR

COMPLETE
PRODUCT
DISCHARGE

EXTERNAL
LOWER
BEARINGS
AND SEAL

MAIN DRIVE
—AT
BOTTOM

STEAM TRAP

PRODUCT
DISCHARGE

TAIL PIPE
PUMP

Courtesy of Buflovak Equipment Div., Blaw-Knox Co.

FIG. 111.   THE BUFLOVAK AGITATED FILM EVAPORATOR

Vapors and liquor are separated in the centrifugal type separator. It utilizes the time proved method of separation, high centrifugal action, coupled with low upward velocities. The finished product is removed from the cone section while the vapors pass to a suitable condenser or venting arrangement. The separator is arranged with such standard equipment as a quick-opening manhole, observation glasses, vacuum controls and a sampler connection. Clean-in-place fittings are also available for wash-down without disassembly.

heating medium must be elevated or the temperature of the boiling liquid must be lowered. In many cases it is advantageous to lower the boiling point of the liquid being evaporated. This can be done by converting the open kettle to a vacuum pan and boiling under reduced pressure which results in a lowered boiling point. As the pressure above the boiling liquid approaches zero, it becomes possible to evaporate at temperatures close to the freezing point of water. At a pressure of 0.0982 p.s.i. (29.72 in. of vacuum) the boiling point of water is 34.6°F.

Vacuum concentration has several advantages. It makes possible the low-temperature concentration of heat-sensitive foods such as orange juice; it can increase the rate of evaporation by increasing the difference between the boiling temperature of the product and the temperature of the heating medium; it makes possible the use of multiple effect systems to be described later.

A common sequence of flow in the vacuum concentration of tomato pulp or fruit pulp follows: A valve is opened to permit high-pressure steam to flow through a large steam ejector or "hog" jet to develop the initial vacuum in the evaporator. When the desired vacuum is reached, preheated pulp is pumped or sucked into the heat exchanger, steam is admitted into the steam chest and boiling begins almost immediately. The vapors are separated and are removed as described below. Once the boiling and vapor removal process starts the vacuum is self-sustaining and the "hog" jet may be turned off.

To maintain the vacuum it is necessary to continually and rapidly remove the vapors boiled off from the product and air or other gases (commonly called noncondensibles) originating in the product or from air-leakage into the equipment. Vapors may be condensed by mixing with cold water in parallel or counterflow barometric condensers provided there is adequate differential between the temperature of the vapors and that of the condenser water. Vapors may also be condensed on surface condensers, which are tubes or plates cooled by water or other refrigerant. The steam chest of a multiple-effect evaporator may be considered as a surface-condenser. Since air cannot be condensed to a liquid by cold water or surface condensers it must be removed by a small steam jet or ejector. The condensed vapors and condenser water are continually removed by a vacuum pump or a barometric leg. The latter is a vertical pipe whose height is determined by the height of a column of water required to balance the desired maximum operating vacuum in the vacuum pan. If the pan is to operate at a vacuum of 29 in. mercury the barometric leg will be 34 ft. high with the bottom opening of the pipe under the surface of water in a tank called a hot-well. The 34 ft. column of water flowing down the barometric leg serves as a pump to remove the condensed vapors and acts as a seal or check valve to prevent air or water from being sucked back. Barometric legs are relatively inexpensive and trouble-free but require large quantities of water, especially at high vacuums. To maintain a 25 in. vacuum in a countercurrent barometric condenser using a water supply at 60°F. requires about 25 lbs. of water for every pound of vapor condensed. Warm water from a barometric leg is frequently used for washing raw product or may be cooled in an evaporative cooler and reused in the condenser.

Single-Effect Evaporators

When vapor from products is not used to heat additional product the evaporator system is known as single-effect. Single-effect evaporators may be modified to furnish vapor to a second evaporator operated at lower pressure or to use vapor coming from another evaporator operating at higher pressure.

Multiple-Effect Vacuum Systems

A vacuum pan is an unusual piece of equipment. At first glance, it appears to do nothing. For every 1,000 lbs. of water that go in, 1,000 lbs. of water come out; for every 1,000 lbs. of water vapor that go in, 1,000 lbs. of water vapor come out; for every 1,000 B.t.u. that go in, 1,000 B.t.u. come out. Water comes in as product water and goes out as steam condensate. Water vapor comes in as boiler steam and goes out as product water vapor. B.t.u. come in with boiler steam and go out with product water vapor.

Heat will only flow "down-hill," from high temperature to low temperature. This temperature difference is commonly called "heat head." The evaporating liquid must boil at a lower temperature than the heating medium in the steam chest or there will be no heat transfer. The water vapor from tomato juice boiling at 212°F. (at atmospheric pressure) may be used to evaporate water from tomato juice boiling at 188°F. under 12 in. vacuum, and this 188° vapor in turn may be used to evaporate tomato juice boiling at 125°F. under a 24 in. vacuum. Each time heat from vapor is reused, the system has another "effect." Where concentration is carried on throughout the year—such as sugar and salt processing—and utility costs are an important cost, 4 and 5 effect systems are used. Because of various engineering and cost factors, there is a practical limit to the number of effects that can be economically used for each product. In the example above, the heat energy in the vapor coming from the third effect contains almost as much heat energy as originally received by the first effect from the boiler. What has been "used-up" is not heat, but "heat head." When this final vapor is condensed in the barometric leg, the heat energy has followed a tortuous path through one or more evaporators from the boiler to the heat-well and the boiler must provide a constant stream of B.t.u. to replenish the heat being lost through the heatwell.

Product vapor coming from a vacuum pan may have its temperature (or heat-head) boosted by mechanical or steam jet compressors. In booster jets, high pressure steam from the boiler is converted to high velocity steam by passing through a venturi-shaped throat to compress vapor coming from the evaporator. The compressed vapor, now at a higher temperature, can be re-used in the steam chest of the same evaporator.

It is possible to have a combination of multiple effects using a series of vacuum pans at different levels of vacuum with or without thermo-compression. Heid and Casten (1961), Parker et al. (1954) and Cruess (1958) have described engineering principles affecting design and use of multiple effect systems.

Heat Pump Evaporators

In direct heat pump evaporators, product vapor is mechanically compressed to raise its temperature and provide a "heat-head" so that it can be re-used as a source of heat in the steam chest. Such a system, manufactured by Henszey, is illustrated in Fig. 109 (p. 485). The system has been called a "boiler-less evaporator" and needs no barometric leg or water supply.

Orange juice and other heat-sensitive liquid foods are commonly concentrated at temperatures below 80°F. to prevent deterioration of color, flavor, stability, etc. This means evaporation under pressures of less than 0.5 p.s.i. At these low pressures the volume of water vapor becomes so large (Heid and Casten 1961) that mechanical recompression requires large and expensive compressors. At atmospheric pressure or 0 vacuum, the boiling point of water is 212°F. and the volume of water vapor at that temperature and pressure is 27 cu. ft. per lb. At 29.4 in. vacuum, the boiling point of water drops to 60°F. and the volume of water vapor at that temperature and pressure expands to 1208 cu. ft. per lb. This is equivalent to expanding the contents of a cubic container, 3 ft. on a side, to a 10 x 15 ft. room, 8 ft. high. Evaporators concentrating orange juice, milk or other heat-sensitive products at these low temperatures and pressures frequently use direct and indirect heat-pumps. In such systems the latent heat of the product vapor is first used to evaporate a secondary low volume vapor (such as anhydrous ammonia) which is then mechanically compressed and condensed to vaporize water from the product. The compressor is used as a heat pump, eliminating the need for a boiler. A pound of water vapor evaporated from orange juice boiling at 60°F. has a volume of 1208 cu. ft. per lb. The water vapor passes through a surface-condenser and condenses to liberate sufficient latent heat to vaporize two pounds of anhydrous ammonia boiling at 45°F. This two pounds of ammonia vapor with a volume of only 7.2 cu. ft. per lb. has the same 1,058 B.t.u. latent heat as the one pound of water vapor with a volume of 1,208 cu. ft. The ammonia compressor compresses the ammonia vapor, raising the temperature from 45° to 100°F. and this "hot" ammonia vapor is condensed to supply latent heat of evaporation to the product.

It should be noted that low temperature evaporators operate at temperatures which permit the growth of microorganisms. Rigid sanitation is mandatory in such operations and equipment design must avoid dead ends, stagnant areas, etc.

CONCENTRATION MATHEMATICS

Among factors and formulas useful in considering engineering aspects of concentration of food products are:

Weight of a gallon of liquid equals 8.34 times the specific gravity of the liquid.
1 cu. ft. per min. equals 448.8 gal. per hr.
1 B.t.u. equals the amount of heat required to raise 1 lb. of water 1°F.
1 b.h.p. (boiler horse-power) equals 33,480 B.t.u. per hr.
    equals 34.5 lbs. water evaporated per hr. at 212°F.
1 lb. per sq. in. equals 2.3 ft. of water at 60°F.
Barometric pressure of 1 ft. water at 60°F. equals 0.443 lb. per sq. in.

Applying some of these conversion factors, packing 100,000 cases of 30 per cent paste (instead of 300,000 cases of 1.045 purée) will require evaporation of the equivalent of 200,000 cases of water.

Example.—Determine the boiler horse-power required to convert 300,000 cases of 1.045 sp. gr. tomato purée to 100,000 cases of 30 per cent tomato paste, assuming an operating season of 1,000 hours.

(1) 200,000 x 4.5 (gal. equivalent of 1 case 6/10s) = 900,000 gal.
(2) 900,000 x 8.34 (lbs. of water per gal.) = 7,500,000 lbs. of water to be evaporated.
(3) 7,500,000/1,000 = 7,500 lbs. of water evaporated per hour.
(4) 7,500/34.5 = 216 b.h.p.

If the boilers are running at full capacity, as is common in tomato processing, the canner may be reluctant to consider purchasing additional boiler capacity. However, if he is using single effect evaporators he may already have the required quantity of steam. To calculate the steam available from a single effect evaporator the conversion factors above can be used to advantage.

Example.—Determine the latent heat energy (in terms of boiler horse-power) in the water vapor generated from the production of 300,000 cases 6/10s of 1.045 sp. gr. tomato purée. Assume an original tomato pulp of six per cent tomato solids and a 1,000 hr. operating season.

(1) 300,000 cases 6/10s of 1.045 purée x 4.5 = 1,350,000 gal.

(2) 1,350,000 x 0.94/0.51 (See Table 95 and conversion formula) = 2,488,000 gal. of six per cent tomato pulp fed to evaporator during season.

(3)   2,488,000 gal. original six per cent tomato pulp.
     —1,350,000 gal. finished 1.045 sp. gr. tomato purée.
     = 1,138,000 gal. of water evaporated during season.

(4) 1,138,000/1,000 = 1,138 gal. of water evaporated per hr.

(5) 1,138 x 8.34 = 9,491 lbs. of water.

(6) 9,491/34.5 = 275 b.h.p.

It is therefore evident that the energy contained in the vapor produced during the concentration of six per cent tomato pulp to 1.045 sp. gr. tomato purée in one evaporator is more than sufficient to concentrate that same tomato purée to 30 per cent tomato paste in another evaporator operating at a higher vacuum and a lower boiling temperature. In the examples above, approximately 9,500 lbs. of water vapor per hr. were boiled off during the concentration of tomato pulp to tomato purée. The latent heat energy which was originally contained in the boiler steam used to effect this concentration is now in the 9,500 lbs. of water vapor. If the tomato purée is now pumped to another evaporator, the heat energy in the 9,500 lbs. of water vapor can be used to convert the tomato purée to tomato paste, an operation which requires the evaporation of only 7,500 lbs. of water.

The reader should be cautioned that the transfer of heat energy from steam condensate to product water vapor is not 100 per cent efficient. There is some loss from radiation, venting, leaks, etc. However, for practical purposes, calculations such as those above can be most valuable in determining plant operating requirements.

Every processor with more than one evaporator has two boiler rooms. One is fed water, the other is fed product. It is possible to produce more steam from a multiple effect evaporator than was initially produced by the fired-boiler. Processors and evaporator engineers take pride in obtaining 2, 3, 4, or more pounds of vapor from product for every pound of steam supplied by the boiler room. By use of multiple effects it is frequently possible to avoid the necessity of additional boiler equipment, and still increase production and lower steam costs. However, multiple effects may require heavy capital investment and steam economy must be weighed against equipment cost.

Fouling

The accumulation of a coat of cooked material on a metal surface, whether on the outside of a coil or the inside of a tube will decrease heat transfer, reduce production and adversely affect product quality. This accumulation is known as fouling or "burn-on" and may require frequent shut-downs for cleaning. Morgan and Carlson (1960) summarized factors leading to fouling of tubes. Adams *et al.* (1955) discussed materials and procedures which affect tomato film deposition on stationary coils. High heating-medium temperatures, high pectin content and high viscosity increase fouling rate. High product velocity, agitated films and polished heating surfaces decrease the fouling rate. Kilpatrick and Breitweiser (1961) on a model forced-circulation, rising-film evaporator increased evaporator capacity about 80 per cent and doubled operating time between clean-outs by replacing commercial pickle finish tubes with polished tubes.

Some California processors handle in excess of 6,000 tons of tomatoes in a 24-hr. period. Evaporators are frequently called upon in such cases to work for six straight days without clean-up. Eventually fouling reaches a point where the time required for clean-up results in less loss in production than the drop in production resulting from poor heat transfer. Continuous operation requires operating techniques resulting in minimum fouling. Open kettles with stationary coils require removal of burn-on several times a day. Internal calandria pans with natural circulation are usually cleaned at least once every 24 hrs. Modern high velocity forced circulation evaporators can run continuously for seven days or more without stopping for cleaning.

Venting and Draining

Both boiler steam in the first stage evaporator, and product vapors used in a second effect, carry entrained air and other gases commonly called "noncondensable gases." When steam condenses in a heat exchanger both the condensate and noncondensable gases must be continually removed or they will form a "blanket" that reduces rates of condensing or evaporation. This is especially important in vacuum pans where the steam chests operate under low pressure steam. There must be adequate vents at any place in the shell where air might accumulate and they should be inspected frequently to insure that they are open and unclogged. It may be necessary to use a small steam ejector or other vacuum source connected to the vents to suck air from the chest.

Condensate will ordinarily flow out through a steam trap by gravity. When pressure in the steam chest is lower than atmospheric it is frequently necessary to use an ejector, pump or barometric leg to remove the condensate. Gage glasses in steam chambers should be kept clean and checked periodically for condensate level. Ordinarily condensed product vapor in a multiple effect system is not suitable for use as boiler feed water since small amounts of entrained solids may be carried over with the vapor (Anon. 1960A).

Measurement of Vapor Pressure

The temperature of saturated steam is related to its pressure. The literature on evaporation makes frequent reference to the pressure of the steam used as heating media or arising from the boiling product. This pressure is expressed as pounds per square inch or as inches of mercury.

Absolute pressure is expressed as pounds per square inch and is abbreviated p.s.i.a. The zero point of a gage calibrated for absolute pressure would be a perfect vacuum.

Gage pressure is expressed as pounds per square inch and is abbreviated p.s.i.g. The zero point of a gage in p.s.i.g. starts at approximately 15 p.s.i.a.; p.s.i.a. minus 15 equals p.s.i.g.

Absolute pressure in inches of mercury is the height of a vertical column of mercury required to balance the pressure being measured. It may be expressed in millimeters, as is common on barometers, or in inches as is common in vacuum pan gages. Atmospheric pressure at sea level is 29.9 in. or 760 mm. mercury. Vacuum is commonly expressed as 29.9 minus absolute pressure in inches.

Example.—20.4 in. absolute pressure is equivalent to 9.5 in. vacuum (29.9–20.4).

Heat Transfer Formula

The amount of water vapor evaporated is directly proportional to the quantity of heat transferred to the product. The amount of heat transferred is determined by the difference in temperature between the heating media and the product, the area of the heating surface and a composite of factors such as thickness of metal wall, agitation of product, fouling of surface, etc., which affect the efficiency of heat transfer. These are all summed up in the basic Heat Transfer Formula: $Q = U \times \Delta T \times A$

Where:

$Q =$ the total heat flow in B.t.u. per hr.,

$U =$ the heat transfer coefficient in B.t.u./hr./sq. ft./degree F.,

$\Delta T =$ the mean (average) effective temperature difference between the hot side and cold side in degrees F., and

$A =$ the surface area available for heat transfer in square feet.

This formula is useful in determining evaporating capacity, boiler horsepower required for evaporating, heating efficiency, etc. Q divided by 1,000 will give the approximate evaporating capacity of a unit in pounds of water evaporated per hour.

The manufacturer of an evaporator will usually supply the square feet of heating surface; or this can be easily calculated from the number of tubes, length and diameter. The temperatures of the heating medium and the boiling product may be obtained from the gage pressure or by direct temperature measurement to derive ΔT. The U factor (coefficient of heat transfer) varies for each particular product and set of evaporating conditions. U factors may run from 40 to 500. Morgan *et al.* (1959) state that they have calculated U factors of 1100 for the flash evaporator previously described p. 483. U factors drop rapidly with viscous products unless special evaporators are used as previously discussed. A practical and easy method of determining U factors is to measure the condensate produced in the evaporator. For practical purposes one can assume that condensation of one pound of steam will evaporate one pound of water from product at boiling temperatures. Example: A steam jacketed open kettle used for evaporation of tomato pulp has an operating pressure of 50 p.s.i.g. in the steam jacket with a heating surface of 60 sq. ft. A 50 gal. drum placed to catch condensate from the steam trap fills in 20 min. What is the coefficient of heat transfer?

$$Q = U \times A \times \Delta T$$

$$U = \frac{Q}{A \times \Delta T}$$

$Q =$ lbs. of water evaporated (steam condensed per hour) $\times$ 1000 (approximate heat of evaporation per pound)
$= 50 \times 3$ (3 drums/hr.) $\times$ 8.34 (lbs. of water/gal.) $\times$ 1000
$= 1,250,000$ B.t.u./hr.
$A = 60$ sq. ft.
$\Delta T = 298°$F. (50 p.s.i.g.) $-$ 212°F. (temperature of boiling product)
$= 86$
$U = \dfrac{1,250,000}{60 \times 86} = 242$

The technique of measuring condensate is a useful tool to the plant manager who wants to know the steam consumption or evaporating capacity of his equipment.

Fouling decreases the U factor; reduced U factors results in reduced heat transfer; reduced heat transfer results in decreased evaporation; decreased evaporation results in less condensate. Continuous or frequent measure of condensate offers a useful method to determine when fouling has reached a point where the evaporator must be shut down for cleaning.

ESSENCE RECOVERY

Volatile substances other than water are "boiled off" in concentrating by evaporation. These include volatile flavors of fruits. It is possible to recover these flavors for return to the concentrated product. A water solution of recovered volatile flavors is called *essence*. These essences may be used by the concentrator or sold as a separate item. Concentrated essences are designated as 100, 150, 200-fold, etc., according to the ratio of the flavor concentration in the essence to the flavor concentration in the natural juice. Walker (1961) reviewed the chemistry, economics, and technology of essence recovery.

INSTRUMENTATION AND CONTROL

Vacuum and pressure gages, thermometers, pressure and temperature recorders and controllers are standard instruments for most evaporator systems. Recording and control of solids is now possible by use of a family of instruments which utilize continuous measurement of refractive index, specific gravity or resistance to neutron flow. Consistency is successfully recorded and controlled in such products as applesauce, tomato catsup, baby food, etc., by an instrument known as the Plastometer. Equipment manufacturers today supply an assortment of automatic valves, variable speed pumps, level controls, measuring instruments, etc., to enable processors to control the solids automatically.

BULK PACKAGING AND HANDLING

Tomato purée and fruit concentrates are frequently processed by the "hot-fill" method. In this technique the product is sterilized by heating above 185°F., filled and closed at that temperature. Closed cans may be passed through a water bath or steam chamber at 190°F. for two minutes to sterilize containers (National Canners Assoc. 1959), and are then cooled. As the container size increases it becomes increasingly difficult to cool viscous concentrates. Hot-fill is seldom practical for containers larger than No. 12 cans although tomato purée is sometimes hot-filled in rectangular five-gallon cans.

The difficulty of slow cooling, with resulting heat damage, is avoided in the Martin Aseptic Canning System (Martin 1951). The product is continuously heated to a high temperature and then rapidly cooled before filling and sealing the sterile product in pasteurized containers. Modifications of this technique are commercially used for packing tomato paste and fruit concentrates in tinned and enameled 55 gal. drums (Anon. 1960B; Anon. 1958).

Advantages claimed for the system include: replacement of 72 No. 10 cans with one 55-gal. drum, elimination of 12 fiberboard cases, possibility of more efficient handling and outside storage of filled drums, convenience of opening for reprocessing, minimum product loss after emptying, and avoidance of heat damage to product during long cooling periods.

The process appears deceptively simple. The concentrate is heated above 190°F. for a few seconds in a shell and tube or a scraped surface heat exchanger, pumped through a scraped surface or vacuum flash-cooling unit (where the temperature is rapidly lowered to about 90°F.) and filled into presterilized drums. The filling and closing operations are performed under aseptic conditions in an enclosed chamber.

The cooled concentrate is subject to recontamination. When the system from the cooling chamber to the filling chamber is under vacuum, possible ports of entry for bacteria such as couplings, T's, valve stems, welds, pumps, etc., are protected by steam jets which continually sterilize the danger points. Special "aseptic" valves and pumps have been designed for this process. It has been estimated that there are more than 150 possible points of contamination between the heat exchanger and the filling station. It is obvious that top-quality engineering and bacteriological design of such a system is mandatory.

There is no limit to the size of the container filled by aseptic techniques such as described above. One large food processor in California successfully ships aseptically packed tomato paste across the United States in railroad tank cars of 10,000 gal. capacity. Processors store sterile tomato paste in tanks of more than 70,000 gal. capacity. Such tanks are kept under positive pressure with sterile nitrogen to avoid oxidation. Economic losses resulting from "mistakes" in such a system limits the technique to processors possessing rigid controls, strict sanitation, and considerable "know-how."

CONCLUSION

The cost, selection, and operation of evaporation systems poses many problems for the food processor. He may well look with envy on the honeybee who successfully concentrates 35 per cent solids flower nectar to 80 per cent solids honey, with a minimum mechanical set-up! The resulting product, honey, is not only universally acceptable and of excellent quality, it is also self-preserving without the use of heat.

Manufacturers of concentrating equipment put out excellent brochures and catalogues which contain much fundamental information and data on concentration and evaporation. A partial list of manufacturers follows:

A P V Co., Inc., 137 Arthur Street, Buffalo 7, N. Y.

Buflovak Equipment Division, Blow Knox Co., 1637 Fillmore Avenue, Buffalo, N. Y.

C. E. Rogers Co., 8731 Witt Street, Detroit 9, Mich.

General American Transportation Co., Process Equipment Division, 135 S. LaSalle Street, Chicago 3, Ill.

Langenskamp, 229 E. South Street, Indianapolis 25, Ind.

Mojonnier Bros. Co., 4601 W. Ohio Street, Chicago 44, Ill.

Oscar Krenz, Inc., Ashby at Sixth Street, Berkeley 10, Calif.

Patterson-Kelly Inc., E. Stroudsburg, Pa.

Pfaudler Co., 1000 West Avenue, Rochester 3, N. Y.

Rodney Hunt Machine Co., 117 Vale Street, Orange, Mass.

Rossi & Catelli, Parma, Italy

Thermovac Inc., 816 E. Hazelton Avenue, Stockton, Calif.

Tito Manzini e Figli, Parma, Italy

BIBLIOGRAPHY

ADAMS, H. W., NELSON, A. I., and LEGAULT, R. R. 1955. Film deposition of tomato juice on heat exchanger coils. Food Technol. 9, No. 7, 354–357.

ANON. 1958. Foods now sterile packed in drums. Canner Packer 127, No. 7, 30–31.

ANON. 1960A. The Engineers Reference Library—Power Handbook. McGraw-Hill Book Co., New York.

ANON. 1960B. Saves with sterile bulk pack. Food Eng. 32, No. 2, 79.

ANON. 1961. Boilerless evaporator saves B.t.u. Food Eng. 33, No. 12, 46–47.

ANON. 1963. New concepts spark evaporation. Food Eng. 35, No. 2, 68–70, 75.

BEISEL, C. G. 1954. Vacuum concentration. In Chemistry and Technology of Fruit and Vegetable Juice Production. TRESSLER, D. K., and JOSLYN, M. A. (Editors). Avi Publishing Co., Westport, Conn.

BROWN, A. H., et al. 1951. Rapid heat processing of fluid foods by steam injection. Ind. Eng. Chem. 43, 2949–2954.

CRUESS, W. L. 1958. Commercial Fruit and Vegetable Products. McGraw-Hill Book Co., New York.

DEDERT, W. G., and MOORE, J. G. 1963. New trends in evaporation. Ind. Eng. Chem. 55, 57–62.

EOLKIN, D. 1957. The Plastometer—a new development in continuous recording and controlling consistometers. Food Technol. 11, 253–257.

HARPER, J. C. 1960. Viscometric behavior in relation to evaporation of fruit purées. Food Technol. 14, 557–561.

HEID, J. L. 1943. Concentrating citrus juices by the vacuum method. Food Inds. 15, No. 5, 62–64, 122; No. 6, 64–66, 110, 111.

HEID, J. L., and CASTEN, J. S. 1961. Vacuum concentration of fruit and vegetable juices. In Fruit and Vegetable Juice Processing Technology. TRESSLER, D. K., and JOSLYN, M. A. (Editors). Avi Publishing Co., Westport, Conn.

HEID, J. L., and KELLY, E. J. 1953. The concentration and dehydration of citrus juices. Canner *116*, No. 5, 9–13, 21.

JOSLYN, M. A. 1961. Concentration by freezing. In Fruit and Vegetable Juice Processing Technology. TRESSLER, D. K., and JOSLYN, M. A. (Editors). Avi Publishing Co., Westport, Conn.

JOSLYN, M. A., and HEID, J. L., 1957. Concentrating and drying in food products manufacture. Western Canner Packer *49*, No. 2, 29–35, 39–44.

KILPATRICK, P. W., and BREITWEISER, E. 1961. Increasing evaporator capacity with polished tubes. Ind. Eng. Chem. *53* 119–120.

LAWLER, F. K. 1960. Revolutionary plate evaporator concentrates orange juice. Food Eng. *32*, No. 3, 60–63.

MARTIN, W. McK. 1951. Continuous aseptic process. Food Eng. *23*, No. 6, 67–70, 134–137.

MILLEVILLE, H. P., and ESKEW, R. K. 1946. Recovery of volatile apple flavor in essence form. Western Canner Packer *38*, No. 1, 51–54.

MOORE, E. I., *et al.* 1945. The concentrating and drying of citrus juices. Proc. Inst. Food Technol. 160–168.

MORGAN, A. I., and CARLSON, R. A. 1960. Fouling inside heat-exchanger tubes. Food Technol. *14*, No. 11, 594–596.

MORGAN, A. I., and WASSERMAN, T. H. 1959. Fouling of evaporator tubes by tomato. Food Technol. *13*, No. 12, 691–693.

MORGAN, A. I., WASSERMAN, T. H., BROWN, D. H., and SMITH, G. H. 1959. Commercial-scale evaporation of tomato products in flash evaporators. Food Technol. *13*, No. 4, 232–235.

NATIONAL CANNERS ASSOCIATION. 1954. Hot-fill—hold—cool procedures for various products in California. Inform. Letter No. 1472. Natl. Canners Assoc., Washington, D. C.

NATIONAL CANNERS ASSOCIATION. 1956. A Laboratory Manual for the Canning Industry. 2nd Edition. Natl. Canners Assoc., Washington, D. C.

NATIONAL CANNERS ASSOCIATION. 1959. Hot-fill—hold—cool procedures for various products in California. Publ. Sheet D-819. Natl. Canners Assoc., Washington, D. C.

NOWLIN, R. L., and HENWOOD, C. I., JR. 1954. Flash evaporation now applied to grape juice concentrate. Wines and Vines *36*, No. 1, 25.

O'CONNELL, J. O. 1954. Instantaneous heating—flash evaporation. Food Processing *15*, No. 7, 14.

PARKER, N. H. 1963. How to specify evaporators. Chem. Eng. *70*, No. 15, 135–140.

PARKER, M. E., HARVEY, E. H., and STATELER, E. S. 1954. Elements of Food Engineering. Vol. 3. Reinhold Publishing Co., New York.

TOWNSEND, C. T., SOMERS, I. I., LAMB, F. C., and OLSON, N. A. 1954. A Laboratory Manual for the Canning Industry. Natl. Canners Assoc., Washington, D. C.

WALKER, L. H. 1961. Volatile flavor recovery. In fruit and Vegetable Juice Processing Technology. TRESSLER, D. K., and JOSLYN, M. A. (Editors), Avi Publishing Co., Westport, Conn.

WATT, B. K., and Merrill, A. L. 1964. Composition of Foods: Raw, Processed, Prepared. Agr. Handbook *8* (revised), U. S. Dept. Agr., Washington, D. C.

CHAPTER 17

M. A. Joslyn

Food Processing by Drying and Dehydration

INTRODUCTION

Drying is probably the oldest form of food preservation. Primitive man, from the earliest time when he first harvested edible plants must have become aware of the fact that certain crops, such as cereal grains, beans and peas, naturally matured and dried while still attached to their stalks and in the dried form could be stored for considerable periods. In imitation of this natural process that occurs in grains and in edible seeds of many plants, early man developed drying as a practical art to preserve other plant products, meats and fish from day to day and season to season. Fruits which matured with a naturally high sugar content and low moisture content, such as dates and figs, undoubtedly were among the first preserved food products. Flavorings of vegetable origin, herbs and spices, used to season or give relish to foods also were harvested dry (such as the seeds of tropical plants—anise, cumin, coriander, caraway, cardamon, fennel, mustard, nutmeg, mace, pepper) or allowed to dry after harvesting as bark, fruits or roots. Spices were anciently grown in the East and in the dried form were used very early. They had a far wider social and ceremonial significance in the East than they ever obtained in the West where the desire for spices was in part, at least, the result of a monotonous diet. Salting, another ancient process of food preservation, which also depends on reduction in available moisture content, usually is associated with drying in early food preservation practices. Smoking prior to drying was introduced at a later period.

Fish split and slowly dried in the wind, meat cut thin and dried in the sun, sun-dried fruit and vegetable products have been known for many thousands of years. In the early history, drying developed empirically without either knowledge of the basic factors involved in preservation or of the factors affecting rate and extent of moisture decrease. Sun and wind currents were utilized exclusively at first and later salting, smoking, sulfuring and other practices were applied as adjuncts. Artificial heat was used in converting sun-drying into evaporation; later hot-air drying was improved by exposure of solid foods to streams of hot-air (dehydration), by atomization of liquid food

M. A. JOSLYN is Professor of Food Technology, Department of Nutritional Sciences, University of California, Berkeley, Calif.

products into heated air (spray-drying), by drying liquid and semisolid foods by contact with heated rollers (drum-drying), and finally by combination of heat and low pressure (vacuum-drying).   Puff-drying in specially constructed and operated vacuum driers (both cabinet and belt), foam-mat driers and other developments to improve drying by evaporation from the liquid phase have been made more recently. Freeze-drying in which the food is frozen and drying occurs by sublimation of water from the solid phase also has been introduced commercially.

Dehydrated foods, particularly vegetables, were produced for military use in the Crimean and Boer wars and their production was stimulated by World War I.   In World War II, because of the possible saving in storage space and the mobility and utility of dried foods, considerable expansion in the production of dehydrated fruits, dehydrated vegetables and the extension of this to milk, eggs and meat occurred.   Commercial production of dehydrated foods, particularly fruits, vegetables, eggs and meat products decreased shortly after the end of World War II.   Commercial production of dried milk products, however, did not decrease as markedly.

Drying and dehydration of foods for military and defense needs still continues to be an important consideration in military planning. Their mobility and stability at ordinary temperatures have been and are of strategic importance.   While in the United States, the ready availability of refrigerated facilities for storage and distribution of both perishable and frozen foods, and the high acceptability of canned and glass-packed foods, have been responsible for the relatively low civilian consumption of dried foods, these considerations do not apply elsewhere.   In the United Kingdom, which produces only a small portion of its total food requirement, the large quantity of food imported annually has focused attention upon the desirability of reducing water content and amount of shipping required.   It has been estimated that the quantity of food imported each year into Britain contains about three million tons of water.   Frozen food production and use, while growing, is still limited.   This is true also in Europe where canned and glass-packed foods, while consumed in sufficient amounts, still are not as widely used as in the United States.   In the developing countries of the world, particularly in Africa, Asia, the Middle East and Far East, where food is in short supply, and refrigeration facilities are limited or nonexistent, dried and dehydrated foods would be the most likely preserved foods to be introduced and used.   Surplus foods from the United States usually have been and will continue to be shipped overseas, as foreign aid, largely in the dried, concentrated form.

While the production of dehydrated foods for the military market (both for our use and that of our allies) markedly decreased after the end of World War II, the desirability and acceptability of various dehydrated products continued to be studied and the U. S. Department of Defense has continued to promote research and development in this field.   In 1951, the United Kingdom actively promoted research and development in food dehydration by establishing a research center and experimental factory at Aberdeen, Scotland, staffed and supplied to develop food dehydration from laboratory, through pilot scale, to full commercial scale demonstration.   This continued to be operated by the Ministry of Agriculture, Food and Fisheries until 1960, (Hanson 1961).   Drying and dehydration of foods also is under investigation in Europe (particularly in Germany and the Netherlands) and elsewhere.

While cereal grains and their products form the bulk of dried foods processed in the world, being followed by sugar, dry beans and peas and oil seeds, the production of dried and dehydrated foods continues to constitute a major portion of preserved foods of commerce.   In 1960

TABLE 97

PRODUCTION OF DRIED AND DEHYDRATED FOODS IN THE UNITED STATES IN 1960[1]

	Tons
Sugar, cane and beet	9,300,000
Coffee	1,460,000
Corn starch	1,100,000
Milk and milk products	1,014,000
Flour mixes	970,000
Beans, dry field	900,000
Peanuts (crop)	890,000
Breakfast foods	860,000
Pet foods	790,000
Macaroni and other paste products	470,000
Corn sweeteners	410,000
Dried fruits	400,000
Potato chips	280,000
Cocoa	275,000
Tree nuts	270,000
Puddings, dry	210,000
Dry yeast	150,000
Peas, field, dry	150,000
Pop corn	145,000
Potatoes and potato products	80,000
Tea	58,000
Spices	50,000
Corn chips	35,000
Vegetables, dehydrated	35,000
Flavor paste, dry	30,000
Baking powder	30,000
Hops	27,000
Eggs	23,000
Pectin	5,000

[1] Source: Canner/Packer Yearbook, Sept. 25. 1961.

over 20 million tons of dried foods were produced or packed in the United States. In the order of production sugar leads the others, as shown in Table 97, although certain cereal products amounted to over four million tons. The production of dehydrated vegetables and potatoes amounted to 115,000 tons (or almost 400,000 tons if potato chips are included) in comparison with 400,000 tons of dried fruits, over one million tons of milk products and only 23,000 tons of eggs.

In the United States the production of dehydrated vegetables which amounted to 750 tons per year during 1925–1937 (largely as dehydrated onions, garlic and chili) reached a high level of over 100,000 tons (including potatoes) in 1944, dropped to 27,000 tons in 1946 and has been increasing since. (The total production in 1960 including potatoes amounted to 115,000 tons.) The production of dried fruits in the United States in 1960 of 400,000 tons, compared with the world production of over 1,300,000 tons. Of this production prunes constituted 139,000 tons and raisins 194,000 tons. Raisins, dates, figs, prunes and currants are the leading fruits dried in the world. During the past decade there has been a considerable increase in the production of dehydrated vegetables for sale in the retail, remanufacturing and institutional civilian markets. The retail items include mainly potato products (granules, flakes, powders), soup mixes, and flaked and powdered seasonings (onions, peppers, garlic). While onions, garlic and peppers have long been used in the manufacturing trade (in the manufacture of chili sauce, catsup, pickles and relishes) this use has expanded, as has also the use of dried meat extracts and other materials mixed with various dried vegetables (carrots, peas, celery, parsley, potatoes, onions, peppers and garlic) in packaged soup mixes, and the use of dehydrated vegetables in canned meat or fish products such as meat and vegetable stew, meat hash, codfish balls, etc., has increased.

The acceptability of standard dried products such as dried milk (whole, nonfat, whey, etc), dried eggs (whole, white or yolk), coffee, cocoa and other beverages has been improved and many of these products as "instant" powders have become popular. Continuous research and development has been responsible for improved reconstitution of dried products, increased storage stability, and improved production. While our knowledge of the physics and engineering of the drying operation, as well as our knowledge of the biochemical changes occurring during preparation for dehydration and subsequent storage, has increased, more information on the fundamental aspects of food dehydration is required before drying and dehydration can expand into a scientifically controlled operation. Recent data on the fundamental aspects of dehydration was reported at the conference held in Aberdeen in 1958, (Soc. Chem. Ind. 1958) and by Saravacos and Charm (1962A.) Among the factors which have contributed to its present success are:

(1) Selection of Raw Materials for Drying on the Basis of Characteristics Best Suited to This Method of Preservation.— In the early development, drying and dehydration was applied as a salvage operation to economically conserve foods produced in surplus quantities. This period was followed by empirical testing to determine the suitability of different varieties of fruit and vegetables, the determination of optimum maturity for drying and the selection of those varieties which are most acceptable in the dried form as determined by color, flavor, texture, nutritive value and storage stability. Suitability to mechanical harvesting in the field and orchard and mechanical handling in the plant were evaluated. While at present it is still not possible to define the characteristics desired in fruits and vegetables objectively, our knowledge of the factors limiting suitability is sufficient to serve as guide to existing practices. This is also true for tree nuts, other plant products and for milk, poultry and eggs, meat and fish products.

(2) Control of Undesirable Changes in Quality During Preparation for Drying and Drying.—As a result of investigation of the factors involved in changes in color, flavor and texture during washing, peeling, cutting and drying, the nature of both the changes due to uncontrolled growth and activity of contaminating microorganisms and of tissue enzymes involved was evaluated. The darkening of cut fruits during drying has long been controlled by empirically developed sulfuring or sulfiting procedures, by the use of various modified oil dips or by blanching. Sulfuring and sulfiting operations for dried fruits were greatly improved prior to World War II (Long *et al.* 1940; Bisson *et al.* 1942) and subsequently blanching and sulfiting of vegetables to improve color and flavor retention were developed largely during World War II. Additional information on both the biological and engineering factors involved in the application of these processes since the war have aided in further improving control of these operations. Investigations of the factors influencing storage stability have led to improvement in quality retention by avoiding or minimizing heat damage during drying. Changes in color and flavor due to nonenzymatic chemical reactions between various constituents such as the reactions between carbohydrates and nitrogenous constituents leading to browning, or the reaction of unsaturated lipids with oxygen leading to rancidification are better understood and controlled.

Undesirable changes in the native proteins of milk, egg and milk products are controlled by better knowledge of the nature of the process involved. Thus the empirically discovered fact that fresh liquid egg cannot be dried without changes in the whipping quality of the resulting product, long known in China, and which led to the traditional use of natural fermentation prior to drying is now better established as a chemical interaction between sugars and egg proteins. Removal of excess sugars by controlled fermentation or by enzymatic oxidation to gluconic acid, commercially used, has resulted in improved egg products. Meat products at present still present problems. They can be only air-dried in the form of precooked minces and are characterized by marked darkening of color, toughening of texture and roast off-flavors. While freeze dehydration reduces the last two changes, darkening in color still occurs. It is less of a problem with poultry flesh.

(3) **More Rapid Reduction of Moisture Content to the Level Required for Optimum Storage Stability Under Conditions of Minimum Damage to Quality.**—As a result of improvement of knowledge of the factors influencing the migration or movement of water from the interior of the product to the outer surface and of evaporation of moisture as water vapor at the surface, hot-air drying has reached the stage where it can yield acceptable fruit and vegetable products. The moisture level required for improved storage stability has been determined for most food products and this level has been attained by combination of multistage drying and in-package desiccation under conditions in which heat damage is minimized. Mass-transfer operations have been improved by recognition of naturally occurring barriers to moisture transfer and their elimination or reduction. Whole small fruits usually dry slowly because of a fairly moisture-impermeable epidermis or outer skin. In some varieties they may be coated with a fairly heavy layer of bloom. By checking the outer surface of such fruits as cherries, grapes and prunes by dipping in dilute lye solutions or in hot water, moisture transfer rates can be greatly increased. With cut vegetables such as potatoes which contain starch, gelatination of starch during blanching results in covering the potato pieces with a starch glaze through which moisture transfer is slow. Proper handling during and after blanching reduces the tendency to form starch glazes during drying. Increasing the surface exposed per unit volume of product by suitable cutting, dicing or shredding to increase moisture transfer ratio; better engineering of combinations of conduction, convection and radiation to supply latent heat of evaporation; and better engineering of moisture vapor re-

moval from evaporating surfaces have resulted in more rapid drying to lower moisture levels.

(4) **Production of Porous Structure During Drying.**—Development of conditions of pressure and temperature under which the structure of the product to be dried could be altered to produce and maintain a highly porous condition has facilitated both drying and reconstitution of the dried product. Porous structures in some foods are best obtained by puff-drying in vacuum shelf or conveyor driers. Foam-mat drying and foam-drum drying techniques have been developed to produce granules or flakes of porous structure. In conventionally spray-dried products the desired porosity can be obtained by agglomeration of the powdered product and subsequent redrying while under agitation on a conveyor drier.

In the production of some types of instant coffee products, the desired structure of particles is obtained by injection as drops of liquid into the top of a drying column of heated air and controlled partial drying with recirculation under conditions of incapsulation, followed by vacuum drying of the resulting discrete partially solidified droplets.

(5) **Retention and Restoration of Volatile Flavors.**—Various methods have been developed to improve retention of flavors in dried foods. These include drying under conditions such that flavor loss during dehydration is reduced by reducing temperature or pressure of the product being dried, by recovery of volatile essences and their return to the product during the drying process, by recovery of volatile flavors and their combination with flavor fixing or holding substances resulting in solid flavor-sealed products which can be granulated and added back to the finished product, or by development of flavor from flavor precursors by the activity of naturally occurring or added enzymes. Garlic and onions, for example, which contain flavor precursors are prepared and dried in a manner to protect the enzymes which liberate the characteristic flavors from their precursors when the product is rehydrated. In vegetables such as cabbage which are blanched before drying and whose natural flavor-producing enzyme is destroyed, precursor-splitting enzymes may be added to the dried product to yield reconstituted cabbage with the characteristic aroma of the fresh. With meat products dried as powders, the desired meat flavor production can be accelerated during preparation of the slurry or mince, recovered and added back after concentration.

(6) **Solvent or Liquid Carrier Dehydration.**—The drying of oil- or fat-containing foods in the chopped, ground or puréed form can be improved by vacuum shelf drying or vacuum concentration in the presence of added oil or fat which increases rate of moisture loss

(Greenfield 1953; Webb 1949).   After dehydration, the excess oil or fat may be separated mechanically and reused.   The resulting products, when properly dried, are of excellent texture and flavor.   Moisture may be separated also by the use of immiscible solvents capable of absorbing water (Baniel 1961).

(7) **Combination of Techniques Yield New Products for Greater Convenience in Use.**—Potatoes are cooked, mashed and dried to give consumers a product which can be prepared for serving with a minimum of time and effort.

Instant coffee, tea, milk and fruit juices are in a similar category. In dehydro-frozen fruits and vegetables, moisture content is lowered prior to freezing, reducing the weight and volume, permitting savings in packaging, warehousing and shipping costs.   Resulting frozen products are quickly and easily prepared, and the flavor and appearance compare favorably with fresh products without partial dehydration.   Partially dried products also can be canned as dehydro-canned products.

(8) **Improvements in Packaging.**—Protective flexible packages of foil, film, fiber and combinations, plus the use of epoxides and other fungicides and bactericides, make it possible to "tenderize" dried fruit by steaming, increasing the moisture content to facilitate consumption as a confection or easy reconstitution.   Fumigated and pasteurized products, protected by suitable packages, have a shelf-life adequate for distribution through normal channels.   Sealing under vacuum or inert gas in tight packages also contributes to improved products.

These are some factors involved in recent improvements in concentrated and dried fruit products.   How these factors are involved in specific applications will be described.

SUN DRYING

Sun drying, in direct or diffused sunlight (shade drying), one of the earliest methods of food preservation, is still used for the production of dried fruits, and also for drying nuts.   It was originally limited to fruits high in sugar content which, when harvested, would dry naturally without hazard of loss from fermentation and molding.   Although marked improvements have been made in the selection of varieties of fruits better adapted to sun drying and in preparation for, and handling during and after drying, sun drying is not as intensively practiced in California as it was when sun-dried cut apricots, pears and peaches were of more acceptable color and texture than those which had been dehydrated.   Today it is possible to simulate the translucency of sun-dried pears and uniformity of color of halved apricots and peaches by suitable blanching treatment before dehydration.

Sun-dried fruit can be produced only in climatic areas with relatively high temperatures, low humidities and freedom from rainfall during the drying season. Inland valleys in California, Australia and countries bordering the Mediterranean are among the important producing areas. A combination of sun and shade drying was customarily used in order to obtain dried fruits of the proper texture and color. Various pretreatments were developed including "checking" with hot water or dilute lye, treatment with oil emulsion, sulfuring and blanching. Fruits most widely dried today are prunes, raisins, apricots, peaches and pears. Of the present annual production of about 150,000 tons of prunes, only one-fourth is sun-dried, three-fourths are dehydrated. Of the present production of 200,000 tons of raisins, about half are dehydrated.

Fruit for sun drying is harvested at optimum maturity, the smaller fruits (currants, grapes, prunes) are sorted, dipped into hot water, dilute lye solution, or in olive oil emulsified in lye solution. Prepared fruit is spread on drying trays, exposed to sun for a day or two, and then stacked to dry in the shade.

The fruit during drying must be protected from contamination with sand, soil and other debris carried by wind and also from excessive dew fall at night. In some Mediterranean countries heavy sandstorms may occur during the drying operation or heavy dew fall may occur at night. The latter will cause rehydration of partially dried fruit and considerable prolongation of the drying period. Occasionally rain will fall and this likewise causes wetting and may result in severe rain-damage to the product.

Apricots are halved and pitted, freestone peaches are halved and pitted, pears are halved and cored, and apples are peeled and sliced. The cut fruit must be sulfured to inhibit browning during drying.

An outline of California practices in sun drying is given in Table 181. Additional details are given in a circular on sulfuring and sulfur house operation by Phaff and Mrak (1948), based on investigation of Long *et al.* (1940) on the sulfuring of fruits for drying. General directions for sun-drying fruits are given in the circular of Mrak and Phaff (1949).

In Australia the traditional practice in sun-drying raisins is to prepare the grapes (Muscat or Sultana) by dipping into an alkaline oil emulsion. Originally the cold oil dip was prepared by emulsification of $1/2$ to $3/4$ pt. of olive oil in 25 gal. of solution containing one pound of potash (potassium carbonate) per four gallons. Only olive oil containing 5 to 10 per cent free fatty acid expressed as oleic acid will give

TABLE 98

OUTLINE OF CALIFORNIA PRACTICES IN SUN DRYING FRUITS

Fruit	Pretreatment	Drying Practices	Treatment During Drying	Drying Time-Days	Yield[1]
Prunes	Dipping in hot lye solutions. Fresh prunes are immersed in 0.25 to 1.0% lye for 5–30 sec. Imperial prunes are checked in boiling water or 0.25% lye	Spread on 3 x 8 wooden drying trays, 75–90 lbs./tray	Imperial prunes turned to prevent molding. All prunes stacked when $2/3$ to $3/4$ dry, usually after 4–5 days	7–14	2.4:1
Silver prunes	Silver plums are lye dipped and then sulfured for 4 hr.	As above	None	7–14	...
Raisins, natural	None	Picked and dried on paper or 2 × 3 trays, 22 lbs./tray in vineyard	Turned on trays after partially dry or rolled into sausages on short pieces of heavy wrapping paper. Stacked 5–6 days after turning	10–25	4.0:1
Soda-dipped raisins	Dipping in 0.5% hot lye solution for 3–6 sec.	As above	As above	10–20	...
Sulfur-bleached raisins	Short lye dip as above, then sulfured for 4 hrs.	As above	As above	10–25	...
Apricots	Cut, pitted, trayed and sulfured for 3 hr.	Dried on 3 x 8 wooden trays	Trays spread in sun for 1–4 days, then stacked.	2–8	5.0:1
Peaches	Cut, pitted, trayed and sulfured 4–6 hr.	Dried on 3 x 8 wooden trays in drying yard	As above	4–8	4.5:1
Pears	Ripened, sorted, washed to remove spray residue, halved, stemmed, sulfured up to 24 hr.	Dried on wooden trays in drying yard	Stacked when partly dry usually after 1–2 days	14–25	...
Nectarines	Cut, pitted, sulfured for 3–4 hr.	As for apricots	As for apricots	4–8	...

[1] Weight of fresh fruit required to produce 1 lb. of dried fruit.

an emulsion satisfactory for dipping on agitation with potassium carbonate. Subsequently other edible oils and even mineral oil were used after emulsification with various wetting agents such as ammonium linoleate, potassium oleate, etc. The dipped raisins are then dried on wire-netting racks beneath a sheet metal roof. This rack-drying and oil-dipping produces light colored raisins of excellent flavor. The alkaline emulsified oil acts by dissolving the waxy constituents of the bloom on the surface of grapes and other components which reduce moisture transfer. Recently Saravacos and Charm (1962B) tested various synthetic surface-active chemicals and found these to promote dehydration of fruits and vegetables.

Fruit maturity at harvest affects both yield and quality. Harvesting all fruit, particularly tree fruit crops, at peak maturity is not practical and investigations have been conducted to determine the compromise maturity when harvesting can begin with least effect on yield and quality. With grapes maturity is determined fairly well by refractometer (Jacob 1942); with French prunes, color of flesh and skin is the most reliable single index. Claypool and Kilbuck (1955) reported that best results are obtained when French prunes are harvested shortly after chlorophyll has disappeared from the skin and flesh.

While sun-drying is more economical as far as equipment and fuel costs are concerned, it requires more labor than dehydration and results in lower yield per ton of fruit dried because of loss in sugars by respiration and fermentation during the long drying period required. Enzymatic and nonenzymatic changes in composition occur during drying and these may lead to deterioration in quality, particularly of color, flavor and texture. Unless scrupulous care is taken in all operations the sun-dried fruit is likely to become damaged by insect infestation and be contaminated by wind-borne dust and dirt or livestock, poultry, rodent and other animal excreta, etc. Because of these factors, mechanical handling and dehydration instead of sun drying is favored. The dehydrated fruit is generally cleaner, of better quality and the dehydration operation can be better controlled. It is possible to remove fruit from the dehydrators at the optimum moisture content for direct packing. Sun-dried fruits, on the other hand, require washing and processing with hot water before packing.

DEHYDRATION

When heat from a source other than sunlight is used to reduce moisture, the process is called "evaporation" or "dehydration." In "evaporation," temperature only is controlled, and natural draft is depended upon to supply hot air and carry away water vapor. In "dehydration" the heated air is circulated by blowers, and temperature and humidity as well as velocity of the air may be controlled and varied to suit specific products or stages in the drying process.

There is great variation in the design and operation of "dehydrators" and they may be divided in classes based upon various factors.

There are direct and indirect heated driers. In direct heated driers hot gases from combustion of the fuel are passed across, through or around products to be dried with or without mixing with heated air. The sensible heat in the gases furnishes latent heat of evaporation for moisture and the cooled gases convey vapor away from products.

In indirect driers, steam, indirectly heated air or electric energy is used to supply required heat of evaporation by radiation, conduction, convection or a combination.

Hot air driers are classed as parallel flow, counter flow, direct flow and cross flow, depending upon the direction of product travel in regard to movement of heated air. In bin, loft and fluidized bed driers, the heated air is blown upward through products.

Driers are also classed in regard to the form in which products are exposed, as spray or film driers (on trays or drums), according to whether operation is by batch or continuous, and according to whether drying is conducted in air or inert gas at atmospheric or subatmospheric pressures (as vacuum driers).

Radiant heating, using electric resistance heaters or steam coils, is limited to special applications. If power costs are low, electric resistance units are convenient to install and easy to control, and may be used in high vacuum drying above or below freezing temperatures (Tappel *et al.* 1943).

Electric heating of air is limited to drying operations of low heat requirements, such as the dehydration of walnuts, and for experimental work.

Conducted heat is used in drum and shelf driers chiefly for liquid and plastic products.

Most fruits and vegetables are dried by circulating hot air over or through products on trays or conveyors. Air may be heated by mixing directly with the gases of combustion of gas or oil, or may be heated indirectly in flues or by steam tubes or (rarely) electric resistance heaters. Solid fuels are not used for direct heated driers because of danger of contamination of products.

In hot air driers the object is to control temperature, humidity, velocity, volume and uniformity of distribution of air in regard to heat transfer and moisture carrying capacity to obtain the most economical drying rate with maximum protection of product quality. Engineering design, based upon nature of products, percentages of water evaporated in various stages of the driers, and air flow characteristics is essential to fully achieve these objectives.

Marked differences in air circulation exist in hot-air blast driers. Natural draft evaporators, used extensively in the early developments of industrial dehydration, today are limited to drying hops and apples.

Apples are dried in natural-draft, loft-type kilns. Peeled, cored, sliced and sulfured apples are spread on slatted floors in the loft of the kiln. Air heated directly by combustion of gas or oil in a furnace, or indirectly by means of steam pipes, rises through the layer of fruit as much as a foot thick. The fruit is stirred occasionally by means of rakes. The hot air is discharged through a ventilator which may be equipped with an exhaust fan to increase circulation. The operation of these driers is on a batch basis, and the product is of fair quality.

In forced draft dehydrators, the air may be circulated by fans of different design and varied arrangements may be used depending on the type of product to be dried and the type of recirculation used. Recir-

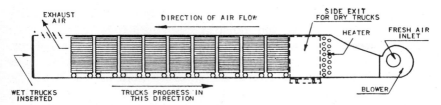

Courtesy of USDA Western Regional Research Lab.

Fig. 112. COUNTERFLOW TUNNEL, TRAYS ON CARTS

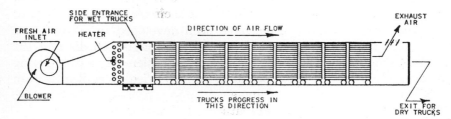

Courtesy of USDA Western Regional Research Lab.

FIG. 113. PARALLEL FLOW TUNNEL, TRAYS ON CARTS

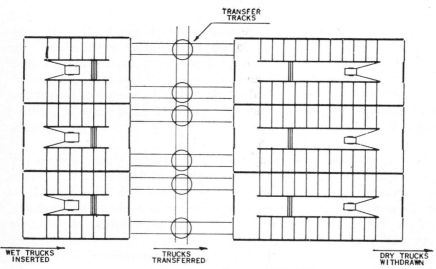

Courtesy of USDA Western Regional Research Lab.

FIG. 114. SEPARATED BANKS OF PARALLEL FLOW FIRST STAGE AND COUNTERFLOW SECOND STAGE DRYING TUNNELS

culation of air reduces costs of heating, but requires careful humidity control to avoid reducing the moisture-carrying capacity and rate of drying.   Tunnel dehydrators are of the countercurrent, parallel-current, cross-flow, center inlet, center exhaust, or multistage types.   The capacity and efficiency of tunnel dehydrators were increased by the use of a primary parallel flow stage and a secondary counter-flow stage.   This drying technique, developed by Eidt (1938) was first applied to apples and later to vegetable products.   Similar combination driers have also been used for apricots and peaches.

Dehydration on trays may be either batch, in cabinets or semicontinuous in tunnels, with trays racked on carts which move in one end of the tunnel and out the other while hot air is circulated transversely or longitudinally.   Tunnel driers have been developed to permit close control of the temperature and humidity of circulated air and the relative amount of new and recirculated air blended in the drying stream.   In a modification, products may be dried on endless, woven wire conveyors in tunnels, giving a continuous process.   Figures 112, 113 and 114 illustrate general features of tunnel driers.

The design and operation of drying tunnels and the evaluation of performance were discussed by Perry (1944) and Perry *et al.* (1946).

Van Arsdel (1951A and 1963B) discussed engineering factors and technology of drying fruits and vegetables.   The time required for drying specific products depends upon properties of the raw material including moisture content, composition, method of preparation, shape and size of pieces to be dried, etc., and also upon characteristics of the dehydrator.   The thickness of layers of material to be dried, the method of support, the degree of exposure to circulating air, the temperature, humidity, velocity and volume of air flow, etc., also are factors.   Although considerable data are available on rate of weight loss in products during drying, there are few data on changes in internal temperatures of individual pieces of products as drying progresses.   This is a major factor in determining quality.

Hot air in tunnel driers supplies heat to warm products to evaporating temperatures, furnishes latent heat of evaporation, and carries away evaporated moisture vapor.   The volume and linear velocity of air, its wet and dry bulb temperature before and after with products, and the weight of products in the drier are information required for determining over-all drying performance.

Initially, drying occurs by free evaporation from the surface of pieces, but later may involve diffusion of both liquid and vapor to the surface of the pieces.   Evaporation inside the pieces is more desirable than migration of liquids to the surface because the liquids carry solubles which tend to seal the product and cause case hardening. Puff-drying techniques are employed to promote evaporation throughout the interior of products. This leads to more rapid drying and more porous nature of the dried material, making it easier to dry to a lower moisture level and also to reconstitute the dried product.

The properties of products undergo constant change as drying progresses. Shrinkage, change in shape and hardness are external manifestations of these changes as the moisture content decreases. Fig. 115 shows how shrinkage changes the shape of diced vegetables during drying.

The total volume of air which must be circulated is determined by the heat transfer requirements as these exceed the moisture carrying capacity of the air in a ratio of approximately seven to one. That is, seven times as many cubic feet of air are required to furnish sufficient latent heat of evaporation needed to transport the evaporated moisture vapor away from the product.

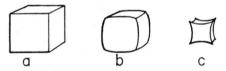

Courtesy of USDA Western Regional Research Lab.

Fig. 115.   Change in Shape of Diced
Vegetables During Drying

(a) Initial appearance.
(b) Appearance after rapid evaporation of surface moisture.
(c) Appearance after completion of dehydration.

In the initial stages of drying, air velocity has a marked effect upon drying rate and is ordinarily held at about 1000 f.p.m. In the later stages air flow at half this velocity will ordinarily remove as much moisture as will a flow at 1000 f.p.m.

The air velocity has a large effect on rate of moisture loss largely because evaporation of moisture at the wet surfaces of solid foods is impeded mainly by the layer of stagnant moisture vapor which forms a film over the surface. Air flowing over this surface removes water vapor, reduces the effective thickness of the film and hastens transfer of moisture by evaporation of water from beneath this film. As the product dries, moisture transfer becomes limited by the rate of transfer of liquid water from the interior to the surface and the over-all transfer process is no longer increased markedly by increase in air flow. In addition to this physical effect, there are practical limitations on air flow in the secondary stages of drying. The particles of food become lighter during drying and thus may be blown off the tray surface.

A high initial rate of drying is desirable with vegetables and other products to reduce sticking to the surface of the drying tray. This requires both a high initial rate of air flow and a high initial temperature. Adherence of the partially dried or dried food pieces or particles quite frequently impedes unloading of both the trays from the tunnel-and-truck dehydrators, cabinet shelf driers or continuous belt driers. This is minimized by rapid initial drying. A fluidized bed drier or belt trough drier may be used as a primary drier to feed partially dried products to a continuous belt drier. Water repellent coatings may be used to line trays or belt surfaces to reduce sticking. Oiling of wooden drying trays, and waxing of metal drying trays was used to reduce sticking in early fruit and vegetable dehydration. More recently polyethylene, polyvinyl chloride and Teflon plastic coatings have been applied successfully to metal surfaces to reduce sticking and facilitate unloading.

In multistage driers, the initial stage is ordinarily operated with parallel flow of air to secure maximum speed, while the second stage is operated counterflow to facilitate control of temperature and humidity and secure lower final moisture content in products. Dry bulb temperatures of 180° to 195°F. are used for the initial stage for such vegetables as cabbage, with trays loaded at two pounds per square foot. In the second stage the dry bulb temperature was lowered to 145° to 165°F. Air recirculation in the primary stage may be as high as 70 to 85 per cent, but in the second stage only 40 to 60 per cent.

During the initial stages of exposure to a stream of hot air, the cut pieces of food act like a fine-grained sponge full of water and the temperature of the product rapidly rises to the wet-bulb temperature of the air stream. Just as the moist wick of a wet-bulb thermometer drops to a temperature below that of the dry-bulb thermometer, so does the temperature of the product during the period of free evaporation drop below the dry-bulb air temperature. Since the wet-bulb

Dry Bulb Temp., °F.	Wet Bulb Temp., °F.	Wet-Bulb Depression
150	120	−30
158	126	−32
166	132	−34
176	140	−36
187	150	−37
194	154	−40
202	162	−40

temperature depression depends only on the humidity of air, the product temperature may be considerably below the air temperature. Thus for a relative humidity of 40 per cent, the wet-bulb and dry-bulb temperatures are given on p. 516. The wet-bulb depression increases with decrease in relative humidity and amounts to 50°F. at 25 per cent relative humidity, and over 90°F. at lower humidities. Thus product temperatures may be considerably below air temperature during the first phase of drying, corresponding to the time required to evaporate about half of the total water present. After that, it begins to rise, and, as the product approaches dryness, its temperature approaches the dry-bulb temperature of the air. Since heat damage during drying is a function of both product temperature and time, it is possible to use much higher temperatures during the initial period of drying when evaporation is rapid than was considered desirable in the early days of dehydration. Thus for countercurrent tunnel dehydration of fruit, the maximum air temperature at end of the drying period recommended varied from 145°F. for pears, to 170°F. for cherries and raspberries, as shown in Table 99. Walnuts were dehydrated at an air temperature not to exceed 110°F. Dehydrated vegetables were dried at maximum air temperatures of 190°F. for onions, 145°F for cabbage, 150°F. for potatoes, and 175°F. for carrots. Today much higher temperatures are used in dehydrating fruits, vegetables and nuts by taking advantage of lowered product temperature control by humidity and shorter drying times.

TABLE 99

TRADITIONAL PRACTICES IN DEHYDRATION OF FRUITS IN CALIFORNIA

Fruit	Preparation	Tray Load, lbs./ Sq. Ft.	Max. Temp. at Dry End, °F.	Humidity at End Period, %	Drying Time, hr.	Drying Ratio
Apples	Peeled and sliced, sulfured 1/2 hr.	2	165	5–10	8	8:1
Apricots	Halved, unpeeled, sulfured 1/2 hr.	2	160	10	12	6:1
Cherries	Lye dipped, sulfured 1/4 to 1 hr.	2–3	160–170	10–25	8–12	...
Figs	Cut and sulfured for 1 hr.	2–3	160	5	10	4:1
Grapes	Lye dipped, sulfured for 1/2–3 hr.	3 1/2–4	160	5	16–24	3.5:1
Peaches	Halved, sulfured for 3 hr.	3	150	20–30	24	5:1
Pears	Halved, sulfured for 24 hr.	3	145	30–40	48	5:1
Prunes	Lye dipped	2 1/2–4	165–170	20–30	24–36	5:1

TABLE 100

DEHYDRATION OF VEGETABLES IN TWO-STAGE DRIERS

Vegetable	Preparation	Blanching-Sulfiting	Tray-load, lbs./sq. ft.	Drying Conditions, °F.	Drying Ratio	Final Moisture Content, %	Final SO₂ Content, p.p.m.
Beans, green	Sized, snipped, cross or French cut	Steam blanched, then sulfited	1–2	180 in primary, 160 in secondary	10:1	4	400–600
Beets	Peeled, cut into dice, half-dice, strips	Steam blanched, not sulfited	1–2	180 in primary, 150 in secondary	14:1	5	None
Cabbage	Cored, shredded	Steam blanched on trays, then sulfited heavily	1–2	190–200 in primary, 150 in secondary	20:1	4	1,500–2,000
Carrots	Peeled, cut into dice, half-dice, strips	Steam blanched, then sulfited	1–2	185–200 in primary, 155 in secondary	12:1	4	500–1,000
Onions	Flame peeled, sliced	None	1–2	190–200 in primary, 130 in secondary	12:1	4	None
Peas, green	Sorted and washed	Steam blanched or water blanched, sulfited	1–2	180 in primary, 160 in secondary	6:1	4	300–500
Potatoes, white	Peeled, cut into half-dice or strips	Steam blanched, then sulfited	1	190 in primary, 130 in secondary	6:1	6	200–500
Potatoes, sweet	Peeled, cut into slices, dice or strips	Steam blanched, then sulfited	1–2	190 in primary, 130 in secondary	6:1	5	200–500
Peppers	Cut, seeded	None	1–2	180–190 in primary, 150 in secondary	10:1	...	...

In current practices, vegetables dehydrated in two-stage tunnels are dried to a moisture content of 50 per cent or less in the parallel current primary tunnel, operated at air temperatures of 190°F.or above in two hours or less, then dried to ten per cent moisture content in a secondary counter-current tunnel at 130° to 150°F. and finally dried to the packaging moisture level in bins operated with low humidity, lower temperature air.   Most vegetables, as shown in Table 100, are blanched to inactivate enzymes involved in producing off-flavors and sulfited, usually after blanching with a solution of sodium bisulfite and sulfite.   While

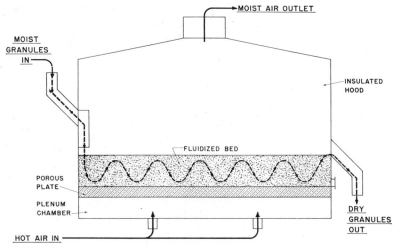

FIG. 116.   FLUIDIZED BED DRIER DEVELOPED BY
USDA WESTERN UTILIZATION BRANCH

this treatment will prevent development of hay-like flavors, it is not sufficient to prevent development of stale rancid flavors in potatoes or loss of carotene in corn and carrots.   The staling of dehydrated low-moisture potatoes has been shown to be due to oxidative rancidity of the lipids present and can be reduced by packaging in atmospheres of low oxygen content or by addition of antioxidants.

The seasonal availability of vegetables other than potatoes which can be stored has presented problems.   It has been possible to increase the length of processing by using commercially frozen vegetables.   The drying characteristics of vegetables such as green beans, sweet corn and green peas change on freezing.   Frozen vegetables will dehydrate more rapidly than fresh, and produce products of improved quality.   This has long been known to be true of potatoes and advantage has been taken of freezing to reduce retrogradation of starch in the production of potato granules.   It is possible also to improve the drying characteristics of potatoes by the use of two-stage blanching based on the traditional French procedure of producing potato puffs. In this process the prepared potatoes are partially blanched, then cooled and again blanched under conditions such that vaporization of moisture occurs in the interior leading to expansion and development of more porous structure during drying.

In experimental tests, dehumidified air at temperatures as low as $10°F$. has been used for drying.   Kaloyereas tested this method in 1950 for drying eggs, carrots, and sweet potatoes and reported excellent retention of color and flavor.   This was confirmed by Lewin and Mateles (1962) who reported data on drying at $24°$ to $30°F$.

Investigators at the U. S. Department of Agriculture, Western Utilization Research Branch, have been active in developing and testing methods and equipment for dehydrating mashed potatoes and other products of military and domestic importance.   Fig. 116 indicates the design of a fluidized bed drier suitable for drying potato granules.   Hot air moves up through the product at sufficient velocity to agitate, partially suspend·and "fluidize" the granules providing uniform drying.

In an air lift drier, built by P & L Welding and Machine Works at Anaheim, Calif., the velocity of the hot air is sufficient to carry the material up through adjustable vanes in the drying chamber before separation of dried granules in a cyclone.

Fig. 117 indicates the design of a transverse belt drier.   Motion of the flexible mesh belt turns and agitates products like diced vegetables which move at right angles to the direction of belt travel while hot air is blown up through the bed at the highest velocity possible without blowing products from the trough.

As drying and freezing techniques improved it was inevitable that combinations of partial drying with freezing preservation should be considered.   Frozen concentrated orange juice is an example of such a product in a liquid food.

In the first stage of drying fruits and vegetables, dehydration progresses rapidly with little change in color or flavor of products.   By dehydrating to approximately half the initial weight, then preserving by conventional frozen food techniques, important savings can be effected in container, storage, and shipping costs.   Dehydro-frozen fruits may be preferred for some applications such as pie baking.   Dehydro-frozen vegetables reconstitute readily and compare favorably with products preserved by freezing without dehydration.

Methods adapted for specific fruits and vegetables have been tested

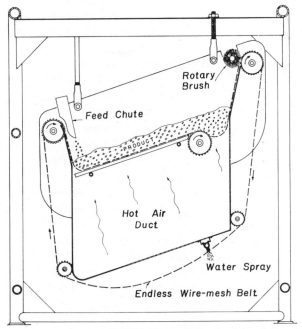

FIG. 117. TRANSVERSE BELT, HOT AIR DRIER

Products move at right angle to belt travel, tumbled by
belt action, air pressure and gravity.

and demonstrated at the U. S. Department of Agriculture, Western
Utilization Research Branch at Albany, Calif. An advantage in dehydro-freezing vegetables is that dehydration may follow directly
after blanching without cooling in water which leaches out some soluble constituents.

ROTARY DRUM AND KILN DRIERS

Single and double drum driers require considerable investment and
are of limited capacity and application. Milk, fruit and vegetable
juices and purées are spread on the outer surface of steam or water
heated drums revolving at atmospheric pressure or under vacuum.
Dried products are removed by suitably designed scraper blades, and
are cooled rapidly to minimize heat damage. Drying is controlled by
varying the moisture content of raw materials (by preconcentration),
also by varying the temperature of the heating medium, the speed of
rotation of drums, and the thickness of layers applied to the surface.
Cranberry sauce, tomato cocktail, pea and bean soups, prepared baby

cereals and apple flakes are among products dried commercially. Low temperature spray drying is tending to replace drum drying for milk solids.

Rotary kiln driers are commonly used for continuous drying of hay, chopped grasses, citrus processing residues, and similar products which may be lifted and tumbled. Direct heated, parallel-flow driers may be used in two stages for maximum efficiency and light colored feed. Wet products enter hot gases from the furnace at temperatures as high as 450°F. Discharge temperature may range from 180° to 250°F. Second-stage driers may be operated with gas entering at 300°F. and being discharged at 160° to 180°F.

Another type of direct-heated drier uses three passes in a single external shell, products being carried along rapidly by the high velocity hot gases, through the center drum, back to the entering end through an intermediate shell, and then reversing once more to the discharge end, just inside the outer shell.

Indirect-heated rotary kiln driers are lined with steam tubes and avoid high inlet temperatures common in direct heat equipment. The tubes act as lifting flights in these kilns.

SPRAY DRIERS

Milk, fruit juice, corn syrup, soluble coffee and many other liquid foods are dried by spraying into a chamber where heated air is circulated to remove water rapidly from the suspended droplets (Fig. 118).

Spray drying of juices is complicated by the tendency of these products to turn into heavy viscous syrups and candies instead of powders. In order to secure powders, it is necessary to lower the moisture content rapidly and cool before particles come in contact with one another on walls of the equipment. Drying aids are extensively added before drying fruit and vegetable juices. These include corn syrup solids, milk solids, gums, pectic substances, methyl cellulose, lactose and sucrose.

The design of equipment is an important factor in spray drying fruit and vegetable juices. Particle size is obviously important since the smaller the droplets, the more rapidly the moisture may be removed. If particles are not of uniform size, large particles may come out wet, making it difficult to properly locate the boundary between drying and cooling zones.

The size and uniformity of droplets formed are determined by the design and operation of the spray-liquor system and this also affects the thermal efficiency and continuity of operation. The spray liquid may be dispersed into the drying chamber by a pressure nozzle, or the

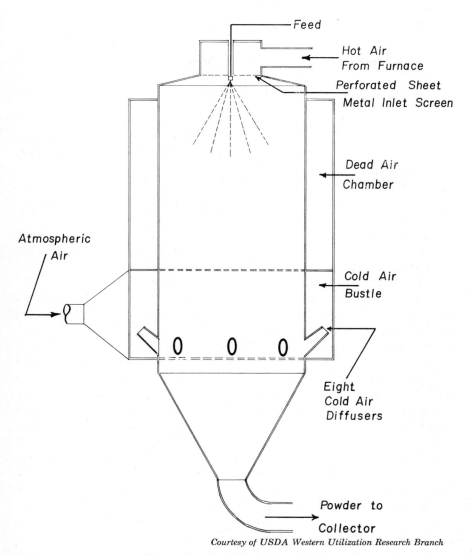

Courtesy of USDA Western Utilization Research Branch

FIG. 118. EXPERIMENTAL SPRAY DRIER SUCCESSFULLY
USED ON TOMATO JUICE

centrifugal or spinning-disc atomizer. The last because of its high
capacity and better control is used commercially for spray-drying
milk, milk products and certain fruit and vegetable juices. In these
atomizers the mechanism of spray formation consists in first dragging
out the fluid into thin flat sheets or filaments. These filaments break
up at the periphery of the rotating disk into particles. The particle

form and size are determined by the thickness of the film formed, and conditions of breaking.   The viscosity or fluidity of the material to be dried and its surface tension determine spraying performance.   While some data are obtainable on the mechanism of formation of particles from filming nozzles from motion pictures taken at 6,000 frames per second by Fogler and Kleinschmidt (1938), similar data for spinning-disc atomizers are not available.   The characteristic particles formed commercially are round and hollow or porous in the interior.   These characteristics are affected by the nature of the material to be dried, the manner of spraying and the subsequent treatment during the drying operation.

The size, shape, and operation of the drying chamber are important to secure dry powders.

Recent advances have improved speed of dissolving and dispersing spray-dried products.   Spray drying tends to produce low-density, fine powders which do not wet readily, floating and clumping so water cannot penetrate uniformly throughout the mass.   "Agglomeration" was developed for spray-dried detergents because fluffy powders tended to cause sneezing.   Coarser granules were desired to avoid this irritation, and also to avoid clumping which delayed dispersion.

Methods were developed for causing the product to dry in the form of flakes or granules.   These have been applied to coffee, milk, and other liquid foods.   In one procedure the liquid to be dried is vacuum concentrated to the optimum density and then injected into the spray chamber with a steam injector which forms beads or bubbles which break into dried flakes which disperse readily.   Fines may be separated by screening, or air separation, and returned to the concentrate for agglomeration into coarser particles.   Other techniques, including vacuum "puff drying" also give granular products which are readily dispersed in water.   Instant milk and coffee "granules" are produced by this and other techniques which will be described.

VACUUM CABINET, BELT TRAY DRIERS

Heat sensitive products may be dried at temperatures ranging from 80°F. to below freezing temperature (by sublimation) in vacuum driers, on trays, drawers or belts.   Latent heat of evaporation may be supplied by transmission from steam, water, or electrically heated shelves or drums on shelves, or by radiation from radiant heat sources. Commercial vacuum driers are designed to remove quickly large volumes of vapor (see Fig. 119).   At low temperature it is necessary to condense the vapors with refrigerated condensers, or compress them in booster jet compressors so they may be condensed at higher temperatures.   Mixing condensers employing lithium chloride brine avoid the problem of removing ice from condenser surfaces, but brine must be concentrated to remove condensate.   In addition, the brine is corrosive.   Booster jets are commonly used for compressing vapors prior to condensing, although surface condensers with ingenious methods for removing the ice are also used.

In atmospheric hot air drying the rate and extent of dehydration are markedly influenced by the distance through which water must travel to an evaporative surface.   Moisture may move to the surface during drying by a single diffusion process in foods that are essentially homogeneous.   In the initial stages where free evaporation occurs, the rate of drying is rapid and constant.   At later stages because of low concen-

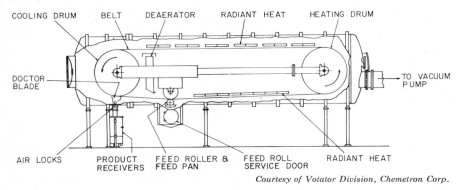

Courtesy of Votator Division, Chemetron Corp.

FIG. 119.   CONTINUOUS VACUUM BELT DRIER

tration gradients and small diffusion coefficient, the rate of drying decreases and can be particularly slow.   Most foods consist of a system of permanent, interconnecting pores or capillaries and possess a surface layer differing in properties from the underlying layers.   The mechanism of moisture transfer during drying of a particular food and the mathematical analysis from which drying times can be calculated are not known except by inference from empirically determined drying rates.   Moisture transfer can occur in both the liquid and vapor state through air or liquid filled pores and through solids.   The mechanism by which water escapes from the interior of large portions of tissue to the evaporative surface in vacuum dehydration is not clear and may be different for different tissues.   Gooding and Rolfe (1955) found that in potatoes the steam forming within the tissues under the low atmospheric pressure produces a system of cavities which may be the channels by which the water vapor escapes.   These cavities enable the vacuum dried potato to reconstitute much more rapidly than air dried potato. A similar effect can be produced in fish, meat and carrot tissue depending upon the manipulation of the drying equipment.

Vacuum dehydration avoids certain objectionable features of hot air drying. Because air is removed, oxidation of unstable constituents may be substantially avoided. Colors, easily oxidized vitamins, and unsaturated fats and oils may be preserved without presulfiting or blanching. Operating at lower temperatures, the effect of heat on flavor may be reduced. Moisture migrates from the interior of discrete particles more rapidly, impelled by vapor pressure in excess of the pressure in the vacuum drier. Vapor formation inside of pieces may cause puffing or cavities which make the dried product sufficiently porous to expedite rehydration. A similar effect in sublimation drying, evaporation of moisture from the frozen product, had led to the use of the term "lyophilic" to products dried by this process. Because of the greatly increased cost of sublimation, drying applications have been limited.

Puff drying at moderate temperatures avoids objectionable surface drying and case hardening and produces dehydrated products of desirable rehydration characteristics. Malted milk products such as Ovaltine have been puff-dried in vacuum tray driers, and more recently ground dried fruit of 20 to 25 per cent moisture and fruit and vegetable juice concentrates have been dried to porous, friable, low moisture products which could be readily ground into powders. Atkinson (1922) patented a process for puff drying by heating in an oven and suddenly applying vacuum to puff, cool and dry. Kristensen (1930) modified this process by heating in steam prior to application of vacuum and this was used also by Moore (1927, 1931, 1935) and others.

By measuring changes in product temperature and observing conditions under which steam formed and puffed the product a process was developed for alternately applying steam and suddenly lowering the pressure. Modifying the pressure to lower the temperature during the final stages of drying fruit juices and purées was observed to overcome a number of obstacles.

Puff drying in shelf driers, as used by Vacu-Dry Corp. was based upon a process for desulfuring cut, sulfured and dried fruit described by Moore (1927). In 1931 the process was modified by (1) evacuating fruit tissue to remove air present in intercellular spaces, then (2) relieving the vacuum with steam at a gage pressure of 15 to 25 lbs. to raise the fruit temperature quickly to 160°F., then (3) evacuating to reduce the fruit temperature to 130°F. (Moore 1931). Grinding the dehydrated fruit (apricots, apples, pears or peaches) facilitated heating of the product. Larger pieces, or even whole fruit could be puff-dried by partially drying in vacuum, then rapidly increasing the pressure by introducing steam, then turning off the steam and suddenly lowering the pressure to simultaneously puff, dry and cool the product. In this process, apples, bananas and raisins are dried for an initial period of 20 to 30 min. in vacuo at 29.5 of mercury to a temperature of 180° to 200°F., the vacuum line is then closed and steam or air is introduced to raise the pressure to 30 to 45 lbs. in 1 to 3 min. The chamber is then rapidly evacuated to original vacuum of 29.5 in. in about one minute and the fruit is maintained at 180° to 190°F. until dried. When the fruit is substantially dry, the temperature of the chamber is reduced rapidly to allow the tissues to become firm and the pressure is slowly raised to atmospheric.

Puffing may be obtained also by raising the temperature and pressure of fruit or vegetable tissue and suddenly releasing the pressure. With cereal and some vegetables the resulting porous puffed structure is rigid enough so that the material may be subsequently dried without change in structure. With most fruits the tissues after puffing will collapse during heating even in vacuo but the desired porous structure, once obtained initially, can be set by cooling prior to continuation of drying.

Recent work at the U. S. Department of Agriculture, Western Regional Research Branch has demonstrated practical applications of puff drying to a number of fruit and vegetable products. Orange juice "crystals" are being commercially produced in Florida. Several instant coffees are produced by related processes, and tomato granules of excellent quality have been produced experimentally by continuous methods having commercial promise (Anon. 1955).

Turkot *et al.* (1956) described a method of limited application for dehydrating fruit juice. After stripping flavoring constituents, sucrose equivalent to the weight of fruit solids is added to juice and the mixture then concentrated in a Turbo-film evaporator to a moisture content less than $2^1/_2$ per cent. The molten product is pumped from the evaporator directly onto chilling rolls. The flavor essence, concentrated to about 1000-fold, is added to the flaked juice and the mixture then packaged with inpackage desiccant. This method is suitable for products such as fruit ades in which the large quantity of added sucrose is not objectionable.

Supplying latent heat of evaporation under high vacuum presents no problem in concentrating liquids which may be circulated rapidly over heat-exchange surfaces. However, it presents an important problem in drying discrete particles of solid materials as there is no air present to transfer heat by conduction and convection. Methods which have been tested and used for supplying heat include: dialectric heating by radio-frequency electromagnetic waves, induction heating, radiant heating by infrared rays, and conduction heating by contact with plate or drum surfaces in the drier.

To increase rate of heat transfer during vacuum dehydration, to allow drying in deep layers and to obtain puffing without interrupting the drying cycle, Webb (1942) introduced the use of a liquid medium as heat transfer medium. The liquid medium (edible fat, ethyl alcohol, glycerin, etc.) is cycled successfully through an external heater and through the food being dehydrated. Puffing in this process is accomplished by momentarily increasing the temperature of the circulating liquid medium in contact with the food. Following puffing and dehydration the food is rapidly and completely cooled by lowering the temperature of the circulating medium. Modifications in this process, including removal of dehydrating liquid from dried foods were proposed in 1949 and 1955. While this process is not applied commercially as yet, a modification of this based on the use of a liquid fat medium as a heat transfer agent in the dehydration of fat-containing foods was patented by Greenfield (1953) and is now used in the commercial drying of meat scrap and is being tested for milk and other products. In the Greenfield process an oil or fat such as that naturally present is mixed with the product to be dried, which is usually ground and the mixture is then pumped into a vacuum evaporator through a heat exchanger. Water vapor is removed from the evaporator and the mixture of dried oil and product is cooled, and the liquid fat or oil is separated from the dried solids by centrifugation and mechanical expression.

Platt *et al.* (1958) also proposed drying food by heating in edible oil *in vacuo* as a means of reducing losses in nutritive value which occur during blanching of vegetables and for improvement in color and flavor.

Swisher (1961) introduced a similar process based on the use of a nonaqueous glycerin corn syrup liquid as a heat-transfer medium and replacement agent for the rapid evaporative removal of moisture from citrus peel and other fibrous fruit such as cranberries and pineapple. A mixture of glycerine and corn syrup is impregnated into the fruit tissue by vacuum make-and-break technique and the impregnated tissue is dehydrated *in vacuo*. Drying rate was increased and flavor retention in the product was improved. Citrus peel so dried is now used commercially in the baking and confectionery industry.

Drying with partially water miscible solvents was introduced in 1958 by Baniel (1961).   In this process, water is removed by mixing a suitable organic solvent with the liquid to be dried; after water transfer has occurred the wet solvent is separated from the partially or completely dried product by decantation or centrifugation, then transferred to or mixed with a secondary water absorbing agent such as saturated salt brine and returned to the product after dehydration.   Since drying under these conditions occurs at constant temperature without external heat it can be applied to temperature-sensitive products.   This process is now used commercially in the chemical industry and is being investigated for possible applications to food products.

Radiant heating by either infrared or radio-frequency waves is limited by engineering factors and dielectric properties of foods.   Radiant heating with infrared waves cannot be used with thick layers or pieces without overheating the exposed surfaces.   High frequency radio waves are costly to generate and when applied to food products being dried in vacuo may result in local overheating.   Sparking may occur also when they are applied in presence of inert gases which would increase efficiency of water vapor transfer.   Investigations now in progress on dielectric properties of foods may overcome these limitations.

Dehydration in vacuum shelf driers, particularly in freeze-drying, has the primary drawback of low rate of evaporation of moisture because of poor energy transfer.   To increase this, dielectric heating has been proposed.   Dielectric heating by radio-frequency fields, however, is limited by two major problems—nonuniform heating caused by variations in thickness and dielectric properties of the material being dried and ionization of residual gas in the vacuum chamber.   Ionization results in voltage breakdown and consequent loss of heat input and causes oxidation or browning of the dried portions.   Harper and Chichester (1960) are investigating the effect of dielectric heating frequency on both these factors.

In order to avoid somewhat similar limitations upon contact heating, Gooding and Rolfe (1955) dried slices of beef, fish, and vegetables between telescoping pressure heating plates in an Atlas Vacuum Dehydration Cabinet.   Tests conducted at the British Ministry of Food Experimental Factory at Aberdeen, Scotland, were successful in quality of products and in drying rates.

After trays are placed between the water-heated plates they are compressed to make contact top and bottom, by a mechanism similar to the Birdseye cabinet freezer.   As shown in Fig. 120, time, temperature, pressure and plate spacing may be varied to secure optimum results with specific products.   Drying time for reducing moisture con-

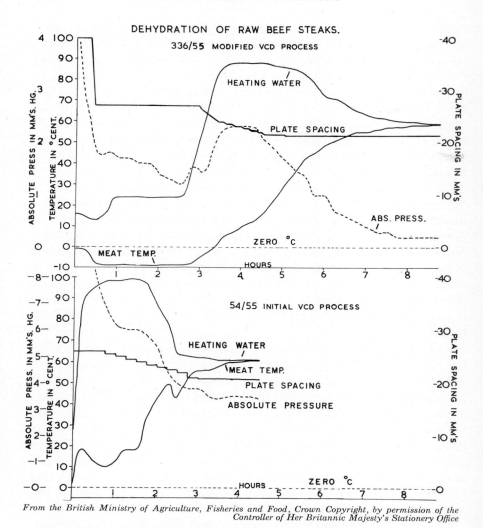

DEHYDRATION OF RAW BEEF STEAKS.

336/55 MODIFIED VCD PROCESS

54/55 INITIAL VCD PROCESS

FIG. 120. CHARTS INDICATING THE FLEXIBILITY OF THE AVCD CABINET

tent to 3 to 5 per cent ranges from 4 to 5 hr.   The unit shown dries approximately a ton of raw material as a batch operation.   Dried products compared closely in appearance, palatability, nutritive value and storage stability with sublimation dried products while costs were appreciably lower.   The process may be modified to provide freeze drying during the early stages (Rolfe 1956) (Fig. 122.)

FLAVOR RESTORATION

Loss of volatile flavor constituents is a major factor in determining the acceptability of concentrated and dehydrated juice products. Milleville (1954) developed a method for recovering apple esters for return to concentrated apple juice. Brown *et al.* (1951) described steam injection preheaters which permit stripping volatile flavors from juice rapidly under reduced pressure and this is used for recovery of flavors from apple, strawberry, and pineapple juices. Some modification of equipment and methods is found desirable for each juice.

When juices are dehydrated to powdered or granular form, flavor essences cannot be added directly, but must be combined with a carrier. Originally anhydrous dextrose was used and the resulting emulsions chilled to harden, then ground for combination with dehydrated juices. More recently, however, volatile flavoring constituents (Griffin 1951; Schultz *et al.* 1956) have been incorporated into melted sorbitol, dextrose or sucrose by addition under conditions favorable for formation of

From the British Ministry of Agriculture, Fisheries and Food, Crown Copyright, by permission of the Controller of Her Britannic Majesty's Stationery Office

FIG. 121. ATLAS VACUUM DEHYDRATION CABINET, WITH TRAY CART SHOWING ON THE LEFT

FIG. 122. ATLAS VACUUM DRYING CABINET OPEN,
SHOWING THE TRAY CART IN OPEN POSITION

stable emulsions. The semiliquid emulsions are then cooled to solidify them and ground to yield solid, relatively stable flavor bases which are added to the fruit powder. In the case of citrus juice powders, cold-pressed peel oil or vacuum concentrated peel oil is used in place of volatile flavor concentrate.

Swisher (1957) developed a solid flavoring compound of essential oils which could be successfully extruded to form amorphous rods. The plasticized compound consists chiefly of corn syrup solids with added emulsifiers for the oils. Essential oils and essence concentrates also may be incorporated during drying by addition at the stage of drying at which the solids present will entrap the volatiles and reduce loss during further drying.

Volatile flavor and odor constituents in fruits and vegetables occur both in the volatile form and also in the form of relatively nonvolatile precursors in which the odorous flavor is chemically combined with other constituents.

To illustrate, garlic oil occurs as alliin, a colorless, odorless precursor. In the presence of moisture the enzyme alliinase splits the alliin to release garlic oil (Stoll and Seebeck 1951). In drying, garlic is sliced rather than crushed to minimize enzymatic conversion to the volatile material. The garlic slices are dried at temperatures which do not inactivate the enzyme. When the ground garlic powder is moistened the enzyme immediately splits the precursor to liberate the characteristic garlic aroma. The development of flavor in onion tissue similarly occurs by an enzymatic conversion of sulfoxide derivatives. Schwimmer and Weston (1961) proposed that enzymatic development of pyruvic acid in onion tissue be used as a measure of pungency.

Similar methods are also used for drying onion powder. In any vegetable tissue where enzyme action is necessary for flavor formation, heat treatment such as blanching may inactivate the enzymes and prevent subsequent splitting of the flavor precursors unless enzymes are added from an outside source. Hewitt et al. (1956) reported that water cress and cabbage which had been blanched and dehydrated were substantially flavorless when rehydrated. But addition of an odorless enzyme extracted from white mustard seed caused the water cress or cabbage to develop characteristic aromas rapidly in the presence of moisture. Enzymes from black mustard seed and from cabbage had a similar effect. Addition of enzymes which will release flavors from precursors opens new possibilities in the utilization of dehydrated vegetables.

COOLING

Powders recovered from spray driers, or obtained by breaking or crushing dried films, or puff-dried materials, as well as dried foods in general and concentrates, should be cooled rapidly to prevent undesirable changes in color, flavor, and nutritive value. This cooling should be carried out under conditions such that exposure to humid atmospheres is avoided and moisture pick-up prevented.

PACKAGING DEHYDRATED FOODS

Handling and packaging techniques must be adequate for specific products. Drying of relatively stable products (some vegetables) may be completed in bins by blowing dry air through the bin.   Hygroscopic products like dried orange juice must be protected against exposure to humid air and must be handled rapidly to avoid oxidation. Packaging with desiccants in hermetically sealed containers is an important means of reducing the moisture content of dehydrated vegetables.   Fig. 123 compares the moisture absorptive capacities of several desiccants, which are placed in packages in sealed, moisture-

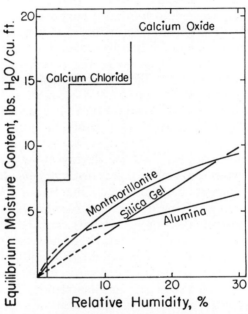

FIG. 123.   MOISTURE ABSORPTIVE CAPACITIES OF CALCIUM OXIDE, CALCIUM CHLORIDE, MONTMORILLONITE, SILICA GEL AND ALUMINA IN LBS. WATER/CU. FT. AT VARIED RELATIVE HUMIDITY

resistant, expandable fiber packets.   The function of these desiccants is to reduce the residual moisture content of products to stable levels under storage conditions which must be met.   The speed and effectiveness of the desiccants is increased when products are sealed under vacuum in tight containers.

For products less susceptible to moisture damage, foil and film packages are used.   Chip board cartons, overwrapped with printed foil are commonly used for tenderized dried fruits.   Transparent films are also used for packaging these products.

RECONSTITUTION

In spite of improvements, packaged dried foods are still subject to deterioration and should be stored at low temperatures and protected from exposure to temperatures above 90°F. Suitable directions for reconstitution must be supplied to consumers. The water used should be free of objectionable off-flavors and low in calcium and magnesium salts. Aeration of juices concentrated during dilution improves palatability, but may increase oxidation during storage even under refrigeration. Powdered foods must be properly dispersed in water and solid dried foods properly reconstituted. Hardness of water may cause serious problems in rate and extent of reconstitution.

The rate of solution and ease of dispersion of powdered foods is still a limiting factor. Hard to disperse powdered foods, such as nonfat milk, whole milk, chocolate milk, etc., may be converted into more readily dispersible form by suitable treatment in which small particles are agglomerated into clusters and the less soluble lactose modification (or dextrose hydrate) is converted into the much more soluble anhydrous β lactose. In this process, dried milk powder is heated under controlled conditions with steam which surface-moistens the product causing clumping. The resulting product is dried in a heated air stream. Continuous units of this type such as the Blaw-Knox and Cherry-Burrell "Instantizers" are available (Anon. 1956A). "Instantizing" has been successfully applied to powdered non-fat milk solids (Lawler 1955) and to instant tea, granulated sugar, onion, garlic powder and other foods.

In reconstitution of powdered dried foods, the rate of absorption of water in reconstituting is affected not only by the size and shape of particles, but also by physical and chemical changes occurring during drying and storage. Denaturation of proteins and irreversible changes in other constituents are involved. These changes are difficult to prevent. Our knowledge of the factors is incomplete. Changes which lead to denaturation and coagulation of proteins may be controlled in part by drying at lower temperatures and by avoidance of excessively low moisture content.

Starches in food products present special problems because they are modified continuously by heat. A typical example is involved in the preparation of dried mashed potatoes. Composition of potatoes, method for cooking and mashing, and the manner of drying determine the texture of reconstituted mashed potatoes. A useful method is to combine dried fines from the dried product with the mashed potatoes going to the driers, so that the moisture content is substantially reduced below critical levels in a relatively short time.

SPECIAL APPLICATIONS

Hot air and vacuum drying are used in the production of specialized products. "Nuggets" and sauces are dried for use in cake mixes, pudding mixes and confections.

Candied and glacéed confections are prepared by blanching fruit in syrup with or without added sulfur dioxide. In one method the fruit in syrup is spread on trays and dried slowly in warm air. The syrup concentrates and penetrates the fruit.

The growing popularity of fruit nectars has resulted in a demand for concentrated fruit purées for use near consuming centers in packing the pulpy fruit drinks. Vacuum concentration of heavy purées presents special problems and a suggested alternate procedure is to partially dehydrate cut fruits prior to puréeing, so purée of the desired consistency is obtained directly (Talburt and Powers 1956).

BIBLIOGRAPHY

ANON. 1955. Superior dehydrated juices from continuous vacuum process. Food Eng. *27*, No. 3, 71–73, 164.

ANON. 1956A. Agglomerates dry milk particles to make readily soluble product. Food Processing *17*, No. 5, 30–31.

ANON. 1956B. This unit puts freeze-drying right on the processing line. Food Eng. *28*, No. 11, 40–41, 143.

ASSELBERGS, E. A., MOHR, W. P., and KEMP, J. G. 1960. Studies on the application of infrared in food processing. Food Technol. *14*, 449–453.

ATKINSON, W. 1922. Drying process. U. S. Pat. 1,415,623. May 9.

BANIEL, A. 1961. Process for the athermal removal of water from aqueous liquors by an organic solvent. U. S. Pat. 2,967,825. Jan. 10. See also J. Applied Chem. (1958) *8*, 711–616; (1959) *9*, 521–525.

BISSON, C. S., ALLINGER, H. W., and YOUNG, H. A. 1942. Some factors affecting the burning of sulfurs used in sulfuring-fruits. Hilgardia *14*, 361–372.

BROWN, *et al.* 1951. Rapid heat processing of fluid foods by steam injection. Ind. Eng. Chem. *43*, 2949–2951.

BURTON, L. V. 1947. Hi-vacuum technics for drying orange juice. Food Inds. *19*, 617–622, 738, 740, 742, 744.

CARLSON, E., WEIR, R. A., and ZIEMBA, J. V. 1956. New way to instantize milk solids. Food Eng. *28*, No. 10, 62–63, 194.

CLAYPOOL, L. L., and KILBUCK, J. 1955. Quality of dried French prunes. Calif. Agr. *9*, No. 8, 13–14.

COPLEY, M. J., KAUFMAN, V. F., and RASMUSSEN, C. L. 1956. Recent developments in fruit and vegetable powder technology. Food Technol. *10*, 589–595.

CRUESS, W. V. 1958. Commercial Fruit and Vegetable Products. 4th Edition. McGraw-Hill Book Co., New York.

CRUESS, W. V., and MACKINNEY, G. 1943. The dehydration of vegetables. Calif. Agr. Expt. Sta. Bull. *680*.

DAVIS, L. E. 1949. Raisin harvesting methods. Calif. Agr. *3*, No. 6, 3–4.

DAVIS, L. E. 1953. Work methods design and work simplification. Advances in Food Research *4*, 37–104.

EDE, A. J., and HALES, K. C. 1948. The physics of drying in heated air with particular reference to fruit and vegetables. Gt. Brit. Dept. Sci. Ind. Res., Food Investigation Special Rept. *53*, 1–50.

EIDT, C. C. 1938. Principles and methods involved in dehydration of apples. Can. Dept. Agr. Pub. *625*, Tech. Bull. *18*.

FLOSDORF, E. W. 1949. Freeze-Drying; Drying by Sublimation. Reinhold Publishing Corp., New York.

FOGLER, B. B., and KLEINSCHMIDT, R. V. 1938. Spray drying. Ind. Eng. Chem. *30*, 1372–84.

GOODING, E. J. B., and ROLFE, J. E. 1955. The vacuum contact-plate dehydration of foodstuffs. I. A first appraisal. J. Sci. Food and Agr. *6*, 427–433.

GREENFIELD, C. 1953. Process of dehydration of fatty materials. U. S. Pat. 2,651,647. Sept. 8.

GRIFFIN, W. C. 1951. Solid essential oil concentrate and process of preparing the same. U. S. Pat. 2,566,410. Sept. 4.

HANSON, S. W. F. (Editor). 1961. The Accelerated Freeze-Drying (AFD) Method of Food Preservation. Her Majesty's Stationery Office, London.

HARPER, J., and CHICHESTER, C. O. 1960. Freeze drying application of dielectric heating. Military-Industry Meeting Rept. 11-14, Research and Development Associates Food and Container Institute, Chicago, Ill.

HARRIS, R. J. C. 1954. Biological Applications of Freezing and Drying. Academic Press, New York.

HAY, J. M. 1955. The vacuum contact-plate dehydration of foodstuffs. II. Equipment. J. Sci. Food Agr. *6*, 433–440.

HAYES, N. V., COTTON, R. H., and ROY, W. R. 1946. Problems in dehydration of orange juice. Proc. Am. Soc. Hort. Sci. *47*, 123–129.

HEISLER, E. G., HUNTER, A. R., SICILIANO, J., and TREADWAY, R. H. 1956. Further studies on the preparation of potato granules by solvent methods. Food Technol. *10*, 276–278.

HENDEL, C. E., and BUN, H. K. 1954. In-package dessication of dehydrated foods. U. S. Dept. Agr., Agr. Res. Admn. Pub. *AIC-373*. Washington, D. C.

HENDEL, C. E., BUN, H. K., and BOGGS, M. M. 1951. Factors affecting storage stability of potato granules. U. S. Dept. Agr., Agr. Res. Admn., Bureau of Agr. and Ind. Chem. Pub. *AIC-303*. Washington, D. C.

HEWITT, E. J., MACKAY, D. A. M., KONIGSBACHER, K., and HASSELSTROM, T. 1956. The role of enzymes in food flavors. Food Technol. *10*, 487–489.

HODSON, A. Z. 1956. Nutritive value of instant nonfat dry milk. Food Technol. *10*, 221–224.

HOWARD, L. B., and CAMPBELL, H. 1946. Dehydro-freezing—a new way of preserving food. Food Inds. *18*, 674–676.

JACOB, H. E. 1942. The relation of maturity of the grapes to the yield, composition and quality of raisins. Hilgardia *14*, 321–345.

JOSLYN, M. A., and HEID, J. L. 1957. Concentration and drying in food products manufacture. Western Canner and Packer *49*, No. 2, 29–35, 39–44.

JUL, M. 1949. The food technologist and the world food crisis. Food Technol. *3*, 279–283.

KALOYEREAS, S. 1950. Report presented at dehydration conference held at Univ. of Calif., Sept. 15, 1950.

KILPATRICK, P. W., LOWE, E., and VAN ARSDEL, W. B. 1955. Tunnel dehydrators for fruits and vegetables. Advances in Food Research *6*, 314–372.

KRISTENSEN, R. 1930. Food product and process. U. S. Pat. 1,778,079. Oct. 14.

LAWLER, F. K. 1955. FE award goes to milk process. Food Eng. *27*, No. 5, 61–62, 184.

LAZAR, M. E., CHAPIN, E. O., and SMITH, G. S. 1961. Dehydrofrozen apples: recent developments in processing methods. Food Technol. *15*, No. 1, 32–36.

LEGAULT, R. R. 1954. Dehydration of juice. *In* Chemistry and Technology of Fruit and Vegetable Juice Production. Tressler, D. K., and Joslyn, M. A. (Editors). Avi Publishing Co., Westport, Conn.

LEGAULT, R. R., and TALBURT, W. F. 1949. Dehydro-freezing improves food quality. Refrig. Eng. *57*, 1175–1177.

LEWIN, L. M., and MATELES, R. I. 1962. Freeze drying without vacuum: a preliminary investigation. Food Technol. *16*, 94–96.

LONG, J. D., MRAK, E. M., and FISHER, C. D. 1940. Investigations in the sulfuring of fruits for drying. Calif. Agr. Expt. Sta. Bull. *636*.

LOWE, E., RAMAGE, W. D., DURKEE, E. L., and HAMILTON, W. E. 1955. Belt-trough, a new continuous dehydrator. Food Eng. *27*, No. 7, 43–44.

MILITARY-INDUSTRY MEETING REPORT. 1960. Freeze-dehydration of foods. Research and Development Associates Food and Container Institute, Inc., Chicago, Ill.

MILLEVILLE, H. R. 1954. Volatile flavor recovery. *In* Chemistry and Technology of Fruit and Vegetable Juice Production. Tressler, D. K. and Joslyn, M. A. (Editors). Avi Publishing Co., Westport, Conn.

MOORE, C. C. 1927. Process of sulfurizing, dehydrating and desulfurizing fruit. U. S. Pat. 1,633,823. June 28.

MOORE, C. C. 1931. Process of sulfurizing, dehydrating and desulfurizing fruit. U. S. Pat. 1,835,237. Dec. 8.

MOORE, C. C. 1935. Process of sulfurizing, dehydrating and desulfurizing fruit. U. S. Pat. 2,035,536. Dec. 10.

MORGAN, A. I., JR., GINNETTE, L. F., RANDALL, J. M., and GRAHAM, R. P. 1959. Technique for improving instants. Food Eng. *31*, No. 9, 86–87.

MORGAN, A. I., GRAHAM, R. P., GINNETTE, L. F., and WILLIAMS, G. S. 1961. Recent developments in foam-mat drying. Food Technol. *15*, 37–39.

MORRIS, T. N. 1947. The Dehydration of Food. D. Van Nostrand Co., New York.

MRAK, E. M. 1941. Some factors in the production of dried fruits. Fruit Prod. J. *20*, 267–276, 293.

MRAK, E. M., and LONG, J. D. 1941. Methods and equipment for the sun-drying of fruits. Calif. Agr. Expt. Sta. Circ. *350*, 1–69.

MRAK, E. M., and MACKINNEY, G. 1951. The dehydration of foods. *In* The Chemistry and Technology of Food and Food Products. Jacobs, M. B. (Editor). 2nd Edition. Vol. III. Interscience Publishers, Inc., New York.

MRAK, E. M., and PERRY, R. L. 1948. Dehydrating freestone peaches. Calif. Agr. Expt. Sta. Circ. *381*.

MRAK, E. M., and PHAFF, H. J. 1949. Sun drying of fruits. Calif. Agr. Expt. Sta. Circ. *392*.

MYLNE, A. M., and SEAMANS, V. S. 1954. Stabilized orange juice powder. II. Changes during storage. Food Technol. *8*, 45–50.

NOTTER, G. K., BREKKE, J. E., and TAYLOR, D. H. 1959. Factors affecting behavior of fruit and vegetable juices during vacuum puff drying. Food Technol. *13*, No. 6, 341–345.

OLSON, R. L., *et al.* 1955. Recent advances in potato granule technology. Food Technol. *9*, 271–275.

PARKER, A. S., and SMITH, A. V. (Editors). 1960. Recent Research in Freezing and Drying. Charles C Thomas Co., Springfield, Ill.

PEEBLES, D. D. 1956. The development of instant milk. Food Technol. *10*, 64–67.

PERRY, R. L. 1944. Heat and vapor transfer in the dehydration of prunes. Transaction Am. Soc. Mech. Eng., 447–456.

PERRY, R. L. *et al.* 1946. Fruit dehydration. I. Principles and equipment. Calif. Agr. Expt. Sta. Bull. *698*, 1–68.

PHAFF, H. J., and MRAK, E. M. 1948. Sulfur house operation. Calif. Agr. Expt. Sta. Circ. *382*.

PLATT, B. S., HEARD, C. R. C., and PELLET, P. L. 1958. Method for the drying of foodstuffs by heating in edible oil in vacuo. Proc. Nutr. Soc. (Brit.) *17*, 21.

POWERS, M. J., TALBURT, W. F., JACKSON, R., and LAZAR, M. E. 1958. Dehydro-canned apples. Food Technol. *12*, 417–419.

POWERS, M. J., TAYLOR, G. H., TALBURT, W. F., and WALKER, L. H. 1956. Dehydro-frozen apricots—preparation. Food Technol. *10*, 489–492.

RICHERT, P. H. 1953. Chemical aspects of dried fruits. J. Agr. Food Chem. *1*, 610–612.

ROCKWELL, W. C., LOWE, E., SMITH, G. S., and POWERS, M. J. 1954. New through-flow rotary drier for the partial drying of apple slices. Food Technol. *8*, 500–502.

ROLFE, E. J. 1956. An improved method for dehydrating meat. Food *25*, 199–205.

SARAVACOS, G. D., and CHARM, S. E. 1962A. A study of the mechanism of fruit and vegetable dehydration. Food Technol. *16*, 78–81.

SARAVACOS, G. D., and CHARM, S. E. 1962B. Effect of surface-active agents on the dehydration of fruits and vegetables. Food Technol. *16*, 91–93.

SCHROEDER, R. L., and COTTON, R. H. 1948. Dehydration of orange juice. Ind. Eng. Chem. *40*, 803–807.

SCHULTES, A. 1955. Prune harvest methods, costs. Calif. Agr. *9*, No. 7, 6–7.

SCHULTZ, T. H., DIMICK, K. P., and MAKOWER, B. 1956. Incorporation of natural fruit flavors into fruit juice powders. I. Locking of citrus oils in sucrose and dextrose. Food Technol. *10*, 57–60.

SCHWIMMER, S., and WESTON, W. J. 1961. Enzymatic development of pyruvic acid as a measure of pungency. J. Agr. Food Chem. *9*, 301–304.

SELTZER, E., and SETTLEMEYER, J. T. 1949. Spray drying of foods. Advances in Food Research *2*, 399–520.

SCHWARZ, H. W., and PENN, F. E. 1948. Production of orange juice concentrate and powder. Ind Eng. Chem. *40*, 938–944.

SLUDER, J. C., OLSON, R. W., and KENYON, E. M. 1947. Production of dry powdered orange juice. Food Technol. *11*, 85–94.

SOC. CHEM. ENG. 1958. Fundamental Aspects of the Dehydration of Foodstuffs. Conference held in Aberdeen, Scotland, March, 1958. Macmillan Co., New York.

STOLL, A., and SEEBECK, E. 1951. Chemical investigations of alliin, the specific principle of garlic. Advances in Enzymology *11*, 377–400.

STRASHUN, S. I., and TALBURT, W. F. 1953. WRRL develops techniques for making puffed powder from juice. Food Eng. *25*, No. 3, 59–60.

STRASHUN, S. I., and TALBURT, W. F. 1954. Stabilized orange juice powder. I. Preparation and packaging. Food Technol. *8*, 40–45.

SWISHER, H. E. 1957. Solid flavoring composition and method of preparing the same. U. S. Pat. 2,809,895. Oct. 15.

SWISHER, H. E. 1961. Fibrous fruit product and process. U. S. Pat. 2,476,159. March 21.

TALBURT, W. F. 1961. Dehydration of juices. *In* Fruit and Vegetable Juice Processing Technology. Tressler, D. K., and Joslyn, M. A. (Editors). Avi Publishing Co., Westport, Conn.

TALBURT, W. F., and LEGAULT, R. R. 1950. Dehydro-frozen peas. Food Technol. *4*, 286–289.

TALBURT, W. F., and POWERS, M. J. 1956. Concentrated fruit purée by partially dehydrating nonsulfited whole fruit, pulping, stabilizing. U. S. Pat. 2,752,253. June 25.

TALBURT, W. F., WALKER, L. H., and POWERS, M. J. 1950. Dehydro-frozen apples. Food Technol. *4*, 496–498.

TAPPEL, A. L., *et al*. 1943. Freeze-dried meat. I. Preparation and properties. Food Technol. *9*, 401–406.

TRESSLER, D. K. 1955. Problems of the dehydration industry. Scientific Monthly *57*, 347–353.

TRESSLER, D. K. 1956. New developments in the dehydration of fruits and vegetables. Food Technol. *10*, 119–124.

TURKOT, V. A., ESKEW, R. K., and ACETO, N. C. 1956. A continuous process for dehydrating fruit juices. Food Technol. *10*, 604–606.

U. S. DEPT. AGR., BUR. AGR., IND. CHEM. 1944. Vegetable and Fruit Dehydration—A Manual for Plant Operators. U. S. Dept. Agr. Misc. Pub. *540*.

U. S. DEPT. AGR. 1959. Management Handbook to Aid Emergency Expansion of Dehydration Facilities for Vegetables and Fruits. U. S. Dept. Agr., Agr. Res. Service, Western Util. Res. and Dev. Div., Albany, Calif.

VAN ARSDEL, W. B. 1951A. Principles of the drying process with special reference to vegetable dehydration. U. S. Dept. Agr., Agr. Res. Admn. Pub. *AIC-300*. Washington, D. C.

VAN ARSDEL, W. B. 1951B. Tunnel-and truck dehydrators as used for dehydrating vegetables. U. S. Dept. Agr., Agr. Res. Admn. Pub. *AIC-308*. Washington, D. C.

VAN ARSDEL, W. B., and COPLEY, M. J. 1964. Food Dehydration. Vol. II—Products and Technology. Avi Publishing Co., Westport, Conn.

VON LOESECKE, H. W. 1955. Drying and Dehydration of Foods. 2nd Edition. Reinhold Publishing Corp., New York.

WANG, H. *et al*. 1953. A histological and histochemical study of beef dehydration. Food Research *18*, 351–359.

WANG, H. *et al*. 1954. A histological and histochemical study of beef dehydration. Food Research *19*, 154–161; 543–556, 557–563.

WEBB, W. R. 1942. Food composition. U. S. Pat. 2,283,302. May 19.

WEBB, W. R. 1949. Food composition. U. S. Pat. 2,473,184. June 14.

WEBB, W. R. 1955. Food composition. U. S. Pat. 2,712,698. July 12.

WELLER, G. 1953. New coating process traps full flavor. Food Eng. *25*, No. 8, 94, 136–137.

CHAPTER 18

M. Karel and
S. A. Goldblith

Processing Aspects of
Freeze Dehydration

INTRODUCTION

Freeze dehydration of foods is commercially established and bids to become a significant means for processing foods within the next decade.

This chapter presents a number of factors (other than those related to engineering and equipment) which must be considered with respect to freeze drying.

RAW MATERIALS

It is particularly true that high quality freeze dried foods cannot be made from poor raw materials. The following operations are involved in freeze drying: (*a*) preparation of foods, e.g., washing, cutting or dicing, blanching; (*b*) freezing; (*c*) dehydration; and (*d*) packaging (frequently under nitrogen).

Steps (*a*) and (*b*) are common to conventionally frozen foods, but here the analogy ceases, inasmuch as freeze dehydrated foods are to be further processed by subjecting them to a high vacuum in the frozen state, subliming the water with a resultant honeycombed structure, containing a great deal of intercellular surface area which water no longer is available to protect.

Effect of Raw Material Quality on Final Product Quality

Since the frozen foods are to be *further* processed by dehydration in a vacuum, it is also logical to state that raw materials for lyophilized foods must be equal to or preferably better than those required for frozen foods. This point is illustrated in Fig. 124 (Goldblith *et al.* 1963).

In order to achieve high quality finished products, the *a priori* requirement of high quality raw materials cannot be overemphasized. Admittedly, the achievement of high quality finished products depends upon successful accomplishment of *all* the operations cited above. Without high quality raw materials, however, all the care in the dehydration step, packaging step, etc., would be in vain. Figure 124 illustrates a further

M. KAREL is Associate Professor of Food Engineering, Department of Nutrition and Food Science, Massachusetts Institute of Technology and S. A. GOLDBLITH is Professor of Food Science and Executive Officer, Department of Nutrition and Food Science, Massachusetts Institute of Technology, Cambridge, Mass.

point in that lower quality raw materials result in more rapid degradation on storage than if one starts with better quality raw materials.

Uniformity of Raw Material as a Factor in Control of Freeze Dehydration Operations

How does one go about assuring high quality raw material supplies? This is a question which is difficult to answer although at first it would seem to be simple. First of all, obviously, one should purchase the highest quality raw materials available. How does one determine this "highest quality?" What does this cost? Obviously, the approach to this

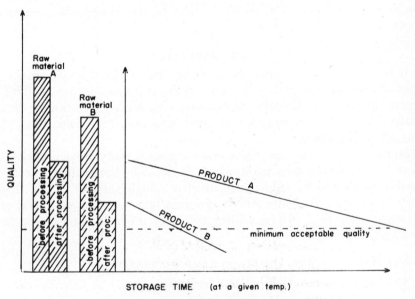

FIG. 124.   DEPENDENCE ON INITIAL QUALITY OF THE STORAGE ;
STABILITY OF A HYPOTHETICAL FREEZE-DRIED PRODUCT

problem resides in the setting of specifications—chemical, physical and/or microbiological—depending on the nature of the product. These specifications must be realistic and must be routinely enforced. On this point, there can be no laxity. Realism in specifications is extremely important. Insistence on *extremely* and inordinately high tolerances can only result in extremely high prices for the materials thus pricing the products completely out of the market place. For instance, if one uses, as an example, raw shrimp which are to be purchased and one sets an unrealistic total plate count such as a value of less than 10^5 bacteria per gram, the cost of such shrimp will be inordinately high inasmuch as but a small percentage of the shrimp which come to the market place have such a low count, and therefore, most of the shrimp would have to be rejected as substandard. Yet, in all likelihood many (but not all) of the shrimp would make satisfactory freeze dried products. Thus, standards must be realistic as well as rigid.

It has been the experience of the writers that specifications must be set up on raw materials dependent on the particular foodstuff being considered. For example, in the case of products such as blanched vegetables, total plate counts should be of a different order of magnitude than of raw sulfited mushroom slices; in the case of chicken meat greater importance is attached to counts of salmonella organisms than in the case of crabmeat, where counts of enterococci are of paramount importance, etc. Chemical and physical specifications are also of importance, dependent upon the particular foodstuff being considered. In the case of chicken meat, for example, minimal values of protein and maximal values of fat and moisture might be specified; in the case of mushrooms, one could specify, in addition to microbiological counts, maximum allowable size variations, maximum numbers of mushrooms with color defects, etc. In other words, the type of specifications for the particular raw materials should be set up in accordance with the nature of the product being considered.

That the quality of the raw material will have an effect on the finished product has been alluded to earlier.

The Aberdeen Group of the Ministry of Foods (Hanson 1961) have shown the importance of consideration of optimal varieties for freeze dehydration and present data on the raw material quality for some 27 different raw materials for freeze dehydration. It is known, for instance, that certain species of shrimp result in high quality freeze dried products whereas others do not; similarly with potatoes and other foodstuffs. Specific tests to be run "at the factory door" on incoming shipments of raw materials will depend, of course, upon the availability of laboratory help and facilities; obviously the more *proper* tests that are run, the better the probability of picking up substandard raw materials (assuming that the proper statistical procedures for random selection of samples is used). Naturally, one wishes to reduce the numbers and types of tests to a minimum in order to keep costs of this testing as low as possible, as well as to perform such tests as can be routinely and quickly done before truckloads of raw material are unloaded. With respect to this, it is well to point out that as a rule where raw materials are sound, wholesome, free-of-defects, of uniform size, etc., they will have correspondingly low microbial counts and be free of off-odors. In the case of seafoods, for example, the same kind of care which results in products of good color, of good texture, freedom from trimethylamine odors, etc., will also result in low microbial counts in the product.

PREPARATION FOR FREEZING

All foodstuffs must be prepared in some way for dehydration, prior to freezing. The manner of preparation and degree thereof will depend upon the particular commodity, the storage conditions thereof, and the use to which it is to be put. Hanson (1961) presents data on this subject for a number of different foods.

Certain foodstuffs present interesting problems. For instance, mushrooms can be hydrated nicely as caps, whole, slices, dice, etc., without any further preliminary treatment prior to freezing. Yet, if one does this, on rehydration, due to the still active polyphenol oxidase enzymes present which leach out into the rehydration water, the products and the water become an undesirable reddish brown. This may be obviated by either a chemical dip with sulfite (which must be declared on the label) or a heat blanch which presents a different problem inasmuch as heat blanching alters the moisture content of the mushroom and adversely affects its rehydrability.

Products which have a skin thereon, e.g., blueberries or peas, must be scored prior to or post-freezing in order to allow for passage of moisture out of the product and for rapid dehydration. With some products, this is achieved by slicing, e.g., strawberries.

Cooked chicken pieces must be boned and diced. This is usually done after cooking, in order to reduce the labor costs. This latter point brings to light other potential problems of contamination of a cooked (and essentially sterile) product during the boning and dicing operation. Thus, in a product of this type, the preliminary operation has to be carefully controlled microbiologically in order to keep down any possible buildup of organisms.

Similar problems are observed with any precooked products of animal or marine origin which are to be handled following cooking, e.g., in the case of shrimp which are size graded, cooked, then peeled, deveined, stacked on trays and finally frozen.

Composite or compounded products, such as fish cakes or meat bars also must be handled prior to freezing. In the case of the meat bars, the procedure used is described by Hanson (1961). Here again care to prevent microbial contamination and multiplication during mixing of the various ingredients and pressing of the bars must be taken. In the case of fish cakes, inasmuch as these products must be porous enough for rapid dehydration following the frying operation, their composition must be different than that normally used for fish cakes to be sold either canned or frozen. Hanson (1961) and the Quartermaster Food and Container Institute for the Armed Forces (Anon. 1962) have suggested formulations which will allow rapid dehydration and rehydration.

Thus, it is apparent that products must be examined individually with regard to the pretreatment to be used. In addition to the normal pretreatment used in preparation for freezing, consideration should be given to the following points: (a) need for water permeability in dehydration and in rehydration; and (b) the water-free nature of the final product, and therefore need for certain preliminary treatments improving final product properties.

EFFECTS OF FREEZING CONDITIONS ON FREEZE DRIED PRODUCTS

The conditions under which the product is frozen prior to the sublimination of ice affect the quality of the final freeze dried product. The effect of freezing is due in part to the following factors (Kuprianoff 1962): (a) ice crystals may cause considerable damage to structural components of the food by mechanical action; (b) under conditions in which a large proportion of water remains unfrozen, the resulting high electrolyte concentration in the unfrozen water may cause protein denaturation; (c) the size and distribution of ice crystals affects rate of dehydration, and consequently also both the duration of drying and the temperature gradients during drying; and (d) the ice structure affects the porosity of the dried material, and thus rehydration and water holding capacity.

The freezing parameters which determine the extent of the changes mentioned above are: (1) rate of freezing; (2) the lowest temperature to which the food is cooled; and (3) extent of dehydration occurring during the freezing period.

It is generally considered that rapid freezing, with the formation of uniformly distributed, small crystals, results in minimum damage to the structure of the food. This is true for both plant tissues in which the main structural polymers are starch and cellulose and for animal tissues in which the structure is due to proteins. This relative freedom from damage may be due to less mechanical action of crystals, or to the short period during which the proteins are exposed to an unfrozen salt solution.

In the case of freezing for freeze drying, however, it is often observed that very rapid freezing does not necessarily lead to optimum product quality. Lusk (1963), for instance, found that slower rates of freezing resulted in better rehydration of marine products than rapid freezing by immersion in liquid nitrogen. Similar observations are reported by Kuprianoff (1962). Apparently the improved rehydration is due to the large pores formed in the food by large crystals resulting from slow freezing. The water holding capacity of the proteins, however, may be impaired under these conditions, and part of the gain in rehydration may be offset by looser binding of the water penetrating into the large pores.

The rate of freezing is not the only important variable in this respect. The equilibrium temperature to which the food is cooled prior to drying, as well as subsequent thermal history, are also of importance. Because of the phenomenon of supercooling, the freezing of eutectic mixtures of water and soluble solids occurs at rather low temperatures, often considerably lower than the temperatures at which the eutectics melt. It is advantageous, therefore, to cool products containing soluble solids to low temperatures, even if subsequently they will be rewarmed during sublimination. The temperatures necessary vary with the nature of the product. Rey and Bastien (1962) report for instance that for the eutectic mixture of water and sodium chloride there is an observable and precise temperature of melting at the eutectic point of —6.88°F. The freezing of this mixture, however, may occur at temperatures as low as —40°F. Similar considerations hold for freezing and eutectic melting of products containing other soluble solids. Orange juice, for instance, shows incipient melting at —25.6°F. and an even lower freezing temperature (Rey and Bastien 1962).

Another factor in the freezing operation is the amount of water evaporated during the freezing step. In evaporative freezing in particular, that is, freezing done by placing unfrozen food in the drying chamber and subjecting it to a vacuum, this consideration is of particular importance. Several dangers are associated with this type of freezing for freeze dried foods, some of which are:

(1) Since part of the water is evaporated by vacuum drying from the liquid state, rather than sublimation, some solute migration and shrinkage may occur, with attendant product deterioration.

(2) At the levels of vacuum used in commercial freeze driers the eutectic freezing point may not be reached at all, and therefore, part of the water is evaporated continuously from the liquid rather than solid state. The properties of the dried materials may then be more typical of vacuum dried, rather than freeze dried, products and, in particular, the texture may be inferior.

(3) There exists a danger of puffing or foaming which in itself may result in undesirable texture. (For some products, however, puffing or foaming may actually be desirable, and is in fact widely practiced in "puff-" and "foam-drying" of foods.)

In view of above considerations it is the current practice to prefreeze food products, usually by blast freezing at temperatures of —40°F. Immersion freezing in liquid nitrogen has been used in laboratory investigation, but is not used commercially to any large extent. Evaporative freezing, however, has been recommended by Hanson (1961) for the following products: cooked minced meats; ham mince; cooked cod flakes; cooked prawns; brussel sprouts; cabbage; and cauliflower.

The present writers feel that even for the products listed above, prefreezing is the preferred treatment, because of quality considerations, as well as from the point of view of efficient freeze drying cycles in the type of cabinet batch drying as is presently used by the industry.

EFFECTS OF DEHYDRATION CONDITIONS ON PRODUCT QUALITY

The engineering aspects of freeze drying have been discussed elsewhere and will not be considered here. The following paragraphs are concerned with the effects of conditions of dehydration on the quality of freeze dried products.

The conditions of dehydration and their effects on quality vary greatly between the two most commonly used types of freeze dehydration, namely, freeze drying with heat input through the ice layer, such as in flask or plate drying of liquids, and heat input through the dry layer such as normally occurs in freeze drying of solid foods (Meryman 1960).

In the second type of drying, which is by far the most important in present commercial practice, the highest temperature in the food is that attained by the surface of the dry layer. The temperature of the ice is determined primarily by the pressure maintained in the chamber. Consequently, with respect to process conditions there are two critical temperatures, which have to be controlled in order to minimize undesirable changes during the process. The first of these is the maximum temperature of the dry layer, and the second the maximum temperature of the ice.

The maximum temperature of the dry layer that can be safely tolerated depends largely on the nature of the product. Severe scorching of the surface must be avoided in any case. In most cases, however, the temperatures must be maintained considerably lower than the scorch temperature because of other deteriorative reactions. Some of the factors limiting the surface temperature are the following: (1) destruction of pigments (carotenoid pigments in vegetables, myoglobin in red meats, astacene in shrimp); (2) denaturation and crosslinking of proteins; (3) rendering out of fat (this not only results in economic losses and often in unsightly appearance, but is also often the cause of imperfect rehydration due to the formation of water-impermeable coating of fat on the internal surfaces of the food); and (4) nonenzymatic browning of high sugar materials.

The actual maximum surface temperatures found to be safe under operating conditions have been reported by several investigators. The general practice appears to be to limit the temperature to less than 140°F. for lean meats, and fish; and to less than 104°F. for fatty materials (Hanson 1961). Our own work indicates that limitation of maximum surface temperature to less than 125°F. is of benefit in maintaining high quality in shrimp, and other crustaceans. On the other hand, some vegetables such as mushrooms may be safely processed at a surface temperature as high as 180°F. without impairment of quality.

The limit on ice temperature is set almost exclusively by the temperature at which eutectic melting occurs. This in turn depends on the content of soluble substances, such as sugar and salt. High sugar items, such as fruit juices, must therefore be processed at a low ice temperature, and therefore at a low chamber pressure. Chamber pressures used commercially at the present time and ranging from 500 to 1,000 microns may not be satisfactory for products of this type.

Two other process variables, in addition to temperature, are of importance in determining quality of the freeze dried product. They are: (1) the final moisture content; and (2) oxygen concentration.

With respect to moisture content, in general, the lower the moisture content, the better the storage stability and quality of the product. It has been suggested that overdrying may result in lowered product quality, but evidence that extremely low moisture contents are damaging by themselves is not convincing. If the low moisture content has been achieved by increasing the temperatures to high levels then, of course, damage to quality is not only possible, but very likely.

In so far as oxygen is concerned, the concentration of this gas during the drying process is extremely low in normal vacuum freeze drying, and presents no problems. Breaking of the vacuum with air at the completion of the process, however, may result in absorption of this gas on inner surfaces of the food, and may make application of inert gas packaging difficult (Thomson et al. 1962). The ideal solution to this problem is to break the vacuum with nitrogen, and to package under this gas without exposing the food to air. It is reported that one organization in Italy does fill and package under nitrogen in a closed-continuous system. This is at present economically not feasible with most of the equipment used commercially, inasmuch as most freeze dehydration installations are multi-cabineted and do not lend themselves to such a procedure. Foods are removed from the chamber into air before inert gas packing in most installations. Even under these conditions, it is highly desirable to break the chamber vacuum with inert gas, and this practice is widespread in commercial operations.

Two other methods of freeze drying have received some attention even though they have as yet no commercial applications. They are (*a*) one utilizing microwave heat input during freeze drying and (*b*) freeze drying at atmospheric pressure with dry gases (Woodward 1963). With respect to effects on quality, their anticipated characteristics are the following:

Utilization of microwaves for heat input in freeze drying has the potential of minimizing damage due to high surface temperatures, since the heat input occurs directly in the ice layer. The difficult aspect with respect to quality is to control the microwave energy input in such a way that ionization, with attendant scorching and uneven input with possible ice melting are avoided. Satisfactory product quality under laboratory conditions has been demonstrated, but there is little knowledge about quality obtainable under commercial conditions (Decareau 1962).

Freeze drying with dry gases at a sufficiently low temperature should also be capable of producing good quality products. The main obstacles to production of foods of high quality in this process are: the use of too high a gas temperature with the danger of eutectic melting, and shrinkage of product. Moreover, if the dry gas contains oxygen there is of course the additional danger of oxidation during dehydration. Large scale experience with this process is as yet not available.

PACKAGING OF FREEZE DRIED FOODS

The shelf-life of freeze dried foods is affected to a large extent by the protection afforded by the package. A. A. Taylor (1963) lists the following four factors in deterioration of dehydrated foods as being amenable to control by protective packaging: (*a*) uptake of oxygen; (*b*) uptake of moisture; (*c*) flavor contamination; and (*d*) mechanical damage. To these factors, one might justifiably add the following: (*e*) contamination by biological agents, such as insects and microorganisms; and (*f*) exposure to visible and ultraviolet light.

The protection actually achieved depends on the properties of the packaging material used, as well as on such package engineering considerations as shape and size of the package, method of closure and conditions of distribution and storage. With respect to the degree of protection that is required, it is possible to classify freeze dried foods into the following three categories:

(*a*) Foods requiring maximum protection against oxygen, water vapor, light and mechanical damage; as well as protection against contamination. Typical examples of sensitive foods falling in this category are: shrimp, crabmeat, lobster, pork, etc.

(*b*) Those foods which require a high degree of protection against oxygen, water vapor, light and contamination; but presenting no major problem with respect to mechanical damage. In this category belong oxidation- and browning-susceptible powders, comminuted foods, and purées. Examples include egg omelettes, fruit juice powders and dehydrated whole milk.

(*c*) Products requiring only protection against water uptake and relatively little danger of oxidation and mechanical damage. Some vegetables such as mushrooms may be cited as belonging to this category.

The following discussion will be concerned primarily with packaging of the most sensitive type of freeze dried products. The general principles will be also applicable to the other types of products, but the requirements are less rigorous and more economical packages may be substituted for the rather expensive packages affording the highest level of protection.

The most rigorous of the requirements for the packaging of sensitive freeze dried foods is the need for packages allowing virtually no diffusion of water vapor and of oxygen. A number of laminations incorporating aluminum foil in combination with one or more layers of plastic materials fulfill this requirement when tested in the form of flat, uncreased sheets (Hanson 1961). Under actual use conditions, and when tested in simulated shipping abuse testers, many of these laminations show a performance which is considerably less satisfactory. Many of the pouches develop pinholes or seal imperfections, which result in infiltration of oxygen, and to a lesser extent of water vapor (Taylor 1961; Shockley 1962).

The number of pinholes per pouch, and the percentage of pouches showing pinholing, depend on type of material used, type of product and method of packaging. A number of laminations have been developed which have been reported to give satisfactory performance, when used in combination with a suitable method for filling, deaeration and sealing. Among the laminations reported suitable for packaging of freeze dried foods are: (1) polymer coated cellophane-polyethylene-foil-polyethylene; (2) polymer coated mylar-polyethylene-foil-polyethylene; (3) coated paper-polyethylene-foil-polyethylene; and (4) mylar-foil-polyvinyl chloride (Shockley 1962; Collins and Boegershausen 1963).

Removal of oxygen from the package headspace is an important prerequisite for the stability of packaged freeze dried foods. A generally accepted maximum level of oxygen concentration is about two per cent based on atmospheric pressure. Many foods, such as dehydrated pork, salmon and others, require even lower levels of oxygen. Lusk (1963) found, for instance, that some oxidation may occur in freeze dried salmon even at an oxygen level of one per cent. Packaging machinery for vacuum or inert gas packaging of freeze dried foods in flexible pouches is commercially available (Cotson and Smith 1963), but each application requires considerable preliminary testing in order to obtain optimal conditions of evacuation, gas flushing type of pouch and conditions of sealing.

The problem of preventing the infiltration of atmospheric water and oxygen is, of course, readily solved by the use of hermetically sealed cans. In fact, in many cases, this method of packaging is used for commercial packaging of freeze dried foods, especially for foods intended for distribution to the institutional market. The advantages of metal cans include the proved impermeability of the container, and the availability of well tested equipment for automatic vacuum and gas packaging. The disadvantages include the larger weight of the cans, especially when one considers the relative low weight of the freeze dried contents. This disadvantage is partially overcome, and some of the advantages of tin cans retained by the use of aluminum cans, such as those used in the marketing of dehydrated soups produced by one company in this country. Cost and greater difficulties in high speed can sealing are the drawbacks of this type of package.

Flexible pouches offer some additional advantages when compared with rigid containers in problems related to mechanical damage to freeze dried foods. Many freeze dried products are very susceptible to breakage, and pulverization. This is due to their fragility and brittleness in the absence of their normal structural component—water. Protection against this type of damage is very difficult to realize, and some breakage and "dusting" is almost inevitable in such brittle products as shrimp and lobster, which lack the plasticizing action of fat, as well as structural rigidity due to water. Some improvement in protection can be achieved however by packaging in flexible pouches having an internal pressure of gas, usually nitrogen, a few inches below atmospheric pressure. Under these conditions, the product is given a snug fit inside the pouch, and there is little breakage due to impact of individual pieces of the product. Impact damage due to shocks to the pouch as a whole are minimized by placing the pouch inside a rigid carton, preferably with attachment of the pouch to several spots on the inside surface of the carton.

The authors have conducted some tests on "dusting" of shrimp in this type of a package, compared with similar damage in shrimp packaged in cans, and found some improvement. Cage (1962) reports results of similar tests, in which he observed very considerable reduction of shrimp dusting in partially vacuumized pouches. It should be noted, however, that the snug fit of the product inside the pouch increases the danger of pinholing of the pouch by sharp edges of the product, and therefore increases the requirement on toughness of the pouch laminate structure.

Automatic machinery for the type of packaging mentioned above has been developed, and is available commercially (Cotson and Smith 1963).

STORAGE

Microbiological Aspects

Storage results in lowered microbial counts on dehydrated products, the degree of reduction in count being, of course, dependent on the following: (1) the nature of the contaminating organisms; (2) the processing conditions during freeze dehydration; and (3) the temperature of storage and length of storage.

Obviously, dried bacterial spores are more resistant during storage at any given temperature than vegetative organisms. The degree of bacterial reduction on storage is dependent on the temperature of storage. Work on this subject has been carried out by Vaughn (1962) using raw, air dried vegetables with the above cited conclusions being reached.

TABLE 101

THE SURVIVAL OF FOUR MICROORGANISMS FREEZE-DRIED IN FOOD MATERIAL AND IN MODEL SYSTEMS AT TWO DIFFERENT PLATEN TEMPERATURES

Platen drying temperature, °F.

	Percentage Survival							
	Beef		Eggs		2% Gelatin		2% Gelatin + 6% Dextrose	
	120°	160°	120°	160°	120°	160°	120°	160°
Salmonella typhimurium	3	1	33	2	2	0	3	2
Staphylococcus aureus	52	14	51	69	54	17	55	17
Streptococcus faecalis	48	43	93	68	30	11	27	12
Pseudomonas fragi	0	0	1.6	0	0	0	0	0
Final moisture, %	0.2	0.5	1.9	1.4	3.0	0.2	0.2	0.2
Drying time, hr.	12	8	9	7	17	13	18	14

[1] From Silverman *et al.* (1963).

The conditions of freeze dehydration to which the organisms are subjected are also important. For instance, in recent studies by Silverman *et al.* (1963) comparing the survival of four different species of microorganisms in two foodstuffs and in two model systems, better survival was obtained when the substrate containing the bacteria were dried at platen temperatures of 120°F. than at 160°F. (Table 101).

The various aspects of the microbiology of freeze dehydration have been considered in detail by Goldblith (1963). In addition to points discussed earlier in this section, consideration is given to the possible needs for consideration of presently available methods of analysis which have been developed for foods processed by other means, the possible production of "metabolic" injury of organisms by freeze dehydration and the consideration of microbiological standards. The latter point, namely that of standards, is also considered by Hanson (1961). Suffice it to say, that in the opinion of the present authors, much more work needs to be done before microbiological standards should be established.

The work alluded to includes the following: (a) consideration, study and evaluation of the extensive data now available in the freeze dehydration industry; (b) establishment of realistic microbiological target goals for various types of foods, raw versus precooked, vegetables, meats, and sea foods, etc.; (c) evaluation of data obtained in plants cooperating in a study such as (b) above; and (d) establishment of standards for various foodstuffs which are realistic, reflect good manufacturing practices and include organisms reflecting public health hazards.

In addition to the above, more data are needed on the growth of organisms during *rehydration*, using inoculated packs of dehydrated foods. Hanson (1961) presents some data. However much more data are needed on studies on rehydration carried on in parallel with similarly inoculated packs of frozen foods and canned foods along with rehydrated lyophilized foods, all stored at temperatures such as 35°, 45°, 55°, 70°, 86°, 98°, 120°F. for varying periods of time. Studies such as these would then give one data upon which to judge whether freeze dehydrated foods offer any greater or lesser microbial hazard, if mishandled, than frozen foods. To date, work on this subject has been limited.

Physical and Chemical Changes During Storage of Freeze Dried Foods

Freeze dried foods are subject to storage changes, due primarily to the following mechanisms (Karel 1963): (1) lipid oxidation; (2) oxidation of other components; (3) nonenzymatic browning; (4) enzymatic reactions; and (5) changes in the proteins and other polymeric constituents.

The extent and rate of deteriorative changes depends on a number of factors, the most important of which are the following: (1) the nature of the food and its treatment prior to storage; (2) time and temperature of storage; (3) oxygen concentration; (4) moisture content; and (5) light intensity.

Oxidation of lipids is one of the most critical problems in extending the shelf life of stored dehydrated foods. The oxidation starts usually with formation of hydroperoxides of unsaturated fatty acids, such as linoleic and linolenic. The peroxides subsequently decompose giving rise to breakdown products having undesirable flavor, and possibly also toxic properties. The peroxides can also react with various fat-soluble vitamins, pigments and flavor compounds, thus further deteriorating food quality. Some of the oxidation products can also react with amino acids thus reducing the biological value of the proteins, and often contributing to nonenzymatic browning.

Exclusion of oxygen, exclusion of light and incorporation of antioxidants are effective in preventing the oxidative changes. Unfortunately, these measures are difficult to apply in the case of freeze dried foods.

Exclusion of light may be readily achieved, but the foodstuffs have a rate of oxidation in the dark that is sufficiently rapid to make this method wholly inadequate. The use of antioxidants is difficult because it is not always possible to apply the antioxidant in such a way as to reach the tissues and tissue layers in which the antioxidant is needed. The large internal surface areas allow the reactions to proceed throughout the food, and simple surface application of the antioxidant, which is often effective in frozen foods, is of little or no value with freeze dried foodstuffs.

Exclusion of oxygen, or, at the very least, minimizing the oxygen pressure within the package, has been the method used to date to control and minimize the rate of oxidation of freeze dried foods. Even with this method, however, freeze dried foods exhibit certain characteristics that make gas packaging difficult to apply.

The first such problem is associated with the slow desorption of gases adsorbed on the porous matrix of the foodstuff. Some investigators have found that, after a simple evacuation-nitrogen flushing cycle, which would lower oxygen concentration to an apparent initial value of less than one per cent the actual amount of oxygen present (and available for reaction with the food) may be as high as 5 to 15 per cent (Thomson *et al.* 1962).

Some research has been done on the use of oxygen scavengers. The classical oxygen-scavenging system consists of glucose and the enzyme glucose-oxidase. In enzyme-catalyzed oxidation of glucose to gluconic acid, oxygen is consumed and hydrogen peroxide is then enzymatically decomposed by catalase to water, and one-half of the oxygen is utilized in the reaction. This system, however, is not suitable for packaging freeze dried foods, because these reactions require water, and the amount of water included in the oxygen-scavenging packet is higher than the maximum level of moisture permitted in freeze dried foods (Scott and Hammer 1961).

Another system, recently proposed by Abbot *et al.* (1961), utilizes hydrogen and palladium catalysts for scavenging the oxygen. This method would appear to have some significant advantages, but much work remains to be done.

A second problem associated with gas packaging of freeze dried foods arises from the extreme sensitivity of freeze dried food systems to oxidation at even extremely low oxygen pressures (Goldblith *et al.* 1963).

This property requires that packaging of oxidation-susceptible freeze dried products must be done under nitrogen with less than one per cent oxygen if meaningful reduction of oxidation rates are to be achieved.

Oxidative deterioration is not limited to foods containing large amounts of fat. Oxidation of pigments may be of great importance in such foods as shrimp which contain very little fat. In this case, the oxidation-sensitive pigment is astacene, which is responsible for the desirable pink color. Oxidation of this pigment results in a yellow discoloration of the product. The extent to which storage in the presence of oxygen may result in destruction of this pigment is shown in Fig. 125 (Lusk 1963).

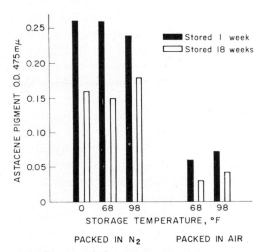

Fig. 125. Loss of Astacene Pigment in Freeze-Dried Shrimp, as a Function of Storage Conditions

Interaction with molecular oxygen may also result in damage to proteins. The nature of the reactions involved is not well understood, except in the case of the protein pigments hemoglobin and myoglobin. In the case of these proteins, oxidation results in brown discoloration due to oxidation of the iron-containing heme group attached to the protein. Proteins may absorb large quantities of oxygen, and this oxygen absorption results in deterioration of such products as meats and fish (Harper and Tappel 1957). It is likely that the oxidation susceptible sulfhydryl groups present in the proteins are the site of this oxidation (Fisher 1962). Another possibility is the involvement of oxygen in nonenzymatic browning (Thomson *et al.* 1962). More research on this aspect of oxidation is clearly needed.

The oxidative changes mentioned above are of primary importance in animal products. In plant materials, the more important oxidative changes include destruction of ascorbic acid, oxidative browning, and oxidation of plant pigments, especially those of the carotenoid group.

Nonenzymatic browning is of considerable importance in both animal and plant materials. There are several mechanisms of browning which can occur in dehydrated materials, differing in initial reactions, but having in common the formation of di- and polycarbonyl compounds, which polymerize to give brown pigments. Reduction of moisture content to very low levels is the most efficient way of preventing this reaction in freeze dried foods. The actual maximum allowable moisture content necessary to give adequate shelf life with respect to browning varies from product to product (Salwin 1959). It is very likely that in order to completely prevent browning, moisture contents would have to be so low that they may become economically unfeasible. Reduction of the water content to two per cent or less, however, slows the reaction down to levels which make the extent negligible for any reasonable shelf life, at normal temperatures.

Enzymatic reactions, such as enzymatic browning catalyzed by the phenolases, lipolysis catalyzed by lipases and oxidation catalyzed by lipoxidase can have significant effects on quality of dehydrated foods. The problem can be solved by blanching prior to dehydration, and in some cases by inhibition of the enzymatic changes by addition of chemicals such as sulfite. If the enzymes are not destroyed by blanching, their activity can be minimized or eliminated completely during the storage period by maintaining the food products at low moisture contents. The maximum moisture contents at which enzymatic activity can occur are lower than those required for bacterial activity but higher than those required for nonenzymatic browning. Enzyme activity has been observed at moisture contents as low as three per cent (Draudt *et al.* 1961), but in general the action of enzymes is not significant at the levels of moisture present in freeze dried foods (1 to 5 per cent moisture) (Acker 1963).

Retardation of enzymatic action by low moisture contents, even if practical ways are found to achieve and maintain such moisture levels, is not the entire answer. At some stage in their "life cycle," freeze dried foods must be rehydrated. Enzymatic action under these conditions becomes very rapid; in fact, in many cases, more rapid than in the original undehydrated material. As an example one might cite the case of enzymatic browning of mushrooms, which occurs within seconds after re-hydration of unblanched freeze dried samples.

There is a need, therefore, for new approaches to enzyme inhibition and control, and these approaches will be developed only by research utilizing the knowledge of the chemist and biochemist as well as the food scientist and food technologist.

The water holding capacity changes which occur during the dehydration process can be further aggravated during storage especially if storage temperatures are high and moisture content is in excess of two per cent. These changes are associated primarily with crosslinking of polymeric structural components of foods, such as cellulose and starch in the case of plant materials, and protein in the case of animal products. The changes in proteins, in particular, have been shown to occur readily in storage, and considerable research on the nature of these changes has been reported.

The changes are not completely elucidated at the present time, but it appears that crosslinking of myofibrillar proteins, that is of actomyosin, is the most important mechanism. Studies on changes in enzymatic activity of these proteins, and on their electrophoretic behavior, indicate that while denaturation may contribute to the acceleration of the crosslinking, it is possible to observe crosslinking and decreased solubility without an apparent denaturation of the proteins (Connell 1962).

Methods for counteracting this aggregation, and the associated increase in toughness consist of maintaining favorable storage conditions, that is low moisture content and reasonably low storage temperatures. Whether oxidation is involved in the toughening process is not definitely known, but crosslinking between oxidation products of fatty acids and proteins has been implicated by some investigators (Fisher 1962).

REHYDRATION

The final step in the life cycle of freeze dried foods is their rehydration. Conditions of rehydration which are of great importance in the final quality of the product include: (1) time; (2) temperature; (3) air displacement; (4) pH; and (5) ionic strength.

The most important changes which can occur during rehydration are: changes in proteins, redistribution of soluble components and enzymatically caused changes. The most important of these are the morphological and physicochemical changes in the protein network which affect the degree of rehydration. Rehydration may be evaluated in terms of total water reabsorbed by the food, or in terms of water holding capacity which is a measure of the amount of water retained by the food after application of pressure (Hamm and Deatherage 1960).

It has been observed that freeze dried foods have a somewhat lower rehydrated moisture content than the raw materials from which they are prepared and that they also have a somewhat lower water holding capacity. Conditions of rehydration are of particular importance in this respect.

It has been observed, for instance, that the rehydration moisture content of meats and fish decreases with increasing temperature. Norman and Auerbach (1963), for instance, found that precooked pork and beef regained considerably more water when rehydrated at 72°F. than when the rehydration was conducted at 180°F.

Steinberg (1960) studied the rehydration characteristics of precooked ground beef and found optimal rehydration when the rehydration fluid was maintained at 34°F. and the rehydration ratio decreased with increasing temperature of the fluid up to 180°F., which was the highest temperature studied. Goldblith et al. (1963) and Lusk (1963) reported similar results obtained with freeze dried shrimp and salmon rehydrated in water at temperatures ranging from 32° to 212°F.

Norman and Auerbach (1963) attribute the effect of temperature to the movement of fat in the hot rehydrating fluid, with clogging of the small interstitial channels formed during freezing. Another theory is that the higher temperatures have a direct denaturing effect on the tissue proteins. This theory is based on work conducted on samples with very low fat contents, which eliminated the complication arising from the presence of fat (Hamm and Deatherage 1960; Lusk 1963). The effect of temperature on rehydration of freeze dried plant materials is less clear cut. Simpson et al. (1955) observed that rehydration of dehydrated potatoes, corn and apple slices improved with increasing temperature, but that the reverse was true for green beans and onion flakes. Hanson (1961) reports that rehydration of most freeze dried foods of plant origin can be accomplished satisfactorily in boiling water.

The pH and ionic strength of the water used for rehydration are important in rehydration of proteinaceous foods. This is due to the polyelectrolyte nature of the proteins, the structure of which, and therefore the water binding capacity, depends on electrochemical properties of rehydrating fluids. Hamm and Deatherage (1960) observed that the water holding capacity of freeze dried beef was at a minimum at the isoelectric point of beef proteins. Lower or higher pH levels improved the water holding capacity. Hamdy et al. (1959) noted that rehydration of freeze dried meats could be improved by rehydration in a solution containing 0.2 M NaCl, 0.01 M KCl and 0.05 M Na-ascorbate, without adversely affecting flavor. Rehydration of beef can be improved also by rehydration in water containing one per cent table salt, without other additives (Steinberg 1960). Similar treatments may also be used to improve rehydration of marine products such as fish and crustaceans. Optimum electrolyte concentrations for rehydration of vegetables are not as clearly defined. Low pH has been suggested, however, as a means for improving the texture of rehydrated dried potatoes (Severson *et al.* 1955).

Other treatments which have been suggested as suitable for improvement of rehydration include the displacement of entrapped air by floating of samples during rehydration, rehydration under vacuum or rehydration of foods previously saturated with a water soluble gas, such as carbon dioxide. Improvement of water penetration by incorporation of wetting agents may also have some merit. Use of proteolytic enzymes in the rehydration water has been suggested as a texture improving treatment, but its use is limited due to possible excessive proteolytic activity resulting in a "mushy" texture.

MARKETING OF FREEZE DEHYDRATED FOODS

Introduction

At the present time, freeze dehydrated foods are produced and sold under the following categories: (*a*) basic products, *per se*, for either the institutional, or retail, market, including (1) shrimp, raw or precooked; (2) crabmeat chunks; (3) chicken meat, slices or dices; and (4) mushrooms, slices, dices, whole caps; (*b*) basic products for industrial use such as for components of soup mixes, dehydrated casseroles (formulated meals), etc. These include meat, fish, shrimp, chicken, crabmeat, mushrooms, carrots, cauliflower chunks, peas, strawberries and other fruits for cereals. (*c*) For the military establishment overseas in commissaries, officers' messes and for troop feeding.

Basic Products

The market for basic products such as shrimp, crabmeat, mushrooms, chicken and the like is dependent largely on the factor of convenience possessed by these foods. These convenience factors reside in the following:

(*a*) ease of preparation—e.g., in the case of shrimp, no cleaning, peeling, or deveining; in the case of chicken meat, no cooking, cleaning, etc.; (*b*) storage at room temperature rather than in the frozen state, thus cutting down the requirements of freezer storage space and allowing for availability of adequate supplies at all times; and (*c*) rapid preparation of large quantities by simple rehydration without problems of defrosting large institutional size containers.

Obviously, products of this type which are processed further beyond the freezing stage will be somewhat more expensive in that they are to be dehydrated and packed under nitrogen.

The marketing of such products in the institutional market place is based on: (a) assumption of and appreciation of savings in labor costs by the user because these operations have been removed back to the factory; (b) reduction in transportation costs inasmuch as refrigerated transportation and handling is not used; and (c) convenience factors.

This is an established and growing business which raises the question, "Why is growth not more rapid?"

The following factors are said to have important influences on this matter, in the United States: (a) the cost of freeze dehydrated foods and (b) consumer education.

Point (b) is extremely important, inasmuch as proper education is needed not only to be certain that the foods are utilized properly by the institutional chef, but also in order to have these chefs appreciate the savings in labor as well as the convenience realized by utilization of lyophilized foods.

Since the over-all food service industry in this country is said to be well over $9 billion annually, there could be quite an opportunity here for freeze dehydrated foods.

Assume, for the sake of convenience, a $10 billion food service industry in 1965 and that of this $10 billion, some ten per cent were frozen foods, and further assuming that only two per cent of the frozen foods were replaced by lyophilized foods, this would be a $10 x 10^9 x 0.1 x 0.02 or a $20 million market potential.

The degree of prophetic accuracy that can be assigned to such figures is not known. In November, 1961, a total sales of $2 billion for freeze dried foods in 1970 was forecast (Lawler 1961). Bird (1963) estimates that by 1967 the freeze dried food products could well reach about 400 or 500 million pounds (raw input) product annually. Assuming an average solids content of 25 per cent, this would represent 100 to 125 million pounds of dried foods which could represent some $500 million to $1 billion in sales dependent on the product composition—somewhat short of the $2 billion figure, but still a significant sales figure.

Of the above figures, the present writers estimate that perhaps 10 to 25 per cent might be in sales in the institutional market. Obviously, these are but "guesstimates" on the part of the present writers.

Industrial Sales

These appear to be looming large in importance in terms of over-all potential for freeze dried basic products. Initially, freeze **dried chicken** meat and some vegetables were manufactured and sold for use in dried soups. Today, there are appearing on the retail market place an increasing number and variety of consumer packages of formulated main course dishes such as shrimp creole, meat loaf mix, ham and eggs, etc. These are now achieving wide acceptance and, hopefully, with good and adequate consumer education, will become increasingly important. An additional example of this is the concept of using freeze dried fruits for sale with dried cereals. The advantage of the use of freeze dried components industrially is in the following:

(a) The freeze dried components used are those primarily responsible for optimal flavor and texture of the dish, e.g., in the meat loaf mix, the meat component; in the shrimp creole, the shrimp, etc.

(b) Thus, these are but a small portion of the over-all product weight and the cost economics of the finished product do not seem as high as in the case of selling simple freeze dried basic products in consumer size packages.

(c) These products offer advantages in convenience, availability, flavor and yet are not excessive in price. Let us examine the statement . . . "not excessive in price." In manufacturing a formulated food or casserole dish, e.g., shrimp creole, one can manufacture this in either of two ways. The first is to make up the entire dish cooked to perfection (including added water), then to freeze, dry and package under nitrogen. The second is to cook, clean, peel, devein and freeze dry the shrimp separately and to mix the dried sauce components (which have been air dried) and package the latter in a foil or a plastic laminate pouch; the rice is packaged also in a separate pouch. In this latter method, only a small portion of the mix (the shrimp) is freeze dried and packaged under nitrogen. The remainder is air dried and consists of relatively inexpensive components. In the opinion of the writers, based on present trends, industrial uses of freeze dried components should constitute a significant and increasingly important portion of the freeze dried food business over the next decade.

Military Uses

Over the past few years, the military establishments in this country and in Europe have been using freeze dried foods in B-ration formulations with increasing success. These have been described in several publications noted in the bibliography attached hereto.

The actions of the Defense Subsistence Supply centers in this country in purchasing increasingly greater quantities of these products coupled with the acceptance of these products by the troops lead one to the conclusion that more and more freeze dehydrated products will be used in the years to come by the military.

It is estimated, by the writers, based on the recent Notifications of Intent to Purchase, that the military is the single biggest purchaser of freeze dehydrated foods at the present time. The uses of freeze dehydrated foods by the government are not only for defense forces, but also for commissary use both here and abroad. Table 102 presents the estimated arrival purchases by the Defense Subsistence Supply Center over the past three years:

TABLE 102

PURCHASES BY THE DEFENSE SUBSISTENCE SUPPLY CENTER OF FREEZE DRIED FOODS
(FISCAL 1962–1964, INC.)

Fiscal Year	Purchases ($)
1962	2.1 million
1963	4.6 million
1964	8.0 million (estim.)

Products on Today's Market Place

The following major U. S. food companies are known to have products on the market place which contain freeze dried components.

Manufacturer	Article
Armour & Co.	Prepared dishes, mushrooms
Borden Foods Co.	Omelette mixes
Campbell Soup Co.	Red Kettle soups
Corn Products Co.	Soup mixes
Thos. J. Lipton, Inc.	Soup mixes
Post Cereal Co.	Corn flakes with strawberries
Wilson and Co.	Meat products

This list, admittedly incomplete, appears to be growing almost daily.

Product Economics

It becomes immediately apparent that the economics of freeze dehydration depend on several factors: (a) cost of raw materials; (b) cost of manufacturing; (c) cost of capital employed; (d) amortization; (e) overhead; (f) profit; (g) shipping; (h) power; and (i) research, development and quality control.

The raw materials represent a major portion of the over-all costs and for this reason, location of the plant in a good raw material area is of paramount importance. As an example we may consider strawberry slices (ten per cent total solids). For each pound of dried strawberry slices, at least ten pounds of frozen strawberry slices would be needed (assuming no losses). At 30 cents per pound of strawberries, this would represent $3.00 for raw material costs. If one could obtain strawberries at any appreciable saving, this would certainly be important in the final price of the finished product.

The remainder of the costs are self-evident. Suffice it to say that as the throughput of a plant is increased or the plant is enlarged to optimal capacity making optimal use of fixed overhead, the costs of water removal decrease. This has recently been discussed by Oetjen (1963). In this country, ultimately, it should be possible to remove water by sublimation at as low as 2 or 3 cents per pound of water removed.[1] At present the cost of water removal is certainly far in excess of this.

Developments in the future leading to the reduction of drying cycles by increasing rates of heat transfer by such techniques as microwaves should result in not only greater throughput but also in better product quality.

Lower costs of freeze dried foods can be obtained by: (a) location of plant in areas of low cost raw materials; (b) choice of optimal design of equipment in accordance with local area, e.g., condensers versus steam jets; (c) maximizing throughput; (d) optimizing product quality; and (e) mechanization as far as possible.

With respect to (d) and (e), one should remember that freeze dried foods, by their very nature, are quite fragile and oxidation-prone. Thus, quality control is an extremely important and costly function. In addition, this is a new and dynamic industry in which companies which are farsighted and research minded insure their own future.

BIBLIOGRAPHY

ABBOT, J., WAITE, R., and HEARNE, J. F. 1961. Gas packing milk powder with a mixture of nitrogen and hydrogen in the presence of palladium catalyst. J. Dairy Research 28, 285–292.

ACKER, L. 1963. Enzymatic reaction in foods of low moisture content. Advan. Food Research 11, 263–330.

ANON. 1962. Fish patties and balls, precooked, dehydrated; limited production. Q.M. Food and Container Inst. for the Armed Forces, Description No. DES-C-195-62, File No. F.S.C. 8905.

BIRD, K. 1963. Freeze drying—a look into the future. U. S. Dept. Agr. Publ. No. E.R.S.-134.

CAGE, J. K. 1962. Packaging freeze dried foods. Modern Packaging 36, No. 4, 153–154, 210.

COLLINS, M. E., and BOEGERSHAUSEN, R. L. 1963. Developing and testing packages for freeze dried foods. Package Eng. 8, No. 1, 55–61.

---

[1] These cost figures relate to amortization, manufacturing costs of water removal and power.

CONNELL, J. J. 1962. The effects of freeze-drying and subsequent storage on the proteins of flesh foods. In Freeze-Drying of Foods, Fisher, F. R. (Editor), Proceedings of a Conference, Chicago, Ill., Apr. 12–14, Washington, Natl. Acad. Sci.-Natl. Res. Council, 50–58.

COTSON, S., and SMITH, D. B. 1963. Freeze Drying of Foodstuffs. Columbine Press, Manchester and London.

DECAREAU, R. V. 1962. Limitations and opportunities for high frequency energy in the freeze-drying process. In Freeze-Drying of Foods, Fisher, F. R., (Editor), Proceedings of a Conference, Chicago, Ill., April 12–14, Washington, Natl. Acad. Sci.-Natl. Res. Council, 147–162.

DIELS, K., and JAECKEL, R. 1958. Leybold Vacuum-Pocketbook (German). Springer-Verlag, Berlin/Gottingen/Heidelberg.

DRAUDT, H. N., DAMON, C. E., HUANG, I. Y., and CHANG, M. T. 1961. Enzyme activity in freeze dried foods. Purdue University, Contract Res. Project Rept., Project No. 7-48-06-031A.

FISHER, F. R. (Editor). 1962. Freeze-drying of foods; Proceedings of a Conference, Chicago, Ill., April 12–14. Washington, Natl. Acad. Sci.-Natl. Res. Council.

GOLDBLITH, S. A. 1963. Microbiological considerations in freeze-dehydrated foods. In Exploration in Future Food Processing Techniques, GOLDBLITH, S. A. (Editor), The M.I.T. Press, Cambridge, Mass.

GOLDBLITH, S. A., KAREL, M., and LUSK, G. 1963. The role of food science and technology in the freeze dehydration of food. Food Technol. 17, No. 2, 21–26; No. 3, 22–24, 27–28.

HAMDY, M. K., CAHILL, V. R., and DEATHERAGE, F. E. 1959. Some observations on the modification of freeze dehydrated meat. Food Research 24, 79–90.

HAMM, R., and DEATHERAGE, F. E. 1960. Changes in hydration and changes of muscle proteins during freeze-dehydration of meat. Food Research 25, 573–586.

HANSON, S. W. F. (Editor). 1961. The Accelerated Freeze-Drying (AFD) Method of Food Preservation. Her Majesty's Stationery Office, London.

HARPER, J. C., and TAPPEL, A. L. 1957. Freeze drying of food products. Advan. Food Research 7, 171–234.

KAREL, M. 1963. Physicochemical aspects of freeze dried foods. In Exploration in Future Food Processing Techniques, GOLDBLITH, S. A. (Editor), The M.I.T. Press, Cambridge, Mass.

KUPRIANOFF, J. 1962. Some factors influencing the reversibility of freeze-drying of foodstuffs. In Freeze-Drying of Foods, FISHER, F. R. (Editor), Proceedings of a Conference, Chicago, Ill., April 12–14, Washington, Natl. Acad. Sci.-Natl. Res. Council. 16–24.

LAWLER, F. K. 1961. Latest in freeze-drying. Food Eng. 33, No. 11, 35–38.

LUSK, G. 1963. Influence of Processing and Storage Parameters on the Quality of Some Freeze-Dried Marine Products. Ph.D. Thesis, M.I.T., Cambridge, Mass.

MERYMAN, H. T. 1960. Principles of freeze-drying. Ann. N. Y. Acad. Sci. 85, 630–640.

NORMAN, W., and AUERBACH, E. 1963. Enhancement of rehydration of precooked, freeze-dried meats. Presented at Am. Meat Inst. Found. Tenth Ann. Res. Rept. Meeting for Ind., March 20, Chicago.

OETJEN, G. W. 1963. Engineering problems and economical aspects of freeze drying. Presented at XIth Intern. Refrigeration Congr., Munich, Sept. 2, Paper No. P-1.

REY, L. R. 1960. Treatise on Lyophilisation. (French). Hermann, Paris.

REY, L. R. 1962. Recent Progress in Lyophilisation. (French). Hermann, Paris.

REY, L. R., and BASTIEN, M. C. 1962. Biophysical aspects of freeze-drying, importance of the preliminary freezing and sublimation periods. In Freeze-Drying of Foods, FISHER, F. R. (Editor), Proceedings of a Conference, Chicago, Ill., April 12–14, 16–24. Washington, Natl. Acad. Sci.-Natl. Res. Council.

SALWIN, H. 1959. Establishing minimum moisture contents for dehydrated foods. Food Technol. 13, 594–595.

SCOTT, D., and HAMMER, F. 1961. Oxygen scavenging package for in-package deoxygenation. Food Technol. 15, 99–104.

SEVERSON, D. E., COOLEY, A. M., and SIMON, M. 1955. Factors affecting the texture of rehydrated potato granules. Food Technol. 9, 223–227.

SHOCKLEY, R. T. 1962. Laminations suitable for packaging freeze dried foods. Food Processing 23, No. 12, 72, 74, 76.

SILVERMAN, G. J., McINTOSH, A. H., PABLO, I. S., SINSKEY, T. J., and GOLD-BLITH, S. A. 1963. Some considerations in the recovery of microorganisms from freeze-dehydrated foods. Paper presented at Meetings of American Public Health Assoc., Kansas City, Kansas, Nov. 12.

SIMPSON, J. I., CHANG, I. C. L., and APPEL, E. C. 1955. Water absorption during reconstitution of dehydrated fruits and vegetables. Food Technol. 9, 608–612.

SMITH, A. U. 1961. Biological Effects of Freezing and Supercooling. Williams & Wilkins Co., Baltimore.

STEINBERG, M. P. 1960. Objective Description of Freeze-Dehydrated Cooked Beef. Rept. No. 8 on Res. Contract No. DA 19-129-QM-1332, University of Illinois, Urbana.

TAYLOR, A. A. 1963. Packaging requirements for freeze-dried foodstuffs. In Freeze Drying of Foodstuffs, COTSON, S., and SMITH, D. B. (Editors), Columbine Press, Manchester and London.

TAYLOR, T. C. 1961. Packaging of freeze-drieds. Food Eng. 33, No. 9, 41–44.

THOMSON, J. S., FOX, J. B., and LANDMANN, W. A. 1962. The effect of water and temperature on the deterioration of freeze-dried beef during storage. Food Technol. 16, No. 9, 131–136.

VAUGHN, R. 1962. Personal communication. University of California, Davis, Calif.

WOODWARD, H. T. 1963. Freeze dehydration without vacuum. Activities Rept. 15, 105–112.

CHAPTER 19

G. E. Brissey and
P. A. Goeser

Aging, Curing and Smoking of Meats

INTRODUCTION

In the discussion which follows, meat in some instances will be classified as to species of origin, e.g., beef, pork, lamb or veal. Mutton and chevon (goat) can be related, in a general way, to comments on lamb, though meat from goats is of no great significance commercially in the United States. Where poultry is to be considered, it will be mentioned specifically. On most occasions, however, when the term *meat* is used it will be in the broad sense of flesh of animal origin.

Once the animal is dispatched, dressed and chilled, the processor must then make a decision as to the use he will make of the meat derived therefrom. Will it be placed in retail channels as fresh or frozen carcasses, primal (wholesale) or retail cuts or will it be prepared for further processing as salted, cured and smoked meats or used for manufacturing meats, such as canned meats, hams, luncheon meats, corned beef, etc., or canned products containing meat—stews, hash, chili, meat sauces, etc., or sausage items—frankfurters, bologna, baked loaves and specialties? Having made the decision the processor will then begin the various tasks of aging, cutting, grinding, chopping, salting or curing, shaping, smoking, canning, cooking and packaging to get the products ready for and into the proper distributive channels.

Though there is some considerable inter-relationship in the preparation of meats for varied end uses, this section will be limited to the aging, salting or curing and smoking of meats. This will include the manufacture of sausage products but not items prepared or preserved for distribution by freezing, canning, dehydrating, radiation sterilization or other means except as possible preliminary preparation steps where applicable, since products prepared by these processes are detailed in another volume of this book.

Neither scientific details nor broad technological aspects can be developed due to the limitations in scope. The reader is referred to the bibliography at the end of this section for more detailed information.

G. E. BRISSEY is General Manager, Quality Assurance Department, and P. A. GOESER is in the Research and Development Center, Swift and Co., Chicago, Ill.

AGING MEAT

"Aging" refers to the process in which fresh meat is stored under controlled conditions for varying periods to increase *tenderness*. Aging is sometimes referred to as *"ripening."* It is a time honored method that is used by meat packers, meat purveyors and some retail meat dealers. In the commercial handling of meat, aging must actually be considered to include the entire period during which meat is held as a fresh product, beginning with the meat packer and ending with the cooking of the specific meat cut in the home, restaurant or institution.

The effects of *rigor mortis* and subsequent cooler age on good quality beef carcasses are shown in Fig. 126. Tenderness rating scale shown is from 1—very poor, to 8—excellent.

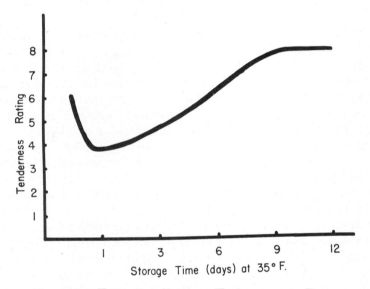

FIG. 126. EFFECT OF AGING ON TENDERNESS OF BEEF

The original approximate beef tenderness value of six at the time of slaughter drops to less than four during *rigor mortis* and gradually increases again to eight with prolonged storage at cooler temperatures or other aging temperatures and conditions. This general effect is noted when aging any of the grades of beef carcasses normally sold through retail channels. The tenderization achieved during aging is attributed to resolution of *rigor mortis* and to autolytic proteolysis.

Aged raw meat compared to fresh meat has higher percentages of protein nitrogen, free amino nitrogen and creatinine but less soluble protein. Aged cooked meat compared to fresh cooked meat has more soluble protein, more protein nitrogen, amino nitrogen and creatinine.

Improved tenderness can be secured by aging at low temperatures for a long time or by aging at high temperatures for a short time. Aging schedules shown in Table 103 will, on the average, provide equal tenderization in beef of similar quality.

TABLE 103

AGING SCHEDULE PRODUCING EQUAL TENDERIZATION OF BEEF

Temperature	Time
32° to 36°F.	2 to 3 weeks
45°F.	5 to 6 days
55°F.	3 to 4 days
68°F.	2 days

In commercial aging at 68°F., surface meat spoilage is partially controlled by ultraviolet radiation, primarily to inhibit airborne bacteria. In experimental work, beef has been aged in one day at temperatures around 110°F. Spoilage at this high temperature of aging was controlled by the use of antibiotics infused into the meat.

In addition to an increase in tenderness, aging does effect some changes in flavor. There is a wide difference of opinion among consumers concerning flavor changes in meat occurring as a result of aging. Two weeks' aging at 34° to 36°F. is generally conceded to improve the flavor of fat and the flavor of lean. Aging beyond two weeks develops more pronounced flavor changes that are due in large part to microbial growth on the surface of the meat. These pronounced aged or *ripened* flavors are sought for and enjoyed especially by gourmets. For many people the pronounced flavor changes due to prolonged ripening are objectionable. Aging beyond two weeks does not provide sufficient increase in tenderness to compensate for the additional cost unless the ripened flavors are essential for a particular trade.

Beef is more commonly aged than pork, veal or lamb. This is due in part to the fact that beef, regardless of quality, lacks in tenderness during the period of *rigor mortis* and for several days immediately following slaughter. Pork is usually not aged. Pork is more uniformerly tender from one carcass to another with less than 20 per cent of carcasses showing lack of tenderness 7 days after dressing. Some aging occurs during the actual merchandising of pork products. Veal carcasses are not aged because of inherent tenderness. They would present an aging problem because of lack of surface fat to provide protection to the meat during the process.   Lamb carcasses are seldom aged as full carcasses.   Occasionally lamb and mutton loins and ribs are aged.   If allowed to age for 7 to 10 days, tenderness of loin and rib chops is definitely improved.   Wild game and fowl are sometimes aged to improve tenderness and to enhance flavor.

Tenderization by aging is costly.   Shrinkage losses due to evaporation and surface trimming will vary from a few per cent on meat carcasses to as much as 6 to 8 per cent on primal cuts.   In addition to investments in aging facilities and longer turnover schedules, increased operating costs are found in all aging procedures.

To provide the least possible surface discoloration and shrinkage due to evaporation, the relative humidity and the rate of air movement in the aging room are controlled.   Relative humidities in the range of 85 to 87 per cent are generally maintained, and air movement of 40 to 60 f.p.m. is desirable.   Evaporation cannot be entirely eliminated because some surface drying on the carcass or meat cut is essential to aid in controlling spoilage due to microbial growth which proceeds very rapidly on moist surfaces.

While aging is usually applied to freshly chilled meat, 24 to 48 hr. following dressing, it may be used on primal cuts such as loins and ribs which have been fabricated from carcasses and chilled 1 to 7 days or more.   In handling primal bone-in and boneless cuts, the meat may be packaged in plastic bags and the air exhausted from the bags.   The bag may or may not be heat shrunk to the meat product. Under such conditions there is no loss due to surface evaporation. Loss in the surface trimming of darkened or spoiled areas is kept to a minimum because of the partial control of surface microbial growth due to air evacuation.   Aging beyond ten days to two weeks may produce some sour meat surfaces under these conditions, due to the growth of anaerobic spoilage organisms.

MEAT SALTING OR CURING

Reason

The initiation of the salting of meats is lost in ancient history. There is little doubt that it was started to improve the character of meats and other foods preserved by smoking as we will note in the section on that subject.   Homer makes reference in his writings to the salting of meats.   The Egyptians are credited with having brought the art of preservation through curing and smoking to a high level of development in their mummification process.

Though the original purpose of salting and curing was primarily for preservation, and at a later time for color and flavor development and fixation, this intent in recent years, except for color and flavor, has with minor exceptions been abandoned.

Ingredients

While the primary ingredient for curing purposes is salt (sodium chloride), other materials have been incorporated historically: saltpeter (potassium nitrate) and sodium nitrate, and in more recent times sugar and sodium nitrite. Spices and seasonings have played their role in special products. Quite recently, as further adjuncts, ascorbic acid and its derivatives, various phosphate compounds, monosodium glutamate and hydrolyzed vegetable proteins have also been utilized.

Nitrate salts have been used to provide the red color of cured meats, though the exact mechanism of all the chemical reactions involved is unknown. The nitrate salt is reduced in the curing process to nitric oxide which reacts with the meat pigment *myoglobin* to produce *nitric oxide myoglobin*. On heat denaturation, this pigment then becomes *nitrosomyochromogen* as illustrated in the following reaction:

$$NO + Myoglobin \rightarrow Nitric\ Oxide\ Myoglobin$$
$$\downarrow + heat$$
$$Nitrosomyochromogen$$

Myoglobin is the pigment of muscle tissue and is directly related to another *heme* pigment, *hemoglobin*. Whereas the hemoglobin transports in the blood stream the oxygen required for metabolism from the lungs of the living animal and returns carbon dioxide to the lungs for expulsion as an end product of the metabolism, the myoglobin is the medium of exchange for the oxygen and the carbon dioxide in the metabolic process.

Sugar was originally added in curing to counteract the harshness of the salt, strictly from a flavor standpoint. Later it was thought to be necessary for assisting in the provision of the required reducing conditions, brought about by bacterial and metabolic processes, needed for the chemical reduction of the nitrate salt to nitric oxide for the formation of the cured meat pigment. In very recent years, it has been shown that sugar is unnecessary for the development of these reducing conditions and, indeed, that artificial sweeteners such as saccharine or sucaryl may be used in lieu of sugar where sweetening only is desired.

Since nitrite is simply one of the reduction products of nitrate in its ultimate reduction to nitric oxide, the Meat Inspection Services of the United States Department of Agriculture in 1925 permitted, with limitations, the use of nitrite *per se* in the curing of meats. The prescription requires that not more than 200 p.p.m. of nitrite (as sodium nitrite) be residual in the finished product.

Ascorbic acid and its derivatives function in two distinct categories. In one, it provides immediate reducing conditions for the production of nitric oxide from sodium nitrite for the curing reaction. In the other, it acts as an antioxidant and protects the cured color from being oxidized by atmospheric oxygen to undesirable colors, such as gray, gray-browns and greens.

While phosphates have been shown to have some effect on the development and stabilization of cured meat pigments, their primary role is that of improving the water binding capacity of the protein. Though the chemical function of the phosphates may not be exactly known, there are at least two factors which are well accepted; they are: (1) the pH, and (2) the phosphate ion effects.

Monosodium glutamate and hydrolyzed vegetable proteins are used as flavor enhancers or intensifiers.

Methods

The curing of meats is accomplished by one of two methods: (1) dry salting or (2) pickling.

In dry salting the meats are rubbed and/or packed with dry salt or dry combinations of the above curing ingredients. In order to prevent bacterial spoilage while the cure materials are being absorbed, the products are usually held at temperatures on the order of 35° to 40°F. Meats cured under these conditions require approximately $1^1/_2$ to 2 days per pound to complete the cure. A variation of dry salting is in the manufacture of sausage, as shall be seen in subsequent discussion, for the curing materials are added in the dry form to the meats as they are being ground, chopped or otherwise comminuted.

A typical dry cure mix for 100 lbs. of pork hams or bellies is: 2 lbs. 4 oz. salt, 1 lb. 8 oz. sugar, and 4 oz. sodium nitrate.

For processing of country hams, the instructions for the cure might be as follows: rub ham with 2 oz. of nitrate of soda and the next day apply, per 100 lbs. of ham, a mixture of 3 lbs. of fine salt and 1 lb. of granulated white sugar.

Several different procedures may be used in pickle curing (commonly called *sweet pickle* curing) of meats. The simplest is that of strictly absorption curing wherein meats to be cured are immersed in a pickle composed of the desired curing ingredients dissolved in water and held in suitable containers under much the same conditions described for dry curing.   In a further effort to prevent bacterial spoilage, the meats may be *stitch*-pumped by means of a hollow perforated needle, attached to a pump which provides the pickle under pressure.   In this manner the pickle is infused into the deep areas where absorption of curing ingredients would otherwise take the longest, with resulting possibility of bacterial activity.

Arterial Pumping of Hams.—A refinement of this procedure is the pumping of curing pickle, in the desired amounts, into the vascular system of the piece of meat being cured.   This provides a relatively

Courtesy of Swift & Co. (Mr. Ed Hois)

FIG. 127.   ARTERIAL PUMPING OF HAMS

uniformly dispersed cure, almost immediately, throughout the entire piece.   The process may be followed by the application of dry cure or immersion in pickle.   Curing by this method drastically reduces the time required.

A typical pumping pickle, having a salometer value of approximately 80° at about 38°F., would be formulated to contain:

        Salt...............................14.5%
        Sugar.............................. 4.0

Phosphate...................... 3.8 (Optional)
Sodium nitrate.................. 0.160
Sodium nitrite.................. 0.075
Sodium isoascorbate............ 0.30 (Optional)

For a curing cover pickle, to be used at the rate of $4^1/_2$ gal. per 100 lbs. of meat, with a salometer value of 50° at about 38°F., the formula might be:

Salt..............................12.5%
Sugar........................... 1.0
Sodium nitrate.................. 0.08
Sodium nitrite.................. 0.08

Courtesy of Swift & Co. (Mr. Ed Hois)

FIG. 128. AUTOMATIC MULTIPLE NEEDLE INJECTION
PUMPING OF BELLIES FOR BACON

A development of quite recent origin is equipment for the *stitch* pumping of meats automatically through multiple needle, manifold heads, where the hollow perforated needles are spaced at relatively short distances (1 to 2 in.). Machines of this type have even been developed for the pumping of bone-in product, the needles being retractably mounted.

TYPES OF CURED MEATS

There are many procedures available for the curing of meats. Any particular cut of meat may be cured and processed in one of several different ways. Since pork hams, shoulders and bellies constitute the major cured items, it seems best to describe the curing in detail of these products first. Cuts from other species as well as miscellaneous other cured items, will be related or described in less detail.

Hams

The curing of hams has undergone drastic revision over the past fifty years. Traditionally, hams were prepared by the dry curing procedure which, as has been previously described, amounts to rubbing the surface of the ham with dry salt or a mixture of dry cure ingredients made in accordance with a "special recipe" of the user. This method of curing provided a product which was well preserved due to the high level of salt absorbed in the curing. The resultant product was harsh in flavor. The amount of time necessary to accomplish the curing was dependent upon the weight of the ham, but took from several days to many weeks. On completion of cure the hams were washed and/or soaked to remove surface cure in preparation for smoking.

By trial and error, it was determined that a better and more uniform distribution of cure could be obtained by curing the ham through immersion in a sweet pickle solution. This method, by providing the curing ingredients already in solution, made for easier absorption. In this manner the possibility of bacteriological spoilage was also reduced. The time involved was approximately the same as for the hams cured by the dry cure procedure. Since the curing ingredients were in solution and in much less concentration than when applied in the dry state, this ham was not as salty as the dry cured ham, but was far saltier than the product which is in general distribution today. Because of the high level of surface salt concentration following curing, this ham was also soaked in water in preparation for smoking.

As a development over the strictly absorption method of sweet pickle curing, some of the curing pickle was injected into the deepest or most remote parts of the ham, or into parts most likely to develop bacterial spoilage. This was accomplished by means of a hollow perforated needle using the technique known as stitch or spray pumping. Immersion in a sweet pickle curing solution followed this treatment. It was not uncommon for hams cured by this process to take 60 to 90 days of cure time.

Because of the high levels of salt—as much as 5 to 7 per cent in the products produced as described above, parboiling was required before final cooking to remove some of the salt.

A revolution occurred in the 1930's with the advent of vascular injection of curing solutions into the ham; this method has been designated *arterial* pumping (Fig. 127). The procedure, with its immediate distribution of curing ingredients into most parts of the ham, along with subsequent immersion of the so-called "pumped" ham into a curing cover pickle for a period of up to 20 days, resulted in a finished product containing about 4 to $4^1/_2$ per cent salt. The resulting ham was the one that was initially proclaimed as the "tender," mild ham, for the arterial method of curing with its attendant processing did, in fact, result in a more tender, less salty product. Over the years there has been a continued demand for milder and milder products resulting from reduction in concentration of salt in the pickle solutions, as well as the length of time in cure. Starting in the mid-1940's the processing of hams by the injection of 8 per cent of 95° salometer curing pickle, then curing in a 60° salometer covering pickle for 15 to 20 days prior to smoking and heat processing gradually changed to a process where the injection is approximately 20 per cent of 45° salometer curing pickle with immediate heat-smoke processing of the pickled product. A product with much less salt has naturally resulted—in the order of two per cent salt.

In the 1950's, as previously mentioned, machines were developed for the stitch or needle spray pumping of boneless hams as a step in the automation of this process. A variation of equipment is pictured in Fig. 128. These machines consisted of multiple mounted, perforated, hollow needles in a manifold head, the needles being inserted into the boneless cuts of ham at spaced intervals as the hams traveled on a conveyor belt. In order to assure complete and thorough distribution of the curing ingredients throughout the hams processed by this procedure, they might be packed for a few days in dry salt, held for one or two days in a curing cover pickle, or repumped after holding for 24 hr. Equipment of this type has also been built for the injection curing of bone-in hams. At this writing this latter equipment has not gained wide spread usage, due to difficulties in obtaining uniform distribution of cure and the desired uniformity of cure gains. No doubt these deficiencies will be corrected as time goes on, since the machine lends itself to automation which is lacking in the arterial pumping of bone-in hams.

By far the vast majority of the sweet pickle hams (which are more commonly referred to in the trade as S. P. hams) are further processed by heat and smoke. Many are boned, if not cured boneless, and used for processing as canned ham; or, they may be pressed into metal forms and then cooked in tanks of water to produce the product known as "boiled" ham.   S. P. hams sold as such have a degree of market distribution particularly in the New England area, and are known as "scotch" hams.

Courtesy of Swift & Co. (Mr. Ed Hois)

Fig. 129.   Trolleys of Smoked Hams Being "Pulled" from a Cabinet-Type Smokehouse

Smithfield, or country cure hams, are traditionally cured by the dry cure process, though, here again, modifications may be made in their curing through the incorporation of portions of the sweet pickle curing procedure.

Hams may be cured regular, that is full shank and unskinned, or they may be skinned and short shank or shankless.   They may also be made skinless, fatted and semiboneless or boneless.

Shoulders

The same curing procedures as described for hams are also applicable to pork shoulders.   The most common practice is to divide the shoulder into two cuts, the lower portion known as the picnic and the upper portion known as the boneless butt which after processing is more familiarly referred to as a Cottage Roll, Daisy, Shoulder Butt, etc.

There is a considerable export business in pork shoulders, particularly in the Caribbean area. One or the other variations of the sweet pickle curing procedures is used to cure the shoulders for this purpose. This may be followed by a period of cure in a dry curing operation in order to insure a very stable product against the rigors of distribution through channels lacking in refrigeration. The stability required may also be attained by adjustments in the strength of the injected pickle and the final drying or smoking process.

Picnics are cured and processed by all of the methods described for hams.

Boneless butts are a natural for automated processing on a manifold needle injection machine.

Bellies

As with hams, the traditional method of curing bellies was the dry curing procedure. Here again sweet pickle curing was an alternate method of choice.

Until the later 1940's the predominant method of curing bellies was the so-called "box-cure" which was a variation of the dry curing procedure. The belly boxes were designed to hold from 800 to 1,200 lbs. of product and were fitted with stout wooden lids. An amount of dry cure was weighed out for a particular box and number of bellies and the cure evenly distributed over the layers of bellies as they were placed in the box. The box was deliberately over-filled, requiring the application of the wooden lid by hydraulic pressure in order to achieve heavy pressure on bellies in the box. The pressure forced air pockets from between the layers and caused the bellies to make their own pickle from the added dry cure mixture. After packing, the boxes were held from 25 to 35 days, depending upon the weight average of the belly, at temperatures on the order of 38° to 40°F. On the completion of the cure time the bellies were pulled from the boxes and sometimes soaked in a mild (10° salometer) pickle for a period of several hours in preparation for heat and smoke processing. The soaking brine *might* contain small quantities of sodium nitrite depending upon the processor.

Though sweet pickle curing was practiced in the preparation of bellies, by and large the procedure used was strictly that of absorption curing. In order to hasten the process, some processors were using variations of hand stitch pumping.   The late 1940's saw the advent of the multiple mounted, hollow, perforated needle manifold head machines for the injection of the curing solution into the bellies (see Fig. 128).   These machines were the forerunners of those developed and described for the ham curing process.   Traditionalists still put the bellies down in a dry cure mixture on pallets following the injection of the curing solution.   It was felt that upward of ten days were required for full maturation and development of the so-called "cured" flavor.   Commercial practice has shown that time in cure is unnecessary, and the bellies are currently "hung off" directly from the pickle injection machine to the smoke trolleys for heat and smoke processing.

FIG. 130.   TROLLEYS OF FINISHED BACON ON COMPLETION
OF HEAT AND SMOKE PROCESSING

Heavy bellies are still cured by the dry curing procedure to produce what is known in the trade as salt pork.   In this instance, the curing may also be speeded up by modifying the dry cure to incorporate hand stitch or spray pumping, or needle injection pumping.

Courtesy of Swift & Co. (Mr. Ed Hois)

FIG. 131. SLICING AND PACKAGING OF BACON

So-called "bean bacon" may be made either by the dry cure or sweet pickle process, using any of their many variations. This product usually comes from the lighter bellies used for salt pork.

Fat backs (the heavy fatty covering removed from the loins) are also cured by variations of these procedures and find wide-spread usage throughout the South and Southeastern portions of the United States as flavoring and seasoning meats.

Pork jowls are handled similarly to bellies.

It is interesting to note that at one time there was a large business in this country in the curing and processing of whole sides of pork. This was accomplished primarily through the use of the sweet-pickle absorption method of processing though dry-salting processes were also used and the finished product was known as Wiltshire Bacon. It was made mostly for export to England and at one time, in rather large quantities. Though there is still quite a demand for this product in England, little if any is made in the United States or Canada. The bulk of the product for England is now made in Ireland, Denmark, Holland and Germany.

BEEF ITEMS

While most beef is sold fresh or used as *manufacturing meats*, there is still a large portion which goes into salted or cured items. The better known of these are corned beef, beef hams (for distribution as sliced dried beef) and beef tongues.   It should be noted that the term "corned" stems from the fact that grains of salt were formerly called "corns."   Salt brines or dry salt cures were made from these "corns" of salt, and hence the meats preserved thereby were termed "corned."

Corned beef is usually prepared from beef briskets, rump butts or shoulder clods.   The briskets are normally cured using a combination of arterial, stitch or spray pumping and cover pickle curing, while the other two cuts generally are cured strictly through absorption curing, though stitch or spray pumping may be incorporated along with it. Curing ages and temperatures for the absorption curing are approximately the same as those for pork cuts i.e., $1^1/_2$ to 2 days per pound at about 38°F.   Preference in the New England area is for corned beef cured without nitrate salts.   Curing in this fashion produces a product which has a gray or gray-brown appearance.   In other sections of the country ascorbic acid or ascorbate salts are incorporated in the curing pickles, so the cured meat in the retail package will have the red or pink appearance associated with *cooked* corned beef.

Beef hams are the boneless cuts derived from the hind leg of beef carcasses.   These cuts are named the *inside*, the *outside* and the *knuckle*.   In the strictly sweet pickle absorption curing of these products, it was common practice to scrub them with a stiff fiber brush using a saturated brine solution (100° salometer) before placing them into the curing pickle.   Depending upon the processor, these hams are now primarily cured by variations of stitch or spray pumping, by hand or through the needle injection machine, followed by a period in cover pickle.   Beef hams cured by this process are used exclusively for further processing into dried beef.   The dried beef hams are sliced wafer thin and sold as chipped or sliced dried beef.

Beef tongues may be absorption-cured in a sweet pickle curing solution, or may be arterially pumped using either or both of the *lingual* arteries followed by absorption curing in a sweet pickle cover solution.   The cured tongues may be sold as sweet pickle tongues, or may be used for canning as canned beef tongues, or may be heat and smoke processed.

MISCELLANEOUS SALTED OR CURED MEATS

The production of barreled beef and pork cuts was at one time the most common of the salted or cured meat products.   This was in the days when the salting or curing of meats was solely a matter of preservation to carry the meats over from the fall and winter slaughtering seasons through the warm periods of the year, since refrigeration was unknown.   Furthermore, it was the only practical means of provisioning ships. It is for this purpose that there is still a demand for these items today, particularly in the fishing fleets. Among the beef cuts treated in this manner are briskets, navels and plates, and in the pork cuts, spare ribs, shoulders and bellies. Product so cured is generally absorption cured in a high salometer salt brine. Following cure, the product is packed into containers using a high salometer salt brine and "capped off" with dry salt. The containers are of wood and known variously as "kits," quarter-, half-, and full barrels depending upon size.

For export purposes, particularly in the Caribbean area, pork snouts, lips, ears and tails may be cured for a period in dry salt or in a salt brine, and then packed in barrels in a manner similar to that described for barreled pork.

Sheep and goat hams have a limited demand in areas of the United States, most particularly in the Southwest. These products are cured and processed in the same manner as described for pork hams.

There is also some limited demand for cured pork spare ribs and pork loins. The spare ribs are cured by absorption curing, whereas the pork loins may be cured by absorption curing or a combination of stitch pumping and absorption curing. Both items are usually further processed by heat and smoke.

With respect to poultry, turkeys and, to a very limited degree, chickens also are cured. These products may be cured after dressing by an absorption cure or by means of a combination of hand spray or stitch pumping and absorption curing. They have limited distribution and are considered to be specialty products. They are distributed usually only after further processing with heat and smoke.

SAUSAGE PRODUCTS

As is so typical in attempting to establish the historical background of meat and/or meat products, it is found that the origin of sausages is lost in antiquity. In the study of any civilization, the earliest reference materials contain mention of sausage products. The terminology sausage is derived from the latin word *salsus*, whose literal translation means *salted* and which has usable translation in "meat minced and highly seasoned and commonly enclosed in the prepared intestine of some animal." Because of their association with pagan rites, sausages were forbidden by the early Christians. Since they enjoyed an extreme popularity, "extra legal" production or bootlegging of these products came to be the accepted order of the day and the bans against their usage were finally removed.

Practically speaking, sausage can be defined as any ground, chopped or comminuted meat mixed with seasonings and/or cure, and formed. Broadly speaking, sausages are classified into two major categories, i.e., domestic and dry or semidry. The domestic variety may be fresh (uncooked and/or uncured), cured and cooked and/or smoked. The dry sausage having historical background in the warmer sections of Europe is generally neither smoked nor cooked. But this is the normal case with the semidry sausage which has its background in the northern or colder sections of Europe.

Many varieties of sausage products take their names from cities, e.g., frankfurters from Frankfort on Main, Germany; wieners from Vienna, Austria; bologna from Bologna, Italy; Goteborg from Gothenberg, Sweden; Lebanon bologna from Lebanon, Pennsylvania. Some products derive their names from countries or geographical areas, for example, Polish sausage and New England cooked specialty. Each ethnic group seems to have developed a whole host of sausage products. The United States, being the great melting pot that it is, has the greatest variety of sausage products manufactured. One can easily believe that there are at least 200 different products to satisfy the demand.

SAUSAGE RAW MATERIALS

Meats from all species of animals are used in the manufacture of sausage products, but those derived from beef and pork are used in the greatest quantity. Beef raw materials are those obtained from boning out the entire carcass, as is the case of *canner* and *cutter* grades of cows or bulls. Other beef raw materials are obtained as trimmings from the preparation of primal or boneless cuts. Pork raw materials are generally derived from the trimming of primal cuts, such as hams, shoulders, loins and bellies. They may also be derived from boning out the usual wholesale cuts of hams and shoulders, particularly those from heavy hogs. Meat manufacturing raw material coming from sheep, mutton and veal is that which is obtained in the preparation or trimming of the wholesale cuts of these meats or the boning of the entire carcass. Various organ or variety meats are also used in the preparation of sausage products, e.g., hearts, tripe, livers, tongue, tongue trimmings, head and cheek meat.

Seasonings are one of the major factors in producing the variety of sausage products. This is undoubtedly due to the tremendous numbers of seasoning materials available. Outside of the commonplace salt, sugar and pepper (black pepper), hundreds of spices and herbs are available to the sausage maker. Examples of some of the common spices and herbs regularly used are the following: anise, basil, paprika, black and white pepper, sage, thyme, mustard, nutmeg and mace, turmeric, sweet bay, capers, caraway, cardamon, cassia, cayenne, celery seed, chives, cinnamon, cloves, coriander, cumin, dill, garlic, ginger, marjoram, etc. All of these materials may be used in the form of the seed or the plant as the flavoring material. There is an increasing tendency to the use of spice extractives rather than the natural spice because of greater uniformity and depth of seasoning. These spice extractives may be in the form of oleoresins or essential oils or combinations thereof. Because of the extremely concentrated nature of these extractives and oleoresins, they are usually distributed on a base material, such as salt or dextrose, in such concentration that the diluted material would then be used in approximately the same weight ratio as though the natural seasoning was used.

Along with seasonings as nonmeat ingredients incorporated in the manufacture of sausage, there are also a variety of fillers or binders. These fillers and binders serve two primary purposes as their names imply. On one hand, as fillers, they simply extend the amount of finished material which may be made from a given amount of meat raw material. On the other, as binders they assist in the stabilization of the protein, fat and water mix, and prevent the "breaking down" or "fatting off" of the meat "emulsion" during the heat processing operation. The material most commonly used for this purpose is nonfat, dried milk solids (dried skim milk). Flours from many other sources are also used; these may be derived from wheat, corn, rice, potato and soy beans. Alginates, along with some of the other wide variety of natural gums, also have a degree of usage for the stabilization of the so-called meat emulsion.

As was noted in the section on cured meats, ascorbic acid and its derivatives, phosphates and protein hydrolyzates from many vegetable protein sources also find wide usage in the preparation of sausage products. They are incorporated for the same reasons as those described for cured meats. The various phosphate compounds are not permitted to be used in the preparation of sausage products in federally inspected meat operations in the United States. Their use however, is quite wide-spread throughout the whole of Europe.

Casings

Casings are a necessary part of the manufacture of sausage in that they assist in the forming, shaping and molding or packaging of the finished product. Until relatively recent times, all sausage products were stuffed into natural or animal casings. Natural casings have been largely displaced by artificial casings, obtained for the most part from regenerated cellulose or other plastic. Less than 20 per cent of sausages, including "dry" sausages, are now produced in natural casings. Depending primarily upon size, shape or origin, trade designations of casings include: small, medium, large, rounds, middles, bungs, bladders, etc.

PROCESSING CONSIDERATIONS

In the preparation of meat products which may be eaten without further heat treatment, destruction of viable *trichinae* organisms is essential. The Meat Inspection Service of the United States Department of Agriculture recognizes three methods of treatment of pork and other meat products subject to *trichinosis*. They are:

1. Heat treatment to insure a minimum temperature of 137°F. in all portions of the meat.

2. Freezing storage according to the following time-temperature schedule:

Temperature, °F.	Time, in days, for 6 in. diameter	Time, in days 6 to 27 in. diameter
+5	20	30
−10	10	20
−20	6	10

3. Specific curing techniques for specific products, related to type of cure, as dry or sweet pickle, whether the meat is ground or in chunks, dimensions of the finished item, etc.

Types of Sausage Products

Since there are such large varieties of types of sausage products manufactured, the best method of describing their manufacture is to put them in categories. For convenience, these categories will be divided into "fresh" sausage, such as pork sausage; "finely comminuted," such as frankfurters and bologna; "coarse chopped," such as Polish and smoked country; "specialty," such as liver sausage and baked loaves; and finally, "dry and semidry" sausages, such as salami and thuringer.

Fresh Pork Sausage.—In the manufacture of fresh pork sausage, fresh chilled selected trimmings from various pork cuts are used. The meats are comminuted or reduced to the desired particle size, by either of two methods: (1) the meats are hashed, or chopped, and mixed with the desired seasoning and flavoring materials; (2) the meats are first coarse ground, mixed with the desired seasoning and flavoring materials, and finally, fine ground to the desired texture. Water or ice may be used during the chopping or grinding operation to facilitate this operation and also to keep the temperature reduced. Some manufacturers, rather than using trimmings for the manufacture of fresh pork sausage, prefer to use the entire boneless pork carcass. A typical seasoning formula for **fresh pork sausage** is as follows: 2 lbs. salt, 3 oz. sage, and 7 oz. pepper (usually white).

Other optional ingredients may be used, depending upon geographical preference; for example, mace is used in some localities, and red pepper is a necessary addition in the South and Southeastern sections of the United States. Many proprietary mixtures are available for flavoring and seasoning fresh pork sausage. Though it is not permitted in federally inspected meat packing establishments, many manufacturers use ascorbic acid in the manufacture of pork sausage to assist in the retention of the desirable red color in the lean meat portions of this sausage.

After preparation of the meat mix, it is put up for distribution in many different forms. It may be distributed in bulk, that is, filled into one-pound bags or stuffed into long lengths of medium hog casings. Probably the bulk of fresh pork sausage is sold as link sausage stuffed in sheep casings. Of relatively recent origin is the forming of fresh pork sausage into links without the use of casings. Also, another recent innovation is the preparation and sale of "brown and serve" links and patties. In products of this latter type, the major portion of the cooking shrink has been taken by the manufacturer; all that is necessary to prepare the product for serving is the warming and browning of the item.

The only type of sausage which may be prepared and sold as fresh pork sausage is that which is made from strictly pork raw materials. There are other fresh sausages available made with the addition of other meat raw materials, in which cereal products or other extenders may be incorporated.

Federal regulations require that fresh pork sausage be made from pork raw materials containing not more than 50 per cent trimmable fat, which means approximately a 55 per cent analytical fat.

Frankfurters or Bologna.—The manufacturing procedures used for the production of frankfurters and bologna are for all practical purposes identical. The significant variation is in the form of the final product and a slight variation in seasoning.

The selected meat raw materials, which consist primarily of beef and

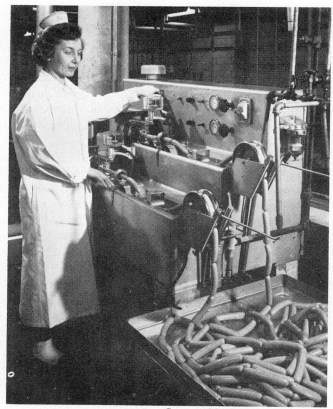

Courtesy of Swift & Co. (Mr. Ed Hois)

FIG. 132.   AUTOMATIC STUFFING AND LINKING
OF FRANKFURTERS

pork trimmings, are first ground or hashed and then chopped to a relatively fine consistency. During the chopping operation, cold water and/or ice are added to facilitate this operation, to contribute to the finished texture and also to keep the temperature reduced during the mechanical manipulation. The cure materials, seasoning and spices are added during the chopping.

A typical cure and seasoning formulation for **frankfurters** based on 100 lbs. of meat is as follows:

3 lbs. 8 oz.	Salt
2 lbs. . . .	Dextrose
6 oz.	Ground white pepper
4 oz.	Ground coriander
2 oz.	Ground nutmeg
$^1/_2$ oz.	Powdered garlic or onion (optional)

$^1/_4$ oz.	Sodium nitrite
$^1/_2$ oz.	Sodium nitrate
$^7/_8$ oz.	Sodium isoascorbate (optional)

In addition to the above, a typical formula for **bologna** might include two ounces of ground allspice and one-half ounce powdered garlic or onion.

Frankfurters may be stuffed into varying sizes of natural casing and linked to different lengths. Or, they may be stuffed into artificial casings (which is the common practice) and made into the commonly accepted *hot dog*.

Courtesy of Swift & Co. (*Mr. Ed Hois*)

FIG. 133. LINKING AND SMOKE STICK LOADING OF FRANKFURTERS

Bologna is designated particularly by the size and shape of the finished product. It may be variously described as ring, small, large or square. However, the same meat formula is generally used to produce all. Following the forming, shaping or stuffing operation, the frankfurters or bologna are subjected to a heating and smoking operation.

Coarse Chopped Sausage.—Sausage products typical of this variety are Polish and smoked country sausage. They are characterized by being coarsely chopped, or of coarse texture, and having cure added (which means the use of nitrite salts) and being smoked; this is in contradistinction to fresh pork sausage. The meat materials are usually prepared by grinding to the desired texture, mixing with the desired curing and flavoring ingredients, followed by stuffing into suitable-sized casings, linking and heat and smoke processing.

Courtesy of Swift & Co. (Mr. Ed Hois)

FIG. 134. LOADING THE CABINET SMOKEHOUSE
WITH TROLLEYS OF FRANKFURTERS

Typical formulation for the curing and seasoning of **Polish sausage** is:

Per Cwt. Meat

3 **lbs.** 8 oz.	Salt
2 **lbs.** ...	Dextrose
$^3/_8$ oz.	Garlic powder
6 oz.	Ground pepper or pepper flavoring
$1^3/_8$ oz.	Ground coriander
$^3/_4$ oz.	Ground ginger
$1^1/_4$ oz.	Paprika
5 oz.	Whole mustard seed
$^1/_2$ oz.	Sodium nitrate
$^1/_4$ oz.	Sodium nitrite

For **smoked country sausage** the formulation is:

Per Cwt. Meat

2 lbs. ...	Salt
1 lb. ...	Sugar

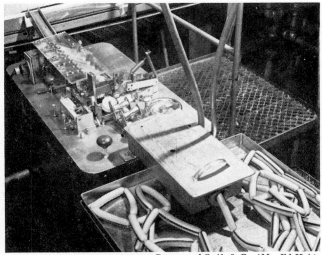

Courtesy of Swift & Co. (Mr. Ed Hois)

FIG. 135. VIEW FROM LOADING END OF SKINLESS
FRANKFURTER CASING PEELING EQUIPMENT

The black stripes on the artificial casings makes for ease
of observing the "skips"—those from which the casing has
not been entirely removed.

$^1/_2$ oz.	Sodium nitrate
$^1/_8$ oz.	Sodium nitrite
$^3/_4$ oz.	Coriander (ground)
$^1/_2$ oz.	Ground caraway
3 oz.	Ground white pepper

Specialty Products.—**Liver sausage** is a good example of one of
the specialty products. A regular formulation for this product
would consist of 50 per cent pork liver and 50 per cent fresh pork
jowls, with the following spice formulation per cwt:

4 lbs. ...	Raw onions
3 lbs. ...	Salt
6 oz.	White pepper
2 oz.	Ground mace
1 oz.	Ground marjoram
$^1/_2$ oz.	Ground cloves

In the preparation of this item the livers are trimmed and washed and
may be leached for a time in a 20° salometer salt pickle. The livers
are then put through a hasher or chopped with the onions; the jowls
are ground and the entire mix is chopped to the desired consistency.

The meat mass can be finished in a variety of ways. It may be
formed into various sizes and shapes in natural or artificial casings,
and then heat and/or smoke processed.

FIG. 136.   CONTINUOUS FRANKFURTER
MANUFACTURING EQUIPMENT

The frankfurters are formed in molds electronically without the
use of casings. Smoking, cooking and chilling are accomplished
as the frankfurters are conveyed through the apparatus.   Production rates are on the order of 1,000 lbs./hr.

Some of the many forms in which products containing liver may be
merchandised are liver sausage, liver loaf, liverwurst and braun-
schweiger.

Other specialty products will include such items as pickle and
pimento loaf, olive loaf, macaroni and cheese loaf, old-fashioned loaf,
pepper loaf, etc. ' The basic raw materials for these items are comparable to frankfurters and bologna, though there may be variations
in grind, as in the case of the old-fashioned loaf.

Since by government definition these items are designated *imitation
products*, they may contain a large variety of nonmeat ingredients.
This is due primarily to the materials used in their preparation, such
as pickle and pimento, macaroni and cheese, olives, etc.   Meat loaves
require the usual seasoning ingredients of salt and sugar as well as the
cured color developing agent—a nitrate salt.

Baked loaves in the finished form are marketed as such, generally to
the delicatessen section or cold meat department of the retail outlet.
There is an increasing tendency to distribute these products in sliced,

Courtesy of Swift & Co. (Mr. Ed Hois)

FIG. 137. PACKAGING SLICED LUNCHEON LOAVES

packaged form as "cold cut" or "sandwich material."

Dry and Semidry Sausage.—As has been previously mentioned, the manufacture of dry or semidry sausages stems from prehistoric times. They were probably developed by a series of gradual steps as the most practical means of preserving for future use those meat cuts which could not be consumed at once, and which were of a character or size not suitable for other methods of preservation.

Though there are many types of dry sausage, one of the larger classes is that of the salamis. While some of the salamis contain a small percentage of beef, the predominant meat for salami is pork and, in some instances, nothing but pork. It was common practice at one time to coarse-grind the meats selected for the salami, mix with the seasonings, spices and cure, and then spread on trays. It was held for up to 24 hr. before giving the final chop or grind and continuing with the process. The more common practice today is a continuous operation in the chopping or grinding, mixing with the seasonings, spices and cure, and proceeding directly with the rest of the operation.

A typical cure, seasoning and spice formula per 100 lbs. of meat for an **Italian style Salami** would be as follows:

3 lbs.	8 oz.	Salt
1 lb.	8 oz.	Sugar
	$^{1}/_{2}$ oz.	Sodium nitrate
	$^{1}/_{8}$ oz.	Sodium nitrite
	2 oz.	Whole white pepper
	3 oz.	Ground white pepper
	$1^{1}/_{2}$ oz.	Prepared fresh garlic

Courtesy of Swift & Co. (Mr. Ed Hois)

FIG. 138.   "ROPING" DRY SAUSAGE IN ARTIFICIAL CASING

After the meat mass has been prepared, it is usually stuffed into hog bungs to form a product of 3 to 4 in. in diameter and up to 20, and in some instances, 30 in. in length.   The stuffed sausage is then "roped" with stout twine to give support to the casing and to provide means for hanging during the drying operation.

The product is then removed to the "green" room where it is hung for up to 72 hr. at 50° to 70°F., with carefully controlled conditions of air velocity and relative humidity.

Since the Italian sausage is not smoked, it is removed directly from the green room to the drying room.   Here again, the air conditions are carefully controlled as to temperature, velocity and relative humidity. Because the meat raw materials are not cooked, the drying time is strictly regulated by the Meat Inspection Services of the United States Department of Agriculture, so as to assure the safety of the product for eating by the consumer without further processing.   In the case of the Italian salami being described, the drying time will be a matter of many weeks.   When the processing of this sausage is completed, it has tremendous shelf-stability under almost any condition.

A typical semidry sausage (sometimes referred to as soft- or summer-sausage) is thuringer. As opposed to the salamis, beef predominates in the meat mixtures used for the preparation of this sausage. The meats are chopped, or ground, to a fineness approximating a $^{1}/_{8}$-in. plate, which is sometimes referred to as "coarse bologna" texture. After mixing the ground meats with the seasonings, spices and cure, the mixture is then stuffed into hog bungs or sewed hog bungs. The sausages are hung in a green room to allow the cure to develop and placed in a cold smoke house. The product

Courtesy of Swift & Co. (Mr. Ed Hois)

Fig. 139.   Dry Sausage Hanging Room

is smoked at a relatively low temperature which is gradually allowed to rise over a one to two day period to approximately 110°F. This allows naturally present bacterial flora to develop and produce the characteristic "tang" of this typical fermented sausage.

In recent years it has been common practice to add cultures of lactic acid producing bacteria to the meats during formulation to speed up the processing operation, and also to insure the development of the desired flavor characteristics.

In some instances, the product may be finished in a sufficiently high temperature to insure its being satisfactory for consumption without being further processed. In other instances, the pork raw

organisms have been shown to be a part of the natural flora of the packing house. Since they tend to the psychrophyllic types, the only thing that time in cure accomplished was to assure their presence in adequate load at the time the cured meats were ready to be smoked. This concept has made for drastic revisions in processing operations in recent years.

There are two primary types of smokehouses in general use today: (1) the multi-floored; and (2) the cabinet (or kiln as it is referred to in England and on the Continent).

Multi-floored smoke houses served their purpose admirably when they were initially designed and installed. The smoking practice at that time was for preservation, which required prolonged smoking of harshly cured product with heavy smoke and relatively low temperature to dry out the product and make it keep, rather than to produce the lightly smoked, mildly cured, succulent product of today. The rigid control of temperature, humidity, air velocity and smoke volume so necessary in the modern operation was practically impossible to

Courtesy of Swift & Co. (Mr. Ed Hois)

Fig. 140.   Mechanical Sawdust Burner and
Smokehouse Controllers

materials used may be certified by other procedures, such as freezing, which are acceptable to the Meat Inspection Services of the United States Department of Agriculture.

SMOKING OF MEATS

The practice of smoke preservation of foods extends far back into prehistoric times and probably stems from the custom of hanging such items as meat, fish, cheese, fowl, etc., near the smoke vent of the dwelling or the cave roof so as to be out of reach. The keeping qualities of the foodstuffs, so exposed, were noted to be greatly improved.

Historically and until relatively recent years, the smoking, with its intendant curing process, was carried out to preserve the meat or other food over prolonged periods. The current consumer demand is for mildly cured, lightly smoke flavored meat products which have only slightly less perishability than fresh meat. There are minor exceptions to this in that there is a very limited demand for products of the Smithfield or country cure ham type and certain highly seasoned, highly smoked, dry or semidry sausages, such as thuringer, smoked salamis and Lebanon bologna.

Smoking, as practiced today, is almost always combined with heat and the following effects, among others, may be listed as resulting from the deposition of smoke constituents and the effects of temperature:

(1) Drying.
(2) Development and fixing of color of lean portions.
(3) A tendering action from increased activity of natural proteolytic enzymes of meat due to the elevated temperature.
(4) The imparting of a desirable finish or gloss on the skin and/or flesh sides of the meat pieces.
(5) The imparting of desirable flavor and odor properties.
(6) The imparting of antioxidants to the fat.
(7) The impregnating of the outer portions of the meat with constituents of smoke which can exert a preservative action.
(8) A reduction of the microbial level present in the meat.

Studies on the development of the so-called "cured" flavor and on

obtain in the multi-floored houses. Hence, the cabinet house was developed where these important factors could be closely controlled.

Some attempts have been made to use continuous smoking operations. Experience has shown that products can be successfully smoked in continuous operations using electrostatic smoke precipitating procedures. Where heating of products to a uniform temperature is also required, much development work remains to be done. In Europe, however, continuous smoking and heat processing operations are extensively used in the smoking of fish.

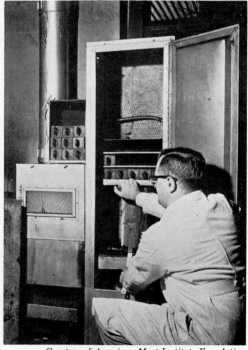

Courtesy of American Meat Institute Foundation

FIG. 141.   FRICTION SMOKE GENERATOR

There has been quite an evolution in the field of smoke generation and again, this has taken place in relatively recent years. Not more than 25 to 30 years ago, smoke was still being generated by smoldering hardwood logs in the pit of the old multi-tiered houses. The practice of sprinkling hardwood sawdust on smoldering logs gradually replaced the logs. The next step was to remove smoke generation to an external burning pit, adjacent to the smoke house. This materially reduced smoke house fires which had been commonplace when the generation had been done in the pit of the house itself. An improvement over this procedure was the development of mechanical sawdust burners which produced a much more uniform flow and volume of smoke with practically no operator attention.

Among recent developments is "friction generation." In this country hardwood logs are pressed onto a rotating disk. In Europe the logs are pressed onto a rotating cylinder. Smoke produced by this type of generator is not entirely comparable to that produced by the more conventional method of smoldering hardwood sawdust.

The chemical analysis of the two types of smoke is shown in the following Table 104.

TABLE 104

FRICTION VS. NON-FRICTION SMOKE

	Sawdust		Friction	
	Steam Volatile	Nonsteam Volatile	Steam Volatile	Nonsteam Volatile
pH	4.00	4.20	3.18	3.00
Total acids (as acetic)	1.28	0.18	4.98	0.21
Total aldehydes (as acetaldehydes)	0.63	0.16	4.78	2.79
Total phenolic (as phenol)	0.07	0.07	0.22	0.07
Moisture	86.7		70.6	

Much more research needs to be done in the area of "cleaning up" friction-produced smoke to make it comparable to that which has had wide acceptance.

Another recent development is that of the use of "cold" smoke on which a United States patent has been issued. In this procedure, hardwood sawdust is combusted in much the same manner as coke is made from coal. In other words, the wood is heated in a closed container, except for a smoke outlet, in the near absence of oxygen over any suitable heating device. The smoke so produced is then "piped" to a closely confined smoking chamber. Experiments with this process have shown that even such items as frozen steaks may be smoked since relatively little heat is involved. Also, since the concentration of the smoke flavor is great, only a matter of minutes is necessary to obtain the desired flavor. Further, because of time and temperature factors, it is not essential to have the meats cured to prevent bacteriological spoilage as is necessary with conventionally smoked products.

The use of suitable pure liquid smokes is now permitted by

the Meat Inspection Services of the United States Department of Agriculture. Liquid smokes may be made strictly from synthetic chemical materials, or from the redistillation or other fractionation of condensates from actual wood combustion.

With respect to smoke flavoring, there are four possible methods: (1) regular; (2) electrostatic; (3) cold; and (4) liquid.

In the smoking of meats in the conventional process, the necessity for critical control of temperature, humidity, air velocity and to some extent, smoke density has been previously mentioned. Regularly smoked meats generally have the smoke applied during their early hours in the smoke house; that is, while the meats to be smoked are still moist on the surface and cool. Most generally, the smoke application is stopped long before the heat processing is completed. For example, in the case of regular smoked hams, those which are taken to an internal temperature of 137°F., the usual processing time is from 18 to 24 hr. depending on weight, but the smoke is applied only during the first 8 to 12 hr. on the average. Sectional likes and dislikes throughout the country enter the picture with regard to desired smoke flavor.

In the electrostatic deposition of smoke, it has been found that "everything" is deposited. In some instances, the flavor of the resulting product from the "smoke" standpoint leaves something to be desired. Various means have been attempted to "clean up" the smoke, that is, filtering through different media, water washing, preliminary electrostatic precipitation, etc., with mixed results. When depositing smoke by this means, it has been determined that in general, it may be done at any stage of the process except the final. It is necessary to give the product a final heat treatment in order to "set" the smoke so that it cannot be wiped or washed off. This method of smoking currently is confined primarily to the fish industry; but it is also used in the smoking of hams, picnics, etc., for canning.

Insufficient work has been done to know about the merits of the "cold" smoking method. Smoke composition, proper conditions with respect to time, temperature, humidity and smoke density are some of the areas which need resolution.

There has been rather extensive activity in recent years with the use of liquid smoking. This encompasses the use of condensates from wood combustion which have been redistilled, or obtained from formulated smoke flavors prepared strictly from pure chemicals. It has been reported that the pyroligneous liquor, free of tar and heavy undesirable constituents, is distilled to yield pure smoke oil (fumeol). This may be made into a 2 to 3 per cent solution for soaking food, or it may be sprayed on the food, or added with the salt or cure. Supposedly, this treatment retards oxidation and bacterial spoilage. Of course, as previously mentioned, the artificial application of smoke flavor to meats has recently been approved by the Meat Inspection Services of the United States Department of Agriculture.

Previously presented was a table indicating the chemical composition of smoke produced by the conventional smoldering of hardwood sawdust and by the more revolutionary method of friction generation from hardwood logs. In addition, there are variations in the composition of smoke produced from various woods, as noted in the following Table 105:

TABLE 105

APPROXIMATE COMPOSITION OF SMOKE FROM VARIOUS WOODS

	Acids	Aldehydes and Ketones	Bases	Phenol
Beech	4.0	2.7	4.0	2.5
Oak	5.2	1.8	1.6	2.7
Plane tree	5.1	5.2	1.8	4.0
Birch	4.0	2.3	3.9	3.4
Pine	12.3	0.1	4.1	3.3
Alder	4.3	3.4	2.8	3.1
Lime	6.0	4.8	3.1	3.8
Aspen	9.1	5.2	4.1	5.2
Fir	6.8	0.2	3.8	4.6

There is still some controversy as to whether high resin containing woods, such as balsam, fir, pine, etc., as opposed to hickory, oak, apple, cherry, etc., are suitable for meat smoking. It would appear that "it all depends on what is desired." It has even been proposed that 20 per cent mesquite roots be mixed with hickory as an ideal wood combination for the smoking of meats. Many of the high resin containing woods are regularly used to smoke fish.

Smoked meats in this country today are consumed for their character and flavor. This is in direct opposition to the fact that a large part of the world's production of smoked meats, including fish, is for the purpose of preservation. In the smoking of meats, the desired end result must be defined—are they to be used for desirable flavor or for preservation?

The aging, curing and smoking of meats serves a real purpose, which is that of supplying a consumer demand. The problem is to discern and satisfy that mandate.

Acknowledgment.—The authors acknowledge with thanks the photo of the continuous frankfurter equipment (Fig. 136) by Ideal

Tool and Manufacturing Co., Chicago, Ill.; the friction smoke generator (Fig. 141) by the American Meat Institute Foundation, Chicago, Ill., and the remaining photos by Ed Hois, Swift & Co.

BIBLIOGRAPHY

AGRICULTURAL MARKETING SERVICE, U.S.D.A. 1961. Beef Muscle Characteristics as Related to Carcass Grade, Carcass Weight and Degree of Aging. Tech. Bull. *1231*. United States Department of Agriculture, Washington, D. C.

AMERICAN MEAT INSTITUTE FOUNDATION. 1957. Four Symposia—Meat Processing. Nutrition. Beef Tenderization. Irradiation. Circ. *35*. American Meat Institution Foundation, Chicago.

AMERICAN MEAT INSTITUTE FOUNDATION. 1960. The Science of Meat and Meat Products. W. H. Freeman and Co., San Francisco.

AMERICAN MEAT INSTITUTE FOUNDATION. 1961. Proceedings of the Thirteenth Research Conference. Research Council, American Meat Institute Foundation, University of Chicago, Chicago.

ANON. 1953. Sausage and Ready-to-Serve Meats. 2nd Rev. Edition. Institute of Meat Packing, University of Chicago, Chicago.

ANON. 1956. Southwestern aroma smoked into sausage. National Provisioner *134*, No. 10, 8, 34.

ANON. 1956. New generator produces smoke by friction. National Provisioner *134*, No. 17, 8–9, 21.

ANON. 1957. Pork Operations. 6th Rev. Edition. Institute of Meat Packing, University of Chicago, Chicago.

ANON. 1961. Books and Pamphlets on the Meat Packing Industry. Institute of Meat Packing, University of Chicago, Chicago.

BENTON, W. 1961. Sausage. Encyclopedia Britannica *20*, 14, 14A. Chicago, London, Toronto.

HUSAINI, S. A., and COPPER, G. E. 1957. Fractionation of wood smoke and the comparison of chemical composition of sawdust and friction smokes. Food Technol. *11*, 499–502.

JENSEN, L. B. 1949. Meat and Meat Food. The Ronald Press Co., New York.

JENSEN, L. B. 1953. Man's Food. The Garrard Press, Campaign, Ill.

JENSEN, L. B. 1954. Microbiology of Meats. 3rd Edition. The Garrard Press, Champaign, Ill.

LOWE, B. 1955. Experimental Meat Cookery. 4th Edition. John Wiley and Sons, New York.

MILLER, A. R. 1958. Meat Hygiene. 2nd Edition. Lea and Febinger, Philadelphia.

NATIONAL LIVESTOCK AND MEAT BOARD. (1948 *et seq.*) Annual Reports from Reciprocal Meat Conferences. National Livestock and Meat Board, Chicago, Ill.

RUSZ, J. 1959. Determination of phenols and aldehydes in smoked meats. Food Manufacture *34*, 59.

TILGNER, I. D. J. 1958. New knowledge with regard to smoke-curing processes. Die Fleischwirtschaft *10*, 649–660, 751–762.

TORIJAMA, Y., NAGAO, S., SUTO, T., and TAKAHASI, T. 1955. Electro-smoke solution speeds curing. Food Engineering *27*, 105, 210.

ZEGILER, P. T. 1952. The Meat We Eat. 3rd Edition. Interstate Printers and Publishers, Danville, Ill.

CHAPTER 20

Zenas Block | # Frying

INTRODUCTION

This chapter will discuss deep fat frying, a process characterized by a volume of fat in the fryer which is grossly greater than the volume of product being processed at any one time.

Frying, a method of heat processing, differs from other heat processing methods in the following principal respects: (1) Cooking is accomplished in a relatively short period of time, generally within five minutes, due to: (a) great temperature differences between heat source (fat) and the food, and (b) the size of the individual food unit cooked is usually relatively small—*usually* less than one ounce in weight. (2) The frying fat becomes a significant component in the end product—varying from as little as ten per cent by weight of the end product (such as in breaded fish sticks) up to 40 per cent by weight or more (e.g., potato chips). (3) Fried products have the characteristic of crispness of the outer surface—to a greater degree than foods otherwise heat processed. (4) The heat transfer medium (frying fat) is subject to change in composition (and often in performance characteristics) during its process life (Carlin *et al.* 1954; Goodman and Block 1952; Melnick 1957; Rock and Roth 1964). (5) There are unique mechanical problems involved in commercial frying operations.

THE FRYING SYSTEM

The frying system can be regarded as consisting of four components: (a) *the mechanical system* which moves product into, through and out of the fryer; (b) *the fat system* which acts as the direct heat source to the product, and an ingredient of the end product; (c) *the thermal system* which provides the means for transferring heat to the frying fat; and (d) *the control system*.

In order to discuss these systems, description in some detail of the specific physical changes that occur in frying processing with most food products is relevant. These changes are: (1) evaporation of water; (2) elevation of temperature of the product to the desired level; (3) elevation of surface temperature to achieve a browning and crisping effect; (4) dimensional changes in the product being fried; (5) removal of frying

---

ZENAS BLOCK is Group Vice President, DCA Food Industries Inc., New York.

fat from the system as an absorbed component of the fried product; (6) replacement of fat to compensate for fat which has been removed; and (7) changes in density of the product being fried during the frying process, which cause it either to float or to remain submerged.

DEFINITIONS OF FRIED PRODUCTS

Surface fried products are products which enter the frying fat and, for most of the frying period, float on the surface of the fat and remain floating until the frying cycle is complete.

Courtesy of D.C.A. Food Industries

FIG. 142.   CONTINUOUS DONUT FRYER WITH VENTED HOOD

Submerged fried products are products which are held under the surface of the fat for most of the frying cycle.

Partially submerged products are products which normally tend to float, but which are held under the surface of the fat for a portion of the frying cycle.

Nonfloating fried products are products which do not float during the frying cycle, and thus are fried submerged without mechanical restraint.

MECHANICAL SYSTEMS

Product Feed

Products which are to be fried may be fed to the fryer in one of two forms. (*a*) as a viscous fluid or (*b*) as discrete solid or semisolid material.

An example of a product which is supplied as a viscous fluid is chemically leavened donut batter (batters of all kinds). Products formed previous to frying are fish sticks, fish fillets, yeast raised donut dough, and potato chips.

Products which are fried from the batter state are deposited in the fryer directly from a depositor (Fig. 142).

Products which are provided in discrete shape are fed to the fryer by means of a conveyor (Fig. 143), or in the case of batch fryers, manually placed on a screen and then lowered into the fryer (Block 1961; Downs 1958).

Conveying Mechanisms Through Fat

Surface Fried Products.—Two types of conveying mechanisms are used. (1) So-called **spacer bar** conveying: The frying product floats between spacer bars, which move the product over the fat surface at the desired

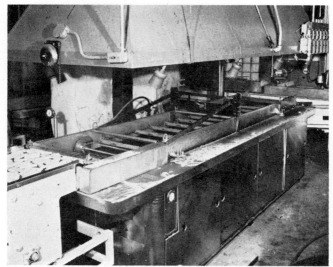

Courtesy of D.C.A. Food Industries
FIG. 143.   FISH STICK FRYER
Showing the automatic feeder and fryer with conveyor belt from fryer.

frying rate. (2) **Fat current** conveying: The fat itself is pumped through the fryer at a rate which establishes the linear surface velocity desired, and thus establishes the frying time.

Spacer bar mechanisms provide extremely accurate frying time control with some nonutilization of frying surface—and with relatively low aeration of frying fat.

Fat current conveying provides maximum utilization of frying surface, with some sacrifice of temperature and time control. With each of these systems, the product must be turned approximately halfway through the cycle, as shown in Fig. 142.

For submerged products the system utilized consists of a **submerger conveyor** which moves the product through the fat without turning the product (since it is continuously under the fat surface), utilizing the flotation tendency of the product to produce necessary contact between the conveyor and the product. In the case of products where dimensional instability is unacceptable (fried pies), two conveyors are operated at equal linear speed. The product is sandwiched between the two conveyors, so that product thickness is controlled, and is conveyed through the fat without turning to an ejector conveyor and out of the fryer, Fig. 144.

Courtesy of D.C.A. Food Industries

FIG. 144.   CONTINUOUS SUBMERGED PRODUCT FRYER

For nonfloating products, completely submerged conveyors are utilized to convey the material through the fryer. Such conveyors might be woven belt conveyors, basket conveyors or any type of conveyor which can hold the product while it is being carried through the frying fat.

Commercial fryers of all designs are usually equipped with variable speed systems, so that frying time may be regulated to the product requirement.

For surface fried products which are nonfloating for the first portion of the frying cycle (their density being greater than that of the frying fat), fryers are designed with **drop plates.** The drop plate is a flat plate or series of stationary flat bars, beneath the fat surface and conveyor, upon which the dropped product may rest until it floats. For such products, fryer design requires careful synchronization of dropping with the motion of the conveyors, so that there is adequate time on the drop plate for the product to decrease in density, rise to the surface, and thus become conveyable without distortion.

A recent innovation in surface frying technology is the so-called moving drop plate. Actually, a short, solid surface conveyor, lying below the surface conveying mechanism, travels at precisely the same rate as the product conveyor, supporting the product in its proper spacing position until the product rises to the fat surface and its further movement is captured by the surface conveyor. This permits high-speed operations without shape distortion.

THE FAT SYSTEM

The fat system consists of the following components:

(a) **The Fat Storage Container.**—Fats which are used for frying may be stored as liquids in bulk with suitable facilities for agitation and temperature control, or in drums. When stored in bulk the fat is supplied to the fryer either directly, or through an intermediate reservoir, in which level is controlled. When stored in drums, if the fat is in the semisolid state, it must be melted either with an immersion heater or by a fat melter (Fig. 145).

(b) **Intermediate Storage.**—Most commercial fryers provide for intermediate storage of fat. This serves the following functions: (1) it is a recirculation storage which avoids contamination of the principal bulk fat storage container with fat which has been subjected to frying treatment; (2) it serves as a means of maintaining fat in a preheated condition close to frying temperatures, so that the fat being added to the fryer does not significantly alter frying temperatures; (3) it provides a point for fat collection from the fryer; the fryer then may be cleaned. Heating methods for intermediate storage tanks are—the use of exhaust flue gases, or heating through dilution with recirculating frying fat itself, or having a prime heating source as in a remote heating system.

The Frying Kettle

The volume of fat in the frying kettle will vary with design. Such design variations are as follows: (1) It may be quite shallow and have no provisions for heating within the kettle itself. A heat exchanger system outside the kettle is used. Fat is moved to and from the kettle at relatively high velocities, depending upon temperature variations permissible for products; that is, the temperature drop permissible during frying. In the case of potato chips, a temperature variation of 50°F. is acceptable. This refers to the temperature drop from input fat temperature to discharge fat temperature. In the case of donut frying, a temperature drop of more than 5°F. is regarded as undesirable.   Another design is the cold-well design.   In this case, the heat source is in the kettle itself, usually gas-fired tubes.   The tubes are positioned above the bottom of the kettle, thus producing a cold zone below the tubes into which foreign matter may settle without burning or interacting with the frying fat.

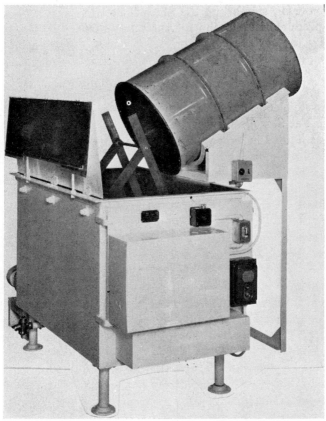

Courtesy of D.C.A. Food Industries

Fig. 145.   Fat Melter and Storage Container
(2000 Lbs. Capacity)

A third alternative design used where there are little or no crumbs or particles discharged to the fat by the frying product is a heated plenum chamber at the bottom of the kettle, which serves as a combustion chamber for gas.   Variation of this latter design consists of electric immersion heating coils lying on the bottom of the kettle.

A recent design utilizes a specially designed kettle bottom through which heat exchanger fluid is circulated at temperatures of approximately

500°F. The fluid is heated in an outside boiler by gas. This design avoids large requirements of fat in the system, and excessive fat circulation and, hence, tends to minimize fat oxidation. Its prime application is in the frying of products which do not deposit foreign material in the kettle through frying.

Good fryer design considers fat turnover rate as a prime factor in design. The fat turnover rate is usually expressed in terms of turnover hours. This is defined as the number of hours during which, arithmetically, the amount of fat removed through absorption by the frying product is equal to the capacity of the fryer (and the fryer reservoir in the case where fat is recirculated) in total pounds of fat. For example, a fryer which holds 1,000 lbs. of fat and which has the capacity to fry 500 lbs. of material per hour, which absorbs 100 lbs. of fat, has a turnover time of 10 hr. In commercial fryer design, it is regarded as desirable to maintain turnover time at something less than nine hours. For reasons which will be discussed, extremely low turnover times are not regarded as desirable, if accompanied by conditions which accelerate oxidation of fat.

THERMAL SYSTEMS

Thermal systems which have been most frequently utilized commercially for frying are gas-fired tubes immersed in the fryer "kettle." Thermal efficiency of such systems is approximately 40 per cent. Theoretical thermal efficiencies in frying system is not more than 75 to 80 per cent because of combustion product condensation limitations in flue gas removal equipment.

(a) **Electric Immersion Heating Coils.**—This heating method is quite efficient, but is not widespread because of high energy cost.

(b) **Heat Exchangers.**—Heat exchangers have been utilized which are both directly and indirectly heated. Indirect heat exchangers utilizing chlorinated hydrocarbon heat transfer fluids have been used in the potato chip industry. The advantage cited for the use of such exchangers is the relatively low contact temperature between the frying fat and the heat source. Very high temperature tolerance in potato chip frying makes the use of such exchangers practical. However, where temperature tolerance is narrow, the volume of fat that must be pumped through the system, the size of the heat exchanger, and the resulting cost of pumping and heat exchanger equipment becomes excessive. There is also a potential problem of excessive oxidation due to high-speed circulation of fat. Heat exchangers in which fat is circulated through a tube surrounded by a chamber in which gas is burned have been used in connection with low fat volume fryers, operated with high fat turnover, together with high pumping velocities and considerable oxidation. A new type of gas fryer tube has been developed, which lowers surface temperature and adds radiant heating effect to the normal conductive heating of fat. This is the so-called "raditube" principle illustrated in Fig. 146.

Thermal efficiencies of a gas fired heater are determined by the efficiency of combustion, which is usually the function of the length of the combustion tube and optimum proportioning and mixing of air and gas. Design may produce variations from 40 to 75 per cent thermal efficiency.

(c) **Hooding and Ventilation Systems for Fryers.**—Under optimum conditions, where fat smoke points are not lowered to frying temperatures, minute quantities of fat are evaporated and must be vented. Frying processes are almost always accompanied by evaporation of considerable

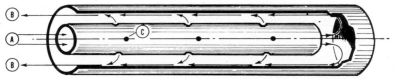

Courtesy of D.C.A. Food Industries

Fig. 146.   Radi-Tube

(A) Flame enters inner tube; passes through tube; leaves inner tube and leaves outer tube along path (B). (C) Represents connections between inner and outer tube.

quantities of water and some steam distillation of volatile materials. Venting requirements are determined by the quantity of water vapor and other gases being produced, and the enclosure of the fryer. Many fryers are enclosed and thus require relatively low air volume movement. However, in variety frying of baked products, such enclosures are regarded as interferences with cleanup processes and flexibility. In such cases, overhead hoods are used. A typical hood is shown in Fig. 142 (p. 602).

In hood ventilator design, it is most important for an engineer to determine air balance at the location. It is frequently necessary to provide makeup air to a room in order to compensate for air being exhausted through the fryer hood. When large quantities of makeup air are required, provision is made for heating incoming air so the room can be maintained at desired temperatures.

A prime element in hood design is protection against condensation dripping back into frying fat. Another major consideration is avoidance of fat drippage into the flame source, to avoid fire hazard.

Every fryer installation should be surrounded with adequate fire safety equipment.

THE CONTROL SYSTEM

Design of temperature control systems for fryers varies, depending on processing requirements. If a process is one which generates relatively large thermal demands as related to the thermal capacity of the system, a modulating thermal control system is required. Such thermal systems raise and lower the gas flame instead of turning gas on and off. This is to avoid lag in response and loss of control of frying temperature with changes in load. Temperature controls with modulating systems can be tight—within plus and minus 2°F. The on and off system which is a thermocouple activating a thermostat switch is less effective as a precise temperature control system, and a range of 10°F. is common. However, on and off systems are less expensive than modulating systems, and are used where there is no great requirement for close temperature control, or where loads are not likely to fluctuate greatly.

FRYING FATS

The choice of the appropriate fat to be used in a specific frying operation is frequently critical. Acceptance or rejection by the consumer, product stability, and the economics of the operation must be considered.

Fats may be characterized by one or more of the following: (1) fat source: animal—beef and lard; vegetable—corn, cottonseed and soy; (2) fat treatment: hydrogenated and refined; (3) fat physical properties: melting point, congeal point, cloud point, AOM and SCI.

Since there is more than a 50 per cent range in cost of fats used for frying, proper choice is ultimately a competitive necessity.

The first, and most significant question that must be answered for a given operation is: To what extent will the fat deteriorate under the expected operating conditions? This involves turnover and oxidation (Stern and Roth 1959; Melnick 1957; Carlin et al. 1954).

All fats deteriorate somewhat during frying because of increase in free fatty acids, hydrolysis, oxidation, polymerization, melt and congeal point drop, flavor and color changes.

The next question is—under that condition will the deteriorated fat satisfy the following: (1) Will its flavor be acceptable in the product? (2) Will its physical appearance—dullness or greasiness, color, be acceptable in the package, as well as when consumed? (3) Will it satisfy the shelf life requirements of the end product? (4) Will the amount absorbed during frying be at the required level? (5) Will its interaction with product coatings be acceptable (sugar toppings, chocolate, breading etc.)? and (6) Will the mouth feel be acceptable (waxiness, greasiness)?

Commercial experience provides guidelines for selection of fats for frying, but whenever possible, direct choice should be made for each specific product—preferably with alternatives to provide mobility to meet changing market conditions.

In the baking industry, hydrogenated lard, and mixtures of hydrogenated lard, beef and soya oil are utilized. Refined lard is often used in high fat turnover donut frying. In the potato chip industry, corn oil is widely used. In the frozen fried foods industry, hydrogenated cottonseed oil is widely used. However, almost every conceivable combination is used for frying.

The lower molecular weight fats, such as coconut and palm oils, are generally unsatisfactory for frying due to foaming tendency and off-flavor formation, due to hydrolysis, resulting in the presence of caprylic and caproic acids.

Fat Absorption

Fat absorption refers to the weight of fat picked up by the frying product per unit weight of end product.

It is sometimes expressed as a finished weight percentage of the end product or as, in the case of donuts, ounces of fat per dozen donuts of specified weight.

Fat absorption, in a controlled frying operation, should be specified at a given level. In all fried products, there is a minimum and maximum quantity required for product identity (Ledden 1958).

Reduction or increase of absorbed fat may alter finished product quality unfavorably.

Factors that determine fat absorption level fall in two groups: (a) feed material factors, including composition and surface characteristics; and (b) process factors including fat composition or "condition."

In a general way, high protein materials and high water absorbers tend to reduce fat absorption, and tenderizing materials such as sugar, shortening, and emulsifiers tend to increase fat absorption.

The behavior of specific products with respect to fat absorption is sufficiently unique to discourage generalization. However, there are a number of generalizations that may be made regarding process factors:

(a) **Frying Temperature.**—In general, fat pick-up varies inversely with frying temperature and consequently it is critical.

(b) **Frying Time.**—May be as little as 20 sec. per side for small cake donuts, or as high as $6^{1}/_{2}$ min. for French crullers.

The time requirement for a specific product is a requirement of composition and size, but relatively minor *changes* in frying time produce almost linear response in per cent change of fat absorption. A five per cent increase in donut frying time for a donut normally absorbing two ounces of fat per dozen will result in an increase to 2.1 to 2.2 oz. of fat per dozen.

(c) **Dough Viscosity.**—In the case of fried "baked" foods, dough viscosity is a significant factor.

In chemically leavened donuts (cake type), lower dough viscosities tend to produce reduction in absorbed fat. Such reduced viscosity may result from increased mixing of dough, elevation of dough temperatures, or increased water in a dough.

The converse is likewise usually true. Exceptions to this generally are found in highly leavened products where lower dough viscosities *increase* fat absorption.

In case of yeast leavened doughs, slack or loose doughs generally produce higher fat absorption if due to higher water content. Optimum mixing for full gluten development in the dough is the principal fat absorption control element.

The mixing operation in all doughs is perhaps the most critical element. Once composition is fixed, the mixing operation and development of gluten develops the gas holding power, i.e., the film strength, and hence the fat repelling properties of the dough.

(d) **Fat Source.**—Unrefined fats yield higher fat absorptions than refined products. With sufficient fat turnover (every nine hours or less) and assuming no aberrant fat oxidizing or hydrolyzing conditions, all refined fats produce substantially equivalent results.

However, frequently aberrant conditions do exist and for this reason fats relatively stable to oxidation are most frequently used. Fats should be free of surface active additives, which increase fat absorption significantly (ten per cent plus). In the baking industry, for lower turnover operations, hydrogenated fats are found to be most suitable.

Fat absorption is readily measured in plant operations daily. The simplest and most accurate method is: (a) before frying—adjust fat level in fryer and holding tanks to a marked level—at the temperature normal to the vessel (i.e., frying temperature in the fryer, holding temperature in the holding tanks); (b) weigh or meter the quantity of fat added to the system during the operating day—adjusting to same levels at the end of the operating day; (c) count the amount of product produced, or tally as produced; (d) calculate the fat usage per unit of product.

In large-scale operations, this may be done over a weekly or a monthly period using opening and closing fat inventories and receipts.

FRYING FISH AND POULTRY PRODUCTS

Many fish, poultry and shrimp products are produced in the breaded, fried state. Such products are usually sold as frozen products. The ranges of frying time encountered vary from a low of 30–40 sec. for small parts to a high of 5 to 6 min. for chicken pieces.

A significant technology has developed with respect to battering and breading compounds, which are designed to control surface color of the end product, as well as fat absorption.

Continuous filtration and/or settling tanks are utilized to separate breading compound which has fallen off during the frying process into the frying fat. The consideration of turnover in these types of operations is as significant as in others. A special consideration in this class of foods is the appearance of the frozen product when removed from the package, with a significant usage of corn oil as a frying fat in order to avoid a dull grey crystallized fat look. However, hydrogenated fats have been developed which have been satisfactory.

Users of corn oil for frying such products state that the flavor of corn oil in the equilibrium state, after some breakdown has occurred, is more compatible with the flavor of the food itself.

In many cases, the object of frying is not to cook the food, but merely to obtain a desired color for the coating material. The instructions for preparation at home are expected to simultaneously raise the product to desired temperature for consumption, as well as finish cooking the product.

SUMMARY

Frying is a relatively low investment method of cooking food and produces foods of unique properties with great consumer acceptance. End product quality and economics is controllable through appropriate action in the selection and control of raw materials, process equipment, process conditions and frying fat.

BIBLIOGRAPHY

ARENSON, S. W. 1950. Shortenings for frying and baking. Food Inds. 22, 1015–1020.

BAILEY, A. E. 1951. Industrial Oil and Fat Products. 2nd Edition, Interscience Publishers, New York.

BENES, C., CARLIN, G. T., and LOGAN, P. 1941. Preparation of French fried potatoes in the restaurant kitchen. Natl. Restaurant Assoc. Research Dept. Tech. Bull. 100.

BENNION, M., and HANNING, F. 1956A. Decomposition of lard in the frying of French-fried potatoes and of fritter-type batters. J. Home Econ. 48, 184–188.

BENNION, M., and HANNING, F. 1956B. Effect of different fats and oils and their modification on changes during frying. Food Technol. *10*, 229–232.

BLOCK, Z. 1951. The selection and maintenance of frying fats. Baker's Dig. *23*, No. 3, 58–59.

BLOCK, Z. 1961. Advances in doughnut technology. Baker's Dig. *35*, No. 5, 124–129.

CARLIN, G. T., HOPPER, R. P., and ROCKWOOD, B. N. 1954. Some factors affecting the decomposition of frying fats. Food Technol. *8*, 161–165.

DOWNS, D. E. 1958. Mechanized fried foods production. Baker's Dig. *32*, No. 2, 52.

FISHER, D. E. 1949. Fat absorption and symmetry in cake doughnuts. Baker's Weekly *144*, No. 4, 88–89.

GOODMAN, A. H., and BLOCK, Z. 1952. Problems encountered in the commercial utilization of frying fats. J. Am. Oil Chemists' Soc. *29*, No. 12, 616–619.

HOLSTON, J. 1955. Weight changes during cooking of fish sticks. Com. Fisheries Rev. *17*, No. 4, 30–33.

JOHNSON, R. N. 1957. Factors affecting the yield, fat absorption, and color of potato chips. Dissertation Abstr. *17*, No. 10, 2242–2243.

LANTZ, C. W., and CARLIN, G. T. 1938. Stability of fats used for deep fat frying. Oil Soap *15*, No. 2, 38–41.

LEDDEN, J. J. 1958. Investigation of desirability and methods of producing low fat in potato chips. Proc. Prod. Tech. Div. Natl. Potato Chip Inst. 42–43.

LEHAULT, B., and BLOCK, Z. 1952. Mechanical production of yeast raised doughnuts through extrusion cutting. Baker's Dig. *26*, No. 6, 122–125.

LIROT, S. J., and NICKERSON, J. T. R. 1956. Quality variables pinpointed for fish-stick makers. Food Eng. *28*, No. 6, 88–90, 189.

MELNICK, D. 1957. Absence of thermal polymers in potato-chip frying oils. J. Am. Oil Chemist's Soc. *34*, No. 7, 351–356.

MELNICK, D., LUCKMANN, F. H., and GOODING, C. M. 1958. Composition and control of potato chip frying oils in continuing commercial use. J. Am. Oil Chemists' Soc. *35*, No. 6, 271–277.

PETERSON, M. B. 1955. The prevention of excessive breakdown of fats and oils in the frying kettle. Proc. Prod. Tech. Div. Natl. Potato Chip Inst. 20–24.

PHILLIPS, R. B. 1958. Recent advances in doughnut producing equipment. Baker's Dig. *32*, No. 2, 72–75.

ROCK, S. P., and ROTH, H. 1964. Factors effecting the rate of deterioration in the freezing qualities of fats. I—Exposure to air. J. Am. Oil Chem. Soc. *41*, 228–230.

RUST, E. M., and HARRISON, D. L. 1960. The effect of method of care on the frying life of fat. Food Technol. *14*, 605–75.

SCHROEDER, W. F. 1957. The use of floating metal covers to minimize fat oxidation. Proc. Prod. Tech. Div. Natl. Potato Chip Inst. 9–11.

SCHROEDER, W. F. 1958. Stack losses in potato chip frying. Proc. Prod. Tech. Natl. Potato Chip Inst. 41.

SMITH, H. L., JR. 1960. Heat transfer in hot fat cooking. Food Technol. *14*, 84–88.

SMITH, H. L., JR., and FREEMAN, W. E. 1955. Automatic remote heating cures frying fats. Food Eng. *27*, No. 3, 60–62, 205.

STERN, S., and ROTH, H. 1959. Properties of frying fat related to fat absorption in doughnut frying. Cereal Sci. Today 4, No. 6, 176–179.

UMPLEBY, J., PINCUS, B., and BLOCK, Z. 1955. Tests to determine range of breader pickup. Quick Frozen Foods 17, No. 6, 63, 68–69.

ZIEMBA, J. V. 1953. Frying breaded fish non-stop; Empire Fish Co. Food Eng. 25, No. 12, 84–85, 138, 140.

ZIEMBA, J. V. 1957. Fast 2-in-1 line makes 68 varieties of product. Food Eng. 29, No. 7, 66–68.

CHAPTER 21

Robert F. Ellis | Metal Containers for Food

INTRODUCTION

Peter Durand's invention, in 1810, of the "tin canister" for preserved foods had a revolutionary effect on packaging practices. Durand launched a new manufacturing industry and gave impetus to the growth of commercial canning.

Metal cans were first introduced into the United States during the 1820's. At that time food cans generally were made by hand during the winter months for use during the next crop harvesting season. It was a slow process; an expert can maker could produce only five or six cans an hour.

Development of the "sanitary" can around 1900 paved the way for mechanization, increasing production rapidly. *More than 49 billion metal cans are now made in the United States annually*, accounting for nearly one-third of all units of consumer packaging, and used for some 2,500 different products.

The principal advantage of the metal can as a package for food is the protection it provides for its contents. Food in an hermetically sealed can is protected against contamination by microorganisms, insects or other foreign substances which might cause spoilage or adversely affect the appearance or flavor of the product. The can also prevents undesirable gains or losses in moisture content. It protects the food from absorption of oxygen, other gases or odors, and from radioactive fall-out particles from the surrounding atmosphere. With some products whose pigments are susceptible to undesirable photochemical reactions, protection against exposure to light is another plus factor for the can.

From a merchandising standpoint, other advantages are: (1) cans lend themselves to high speed mechanized handling, filling, sealing and casing; (2) they can be displayed advantageously by the retailer; and (3) they can be stored and used easily by the consumer.

The extent of canned food production in the United States is indicated in Table 106, prepared from data published by the National Canners Association. This table does not include the millions of cans

Robert F. Ellis, Customer Service Group, Research and Development, American Can Co., Barrington, Ill.

used for soft drinks and other beverages, pet foods, frozen foods and nonfood products.

Rigid metal containers for food products include cans, pails and drums. Although aluminum cans are now used for some products, steel is still the base metal for most food and beverage containers. About four million tons of steel and 22,000 tons of tin are used each year for this purpose by can manufacturers in the United States.

TIN PLATE CANS

The common term "tin can" is really a misnomer. Actually the can is made of steel bearing only a thin coating of tin. Many modern cans contain less than a quarter of one per cent of tin, and "tinless" cans are not uncommon.

TABLE 106

TRENDS IN CANNED FOOD PRODUCTION—1938–1962[1]
In millions of standard cases

Year	Fruit	Juices	Vege-tables	Special-ties	Milk	Fish	Meat[2]	Total
1938	40	39	122	67	49	17	7	341
1940	49	55	133	79	58	19	12	405
1942	59	73	194	54	83	18	43	524
1944	57	95	170	69	82	18	43	534
1946	83	105	201	102	74	21	30	616
1948	66	94	158	111	81	24	24	558
1950	77	109	166	113	68	30	27	590
1952	77	109	194	120	66	26	30	622
1954	83	99	183	125	59	28	32	609
1955	92	99	197	128	60	26	33	635
1956	99	123	235	130	59	31	38	715
1958	92	109	222	132	54	34	37	680
1960	104	105	217	136	51	35	39	687
1961	109	103	237	138	50	33	40	710
1962	111	107	248	140	46	37	42	731
1963	103	107	231	169	45	34	43	732
1964[3]	124	114	227	175	44	35	46	765

[1] Courtesy of National Canners Association, Division of Statistics and Economics.
[2] Excluding meat soups and canned poultry which are included in specialties.
[3] Preliminary

Tin plate is an ideal material for food containers. Although tin is not completely inert to all foods, container corrosion and any product changes are slight when the proper combination of materials is chosen. Among the factors which must be considered by the can manufacturer are: (1) chemical composition and physical properties of the base plate, (2) thickness of the tin coating, (3) application of protective coatings or enamels, (4) container construction and (5) relative corrosivity of the product which is to be canned.

Thousands of test packs have been made by can manufacturers and the steel mills to determine both the corrosivity of representative food products and the effect on storage life of varying the type of base steel and tin coating weight.

In hermetically sealed cans of food, container corrosion is usually a gradual process. Tin, in contact with the product, sacrificially corrodes to protect any small exposed areas of base steel and iron-tin alloy. The tin coating gradually disappears and the area of exposed steel and alloy increases. Eventually, a point is reached where the steel, initially well protected, is attacked rapidly. During this process, hydrogen is evolved so that the ultimate result may be the production of enough gas to distend the can ends.

Normally, such "hydrogen swells" do not occur until nearly all the available tin has been consumed. However, if the steel is of poor quality or of the wrong chemical composition, container service life may be shortened.

Low carbon steel is used for can manufacture. Research studies have shown that chemical composition of the base steel is of primary importance in obtaining adequate service life for corrosive products. The metalloids phosphorus and silicon are particularly critical. However, other trace metals such as copper, nickel, and molybdenum may also affect the corrosion resistance of the plate.

Can manufacturers have set up rigid chemical specifications for base steels (see Table 107). These specifications recognize four basic types of steel required for the different classes of food products, and a fifth type used only for beer can ends.

TABLE 107

CHEMICAL SPECIFICATIONS FOR BASE STEELS[1]

Element	Percentage Permitted				Beer End Stock
	Type L	Type MS	Type MR	Type MC	
Manganese	0.25–0.60	0.25–0.60	0.25–0.60	0.25–0.60	0.25–0.70
Carbon	0.12 max.	0.12 max.	0.12 max.	0.12 max.	0.15 max.
Phosphorus	0.015 "	0.015 "	0.02 "	0.07–0.11	0.10–0.15
Sulfur	0.05 "	0.05 "	0.05 "	0.05 max.	0.05 max.
Silicon	0.01 "	0.01 "	0.01 "	0.01 "	0.01 "
Copper	0.06 "	0.10–0.20	0.20 "	0.20 "	0.20 "
Nickel	0.04 "	0.04 max.	No limitations specified		
Chromium	0.06 "	0.06 "	"	"	"
Molybdenum	0.05 "	0.05 "	"	"	"
Arsenic	0.02 "	0.02 "	"	"	"

[1] *Adapted from* R. R. Hartwell (1956).

Type L plate is a specially prepared steel which is low in phosphorus and residual metals. It is more difficult to produce and consequently sells at a slight premium.   This type of plate is ordinarily specified for the most strongly corrosive products, such as red cherries, dried prunes in syrup, berries and pickles.   Type MS plate is similar to type L but has a higher copper content, and is now preferred for sauerkraut cans. Type MR steel is specified for mildly acid fruit products, such as citrus fruits and juices, peaches, pears and pineapples.   It has a slightly higher phosphorus content than type L plate and no specified limits on most residual metals.

A variety of plates is available for such low acid products as meats, fish and most vegetables, and for dry or frozen packs.   Choice of the steel base for products in this group more often is dictated by economic considerations than by product corrosivity.   Both continuously annealed type MR steel and box annealed type MC (rephosphorized) steel are used.

A number of representative canned foods are listed in Table 108, grouped according to corrosivity and types of steel base required.

TABLE 108

GENERAL CLASSES OF FOOD PRODUCTS AND TYPES OF STEEL BASE REQUIRED

Class of Foods	Characteristics	Typical Examples	Steel Base Required
Most strongly corrosive	Highly or moderately acid products, including dark colored fruits and pickles	Apple juice Berries Cherries Prunes Pickles	Type L
. . . Moderately corrosive	Acidified vegetables Mildly acid fruit products	Sauerkraut Apricots Figs Grapefruit Peaches	Type MS Type MR
Mildly corrosive	Low acid products	Peas Corn Meats Fish	Type MR or MC
Noncorrosive	Mostly dry and non-processed products	Dehydrated soups Frozen foods Shortening Nuts	Type MR or MC

Strength Factors

Can manufacturers also must consider the strength of the plate. Thickness, or gage, of the plate is of course one factor.   Most tin plate specifications are expressed in terms of the "base box," an industry measure which should be explained here.   Originally, tin plate was sold in only one size sheet, 14 x 20 in., and bundled 112 sheets to a package.   The total area of plate in such a package, 31,360 sq. in. or

TABLE 109

TIN PLATE BASIS WEIGHT STANDARDS[1]

Basis Weight, lbs. per base box	Equivalent Weight, lbs. per sq. ft.	Approximate Thickness, in.
55	0.2526	0.0061
60	0.2755	0.0066
65	0.2985	0.0072
70	0.3214	0.0077
75	0.3444	0.0083
80	0.3673	0.0088
85	0.3903	0.0094
90	0.4133	0.0099
95	0.4362	0.0105
100	0.4592	0.0110
107	0.4913	0.0118
112	0.5143	0.0123
118	0.5418	0.0130
128	0.5878	0.0141
135	0.6199	0.0149

[1] From American Iron and Steel Institute (1960).

TABLE 110

MECHANICAL PROPERTIES OF TIN PLATES

Temper Number	Ideal Hardness (R30-T)[1]	Ductility, in.[2]	Average Ultimate Tensile Strength, lbs. per sq. in.	Characteristic
T-1	49	0.32	47,000	Soft for deep drawing
T-2	53	0.30	50,000	Moderate drawing
T-3	57	0.28	55,000	General purpose
T-4	61	0.26	59,000	General purpose
T-5	65	0.24	64,000	Strength
T-U	65	0.27	64,000	Strength of T-5 with greater ductility
T-6	70	0.20	75,000	Greater strength

[1] Specified range for all tempers is ±3 points from ideal Rockwell hardness values.
[2] Expressed as minimum expected cup test values.

217.78 sq. ft. came to be known as a base box. The weight of a base box varies with the thickness of the steel, as is shown in Table 109.

Plates with various physical requirements are needed for making suitable containers for the many types of products canned today. Juices, for instance, are filled into cans at near-boiling temperatures, then cooled. Absolute pressure in the cooled cans is lower than the outside pressures, exposing the cans to severe paneling or collapsing forces. With processed products, such as cream-style corn, some 20 to 35 p.s.i. of pressure develop in the can during processing and cooling. Beer can ends are subjected to even greater pressures, as high as 85 p.s.i. during pasteurization. Strong, stiff plate is needed to meet these requirements. On the other hand, certain drawn cans such as the oval fish can, require the use of soft, ductile plate. The stiffness of the plate is controlled in the steel mill by cold rolling the surface after the annealing operation.

By converting the can requirements for ductility, paneling and buckling resistance into mechanical properties of the sheet steel, can manufacturers have set up a temper classification for tin plate. It consists of seven tempers, from the softest plate practical for the tin mills to produce (T-1) to the stiffest plate feasible for the can manufacturer to use (T-6). Table 110 shows the mechanical properties of tin plate tempered to varying degrees of hardness.

Tin plates with T-1 or T-2 temper are used for drawn container parts, such as fish can bodies and slip covers. T-3 and T-4 are general purpose tempers used for the ends and bodies of many processed food cans. T-5 plate is specified where higher resistance to buckling is required, such as in the ends of cans for products such as peas, corn and spinach, or where high resistance to paneling is required, such as in the bodies of vacuum packed cans. T-6 plate is not made for food cans, and is used only for beer can ends.

Recent changes in plate production methods have made possible the production of continuously annealed plate. Continuously annealed plate has more uniform mechanical properties than the conventional coil annealed material. It has the strength of high phosphorus plate (MCT-5) in a more widely usable steel composition, yet has adequate ductility to make most of the parts normally requiring lower temper. This material is classified as T-U (universal temper) plate.

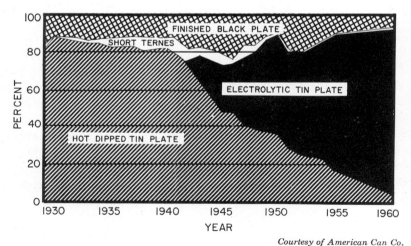

Courtesy of American Can Co.

FIG. 147. PRODUCTION OF ELECTROLYTIC AND HOT DIPPED TIN PLATE
(1930–1960)

Tin Coatings

The thickness, uniformity, and manner in which the tin coating is applied affect the resistance of tin plate cans to perforations and corrosion.   Prior to World War II practically all tin plate was made by immersing sheets of black plate in molten tin.   Now less than six per cent of all tin plate is hot dipped (see Fig. 147).   Electrolytic plating has become the more important and economical method for applying tin.

Almost all the hot dipped tin plate used in the United States today is in the lighter "coke" grades.   The major portion of this is "common coke" (1.25-lb.) plate, which averages about 1.10 lbs. of tin per base box.   There is a lesser use of "standard coke" (1.50-lb.) plate, which carries an average coating of 1.35 lbs. of tin per base box.

Hot dipped tin plate is still used today for a limited number of the more corrosive products and for certain vegetables which are best when packed in plain cans since they require the solution of a small, harmless amount of tin.

The increasing use of electrolytic plate has meant a trend to lower tin coatings on food cans. Consumption of tin for all tin products has decreased from an average of 1.30 lbs. per base box in 1935 to 0.52 lb. per base box in 1959.   The tin coating on most food cans is only 15 to 80 millionths of an inch thick on each side of the plate surface.   The steel base is about 100th of an inch thick.

The electrolytic tinning process permits a close control over the tin coating.   Light but uniformly distributed coatings can be applied. The most common tin coating weights are 0.25-, 0.50-, -0.75- and 1.00-lb. per base box.   Some 70 per cent of the electrolytic plate production in the United States is made with 0.25-lb. tin coating (No. 25 plate).

With the widespread use of electrolytic plate for most canned products, can manufacturers have turned to "differentially coated" plate for further economy.   Such plate has a heavier (1.35-, 1.00-, 0.75- or 0.50-lb.) coating on the surface which becomes the inside of the can, and a light (0.25-lb.) coating of tin on the outside surface.   Thus, product protection is provided where it is needed, while a lighter tin coating, adequate for exposures under most normal distribution conditions, is applied to prevent exterior rusting.

Lightweight Tin Plate

In 1960, the United States Steel Corp. introduced "Ferrolite" plate, a new type of tin plate for cans.   This new "double reduced" plate is thinner than conventional tin plate, but unusually stiff for its gage. It is cheaper to produce and is sold at a lower price per base box than the regular product. Similar types of double reduced (2CR) tin plate have since been developed by other steel suppliers for use in food and beverage containers.

In manufacturing lightweight tin plate, the steel is first cold reduced to about twice the desired thickness. It is then annealed, and sent through a second series of reducing rolls. The plate is not tinned until *after* it has been double reduced to its final thickness. The end product is a lightweight plate which is versatile and strong, and which has the expected bright tin finish.

As with any new container material, extensive test packs and canning trials have been made to determine the best commercial uses for lightweight plate. Today a wide range of food and beverage products are packed in this type of container, and 2CR plate accounts for over 30 per cent of tin plate usage.

ALUMINUM CANS

There is increasing interest in the potentialities of aluminum as a container material. All-aluminum cans or combination cans with aluminum bodies and tin plate ends have been used commercially with frozen citrus concentrate, beer and some meat and fish products.

The advantages of aluminum which are establishing its use are: (1) it is light in weight; (2) it is resistant to atmospheric corrosion; (3) it generally is not stained by sulfide-bearing products; and (4) it can be shaped into containers by several different methods. Some disadvantages are: (1) it is impractical to close body seams by soldering; (2) heavier gages are required to obtain strengths comparable to tin plate; (3) aluminum ends are difficult to open with some widely used can openers; (4) aluminum severely bleaches some products; and (5) container service life is considerably less than that of tin plate for most aqueous products.

In considering new uses for aluminum cans, it is important to understand the corrosion behavior of aluminum. The excellent resistance of aluminum to atmospheric corrosion is due to a protective skin of aluminum oxide on the plate. This oxide is not only chemically inert but rapidly repairs itself if damaged, so long as oxygen is available to reform the film.

Inside the modern food can, however, only limited quantities of oxygen are present so the oxide film provides less protection. Test packs in the American Can Co. laboratories have shown that aluminum cans for most processed foods will require inside enameling for adequate shelf-life.

Soldered side seams are still considered impractical for aluminum cans. Seamless cans have been manufactured by drawing or impact extrusion, and aluminum cans with cemented side seams developed for some applications. Aluminum cans with welded side seams have been fabricated experimentally.

Container strength is one factor which may limit expansion of aluminum into some product fields. Aluminum cannot be substituted for tin plate on a gage-for-gage basis. With present alloys, the gage must be increased about 35 per cent over that of tin plate to provide equal strength for resistance to paneling, buckling and denting. The extent to which heavier gages will be required is likely to dictate the future of aluminum as a container material for processed foods.

ENAMEL COATINGS

Can enamels are baked organic coatings which are applied to preserve the attractiveness of the food, improve the interior or exterior appearance of the container, and/or increase the shelf-life of the can. In some cases, coatings also make it possible to use more lightly coated and, consequently, less expensive grades of tin plate. The coatings are normally applied by roller to the flat sheet and are baked at temperatures below the melting point of tin.

TABLE 111

GENERAL TYPES OF CAN COATINGS

Coating	Typical Uses	Type
Fruit enamel	Dark colored berries, cherries and other fruits requiring protection from metallic salts.	Oleoresinous
C-enamel	Corn, peas, and other sulfur-bearing products, including some sea foods.	Oleoresinous with suspended zinc oxide pigment.
Citrus enamel	Citrus products and concentrates.	Modified oleoresinous
Seafood enamel	Fish products and meat spreads.	Phenolic
Meat enamels	Meat and various specialty products.	Modified epons with aluminum pigment.
Milk enamel	Milk, eggs, and other dairy products.	Epons
Beverage can enamel (noncarbonated beverages)	Vegetable juices; red fruit juices; highly corrosive fruits; noncarbonated beverages.	Two-coat system with oleoresinous type base coat and vinyl top coat.
Beer can enamel	Beer and carbonated beverages.	Two-coat system with oleoresinous or polybutadiene type base coat and vinyl top coat.

Until World War II, most can enamels were essentially baking varnishes prepared from chinawood oil and natural resins. During the war chemists began to formulate interior and exterior coatings from domestic drying oils and synthetic resins. Today most can coatings are made from synthetic materials which provide even better performance than the prewar formulas. The use of synthetics also allows more "tailoring" of enamels to meet the requirements of specific products than was possible previously (see Table 111). Choice of the proper enamel is very important in selecting the best can for a specific product.

When used in lining food containers, a can enamel must meet several requirements: (1) it must impart no odor or flavor to the food; (2) it must be acceptable for contact with foods under the Food Additives Amendment regulations of the Food and Drug Administration; (3) it must protect the can and contents during the required service life; (4) it must not flake off the plate during can manufacture or in subsequent storage; (5) it must be nominal in cost, easy to apply, and quickly cured; and (6) it must withstand all temperatures encountered during processing and normal storage.

The original can enamels were developed for use with highly colored fruit products, such as cherries and berries, which fade when they are packed in plain cans. Present day fruit enamels, formulated from oleoresins, serve this purpose.

Many vegetables, such as peas and corn, contain sulfur-bearing protein constituents. During processing these compounds break down, yielding sulfur residues which react with the tin and iron of the container to produce dark colored metal sulfides. These deposits are similar to the tarnish found on a silver spoon in contact with eggs. Like this tarnish, "sulfur black" in cans is perfectly harmless, but is objectionable because of its appearance. In the C-enameled can, now used for many sulfur-bearing foods, a zinc oxide pigment in the oleoresinous coating effectively traps the sulfur compounds before they can cause discoloration.

Various types of phenolic and epon based coatings are available for fish, meat and dairy products. Release agents sometimes are added to meat enamels to prevent the contents from sticking to the container.

Special two-coat enamel systems have been developed for beer and other beverages which require additional protection against flavor changes. Striping materials can be used to provide further coverage at the side seam area. These are quick drying enamels, sprayed inside the can after it is formed.

Enamel coatings are not used in cans for such products as applesauce and grapefruit sections, where the reducing action of the tin salts retards darkening or flavor changes during storage.   Uncoated cans are also considered desirable for green asparagus as the dissolved tin helps to prevent "tannate" discoloration when the can is opened.

In some instances "combination" cans with plain tin plate bodies and enameled ends are specified to reduce container costs through the use of lighter tin plate, or to expose some tin where this has a beneficial effect.

The outside of cans may be coated to decorate, to camouflage or to retard rusting.   During the war many cans of food for the armed forces were coated with olive-drab colored, rust inhibitive, camouflage coat-

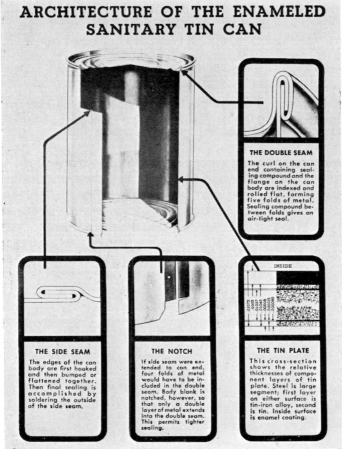

ARCHITECTURE OF THE ENAMELED SANITARY TIN CAN

THE DOUBLE SEAM
The curl on the can end containing sealing compound and the flange on the can body are indexed and rolled flat, forming five folds of metal. Sealing compound between folds gives an air-tight seal.

THE SIDE SEAM
The edges of the can body are first hooked and then bumped or flattened together. Then final sealing is accomplished by soldering the outside of the side seam.

THE NOTCH
If side seam were extended to can end, four folds of metal would have to be included in the double seam. Body blank is notched, however, so that only a double layer of metal extends into the double seam. This permits tighter sealing.

THE TIN PLATE
INSIDE
This cross-section shows the relative thicknesses of component layers of tin plate. Steel is large segment; first layer on either surface is tin-iron alloy, second is tin. Inside surface is enamel coating.

Courtesy of American Can Co.

Fig. 148.   Architecture of the Enameled Sanitary Can

ings. In recent years, the use of multicolored lithography on cans has increased rapidly. Plate is lithographed in the flat before the cans are formed. Each color is applied separately, and the register and color values must be checked regularly to obtain the desired decorative effects.

CAN MANUFACTURE

Modern can manufacture is a highly mechanized operation in which can bodies are formed at speeds as fast as 600 units per minute. First, the interior enamel and the outside lithography, if used, are applied to the flat sheets of plate. The coated sheets are then cut into the proper size for individual can bodies. These "body blanks" are fed into a bodymaker which notches, edges and curls the plate so that the opposite sides lock together (see Fig. 148). The four thicknesses of metal which meet at the side seam are "bumped" flat and soldered, forming a cylindrical shell. For some nonprocessed products, such as frozen citrus concentrates, a special organic cement may be used in the side seam instead of solder.

The next operation on the can line is the flanger, which puts a flared rim on both ends of the can body. When needed, a second coat of enamel is sometimes sprayed into the formed can body or a protective

Courtesy of American Can Co.

Fig. 149. Bodymaker Forms the Metal Cylinder of the Can Body in a Series of Automatic Operations

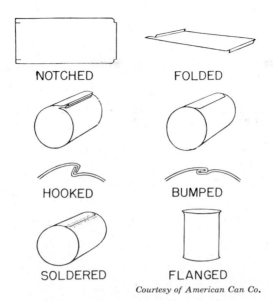

NOTCHED   FOLDED

HOOKED   BUMPED

SOLDERED   FLANGED

Courtesy of American Can Co.

FIG. 150. SEQUENCE OF CAN MANUFACTURING OPERATIONS

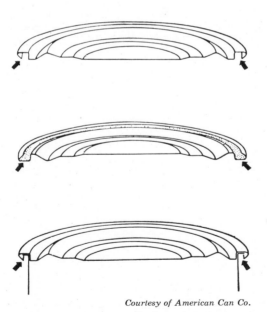

Courtesy of American Can Co.

FIG. 151. INSIDE CURL OF THE CAN END IS LINED WITH
SEALING COMPOUND, A RUBBER GASKET MATERIAL

TABLE 112

SOME COMMON CAN SIZES[1]

Can Name	Can Dimensions[2]	Approx. Net Wt.[3]	Net Contents Liquid Product[4]	Some Products for Which Ordinarily Used
2z Mushroom	200 x 204	3 1/4 oz.	3 1/4 fl. oz.	Mushrooms
5z Baby food	202 x 214	4 3/4 oz.	4 1/4 fl. oz.	Baby foods, chocolate syrup
6z	202 x 308	6 oz.	5 1/4 fl. oz.	Tomato paste, tomato sauce, juices
6 1/2 z	202 x 314	6 oz.	6 fl. oz.	Frozen concentrates, juices
Evaporated milk	206 x 208	6 oz.	6 fl. oz.	Evaporated milk
Meat spread	208 x 109	3 oz.	2 3/4 fl. oz.	Meat spreads
....	208 x 208	1/2 lb.	4 3/4 fl. oz.	Meat products
4z Pimiento	211 x 200	4 3/4 oz.	4 fl. oz.	Pimientos, chopped olives
....	211 x 208	7 oz.	5 1/2 fl. oz.	Cranberry sauce
4z Mushroom	211 x 212	6 3/4 oz.	6 1/2 fl. oz.	Mushrooms
8z Short	211 x 300	7 3/4 oz.	7 fl. oz.	Baked beans, tomato sauce, shrimp, specialties
8z Tall	211 x 304	8 1/2 oz.	7 3/4 fl. oz.	Vegetables and fruits, juices, specialties
No. 1 Picnic	211 x 400	10 1/2 oz.	9 1/2 fl. oz.	Vegetables, some fruit juices, soups, meat, fish, specialties
Beer	211 x 413	......	12 fl. oz.	Beer and carbonated beverages
Half-quart beer	211 x 604	......	16 fl. oz.	Beer
16z Domed	211 x 604		8 fl. oz.	Whipped cream, toppings
No. 211 cylinder	211 x 414	13 oz.	12 fl. oz.	Fruit juices, nectars, tomato juice
Evaporated milk	215 x 315	......	14 1/2 fl. oz.	Evaporated milk
4z Flat pimiento	300 x 108	4 oz.	3 3/4 fl. oz.	Pimientos
....	300 x 308	11 1/2 oz.	11 1/4 fl. oz.	Pork and beans
Chocolate syrup	300 x 315.5	1 lb.	13 fl. oz.	Chocolate syrup
....	300 x 402	14 1/2 oz.	13 fl. oz.	Infant formulas
No. 300	300 x 407	14 1/2 oz.	13 1/2 fl. oz.	Vegetables, some fruits, juices, soups, meat, fish, pet foods, specialties
....	300 x 409	1 lb.	14 fl. oz.	Meat products
No. 300 cylinder	300 x 509	1 lb. 3 oz.	1 pt. 1 fl. oz.	Soups, pork and beans, specialties
1/4 lb. Flat	301 x 106	3 3/4 oz.	3 1/2 fl. oz.	Salmon
No. 1 Tall	301 x 411	1 lb.	15 fl. oz.	Fruits, some vegetables, juices, fish, specialties
No. 303	303 x 406	1 lb.	15 fl. oz.	Most commonly used size for vegetables, fruits, juices, soups, specialties
No. 1/2	307 x 113	7 oz.	5 3/4 fl. oz.	Tuna
1/2 lb. Flat	307 x 200.25	7 3/4 oz.	6 1/2 fl. oz.	Salmon

Container	Dimensions[2]	Net weight[3]	Fluid capacity[4]	Typical products
No. 1 Flat	307 x 203	9 oz.	8 fl. oz.	Pineapple
No. 2 Squat[5]	307 x 208	......	9 fl. oz.	Sausage, fish flakes, coffee
12z Vacuum	307 x 302	½ lb.	......	Nuts
No. 95	307 x 306	12 oz.	13 fl. oz.	Vacuum packed corn
No. 2	307 x 400	1 lb. 1 oz.	1 pt.	Breads, sea foods
Jumbo	307 x 409	1 lb. 4 oz.	1 pt. 2 fl. oz.	Vegetables, fruits, juices, soups, specialties
32z (Quart)	307 x 510	1 lb. 9 oz.	1 pt. 7 fl. oz.	Pork and beans, mushrooms
No. 1¼	307 x 710	2 lb. 2 oz.	1 qt.	Fruit juices and drinks
Shortening[5]	401 x 207.5	14½ oz.	12½ fl. oz.	Pineapple
No. 2½	401 x 307.5	1 lb.		Shortening
	401 x 411	1 lb. 13 oz.	1 pt. 10 fl. oz.	Fruits, some vegetables and juices, meat products
	401 x 509	2 lb. 3 oz.	1 qt.	Frozen concentrates
	401 x 602	2 lb. 6 oz.	36¾ fl. oz.	Spaghetti, beans in tomato sauce
No. 3 Cylinder	404 x 309	1 lb. 8 oz.	22 fl. oz.	Meat products
	404 x 700	3 lb. 2 oz.	1 qt. 14 fl. oz.	Fruit and vegetable juices
Vacuum Coffee[5]	502 x 308	1 lb.	......	Coffee
Vacuum Coffee[5]	502 x 607	2 lb.	......	Coffee
Shortening[5]	502 x 514	3 lb.	......	Shortening
No. 10	603 x 700	6 lb. 10 oz.	3 qt.	Institutional size for vegetables, fruits, juices, meat, and fish products, soups, specialties
	603 x 812	8 lb. 4 oz.	1 gal.	Soft drink syrups
12z Oblong[5]	314 x 202 x 303	12 oz.	......	Meat products
Pullman Base[5]	402 x 310 x 608	3 lb.	......	Meat products
Pullman Base[5]	402 x 310 x 1208	6 lb.	......	Meat products
Pullman Base[5]	414 x 410 x 1100	8 lb.	......	Meat products
Miniature Base Ham[5]	512 x 400 x 211	1 lb. 8 oz.	......	Ham, pear-shaped
#1 Base Ham[5]	710 x 506 x 300	3 lb.	......	Ham, pear-shaped
#1 Base Ham[5]	710 x 506 x 312	4 lb.	......	Ham, pear-shaped
#2 Base Ham[5]	904 x 606 x 308	5 lb. 3 oz.	......	Ham, pear-shaped
#4 Base Ham[5]	1010 x 709 x 412	10 lb. 3 oz.	......	Ham, pear-shaped
¼ Drawn	405 x 301 x 0145	3¼ oz.	......	Sardines
No. 1 Oval	607 x 406 x 108	15 oz.	......	Sardines, sea foods

[1] Adapted from American Can Co., *The Canned Food Reference Manual.*

[2] In inches and sixteenths of inches. Dimensions vary slightly within manufacturing tolerances. Diameter is listed first, followed by height.

[3] The net weights of various foods in the same size can will vary with the density of the product. The weights cited are for foods of average density, except where the container is largely used for one specific class of product.

[4] The volume figures cited are average commercial fills.

[5] Key-opened cans.

stripe is applied on the inside side seam area. Finally, one end is double-seamed onto the can body. The cans are then tested under air pressure in equipment which automatically rejects any that have imperfect seams.

Can ends are punched from enameled or uncoated sheets of plate which have been cut into strips of proper size. The edge of the end is curled, forming a groove into which a heavy liquid rubber sealant is flowed. This gasket-like material, when dried, provides an hermetic seal in the doubleseam between the body and end. One can end is double-seamed on the can by the manufacturer, the other end by the packer at the canning plant after the can is filled.

Circumferential beads are used on some types of can bodies, principally the larger sizes, to increase container resistance to handling abuse and paneling pressures. In effect, beads strengthen a tall can body by making it into a column of shorter can bodies.

Cylindrically shaped, double-seamed sanitary cans of various heights and diameters still account for the great majority of cans used as food containers (see Table 112). However, a number of special constructions are made, including oblong key-opening cans for meat products, "pear" shaped key-opening cans for ham, seamless drawn cans for sardines, key-opening reclosure cans for shortening and coffee, aerosol cans for whipped cream and other pressurized foods, and slip-cover cans for lard, frozen fruit, and dried foods that do not require hermetic closures.

Quality Control of Cans

Can manufacturers have the responsibility of supplying containers which will give adequate performance when used under acceptable canning procedures. Rigid control of both can materials and production techniques is necessary to be sure that the finished containers meet the manufacturers' quality standards.

Tin plate suppliers have a continuing program for improving the quality of their product. Can manufacturers work closely with the mills, bringing to each supplier's attention any plate deficiencies or areas where quality improvements are needed.

The can manufacturer assumes the responsibility for the quality of the tin plate in the finished can. One of the characteristics of corrosion resistant tin plate is the extent to which the tin coating protects the base plate. Microscopic pores or flaws in the tin may expose the base steel, accelerating corrosion in the can. Tests have been developed for checking the continuity of the tin coating and other variables which may affect corrosion resistance. Among the tests commonly used are pickle lag, iron solution value (ISV) and tin crystal size.

In the pickle lag test, a detinned sample of plate is immersed in hydrochloric acid. The rate at which hydrogen is given off by the corroding plate is recorded graphically. Good plate is attacked at a constant rate throughout the test, whereas the attack on poor plate is more erratic.

The iron solution test simulates the reactions within a filled tin can. It measures the amount of iron dissolved from a tin plate specimen immersed for several hours in an acid solution. The dissolved iron tends to discolor the otherwise clear test solution and can be measured spectrophotometrically.

The size of tin crystals in the tin coating also has an important bearing on its corrosion resistance. Large crystals are desirable. Test samples are etched for 10 to 15 sec. in an acid solution to bring out the pattern of crystals on the plate surface.

More recently, a test has been developed for evaluating the electrochemical characteristics of the base steel and the iron-tin alloy layer

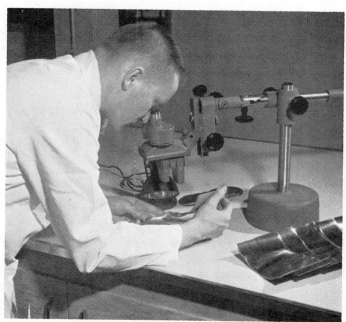

Courtesy of American Can Co.

FIG. 152. ENAMELED CAN BODIES FROM PACKED CANS ARE EXAMINED UNDER MAGNIFICATION FOR COATING AND TIN PLATE PERFORMANCE

which lies between the tin and the steel.   Proper control of the alloy layer on a plate can mean the difference between "average" and "superior" corrosion resistance.

Surface properties of the plate, such as those affecting enamel adhesion, hardness and flexibility, also can be determined.

Can manufacturers and packers sometimes check the continuity of enamel coatings on finished cans through a conductivity test.   The test instrument evaluates enamel coverage by measuring electrochemical current flow between the can wall and the electrode of the instrument.   The amount of current, measured in milliamperes, is a rough indication of the amount of metal exposed.

DELIVERY AND HANDLING OF CANS

Cans are usually delivered to the canning plant in bulk quantities packed in railroad cars, trailer trucks, or cartons.   Where distances of over 100 miles are involved, most cans are shipped in tiered rows, bulkloaded into railroad cars.   Loading and unloading of the cars is necessarily a manual operation, but multirow handling forks can be used to pick up a number of cans at a time.

Next in volume of cans handled are shipments in kraft paper bags or "carriers."   The cans are pattern-stacked vertically with paper or chipboard separators between each layer of cans.   Semiautomatic unloaders for bagged cans are available which operate by sweeping a single layer of cans at a time into a runway.   Paper carriers are good for warehousing cans in the manufacturer's or user's plant, but are relatively expensive and do not provide as much protection as do other packaging methods.

Fiberboard cartons are an ideal shipping package for protection and can be handled efficiently by many plants.   They are best employed by packers who use large quantities of cans of the same size and label, use a limited number of different cartons, and know in advance the type of cartons they will use as shippers.   In the latter case, the cartons of empty cans are delivered with only the top or bottom flaps glued in place; the flaps of the other end are sealed by the packer after the containers have been filled and repacked in the carton.

The use of automation in can handling operations at the canning plant has increased rapidly in recent years.   Automatic unloading is done at speeds up to 2,000 cans per minute for the small can sizes.

Several different methods of delivering cans for automatic line feeding are now being operated successfully where reuse of packing materials is economically attractive.   Among these are "jumble packed" cartons or large returnable boxes into which the empty cans are poured at random. Flaps are closed and tied with cord for delivery. At the canning plant the jumbled cans are dumped into an automatic unscrambler. With an efficient setup of this type, a single operator can easily handle as many as 1,000 cans per minute of small or medium size. The empty cartons are collapsed and returned to the can factory for reuse.

The jumble packing system has also been extended to specially fitted highway trailers in which bulk loads of jumbled cans are hauled for short distances.

The best and fastest growing method for handling empty cans is bulk pallet delivery. Cans are stacked vertically on wooden pallets with chipboard separators between each layer of cans. The cans and pallets are shipped as a unit containing from 2,000 to 4,000 cans, depending on the can size. Loads are wrapped with corrugated fiberboard or kraft paper and taped at the edges to protect the cans and keep the load in shape during transit.

STORAGE OF EMPTY CANS

With the use of lighter tin coating weights on most cans today, the importance of good storage practices cannot be over-emphasized. Storage facilities should be dry, properly heated and adequately ventilated. Otherwise rust may be a problem.

Empty cans should be stored in a dry and sheltered area, away from open windows, leaky pipes, steam lines, or other sources of moisture. They should be packed in dry cartons, paper carriers or at least covered with tarpaulins or heavy paper.

Whenever possible, bulk or packaged cans should be stored on raised platforms away from direct contact with the floor. Enough space should be left between pallets of stacked cans to permit proper ventilation in the storage area.

Sweat rusting may occur on empty cans during storage unless special precautions are taken. Moisture will condense on exposed can surfaces whenever it is present in the air and the can temperature is well below the dew point of the surrounding atmosphere. Ideally, cans should be kept at least as warm as the temperature of the storage area and not exposed to high humidities. This may be accomplished by proper heating and air circulation in storage quarters.

Sudden increases in temperature and humidity should be avoided. Cold cans will sweat when they are brought into a warm, humid room. Similarly, sweat rust may occur if warm outside air is suddenly let into a cool warehouse. In Northern states this situation often prevails during the spring months when warehouses are likely to be cooler than the outside air.   When sudden atmospheric changes occur, warehouse doors and windows should be kept tightly closed until the temperature of the cans can be brought up to that of the outside air or slightly higher.   Planned changes in warehouse temperatures should be made gradually.

Some canners set up "tempering rooms" into which cans that are about to be used (or filled cans which have been stored for later shipment) are brought.   Initially, these rooms are held at the same temperature as the warehouse, then are closed off and gradually brought up to the outside temperature by proper heating and ventilation.

Special attention must be given to cans stored in warehouses located near seacoasts.   Precautions should be taken to prevent the deposition of air-borne ocean salt on the cans, as this will accelerate corrosion.

CLOSING MACHINE OPERATIONS

For use in food processing operations, cans are normally washed and steamed in continuous washers ahead of the filling operations. Methods of food processing are described in other chapters of this book.   Whatever method is employed, it is important that the container be sealed hermetically to prevent the invasion of spoilage organisms.   Can closing machines may be purchased or leased from the manufacturer.

The simplest and probably the most widely used procedure is regular closure in which the can end is merely double-seamed onto the filled can.   This style of closure is suitable for several classes of products: (1) those not adversely affected by residual air in the container and not requiring vacuum in the closed can (e.g., popcorn); (2) hot filled products in which headspace vapors provide the necessary degree of oxygen removal and thermal condensation and contraction on cooling create an internal vacuum (e.g., fruit juices, soup, cream-style corn); and (3) products which receive a thermal exhaust after being filled into the can (e.g., fruits, sweet potatoes).

With the advent of high-speed canning lines, the need arose for a method of closure which would be simple, relatively inexpensive, and would produce a vacuum without the use of an exhaust box.   Steam flow closure was developed to fill this need, and has proved to be very successful.   With this method, steam is jetted into the headspace of the can immediately before and during assembly of the can and cover. The steam displaces the air in the headspace, and when the steam in the closed can condenses, a vacuum is formed.

For successful use of steam flow closure, a product must be brine or syrup packed, with a relatively unobstructed "headspace" above the liquid level. If the cans are overfilled, the volume of steam entrapped in the closed can will not be enough to provide an adequate vacuum. Also, no appreciable air pockets should be left below the liquid level of the product as this air will not be removed by steam flow closure.

Large fruit packers on the West Coast use a special procedure in which vacuum syruping is combined with steam flow closure. Cold fruit is filled into the can; then a vacuum is drawn to remove air and cellular gases, and the vacuum is replaced with syrup. Headspace air is removed by steam flow before the can is closed, producing a vacuum in the sealed container.

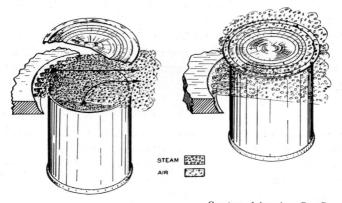

STEAM

AIR

Courtesy of American Can Co.

FIG. 153. OPERATING PRINCIPLE OF STEAM FLOW CLOSURE

Gas flow or low oxygen closure operates on the same principle as steam flow except that an inert gas such as nitrogen or carbon dioxide is jetted into the headspace of the can at the time of closure. This method of closure is used for special applications, such as beer and carbonated beverages, where the air content of the can must be reduced to a minimum without producing a vacuum.

A fourth method, vacuum closure, involves removing the air from the can in a vacuumized chamber and completing the double-seaming operation while the can is still under vacuum. Vacuum closure removes air very effectively, and is the only method of closure suitable for dry packed products such as nut meats, coffee and potato sticks, which are highly sensitive to oxidation and yet contain numerous air pockets within the filled can. This type of closure also is used for most meat products which are handled and filled in an uncooked or refrigerated state, and for vacuum packed whole kernel corn.

Vacuum-gas closure is a special method which is used with certain types of dry packed, oxygen-sensitive foods for which regular vacuum closure is not suitable. Applications include large can sizes which would panel or collapse under high vacuum closure, and powdered products, such as dry milk, which would be blown out of the can if subjected to the rapid suction of a conventional vacuum machine. Air and atmospheric gases are removed slowly from the can, and the resulting vacuum is then replaced with an inert gas.

Accurate control of closing machine operation is essential to avoid spoilage. Poor seams may result from faulty adjustments or worn parts. Can manufacturers have closing machine specialists who are available to assist canners with proper maintenance and adjustment of closing machines. Another factor which may affect vacuum retention and prevention of spoilage is can handling. It is important to avoid damaging bumps and dents on the double-seams through rough handling, especially while the cans are still cooling. Chlorination of the cooling water may be advisable, especially if the water is reused, or has a high bacterial count.

FILLED CAN HANDLING

Labor-saving methods have been developed for handling filled cans at the cannery so that it is now possible to maintain continuous high speed operations. Filled can runways are geared to remove cans from the closing machines at an increased rate of speed. Otherwise line jams and production stops are apt to occur when the cans crowd back to the closing machine.

Because of their weight, filled cans are subject to damage from sudden impacts. For this reason, gravity runways should be used only for short distances and for small cans. The angle of drop should be slight, and vertical drops should be avoided completely. A water bath is sometimes used to cushion the fall.

Vertical retorts are still the most widely used equipment for the heat processing of food. Until recently, most vertical retort crates were filled by "strapping." With this method, cans are discharged from the closing machine onto a table adjacent to the empty retort carts or crates. A large strap, held at each end by the operator, is used to gather a quantity of cans. The cans are slid off the table into place in the retort crate. About 300 cans per minute can be handled without serious damage to the cans.

Several different types of equipment have been developed for loading and unloading retort crates automatically. One method employs crates with false bottoms and a hydraulic lift which positions the bottom level of the crate with the discharge table of the closing machine. After one layer of cans has been filled, the lift is dropped one can height, a perforated divider inserted, and the next layer accumulated. This process is reversed for unloading.

Rapid handling is achieved in reel-type continuous retorts and coolers. This type of unit consists of a long cylindrical vessel equipped with a rotating reel and suitable valves through which the cans enter and are discharged. While such equipment is costly, it is fully automatic and economical to operate.

Warehousing of filled cans has similarly been mechanized with cases being palletized for stacking by fork lift truck. Several different models of palletizers have been developed which do the job automatically and efficiently. Some of these machines will turn the cartons as they are received from the feed-in conveyor, reversing each layer so that there is an interlocked package. Such equipment is expensive but is considered economically sound for large canning plants where 15 or more cartons per minute may be handled.

Protection of Cans from Corrosion

The Can Manufacturers Institute (1958) has issued suggestions for preventing internal corrosion and external rust on cans. Canners are advised to consider the following factors affecting internal corrosion:

(1) **Container Fills Should be Controlled Closely.**—Proper fills delay the formation of hydrogen springers by providing a reasonable headspace that acts as a reservoir to hold the first hydrogen gas evolved in the corrosion process. This headspace is largely ineffective, however, if it is not exhausted of air and other gases, and a good vacuum established in the can.

(2) **Elimination of Air.**—Every effort should be made to minimize the volume of air entrapped in the sealed can. This may involve both adequate preparation of the raw product and thermal or mechanical exhaust of the can. Syrup and brines should be boiled prior to use and added as hot as possible.

(3) **Adequate Cooling.**—Immediately after the sterilization period the cans should be rapidly cooled until only enough heat remains to dry the containers and prevent rust. The preferred method is to cool in water to 95° to 105°F., and allow the cans to dry before casing. Under no circumstances should cans be cased at temperatures above 95°F. or "stack-burn" will occur. Similarly, cans should not be stacked in solid blocks in the warehouse if the can temperatures are above 85°F.

(4) **Storage Temperatures.**—Corrosion is a chemical reaction which is accelerated by increases in temperature. Container service life at 100°F. may be from one-seventh to one-third that obtained at 70°F., depending on the product. Cool storage temperatures help to retard corrosion and maintain the initial quality of the canned food.

(5) **Corrosion Accelerators.**—A number of substances are capable of reducing the shelf life of food cans to less than one-quarter that expected. Spray residues, some sulfur compounds and minute quantities of metal (particularly copper) dissolved from equipment are among the corrosion accelerators known to have caused trouble.

External rust on cans may be caused by:

(1) **Abrasion** of the tin coating or lithography in can tracks, twisters, unscramblers, or other can handling and processing equipment.

(2) Excessively sharp or deep code **embossing** on the can ends.

(3) **Product residues** on the exterior surfaces. Sealed cans should be washed immediately after closing to remove salt or acid brines. Excessively high concentrations of alkaline detergent solutions should be avoided in washing grease from cans. The cans should be rinsed in fresh water immediately after such detergent sprays.

(4) **Improper Retort Venting.**—Air should be removed from steam retorts rapidly and completely at the beginning of the process.

(5) **Water Temperature.**—In boiling water processes, the water should be kept at a full boil, not merely "rolling."

(6) **Chemical composition of the water** used in processing and cooling. Water of high natural alkalinity or containing alkaline residues will etch or spangle cans, leaving them more vulnerable to rusting during storage. Appreciable concentrations of chlorides, sulfides or sulfates in the processing or cooling waters also may cause rust formation. Chemical treatment of the water sometimes is necessary.

(7) **Residual Moisture.**—Cooling water should be drained from the cans promptly and thoroughly. An air or steam blast is sometimes used to remove excess water from the tops. When cooled to 95° to 105°F., enough heat is left in the cans to dry any moisture remaining on the exterior surfaces. Cans should not be cased until they are thoroughly dry.

(8) **Inadequate Storage Facilities.** The recommendations mentioned earlier concerning storage of empty cans apply to filled can storage.

BIBLIOGRAPHY

AMERICAN CAN CO. 1943. Canned Food Reference Manual. American Can Co., New York.

AMERICAN IRON AND STEEL INSTITUTE. 1960. Steel Products Manual—Tin Mill Products. American Iron and Steel Institute, New York.

BRIGHTON, K. W. (Editor). 1947. The development of sealing compounds. Res. Bull. 9. American Can Co., Maywood, Ill.

BRIGHTON, K. W., and PEARCE, W. E. 1961. Progress in metal containers. Proc. Fourth Internatl. Congr. on Canned Foods, 171—193., Berlin, Germany.

CAN MANUFACTURERS INSTITUTE. 1958. How to Obtain Best Service from Food Cans. 2nd Edition, Can Manufacturers Inst., Washington, D. C.

CAN MANUFACTURERS INSTITUTE. 1960. The History of the Metal Can and its 150 Years of Service to Man. Can Manufacturers Inst., Washington, D. C.

CIBOCH, L. 1954. Literature of canning and preserving. Advan. Chem. Ser. 10, 280–285. American Chemical Society, Washington, D. C.

CLIFCORN, L. E. 1958. Cool storage maintains quality in canned foods. Food Processing 19, No. 5, 27, 35.

ELLIS, R. F. (Editor). 1952. The inside side seam stripe. Research Bull. 21. American Can Co., Maywood, Ill.

ELLIS, R. F. (Editor). 1961. New materials and manufacturing techniques for the metal can. Research Bull. 40. American Can Co., Maywood, Ill.

GOTSCH, L. P., EIKE, E. F., and BRIGHTON, K. W. 1959. The status of aluminum for food cans. Natl. Canners Assoc. Inform. Letter 1720, 99–104.

GUEFFROY, W. A., and BRAUN, O. G. 1956. Automatic handling of cans in the modern canning plant. Natl. Canners Assoc. Inform. Letter 1570, 81–85.

HARTWELL, R. R. 1951. Corrosion factors related to the use of tin plate for food containers. Food Technol. 5, 402–408.

HARTWELL, R. R. 1954. Trends in the use of tin in the container industry. Tin. 23, 57–60, 62. Tin Publications Ltd., London, England.

HARTWELL, R. R. 1956. Choice of containers for various products. Proc. Third Internatl. Congr. Canned Foods, 128–148, Rome-Parma, Italy.

HOTCHNER, S. J., McKIRAHAN, R. D., and LACHELE, C. E. 1959. Control of quality of sheet metal materials for containers. Proc. Am. Soc. Quality Control, 179–189.

IVES, M. 1957. Safety evaluation of food packaging materials. J. Am. Dietet. Assoc. 33, 347–351.

JOSLYN, M. A. 1956. Metal containers—in food products manufacture. Western Canner Packer 48, No. 4, 24–26, 31–34, 36.

LUECK, R. H., and BRIGHTON, K. W. 1951. Twelve years of technical progress in the United States canning industry. Proc. Second Internatl. Congr. Canned Foods, Paris, Sect. 14, 1–18.

McKIRAHAN, R. D., CONNELL, J. C., and HOTCHNER, S. J. 1959. Application of differentially coated tin plate for food containers. Food Technol. 13, 228–232.

NATIONAL CANNERS ASSOC. 1955. The ABC's of Canned Foods. Natl. Canners Assoc., Washington, D. C.

NATIONAL CANNERS ASSOC. 1964. Canners Statistical Handbook. Division of Statistics and Economics, Natl. Canners Assoc., Washington, D. C.

PILCHER, R. W. (Editor). 1947. The Canned Food Reference Manual. 3rd Edition. American Can Co., Maywood, Ill.

PILCHER, R. W., and PEARCE, W. E. 1960. Can production and canning: a record of progress. Southern Food Processor 21, No. 9, 4–6, 13–15.

STEVENS, H. P., and BRIGHTON, K. W. 1954. The story of can enamels. Can. Chem. Process. Oct., 72–80.

STEVENS, H. P., and ELLIS, R. F. 1960. Can coatings now tailor-made for top product protection. Can. Packaging *13*, No. 8, 46–48.

STOLK, W. C. 1960. Revolution in Containers. Address to the Newcomen Soc. in North America. Princeton Univ. Press, Princeton, N. J.

WILLEY, A. R., KRICKL, J. L., and HARTWELL, R. R. 1956. Steel surface properties affect internal corrosion performance of tin plate containers. Corrosion *12*, No. 9, 433t–440t.

CHAPTER 22

Frank H. Wright | Glass Containers

INTRODUCTION

Glass containers used for food packaging in 1960 amounted to 9,200,000,000 units—41.3 per cent of the 22.3 billion containers shipped. Of these shipments, wide mouth food containers constituted about 70 per cent of this total, and narrow neck, the remaining 30 per cent. This ratio has been approximately maintained over the past 25 years. Figs. 154 and 155 show the trend in use of wide and narrow mouth containers through 1960. These figures represent "packer's ware" and do not include dairy product containers, which represented an additional 261 million bottle shipment.

Glass containers are selected for a wide variety of foods because:

(1)   Glass is inert chemically, and does not react with foods to produce flavor changes.

(2)   Glass is impermeable and nonporous.

(3)   Glass is odorless and sanitary.

(4)   Glass is transparent, permitting the contents to be inspected at the time of packing and at the point of purchase to stimulate impulse sales in self-service super-markets.

(5)   Glass containers have great strength—and they are being made stronger, yet lighter and thinner each year.

(6)   Glass containers are easy to open and reseal to store unused contents. Many have numerous reuse purposes.

(7)   Glass containers may be made in a wide variety of shapes, sizes and colors.

(8)   Properly designed glass containers have high conveyor line speed and stability.

(9)   With glass containers, vacuum-fill, as well as gravity-and-pressure-fill and vacuum-closing, are easily accomplished.

(10)   Many foods packed in glass have a high storage stability and extended shelf-life.

New food specialties are often introduced in glass to take advantage of its sales appeal (e.g., processed dates, figs, prunes, nuts and cocktail specialties, etc.). Colorful products such as beets, pimentos, cherries,

FRANK H. WRIGHT is West Coast Manager of Glass Container Manufacturers Institute, Inc., San Francisco, Calif.

GLASS CONTAINER SHIPMENTS
WIDE MOUTH FOOD
INDEX:— 1939 = 100

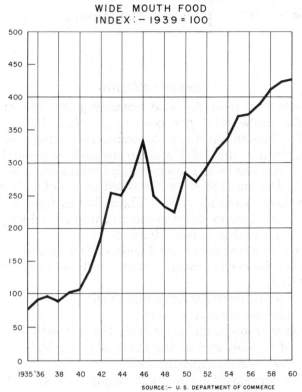

SOURCE:— U. S. DEPARTMENT OF COMMERCE

Fig. 154.　Wide Mouth Glass Container Shipments for
Foods, by Year

carrots, berries and red cabbage are especially appealing in glass containers.

Gourmet foods, and the constantly improved and expanding lines of pickled items and relish products, are packed, preferably in glass, as the best package to display appetite-exciting appeal, preserve delicate flavors, and provide the protection of positive reseal to protect these qualities when the contents are partially used at one serving.

Instant products in many lines, because of their hygroscopic characteristics, use glass for packaging. In this area, one of the largest users of glass containers is soluble "instant" coffee. Coffee men point out that current soluble coffee sales, glass packed, represent about one-third of all household coffee consumption, and are of the opinion this may rise to 50 per cent within the next five years.

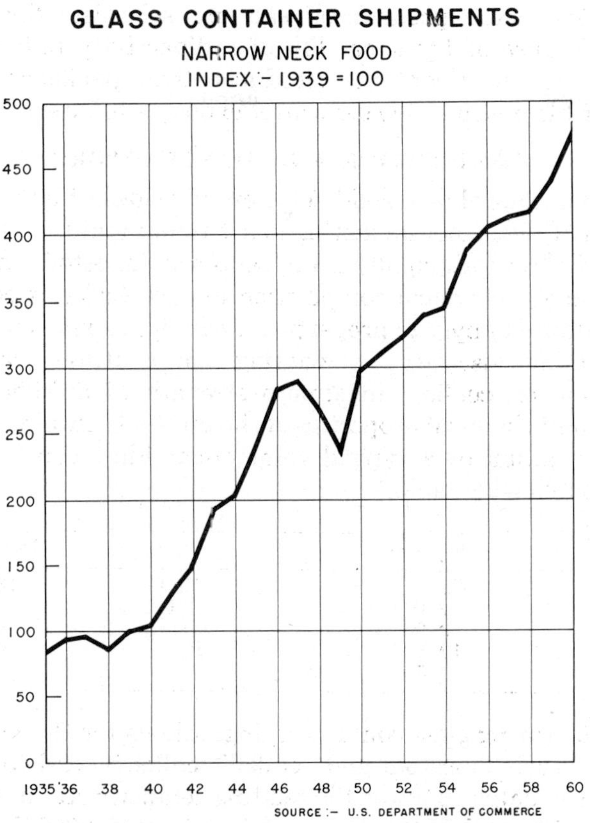

GLASS CONTAINER SHIPMENTS

NARROW NECK FOOD
INDEX :- 1939 = 100

SOURCE :- U.S. DEPARTMENT OF COMMERCE

FIG. 155. NARROW NECK GLASS CONTAINER SHIPMENTS
FOR FOODS, BY YEAR

Instant cream, vichyssoise, tea, bouillon and other convenience products require more glass packaging each year.

Food processors should not restrict their thinking to packaging their products in package material considered "historical" to the particular item. Many staples, as well as other items, have been requested in glass by housewives, who are the ultimate consumers.

An alert merchandising manager or packaging engineer can visualize many products that are not predominantly packed in glass at the present time, which would move rapidly from retailers' shelves if so packed, and thereby capitalize on these stated preferences.

It is interesting to note qualities of glass containers revealed in Civil Defense Authority tests conducted at Frenchman's Flats, Nevada in 1955. Food products of many varieties in glass containers stored 4,700 ft. from ground zero—the point where the atomic device was exploded—were pronounced safe by scientists for emergency feeding. Because of the short life of radioactivity induced in glass containers and their contents, products thus packaged were pronounced usable within a few days after exposure to intense radiation.

COMPOSITION AND MANUFACTURE

Glass is an amorphous, solid solution of oxides of silicon, calcium, sodium and other elements existing in a vitreous state. The basic raw materials of glass (principally sand, soda ash, limestone) are carefully selected, and the chemical composition of each batch is controlled to obtain the desired physical properties (fusibility at reasonable temperatures, suitable viscosity at working temperatures, resistance to devitrification on cooling, maximum strength of finished container, and the desired chemical properties of the finished container).

The composition of a typical commercial Flint container glass is given in the following table.[1]

	Per cent		Per cent
SiO_2	72.7	Na_2O	13.6
Al_2O_3	2.0	K_2O	0.4
FeO	0.06	SO_3	0.3
CaO	10.4	F_2	0.2
BaO	0.5		

In manufacturing glass containers, ingredients for the batch including sand, soda ash, limestone and "cullet" (cullet is crushed glass introduced into the batch to lower the melting temperature) are accurately measured and heated to temperatures in excess of 2,600°F., using gas, oil or electric energy or a combination of any two, to supply heat. After the glass is melted and refined, containers are formed by introducing the molten glass into molding machines, either by extrusion or suction, so that a "gob" sufficient for each individual container is sheared into the first mold (the blank mold) where the shaping of the container is started, then transferred to a finishing mold, blown to final shape, partially cooled and released.

The formed container is reheated to 1,200°F. on a conveyor as it passes through a tunnel called the "Lehr," then cooled gradually to anneal or temper the glass. The cooled containers are inspected and then cased for shipment in cartons equipped with dividers to hold the containers in position and prevent direct contact between them. Note must be taken that some ware other than food containers is now being bulk loaded on pallets at the manufacturer's plant, and it is possible

[1] Source: Handbook of Glass Manufacture. Anon. Ogden Publishing Co., 55 W. 42nd St., N.Y.C. 1953

this practice may extend, to some extent, to the shipment of food containers. Rigid periodic tests of samples from all molds are made as a basis for careful quality control.

As a result of improvements in equipment and technology, lighter, stronger containers are being produced at increasing speeds. Packers' lines are being operated at speeds of over 750 containers per minute, while speeds of 1,000 containers per minute are anticipated through improvements in uncasers, unscramblers, single-filing equipment, fillers, cappers, labelers and casing machines. Inspection of containers and contents is now being performed electronically in an increasing number of packers' plants, eliminating the effect of operator fatigue or error.

Container Design and Specifications

Designing a new container, or redesigning a container, is in most cases a mutual problem of the container manufacturer and the packer. The problems of one customer or group of customers are not necessarily those of all customers using glass. For packing heat-processed foods, a container resistant to temperature differences is required. Carbonated beverages and beer require containers capable of withstanding internal pressures.

Few packers will undertake to write their own specifications. When a food processor reaches the decision to package a particular product in glass, he will find that glass container manufacturers usually have furnished containers for similar products and can make recommendations based on broad past experience.

Selection can be made from Glass Container Manufacturers Institute designs showing recommended specifications for approximately 66 kinds of containers of various designs. Of these, 31 are used for food products, each available in an assortment of capacities, thus offering in the neighborhood of 200 different containers. These recommended container design standards are available to glass container manufacturers, and most are manufactured by several. Packers can, therefore, almost always obtain glass containers of suitable capacity and design from standard recommendations, or from a stock design in which a given manufacturer may specialize.

The packer may possibly reach a decision to have a private mold manufactured for his exclusive use. If one decides upon specifications of his own, it is recommended that he: (1) define requirements clearly (or specifications may fail because they do not set down their purpose); (2) work out details with supplier; otherwise, impractical specifications may be called for.

Specifications should include: (a) an appropriate description of container and finish; (b) size and dimensions of container, including: ideal capacity; ideal height; maximum ideal diameter; maximum ideal weight; and tolerances either way for these dimensions.

Limitations or requirements imposed on containers by equipment in a packer's plant are important. These requirements, may be influenced by equipment for automatic uncasing, washing or cleaning, filling, labeling and casing, coupled with the methods used for conveying or transferring containers from one operation to the next in line. Food packers are primarily interested in containers which will protect and display products to maximum advantage and yet be economical. In addition, containers must fill and label well and run easily in packing lines.

The retailer is primarily interested in whether the package will sell, and is likely to ask questions such as, "Does it have eye appeal? Will it generate confidence? Will it complement the product? Is it a good mass display package? Will it stack?"

The consumer will, at least mentally, ask, "Is the package easy to handle? Will it fit in home cupboards and refrigerators? Will it look nice on the table? Does it have reuse value?"

After requirements and specifications have been thoroughly discussed by the food packer and the glass container manufacturer, artist's sketches, working drawings, preliminary models, displacement tests and specification adjustments, finally result in the production sample molds. Each of these steps is necessary in engineering a new container design for a private mold.

One of the most exacting factors in designing a container is the establishment of proper capacity, determined in regard to volume or cubic content stated in fluid ounces. If a product is to be sold by weight, the bulk or specific gravity of the product must be determined and the volume of this weighed quantity calculated. To illustrate variations in the volume for containing weighed quantities of specific products: a pound of honey is usually packed in a jar having an overflow capacity of $11^1/_2$ fluid ounces, while the same jar will hold three-quarters of a pound of peanut butter. A pound of jam may be packed in a $12^1/_2$ fluid ounce jar, but only 6 oz. of soluble coffee will go into a jar almost double that size.

Increased filling-line speeds focus greater attention on the importance of the stability of containers on fast moving conveyor surfaces. Height of center of gravity, location of point of contact of bottle to bottle, adequate bottom bearing surface, and method of contact with pushing devices, all must be considered in container design.

Improved containers are constantly being produced, and as previously mentioned, there has been a marked advance in technology of glass container manufacture in the past 15 years. The glass industry is producing containers today which are lighter in weight, but stronger in their resistance to impact and internal and external pressures, and which will withstand greater temperature differences. This has been accomplished through improved chemical control of the raw materials and the finished glass, more scientific shaping of the container, more rigidly controlled furnace temperatures, higher handling speed of the molten glass, more accurate control of time and temperature factors in the forming process, better control of mold cooling, lubrication and design, and improved annealing or tempering, coupled with ameliorated methods of handling hot ware.

Historically, food containers fall into two general classifications depending on the size of the bottle opening; namely, "wide mouth" or "narrow neck." The nature of the food product determines which type is used.

Wide mouth containers are used for packing such items as baby food, dessert topping, dried milk, fruits, honey, peanut butter, instant coffee or tea, jams, jellies, mayonnaise, pickles, relishes, cocktail snacks and vegetables. Products such as catsup, extracts, juices, salad oil, liquid seasoning, syrups, sauces and vinegar are usually packed in narrow neck containers although wide mouth and narrow neck containers are often used interchangeably, according to the preference of a packer.

Container designs change to keep pace with trends in displaying foods and consumer preferences. For years housewives have been in the habit of reusing glass containers. This has resulted in designs for freezer jars which have gained popularity, and the "cocktail" packs of various seafoods and preserves. Containers used for these packs make pleasing and durable serving ware. The old "jelly glass" long used for water tumblers has been refined so that, when emptied of product, it is an attractive drinking glass which has been widely accepted. Another popular design is the decanter container now used for packing many juices, as it makes an ideal container for storing liquids after the original product has been used.

One ingeniously designed jar is tapered to match the taper of asparagus spears, thus affording optimum protection and display for the product. It is labeled and stacked "upside down," that is, with the closure cap at the bottom.

Manufacturers are constantly changing and modifying glass package designs. One example of a design improvement is the heeled-in

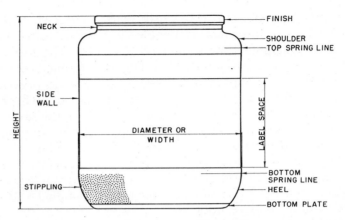

FIG. 156. NOMENCLATURE FOR GLASS CONTAINERS FOR
FOODS

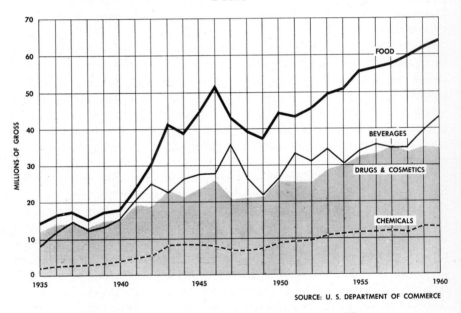

SOURCE: U. S. DEPARTMENT OF COMMERCE

FIG. 157. GLASS CONTAINER SHIPMENTS FOR VARIOUS
USES, BY YEAR

base which eliminates impact and abrasion in that area during filling
and casing. Other examples are the use of stippling or knurling in
certain areas to increase strength, bottom indentations which fit over
the closures of similar containers, thereby improving stacking characteristics on grocers' shelves, and the "form fitting" sidewall designs
which facilitate handling by the consumer.

FIG. 158. 71½ BILLION GLASS CONTAINERS GO TO MARKET EACH YEAR, EQUIVALENT TO ALMOST 396 FOR EACH MAN, WOMAN AND CHILD

The major use is to contain food products for home and institutional use.

Container Description

The important parts of a glass container, diagrammed in Fig. 156, are shoulder, heel, side wall, label space, body diameter and finish. The finish, so-called because in the old days of hand-blown bottles, this was the last part made, is that part of a glass container which engages the cap, closure or cork. The key dimensions are over-all height, body diameter, neck diameter and label space. These dimensions for the various more commonly used containers are indicated in Figs. 160, 161, 162 and 163.

Finishes and Closures

A glass container becomes a useful package to the food processor only when it is properly capped or sealed. Originally, this was accomplished by forcing a cork into the bottle. Now there are commercially accepted specifications for some 65 finishes in hundreds of sizes to fit closures made of metals, plastic, cork, rubber and paper. These closures cover a wide range of design, encompassing pry-off, screw-thread, lug, crown, a variety of milk bottle caps and the various friction finishes providing a "corkage" feature for plastic, rubber or cork stoppers.

FIG. 159. FORMING GLASS CONTAINERS
An accurately measured portion of molten glass is molded
to the desired shape, then conveyed through exactly controlled annealing ovens to impart toughness.

In connection with closures, food packers are primarily concerned with three elements: the "finish" on the container itself; the
gasket or liner which forms the seal; and the cap which may be pry-off
screw, lug, crimp-on (crown and milk bottle) or shaker-disc design.
Although dimensions of containers are stated in inches, dimensions of
finishes and closures are stated in millimeters, probably a heritage
from the French origin of the first commercial metal cap.

Metal caps may be of tin plate or aluminum, and are usually coated
with organic compounds.

GCMI ITEM NO.	CAP. O'FLOW FL OZS.	WT. MAX. OZS.	A	B MAX.	C	D	E	SPECIMEN FINISH
10-14	4 1/4	3 3/4	3 25/64	2 1/16	35/64	1 49/64	1 3/4	48 - 400
10-20	6 1/4	4 1/4	3 55/64	2 9/32	5/8	2 1/16	1 15/16	53 - 400
10-24	7 3/4	4 1/2	4 1/8	2 25/64	21/32	2 5/16	2 3/32	58 - 400
10-26	8 3/8	4 3/4	4 9/32	2 1/2	11/16	2 9/64	1 15/16	53 - 400
10-27	8 3/8	4 3/4	4 9/32	2 29/64	11/16	2 3/8	2 3/8	58 - 400
10-28	8 3/4	5 1/2	4 11/32	2 1/2	5/8	2 31/64	2 3/32	58 - 400
10-30	9 1/2	5 1/2	4 31/64	2 35/64	41/64	2 9/16	2 3/32	58 - 400
10-36	11 1/2	6	4 25/32	2 3/4	49/64	2 7/16	2 3/32	58 - 400
10-40	12 1/2	6 1/4	4 27/32	2 53/64	49/64	2 1/2	2 3/32	58 - 400
10-48	15 1/2	7	5 1/8	3 1/32	13/16	2 11/16	2 5/16	60 - 440
10-50	16 1/2	7 1/2	5 7/32	3 1/8	27/32	2 47/64	2 3/16	63 - 400
10-51	16 1/2	7 1/2	5 7/32	3 1/8	27/32	2 47/64	2 5/16	63 - 400
10-52	17	7 1/2	5 11/32	3 7/64	27/32	2 55/64	2 5/16	63 - 400
10-53	18 5/16	8 1/4	5 3/8	3 17/64	29/32	2 49/64	2 5/16	63 - 400
10-60	22 3/4	9 1/2	5 7/8	3 29/64	15/16	3 11/64	2 5/16	63 - 400
10-62	24	10 1/8	5 7/8	3 35/64	61/64	3 3/16	2 5/16	63 - 400
10-63	24 1/2	10 1/2	5 6/16	3 9/16	31/32	3 7/32	2 5/16	63 - 400
10-67	27 1/2	11	6 1/4	3 43/64	1	3 25/64	2 5/16	63 - 400
10-71	30 1/4	11 1/2	6 9/16	3 47/64	1 1/32	3 39/64	2 5/16	63 - 400
10-72	31	11 1/2	6 9/16	3 47/64	1 1/32	3 39/64	2 5/16	63 - 400
10-75	32 5/8	11 1/2	6 3/4	3 53/64	1 1/16	3 45/64	2 5/16	63 - 400
10-77	34	12 3/4	6 13/16	3 59/64	1 3/32	3 45/64	2 5/16	63 - 400
10-81	48 3/4	18 1/2	7 11/16	4 13/32	1 1/4	4 11/64	2 5/8	70 - 400

NOTES:-

1. WHEN OTHER FINISHES ARE USED, CAPACITY, WEIGHT AND HEIGHT SPECIFICATIONS ARE ADJUSTABLE WITHIN THE REQUIREMENTS OF THE FINISH USED. SEE NOTE 2.

2. HEIGHT (DIMENSION 'A') IS BASED UPON USE OF SPECIMEN FINISH SHOWN.

3. THE SPECIFICATIONS SHOWN MAY VARY MODERATELY ACCORDING TO COMMERCIAL TOLERANCES AND INDIVIDUAL MANUFACTURERS PRACTICE.

4. 'B' DIMENSION IS VARIED TO MAINTAIN CAPACITY.

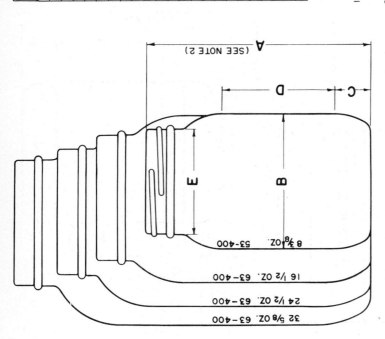

FIG. 160. STANDARD DIMENSIONS OF PLAIN ROUND JARS

GCMI ITEM NO.	CAP. O'FLOW FL.OZS.	WT. MAX. OZS.	A	B MAX.	D	E	F	SPECIMEN FINISH
15-46	$14\frac{3}{4}$	$6\frac{5}{8}$	$4\frac{1}{2}$	$3\frac{3}{64}$	$2\frac{1}{4}$	$2\frac{23}{64}$	$\frac{3}{4}$	63-1710
15-47	15	$6\frac{5}{8}$	$4\frac{1}{2}$	$3\frac{1}{8}$	$2\frac{1}{4}$	$2\frac{15}{32}$	$\frac{3}{4}$	66-1710
15-53	17	$7\frac{1}{4}$	$4\frac{11}{16}$	$3\frac{1}{4}$	$2\frac{3}{8}$	$2\frac{15}{32}$	$\frac{13}{16}$	66-1710
15-71	$28\frac{3}{8}$	$11\frac{1}{4}$	$4\frac{7}{8}$	$4\frac{3}{32}$	$2\frac{1}{4}$	$3\frac{9}{64}$	$1\frac{3}{64}$	83-1710

NOTES:—

1. WHEN OTHER FINISHES ARE USED, CAPACITY, WEIGHT AND HEIGHT SPECIFICATIONS ARE ADJUSTABLE WITHIN THE REQUIREMENTS OF THE FINISH USED. SEE NOTE 2.

2. HEIGHT (DIMENSION 'A') IS BASED UPON USE OF SPECIMEN FINISH SHOWN.

3. THE SPECIFICATIONS SHOWN MAY VARY MODERATELY ACCORDING TO COMMERCIAL TOLERANCES AND INDIVIDUAL MANUFACTURER'S PRACTICE.

4. 'B' DIMENSION IS VARIED TO MAINTAIN CAPACITY.

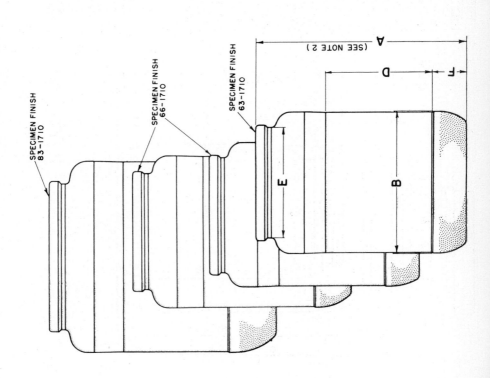

FIG. 161. STANDARD DIMENSIONS OF SHOULDER-TYPE FRUIT AND VEGETABLE JARS

GCMI ITEM NO.	CAP. O'FLOW FL.OZS.	WT. MAX. OZS.	A	B MAX.	C	D	E	SPECIMEN FINISH
29-16	5	$3\frac{9}{16}$	$3\frac{17}{32}$	$2\frac{7}{64}$	$\frac{11}{16}$	$2\frac{7}{32}$	$1\frac{49}{64}$	48-1740 OR 48-870
29-25	8.2	$5\frac{1}{8}$	$3\frac{7}{8}$	$2\frac{17}{32}$	$\frac{41}{64}$	$2\frac{39}{64}$	$2\frac{5}{32}$	58-1740 OR 58-870

NOTES:—

1. WHEN OTHER FINISHES ARE USED, CAPACITY, WEIGHT AND HEIGHT SPECIFICATIONS ARE ADJUSTABLE WITHIN THE REQUIREMENTS OF THE FINISH USED. SEE NOTE 2.

2. HEIGHT (DIMENSION 'A') IS BASED UPON USE OF SPECIMEN FINISH SHOWN.

3. THE SPECIFICATIONS SHOWN MAY VARY MODERATELY ACCORDING TO COMMERCIAL TOLERANCES AND INDIVIDUAL MANUFACTURER'S PRACTICE.

4. 'B' DIMENSION IS VARIED TO MAINTAIN CAPACITY.

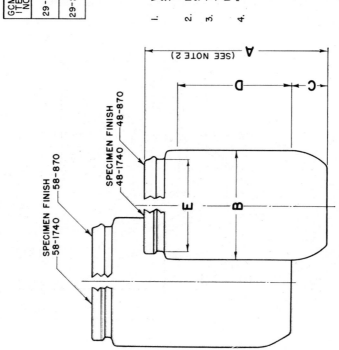

FIG. 162. STANDARD DIMENSIONS FOR BABY FOOD JARS

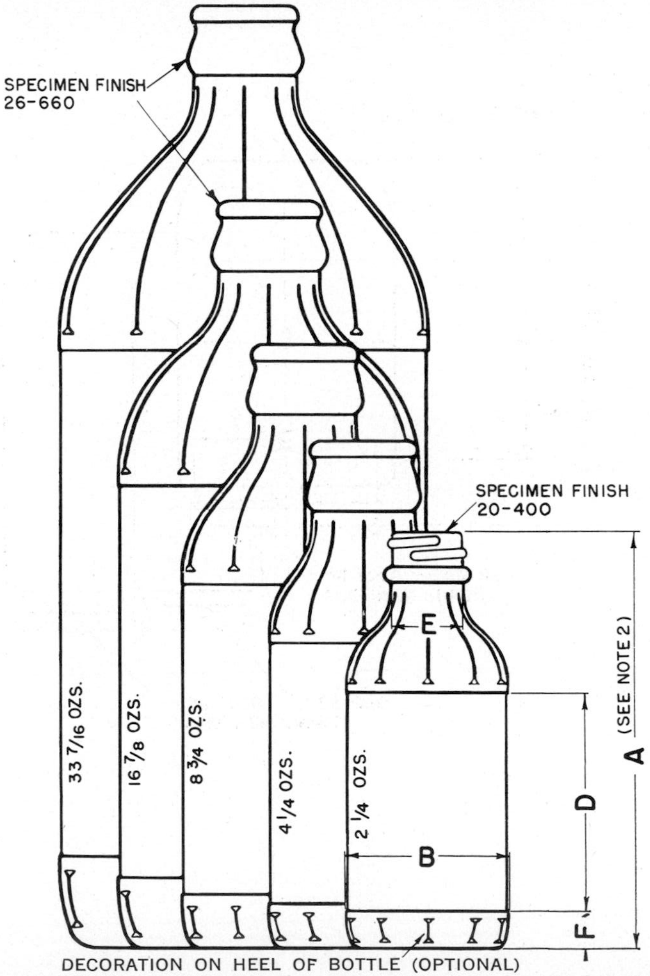

GCMI ITEM NO.	CAP. OF LOW FL. OZS.	WT. MAX. OZS.	A	B MAX.	D	E	F	SPECIMEN FINISH
50-08	$2\frac{1}{4}$	3	$4\frac{3}{32}$	$1\frac{37}{64}$	$2\frac{5}{32}$	$\frac{11}{16}$	$\frac{3}{8}$	20-400
50-14	$4\frac{1}{4}$	$4\frac{1}{4}$	5	$1\frac{7}{8}$	$2\frac{9}{16}$	1	$\frac{7}{16}$	26-660
50-21	$6\frac{19}{32}$	$5\frac{1}{2}$	$5\frac{5}{8}$	$2\frac{5}{32}$	$2\frac{9}{16}$	—	$\frac{1}{2}$	26-660
50-28	$8\frac{3}{4}$	$6\frac{1}{2}$	$5\frac{31}{32}$	$2\frac{13}{32}$	$2\frac{27}{32}$	—	$\frac{17}{32}$	26-660
50-40	$12\frac{3}{4}$	$8\frac{1}{2}$	$6\frac{49}{64}$	$2\frac{11}{16}$	$3\frac{1}{16}$	—	$\frac{5}{8}$	26-660
50-50	$16\frac{9}{16}$	$10\frac{1}{2}$	$7\frac{3}{8}$	$2\frac{29}{32}$	$3\frac{1}{2}$	—	$\frac{11}{16}$	26-660
50-51	$16\frac{7}{8}$	$10\frac{1}{2}$	$7\frac{3}{8}$	$2\frac{61}{64}$	$3\frac{7}{8}$	—	$\frac{11}{16}$	26-660
50-52	$17\frac{3}{8}$	$10\frac{1}{2}$	$7\frac{7}{8}$	$2\frac{63}{64}$	$3\frac{7}{8}$	—	$\frac{11}{16}$	26-660
50-64	$25\frac{3}{8}$	14	$8\frac{3}{8}$	$3\frac{11}{32}$	$4\frac{7}{16}$	—	$\frac{25}{32}$	26-660
50-75	$32\frac{3}{4}$	17	$9\frac{3}{8}$	$3\frac{35}{64}$	5	—	$\frac{29}{32}$	26-660
50-76	$33\frac{7}{16}$	17	$9\frac{5}{16}$	$3\frac{39}{64}$	5	—	$\frac{29}{32}$	26-660
50-77	34	17	$9\frac{5}{16}$	$3\frac{21}{32}$	5	—	$\frac{29}{32}$	26-660
50-81	$48\frac{1}{2}$	22	$9\frac{19}{32}$	$4\frac{15}{64}$	$5\frac{3}{16}$	—	$\frac{15}{16}$	26-660
50-85	$58\frac{1}{8}$	$25\frac{1}{2}$	$9\frac{13}{16}$	$4\frac{17}{32}$	$5\frac{9}{32}$	$1\frac{3}{8}$	$\frac{31}{32}$	36-700
50-91	$105\frac{5}{8}$	37	$10\frac{5}{32}$	$6\frac{5}{64}$	$4\frac{3}{16}$	$1\frac{3}{8}$	$1\frac{7}{16}$	36-700

NOTES:-

1. WHEN OTHER FINISHES ARE USED, CAPACITY, WEIGHT AND HEIGHT SPECIFICATIONS ARE ADJUSTABLE WITHIN THE REQUIREMENTS OF THE FINISH USED. SEE NOTE 2.

2. HEIGHT (DIMENSION 'A') IS BASED UPON USE OF SPECIMEN FINISH SHOWN.

3. THE SPECIFICATIONS SHOWN MAY VARY MODERATELY ACCORDING TO COMMERCIAL TOLERANCES AND INDIVIDUAL MANUFACTURERS PRACTICE.

4. 'B' DIMENSION IS VARIED TO MAINTAIN CAPACITY.

FIG. 163. STANDARD DIMENSIONS FOR SHORT LINE, ROUND FOOD LINE GLASS CONTAINERS

A familiar and widely used closure in food packing is the screw cap. This closure is most often made of tin plate with a liner of pulpboard laminated to a layer of paper which has been specially faced or coated with a suitable material or has a layer of plastic film applied, according to the nature of the product to be packaged. Some of the common types of paper liners are "pulp and oil," "pulp and oil waxes," "vinylite" and various other plastics.

With screw caps, a "pilfer proof" film type seal is often incorporated. This consists of a special film seal superimposed on the liner inside the cap. After the container is filled with product, a thin coating of adhesive is applied to the sealing surface of the finish. Upon application of the closure, this seal is fixed to the finish and provides a relatively moisture-proof seal even with the closure partially loosened or removed. Due to the moisture-resistant characteristics of this pilfer-proof seal, it is widely used with hygroscopic products, such as soluble coffees, teas, creams and bouillons, but it is by no means limited to this type of product because it is enjoying wide use in the wine industry, especially with dry table wines.

Flowed-in or cut rubber gaskets are used also in screw caps if it is desired to retain vacuum through quick sealing of hot-packed products. Usually the rubber gasket is in the form of a ring which engages the top of the glass finish.

Screw-type finishes for wide mouth containers are manufactured in two basic designs: namely, shallow thread and deep thread. Appearance is the controlling factor in the over-all design, and no appreciable difference is apparent in sealing characteristics, although there is more closure purchase by the greater thread contact in a deep thread cap. Purchase approximates 270° in an average shallow thread finish, and 230° to 330° in the average deep thread finish. For home canning, deep-thread finishes afford a slightly higher number of degrees of purchase, averaging in the neighborhood of 360°.

A variation of the screw cap is the so-called lug-type cap where, instead of a "C.T." or *continuous thread* finish on the glass container, there are 2, 3, 4 or 6 lugs or cams molded on the finish. These are engaged by corresponding lugs on the closure. One obvious advantage of this type cap is that it may be conveniently removed.

Lug caps come supplied with any of the liners mentioned above and are generally applied with the same automatic capping equipment used for other screw caps. With rubber gaskets, they are particularly adapted to the sealing of hot-packed products, and many food packers are successfully achieving hermetic seals with moderate vacuum in hot-packed, but not retorted, foods such as jams and jellies.

A closure which is becoming increasingly popular is the specially designed lug cap (marketed under various trade names) applied to the container with high speed automatic capping equipment, and capable of holding a vacuum of any degree in the headspace of the jar or bottle.

This closure in the 48-mm. size has revolutionized baby food packing, and is being used successfully with a variety of food products up to an 83-mm. size.

Another variation of the screw cap is the "roll-on" cap, an aluminum cap which comes as a shell without threads, where the threads are formed over the glass threads of the container at the time the cap is applied. Originally, these caps were used only on narrow neck containers, but now baby foods are packed using these closures in 48- and 53-mm. sizes, and it is anticipated that "roll-on" caps will be used in packing jams, jellies, pickles and relishes using sizes up to 65 mm.

One of the most common closures used by packers of fruits and vegetables is the pry-off closure, easy to open with key or "lid flipper" openers, and easy to reseal airtight with hand pressure. This type of closure affords great product protection and long shelf life.

Pry-off closures fall into two principal categories; namely, side seal and top seal. Both are manufactured from tin plate, with a lubricated rubber or plastic gasket flowed in or molded.

In both types of pry-off closures, they are so constructed that the skirt of the cap is seated over the finish of the jar.

In the side seal finish and closure, the seal is accomplished by pressure of the closure gasket against the outside of the finish perimeter.

The top seal pry-off closure accomplishes the seal through gasket contact with the top of the finish, and the closure is held in place by headspace vacuum alone. Products packed in containers using this type of closure include various cheese packs and preserves. However, packers now are switching to the side seal pry-off finish and closure.

Care must be taken to prevent loosening or "blow-off" of pry-off closures during heat processing. In acid foods processed in atmospheric cookers, this protection is provided by special design of closure and glass finish so that the gasket is mechanically engaged with a uniformly contoured glass bead formed in the finish. In nonacid foods processed under pressure in retorts, air and steam pressure are applied to maintain an external pressure during the heating stage and air pressure during the cooling stage.

Gaskets must retain their resilience at retorting temperatures to insure proper sealing, and various gasket compositions have been developed using synthetic rubber bases or plastics which have desired characteristics.

A closure sometimes used for packing juices is the crimped-on crown closure, consisting of a shell made of tin plate with a composition or cork liner. Frequently a spot of foil, lacquered paper or plastic is positioned on the surface preventing the product from coming in contact with the liner. This crown gives a hermetic seal and will retain internal pressures of a high order.

Larger diameter crimp caps are used on milk and fresh refrigerated citrus juice bottles (36 mm.), spring and distilled water bottles (56 mm.), and on jars of fresh oysters (70 mm.).

Ground, dry seasoning manufacturers have required the development of a new closure and finish combination called a "shaker disc" finish. In most cases, this consists of a conventional screw cap of tin plate with a perforated polyethylene or foil fitment inserted in the mouth of the container at the finish to facilitate sprinkling of the contents when used. In order to provide a means of engagement between the fitment and the glass finish, the basic specifications of the glass thread finish are frequently modified to provide the required sealing characteristics. It is readily understandable that numerous problems had to be solved with this finish, due to the different materials in the components and the fact that in many instances, three different manufacturers are involved in producing the glass container, the fitment and the closure.

Obviously, it is necessary for the packer to determine which type of closure suits a product before it is possible to specify the glass container. A finish and suitable closure must be carefully selected during the planning of the package, since they are interrelated, and one cannot be changed without changing the other. Proper choice of closure is of utmost importance to the satisfactory performance of the complete glass package.

Coatings

Pristine glass containers, as they come through the annealing oven, as yet untouched by human hands, are at their maximum peak of strength. Glass-to-glass contact which occurs during inspection and packing may create microscopic abrasions or "tears" in the glass surface which lower the "built in" strength of the container. Coating the containers at the exit of the annealing oven with materials such as sultur compounds, polyoxyethylene stearate, carbo-waxes, glycols and silicone compounds increases the lubricity of the glass, eliminating the seizing of the pristine glass and thereby preserving its strength, and in the case of some of the aforementioned materials, a bond is created with the glass surface which actually increases the surface strength.

No coating materials are used by the glass container manufacturers which do not comply with the Food and Drug Administration regulations.

Exterior coatings on glass containers act as lubricants to smooth and increase the efficiency of high speed filling lines. Food packers have also found that in addition to increased line speed, the noise incident in the filling line areas is decreased since coating tends to change direct impacts into glancing blows, and the bottles have a different sound. Further, from a purely aesthetic standpoint, the appearance of coated glass containers is better than uncoated ones, as they are more glossy.

In addition to the coating at the glass container manufacturing plant, some packers have installed surface coating equipment at the start of their fill lines.

There is a continuing study of interior coatings for the fire-polished inside surface of glass containers as this is sometimes specified by packers to improve pouring and foaming-at-fill characteristics of certain products.

Labeling

Labels serve to identify products and brands, provide space for instructions, and sales messages, and for information required by food laws including net contents, ingredients, etc. Labels used on glass containers include: (1) spot and wrap-around paper and foil labels; (2) vitreous fired enamel labels fused into the surface of the glass; (3) thermoplastic labels; (4) lithographed designs upon the metal caps of containers.

Spot labels may be applied with water-soluble adhesive or thermoplastic adhesive. The labeling space, or panel for spot labels, may be cylindrical, conical or plane, raised from the surrounding area or indented below the surrounding area. The surface should not be irregular or warped and should not have too sharp a radius, or labels cannot be dependably or smoothly attached.

Odd-shaped labels should be so designed that very acute angles in their termination are avoided, as it is very difficult to get a good adhesive spread on those points. Round labels which contain reading matter and require definite positioning should not be used. An operator will experience great difficulty in placing a round label in a definite position in the labeling machine hopper; and due to vibration of the machine, once they are placed they are likely to turn so that upon application to the container, they will be positioned improperly. If a round label is required for a particular product, a flat may be cut from the diameter of the circle, or ornamentation extending beyond the circle may be added. Either of these methods will allow the labels to be definitely positioned in the label feed.

Paper-backed metal foils or metallic seals are being seen with increasing frequency as they give a rich look to the finished package. Though this type of label has decreased somewhat in cost, it is higher than paper labels and is not used generally except for specialty items in the food processing industry.

Selection of proper adhesives for label application is a highly technical and specialized field. Food products marketed from retailers' refrigerators and freezers require moisture-proof or moisture-resistant adhesives to prevent label soak-off. Climatic conditions, storage, shipping, stock used for label, container shape and size, whether the glass container is coated or uncoated, and the point where the label is applied in the processor's line, to mention a few, are factors which must be taken into consideration when choosing an adhesive.

Thermoplastic labels have been gaining a degree of popularity due to advantages which many food processors feel offset slightly higher costs. A partial list of considered advantages, besides the elimination of a separate adhesive, are: over-all adhesion, no moisture to distort paper fibers, moist as well as dry bottles can be handled, and high speed production can be achieved.

Sometimes the use of thermoplastic labels is called "dry" labeling, as the use of glue and water is eliminated. Thermoplastic labels are manufactured from paper coated with plastic, which, by the application of heat at properly controlled temperatures, becomes tacky and anchors to the container for full surface adhesion.

Wrap-around labels can be used only on round containers, but production speeds are higher than for spot labeling. The label panel is often recessed to avoid scuffing of the label. Varnished labels accomplish much the same purpose without recessing. The quality of wrap-around and spot labels is affected by the weight and grade of the paper, the lithography, and by the varnish or plastic coating. Lighter paper is used more often for wrap-around labels than for spot labels. Suitably coated, the lighter paper can give the feel and appearance of heavier stock.

Still another type of label or container decoration is vitreous fired enamel. This ceramic decoration is usually applied at the glass container manufacturer's plant, and fired into the glass at over 1000°F. in long ovens resembling Lehrs, which gradually increase, then decrease the temperature, to fuse the applied enamel. Vitreous labels are a permanent and integral part of the container and cannot be washed

off.   Modern techniques make it possible to reproduce the most complicated designs or trademarks in many colors or combinations of
colors.

Vitreous enamel is probably most extensively used on containers
for soft drinks and dairy products, as many of the bottles used to
package soft drinks and milk are returnable.   Returnable beverage
bottles average about 23 trips, and milk bottles over 30 trips, before
loss or retirement, thereby making the additional cost for this type of
label inconsequential.

The most familiar use of vitreous enamel by food packers is as
decoration on tumbler packs of cheese, jelly, and preserves, where the
container is designed for reuse in the home.   Some use is made, particularly for salad oils, of vitreous fired enamel for quantitative measurements on the side of the container to assist the homemaker in accurately dispensing the product for recipes.   Food processors do not,
by any means, confine themselves to the above use of vitreous fired
enamel.   Many premium products, gourmet items and specialties are
packed in glass containers with vitreous fired labels to impart the desired quality impression of the product to prospective buyers.

Sealing bands of plastic material, which cover all or a portion of the
closure skirt and extend down over the neck of the container, are used
by many food processors.   These sealing bands offer additional protection against pilferage and contamination at the base of the closure
and top of the bottle neck.   However, their prime purpose consists of
dressing up the container and providing additional space for advertising and product identification.

A number of companies manufacture these bands, offering a wide
variety of sizes, choice of plastics, color ranges and combinations.
Application in some instances is manual, but to maintain the required
high output needed in today's economy, virtually all are now machine applied.

SHIPPING BOXES

There was a time when glass containers were delivered "jumble
packed" to customers in burlap bags.   Now, casing is an integral part
of the glass container industry, with glass containers being delivered
to food processors in shipping boxes manufactured to their requirements and specifications.   The glass container manufacturers, together with customers they serve, represent one of the largest users of
fiber shipping boxes.

Performance of these packaging materials, including paperboard
boxes and interior packing (interior packing is discussed in more de-

tail in a subsequent section of this chapter), is of the greatest importance to glass container manufacturers and represents a substantial
item of cost.   The Glass Container Manufacturers, Institute maintains a completely equipped and excellently staffed packaging laboratory in East Lansing, Mich., for the purpose of studying, experiment-
ing with and testing various materials and box design developments.
This laboratory has been in existence since 1947.

Fiberboard boxes for all kinds of glass containers must usually meet
requirements specified by the Federal Government, the carriers, or by
customers, where some specific attribute is important.   By far the
greatest proportion of the boxes used by the food industry are "reshippers" which serve to carry the empty glass containers from the glass
manufacturer to the food processor, bottler, or packer, and then carry
the filled glass container to the ultimate customer.   Reshippers may
be made in many styles, but two styles are in most common usage.

These two styles are the Regular Slotted Shipping Box (RSC) and
the Center Special Slotted Shipping Box (CSSC).   The Regular
Slotted Box is in more general use than any other style because it is
adapted to the shipment of the many designs and sizes of glass containers.   This style of box makes efficient use of the box material being wasted due to special flaps, etc.   All flaps are the same length,
with the outer flaps meeting at the center of the box, while the inner
flaps do not meet.   The space between the inner flaps varies, depending upon the relation of the length to the width of the box.

When the product to be shipped does not require the protection afforded by two thicknesses of corrugated fiberboard over the entire
areas of top and bottom, this shipping box is safe, convenient and
satisfactory.   However, when two thicknesses of corrugated fiberboard are required at top and bottom, fill-in or plug pads between the
inner flaps are often used with the regular slotted box.

With the Center Special Slotted Box the end flaps are of greater
length than the side flaps, thereby insuring that all meet.   In this
style of slotted box, the inner flaps and outer flaps meet in the
center of the box.   It is similar to the regular slotted shipping box
with the exception that the Center Special Slotted Box affords more
cushioning at the top and bottom because those areas are entirely
covered by two thicknesses of corrugated fiberboard.   This means
that no fill-in pad is necessary to provide a level bottom.

Regulations specifying strength for corrugated fiber box materials
are most frequently given in terms of bursting strength.   This is the
value that appears on the box certificate located on the bottom of
each box.   The bursting strength test (Mullen or Cady) is the pres-

sure required to rupture a paper or paperboard when it is tested in a specified instrument under specified conditions. The units of measure are frequently referred to as pounds, Mullen Test, or pounds, Cady Test.

While boxes may be fabricated of almost any strength of corrugated board from 125 lbs. Mullen Test to 275 Mullen Test or higher, the most commonly used strengths or grades are the 175-lb. and 200-lb. Mullen Test materials. Gross package weights most frequently shipped lie in the range of 20 to 65 lbs., and carrier requirements for box strength are tied to the gross package weight.

Interior Packing

Interior packing elements such as partitions, separators, shelfs, liners, pads, etc., are important for glass products in order to keep the containers from glass-to-glass contact, and to provide a cushioning effect. Partition designs and materials are numerous, and again only those in most common use by food processors will be discussed.

Laboratory studies, combined with shipping experience, determine the optimum partition type to be used, which must be the result of a balance of protective qualities and economics. Full height or shoulder height partitions may be used by food processors. Either may be fabricated of various grades and thicknesses of corrugated or solid fiberboard. In addition to forming individual cells for each container, the full height partition also supports the box to give it more compressive strength and greater rigidity than shoulder height partitions. Also, if the box is shipped upside down, there is the possibility the shoulder height partition may become dislocated, thereby leaving the bases of the glass containers unprotected. Shoulder height partitions facilitate packing and unpacking and, are less expensive.

The protective qualities of partitions are dependent upon the quality of the paperboard from which they are fabricated. Both the facing material of the board and the corrugating medium used for the flutes are important. The cushioning effect of the board used in the interior packing is commonly judged by the flat crush resistance. The flat crush resistance is measured in a compression tester under specified conditions and represents the pounds of force required to crush the flutes of each square inch of board specimen. Double wall boards give a great deal more cushioning effect than single wall boards.

The following boards are used exclusively for partitions and other interior packaging in the boxes used by the food processing industry.

(1) **0.009 Chip and Chip, Double Faced Corrugated Board** fabricated with chip liners and chip corrugating medium is considered

non-test partition material. This type of material generally is used whenever the specifications or intended usage do not require test material. 0.009 refers to the caliper (in inches) of the component material.

(2) **175 or 200-lb. (Mullen) Test Material.**—Frequently specifications and intended usage dictate that test material of 175- or 200-lb. bursting strength be used. In general this material gives more protection to the glass container and stands up to repeated vibrations and impacts much longer than does the previously mentioned paper board.

(3) **0.009 Chip and Chip Double Wall Board.**—Laboratory work and shipping experience are indicating more and more that the separation between glass containers is frequently more important than the use of extra heavy outer boxes or the use of liners in the boxes. For example, double wall partitions have been used extensively in liquor cases.

(4) **200-lb. Double Wall Board.**—This double wall material with a bursting strength test of 200 lbs. may be used where protection superior to that afforded by chip and chip double wall board is desired.

(5) **0.040 to 0.047 Solid Chip Board.**—This material may be used satisfactorily with the smaller sizes of glass containers where cushioning is not necessary and only separation to prevent glass-to-glass contact is desired. The material is also satisfactory with some larger special bottles of exceptional strength such as the returnable beer bottle. The 0.040 and 0.047 refer to the caliper (in inches) of the chip board. In general, it may be stated that the greater the caliper of the chip board, the greater the protection offered the glass containers.

Rule 41 of the Consolidated Freight Classifications, among other things, outlines in great detail packing requirements for the shipment of items in glass containers. Time and space do not allow covering this rule in detail. However, mention will be made of several points which are of particular interest to food processors.

(1) Gross weight of glass container or earthenware containers and contents packed in fiber boxes must not exceed 65 lbs.

(2) Contents must completely fill the box.

(3) Corrugated fiber boxes, partitions, shells, liners and pads, must have A or C flutes, except containers having net weights not exceeding 25 oz. may have boxes, partitions and pads of B flute corrugated board. Other types of interior packing are also permitted.

(4)　　Liquids in glass or earthenware containers exceeding one gallon capacity will not be accepted in fiber boxes.

(5)　　All partitions are not to be less than full shoulder height.

(6)　　Tiers or layers of containers to be separated by pads of same board as partitions, except pads not required between cartons.

Product Packing

Glass containers as received by the packer are usually cleaned and washed, preheated or sterilized for hot-packed foods. Specially designed cleaners are used to remove all fiber particles, "carton dust," or foreign matter that may be present. These may be air-cleaners in which the jar or bottle is inverted and swept out with air or spray, or immersion washers. The glass containers are frequently inspected after uncasing, both before and after cleaning, for the presence of undesirable defects.

Conveyor lines for glass packing should be suitably designed to protect the ware from unnecessarily rough handling, excessive abrasion, and breakage. New plastic materials with "built-in lubricity" such as Teflon when used for conveyor chains, guide rails and star wheels have contributed materially to solving these problems.

Packers considering installation of a new packaging line normally consult container manufacturers to minimize possible areas or points in the line where problems might be encountered. If handling steps not previously used are involved, points to watch are unusual abuse during handling, overloading, bruising and abrading.

In the event a new container is projected, all the handling steps should be checked, including washing, pasteurizing or any form of heat processing and cooling.

If packing problems in a processing line using glass should occur, it is wise to advise the glass supplier immediately, so their technical staff can examine the problem first-hand. Service engineers, through long experience, can many times immediately spot derangements which would go undetected by even an experienced operating man.

Examples of line speeds for various end uses of containers, which are in most cases limited by filling speeds, are baby foods at 500 to 720 per minute; catsup up to 450, with an occasional line running at approximately 500 per minute; 24-oz. juice bottles and some quart juice bottles 300 per minute with 16-oz. juice bottles occasionally reaching 400 bottles per minute; No. 303 and 300 jars up to 450 bottles per minute; mayonnaise at 240 to 300 per minute; and instant coffee as high as 360 jars per minute.

Glassware may be examined by a processor's quality control section to determine that the glass fulfills the requirements and specifications. Prerequisites for effective sampling are trained, experienced inspectors, a large enough sample, a definite checklist or set of specifications which have been compiled in agreement with 'the glass supplier of the specific lot to be checked. Packers who wish to conduct acceptance sampling must be prepared to spend money for a correct, rather than half-hearted job. Procedures should be carefully organized and backed by a thorough knowledge of glass manufacture, and the principles of statistical quality control.

Accepted ware commences its journey through the packing line by being uncased automatically, or in some smaller food processing plants, by hand. The containers are then "unscrambled," or single filed to be conveyed to cleaning equipment to insure that any carton dust that may have filtered into the container through shipping and handling is removed. Air cleaning is accomplished, with the container upright or inverted, by suction and/or multiple jets of air directed into the jar to create a swirling action. Another type of jar cleaner is a water rinser which operates on the same jet principle using water which is sprayed into the inverted container. It is after this point that some food processing plants spray the containers with any one of a number of coatings to lubricate the containers for their trip through the remainder of the filling line cycle.

Containers may then be given one or more visual inspections, or inspected by highly sensitive electronic equipment which rejects ware automatically if a flaw or foreign matter is detected. They then are filled to predetermined headspace which is adjusted to the product and the nature of the fill.

Headspace must be allowed to provide for expansion of liquid products. Some hot-filled products tend to take care of this requirement automatically, developing a vacuum after they have cooled. Others are headspaced mechanically. With cold-filled liquid packs, correct headspace is important. To determine proper headspace, it must be remembered that water will increase 2 to 3 per cent in volume as the temperature rises from 50° to 150°F.

Filled containers are closed by capping machines which either press or screw the closure on with torque-controlled mechanisms which insure adequate tightness for proper seal, yet which can be easily opened by hand.

From filling and capping, the containers many times are routed through a washer to remove possibly spilled product, to the retorting section, or to a holding and cooling section. Process time and temperatures for low-acid glass packed foods, together with much helpful

DIAMOND, F. 1953. Story of Glass. Harcourt, Brace and Co., New York.

GUSE, V. C. 1951. Crown handling and use. Research Dept. Bull. *24*. Continental Can Co., New York.

KOHMAN, E. F., and COLE, R. L. 1953. Surface darkening of food in glass containers with metal caps. Food Technol. *7*, 174–175.

LIVINGSTONE, G. E., SOLSTAD, M. R., VILECE, R. J., and ESSELEN, W. B. 1954. The role of trace metal contaminants in the discoloration of glass packed baby foods. Food Technol. *8*, 313–316.

MOREY, G. W. 1954. The Properties of Glass. A.C.S. Monograph. 2nd Edition. Reinhold Publishing Corp., New York.

PHILLIPS, C. J. 1941. Glass—The Miracle Maker. Pitman Publishing Corp., Chicago, Ill.

PHILLIPS, C. J. 1960. Glass—Its Industrial Applications. Reinhold Publishing Corp., New York.

POWERS, J. J., PRATT, D. E., and MORRIS, W. 1952. Comparative heating rates of bentonite suspensions in jars processed in boiling water and in steam at atmospheric pressure. Food Technol. *6*, 246–248.

SCHOLES, S. R. 1935. Modern Glass Practice. Industrial Publications, Chicago, Ill.

SCOVILLE, W. D. 1948. Revolution in Glass Manufacturing. Harvard Univ. Press, Cambridge, Mass.

TOOLEY, F. V. 1953. Handbook of Glass Manufacturing. Ogden Publishing Co., New York.

YARNICK, N. S. 1955. Determination of gas in glass packed food products. Food Technol. *9*, 192–193.

CHAPTER 23

C. Olin Ball | Flexible Packaging in
Food Processing

INTRODUCTION

Food is packaged for four primary reasons: (1) to protect the product from contamination by macroorganisms, microorganisms and filth; (2) to retard or to prevent either loss or gain of moisture; (3) to shield the product from oxygen and light and (4) to facilitate handling.

This chapter is concerned with "flexible" packaging, involving films, foils, papers and paperboards which are wrapped about a product, or if preformed, require physical support during filling. This excludes rigid cartons of paperboard.

Among the properties of flexible packaging materials of importance to food processors are: (1) permeability to moisture, oxygen, nitrogen, carbon dioxide and desirable or undesirable volatiles; (2) dimensional stability with change of temperature, humidity, etc.; (3) temperature range for practical utilization; (4) sealability; (5) grease resistance; (6) wet and dry strength; (7) cost; (8) tear, puncture and crease resistance; (9) reaction to ionizing radiations; (10) freedom from contaminating odors, flavors, and solubles, etc.; and (11) appearance and feel, involving texture, gloss, transparency, and printability.

Flexible packaging materials of suitable characteristics are used for packaging food products sterilized by heat or ionizing radiations, as well as "dry" products and perishables stored under refrigeration.

No flexible package equals the protective features of metal and glass containers which are almost universally used for holding sterilized perishables for prolonged storage without refrigeration. For short term storage under favorable conditions, complete imperviousness to oxygen and moisture may not be necessary. For long term storage of perishables, flexible packages must be impervious to gases and water vapor *under commercial handling*.

Metallic foil plastic laminate packages perhaps meet physical requirements for sterile food packages except for strength. Intact, heavy foil is not penetrated by gas or vapor; however, in commercial handling, cracks and splits occur. Increasing thickness of either foil or laminated plastic layer is helpful in giving strength and resisting perforation. Thick foil is completely impervious, and increased

C. OLIN BALL is Consultant in Food Science, Technology, and Engineering, New Brunswick, N. J.

thickness reduces the permeability of plastic films to gas and vapor. Another method for reducing rates of vapor and gas transmission through plastic films is to apply to the surface of the film a coating of material having a lower rate of transmission than the basic material of the film. For instance, a manufacturer of films reported that a coating of a thermoplastic resin applied to a one-half mil polyester film to make the film heat-sealable, reduced water vapor transmission by 77 per cent and gas transmission by 89 per cent.

Rubinate (1961) and associates have made notable progress toward bringing the flexible package composed of foil laminate to a near-practical point for use with heat processed foods in rations for the armed forces. The point of actual use on a trial basis has been reached. No doubt many new problems will have to be solved before the packing of heat processed ration foods becomes general practice but certainly gigantic strides have been made in that direction.

It is well to keep in mind the fact that foods for which flexible packages have been used include only those which, during their storage life, can tolerate a change in moisture content as well as in the composition of gas within the package, particularly in respect to content of oxygen and nitrogen, the principal components of air.

PROPERTIES AND PERFORMANCE

The relatively immense size and the chain-like conformation of the polymeric molecules of the organic materials used in flexible packages for food account for the strength and the flexibility of the materials. In paper, these are cellulose molecules; in plastic films, the basic plastic molecules. Many edible substances, as for example, proteins, nucleic acids and cellulose, are polymers. It is reasonable to expect, therefore, that we may some day have packages for many kinds of food which will be eaten along with their contents, just as sausage casings of animal origin are eaten today. Such a practice will in all probability be limited to foods that must be prepared for eating with the use of water or heat, or both, in order either to dissolve or to soften the packaging material to make it suitable to eat. Special sanitary precautions in handling this type of food will have to be exercised in order to keep packages clean. The most logical use for this type of packaging will probably be with individual or family portions packed in groups in master containers comparable to present packaging of pharmaceutical preparations in gelatin capsules.

Flexible packages are rapidly expanding their foothold in the food industry because they possess a combination of desirable attributes, namely, economy, light weight and compactness both of empty and filled packages. Transparency provides an additional reason for using flexible packages for some products, including candy, nuts, fresh, cured and frozen meat, cheese, dried milk, dehydrated products of all kinds, fresh, frozen and dried fruits and vegetables, and cereal products, both manufactured and raw. These foods might be better preserved in containers that would protect them completely from oxygen of the air as well as from changes in moisture content. Because of the advantages named above, the use of flexible packages seems justified. Where transparency is not important and economic requirements of the situation are met, packages may be made of sheet containing metal foil to give extra protection against transmission of air, water vapor, and other contaminants.

Shelf-Life Determination

Shelf-life of a packaged food involves two primary factors, reactivity of the food with deteriorating substances (or influences) and capacity of the package to protect the food from these substances (and influences). The slow-but-sure method for determining the shelf-life of a packaged food is to conduct a complete, well-planned test of the food in its package held under the full range of storage conditions which obtain in practice. Some tests may be shortened by storage at elevated temperatures, but before results of such tests can be interpreted, a correlation must be established between shelf-life at the elevated temperature and shelf-life at temperatures that will obtain during commercial handling.

The basic mathematical procedures for establishing these relationships have been developed (Ball and Olson 1957; Brickman, 1957, 1961) and several workers, including Van Arsdel and Guadagni (1959) and Olson (1960) have made significant advances in applying the procedures to the prediction of shelf-life of packaged foods.

Laboratory tests which quickly give information of a comparative nature consist of subjecting the unpackaged food, under controlled conditions, to deteriorating influences like those encountered in practice, supplemented by objective measurement of the properties of the packaging materials, upon which the protective capacity of the packaging material depends.

Protection against Microorganisms

Deterioration in food may be chemical, biological or physical. Strictly speaking, all changes may be included under the designation "chemical" because the changes that have biological origin (spoilage) and those having physical criteria (color, flavor or texture change) are basically chemical. There are well-known principles on the basis of which easily observed properties of the food product will reveal the degree of susceptibility to microbial attack. Since flexible packages do not yet seem to be ready for use in commercial marketing of sterilized perishable foods, discussion of microbial attack will be limited to the observation that, if a food is subject to attack by microorganisms, spoilage may in some cases be delayed by packaging in flexible materials. Unless the food is sterile in the sealed package, however, it will eventually spoil.

Protection against Oxygen

Next to microorganisms, oxygen is probably the most destructive of the agents that have access to foods in flexible packages. Thus, the most widely used tests to indicate the shelf-life of foods are those designed to reveal the effects of oxidation. These effects are usually the most serious in unsaturated fat-containing foods, although oxygen produces quality-destroying changes also in foods containing little or no fat. Deterioration of color is usually a significant element in such changes, but fresh meat, under certain circumstances, experiences an improvement in color through contact with oxygen.

Three of the several accelerated tests in use for determining the rates of oxidative reactions in foods are: the Active Oxygen Method (AOM); the Schaal Oven Method; and the Oxygen Bomb Method.

Testing Flexible Package for Food

Each method has its own way of measuring the rate of oxygen consumption by the food. Of the three methods, the bomb test is claimed by its originator, Eastman Chemical Products, Inc., to be both the most accurate and the least time-consuming. Data indicating comparisons in respect to time and accuracy are given in Table 113, (Anon. 1957).

An oxygen bomb of one type consists of a metal alloy cylinder with a screw cap which provides a hermetic pressure seal for the bomb. A

TABLE 113

COMPARISON OF THREE METHODS OF MEASURING RATES OF OXIDATION

Name of Method	Relative Test Times (Basis: 1 for Oxygen Bomb)	Approximate Error, 95 % Confidence Limit
Schaal Oven	40–50	$\pm$ 40 %
A O M	1.5	$\pm$ 16 %
Oxygen Bomb	1.0	($\pm$ 4 hr.)

metal tube for vacuumizing and gassing the bomb connects with an opening in the center of the cap. The food sample is held in a glass jar which fits within the bomb. To perform a test, a weighed sample is placed in the bomb. The bomb is purged with oxygen at 50- or 100-lb. per sq. in. gage pressure at room temperature and is then submerged in boiling water, causing the pressure to increase. Timing begins when the curve on the pressure recorder chart levels off at its highest point. While the bomb is held in boiling water, the rate of reduction in pressure indicates the rate of oxygen consumption by the sample. The end of the test is arbitrarily set at the termination of the second two consecutive 15-min. periods during each of which a pressure drop of two pounds or more is observed.

Neither the oxygen consumption rate nor any other characteristic of a food product which is significant from the standpoint of package requirements is to be taken for granted on the basis of tests made on another food product of the same general class. Until more basic information on foods is available, pitfalls resulting from insufficient knowledge of oxygen consumption rate will be avoided only by conducting tests on each food.

Protection Against Change in Moisture Content

Brickman in two papers (1957, 1961) dealing primarily with water vapor transfer rate, covered in excellent manner the engineering aspects of evaluating the package requirements of a product.

Brickman (1957) determined, for the *normal moisture content of the product* and the *failure-point moisture content of the product*, the values of the relative humidity and temperature of the surrounding atmosphere, at which equilibrium of moisture content is maintained in the product. The failure-point is the per cent of moisture content at which the product becomes unacceptable to the consumer. This point may be either a maximum or a minimum moisture content; thus, it may be associated with transmission of moisture through a package wall either outwardly or inwardly. The procedure to follow in making an evaluation is: (1) plot "equilibrium per cent of moisture content" against "per cent relative humidity" at a given temperature; (2) calculate the amount of water that would have to pass through the walls of a package, in order to change the moisture content of the food from its normal content to its failure-point content; and (3) choose, for testing with the product, packaging materials on which property-measurement tests have indicated that their water vapor transfer rates (WVTR) are within a satisfactory range to provide a reasonable shelf-life.

The product is sealed in packages made of the chosen materials and held in storage for 90 days under controlled conditions of temperature and relative humidity and, through periodic examinations, the rate of change in moisture-content of the product is determined.

Brickman (1961) recently presented a "new pouch method" for determining WVTR, which has the advantages of (1) eliminating the necessity of using certain accessories and items of equipment that are required in other methods, and (2) simplifying the obtaining of permeability values over a wide range of temperature and humidity conditions. A temperature range of from 0° to 100°F. and a relative humidity range of from 30 to 95 per cent are suggested, for twelve combinations of which Brickman gives pressures in millimeters mercury as follows: At 0°F., 0.91, 0.62 and 0.29 for relative humidities of 95, 65 and 30 per cent, respectively; at 38°F., 46.71, 31.96, and 14.75 for the three relative humidities, respectively.

Brickman (1957) plots, for each combination of storage temperature and relative humidity used in the tests, the weight loss or gain, expressed as per cent of the original weight of the loaded bag or pouch, against days in storage. A simple linear curve is plotted for each packaging material. If the failure point of moisture content is not reached within what is regarded as a reasonable shelf-life, the packaging material is considered satisfactory from the standpoint of WVTR. A similar procedure is followed in respect to rate of oxygen transmission.

In describing his pouch method, Brickman (1961) takes a further step in his data analysis by plotting as "practically linear lines" on semilog paper the relationship between WVTR and temperature on the pattern of the reaction kinetics equation of Arrhenius, in which temperature is expressed as the reciprocal of absolute temperature.

The present author prefers a method different from that followed by Brickman for plotting the final curves in this evaluation. Instead of plotting time against weight loss or gain, it seems better to plot time against a value which represents the difference between the *per cent of moisture in the packaged product* and the *equilibrium per cent moisture content* corresponding to the storage temperature and relative humidity combination used in the test. The resulting curves should be straight lines on semilog paper. Plotting in this manner validates extrapolation of the curves beyond the 90-day test period as straight lines. It would seem difficult to justify straight lines on linear coordinates to express the relationship between time and weight loss or gain for this certainly should not be a linear relationship. In fact, the plotting of time against weight loss or gain as a linear relationship cannot be rec-

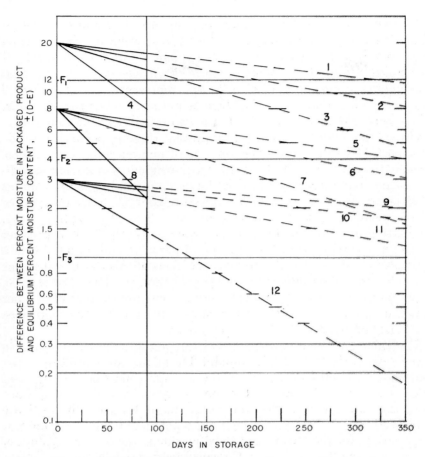

FIG. 164. RELATIONSHIP BETWEEN STORAGE TIME AND
THE QUANTITY $\pm (D - E)$

When D equals the per cent of moisture in the packaged
product (at zero time, this is the "normal product moisture")
and E equals the "equilibrium percent moisture content"
of the product corresponding to the storage temperature
and relative humidity combination used in the test.

onciled with the Arrhenius plot of WVTR against temperature. In
other words, if one is correct, the other is not. The writer's suggested
graphical treatment of the data, illustrated in Fig. 164, is free of the
above noted inconsistency, since the data, as presented in Fig. 164,
plotted for different temperature or different relative humidity conditions, is directly transferable to linear curves on semilog paper expressing numerous different relationships, for example, time vs. temperature, time vs. relative humidity, or WVTR vs. temperature.

Three examples of the suggested plotting are shown in Fig. 164, in which the log (vertical) scale is "difference between *per cent moisture in packaged product* (represented by symbol *D*) and *equilibrium per cent moisture content corresponding to the storage-temperature and relative-humidity combination used in the test* (represented by symbol *E*)." The linear (horizontal) scale is "days in storage." The *per cent moisture in packaged product* at zero-time is the normal per cent moisture.

Three sets of curves in Fig. 164 represent three hypothetical products, each of which could have any one of innumerable designations. As examples, the first set of curves, which originates at 20 on the ordinate scale, may represent a product having a normal moisture content of 28 per cent and an equilibrium moisture-content under the storage conditions of this test of eight per cent $(28 - 8 = 20)$; the second set, originating at eight on the ordinate scale, may represent a product having a normal moisture content of 13 per cent and an equilibrium moisture content under the storage conditions of this test of 5 per cent $(13 - 5 = 8)$; the third set, originating at three on the ordinate scale, may represent a product having a normal moisture content of $4^1/_2$ per cent and an equilibrium per cent moisture content under the conditions of this test of $1^1/_2$ per cent $(4^1/_2 - 1^1/_2 = 3)$.

The value on the ordinate scale which represents the failure-point in every case is the actual failure-point D_F minus the equilibrium per cent moisture content, E, under the storage conditions of the test being run. If the failure-point of the first product is 20 per cent moisture, the value representing the failure-point level on the ordinate scale is $20 - 8 = 12$. Assuming failure-points of 9 and $2^1/_2$ per cent, respectively, for the second and third products, the ordinate values of $9 - 5 = 4$ and $2^1/_2 - 1^1/_2 = 1$, respectively, are failure-point levels. On Fig. 164, the failure-point levels are designated F_1, F_2 and F_3, respectively. The curves, numbered from 1 to 12, inclusive, represent different packaging materials. The storage-periods to failure-point, expressed in days, for the twelve packages are, respectively, as follows: 320, 200, 123, 50, 350, 252, 150, 50, 350, 350, 350 and 134.

The three sets of curves of Fig. 164 may be used also to indicate the performance of different packages for products that are degraded by the absorption of moisture through the walls of the package. In this case, the ordinate scale represents $- (D - E)$ instead of $+ (D - E)$.

We shall say that the first set of curves represents results of tests with a product having an equilibrium per cent moisture content, E, under the storage temperature and relative humidity used in the test, of 28. The normal moisture content, D_N, of this product, represented by the point where the curves originate, is $E - 20 = 8$ per cent. We shall say also that the failure-point moisture content of D_F of this product is 16 per cent. Therefore, the horizontal line at $- (16 - 28) = 12$ marks the failure-point level just as it did for the first product discussed. Following a similar line of reasoning, if we consider that a product has an equilibrium moisture content E of 15 per cent, a normal moisture content of $E - 8 = 7$ per cent, and a failure-point moisture content D_F of 11 per cent and another product has an equilibrium moisture content E of 6 per cent, normal moisture of $E - 3 = 3$ per cent, and a failure-point moisture content D_F of 5 per cent, we find that the curves 5, 6, 7 and 8, together with their failure-point line, $- (11 - 15) = 4$, and the curves 9, 10, 11 and 12, together with their failure-point line, $- (5 - 6) = 1$, represent these two products. The specifications of the last three products, of course, were expressly selected for the purpose of illustration—to make the products fit the curves which were already shown in Fig. 164. In the use of this system of evaluating packages, curves like those of Fig. 164 are, of course, plotted from actual data from tests with the packaged products. This system is, as was indicated, applicable to the evaluation of packages as protectors against oxygen-degradation of products, although the techniques and interpretations in this case are somewhat more difficult than those applying to the moisture problems because the failure-point in respect to oxygen effect is more difficult to define.

Examples of food products in which the failure-point may be reached through reduction in moisture content are raw popcorn, dried fruits and syrup. Products in which the failure-point may be reached through increase in moisture content include dehydrated vegetables and milk, hard candy and corn chips. Oxygen is deleterious to many products, including vegetable and animal oils, whole milk powder, shelled nuts and dehydrated vegetables. Oxygen generally is beneficial to the color of fresh meat but it accelerates the growth of spoilage organisms in the meat. Oxygen promotes mold growth and affects flavor and color. Increase in moisture also promotes the growth of microorganisms as well as some chemical and physical changes in a food product. On the other hand, in some products, carrots, for example, excessively low moisture content accelerates color destruction.

Obtaining and Utilizing Information

With practice, one can analyze the results of an oxidation test and of tests for equilibrium of moisture content and failure-point of moisture content of a product in conjunction with the results of measurements of the characteristics of different packaging materials and arrive at a reasonable judgment on the selection of the best package for the food product.   One important factor in this connection is the relationship between area of package surface and the amount of product in the package, as will be shown later.

There are many laboratory tests to measure chemical and physical properties of flexible packaging materials.   From a performance standpoint, the chemical properties of inertness, stability and grease-proofness are as important as the physical properties of strength and rates of transmission of oxygen and water vapor.   Usually, if dry physical strength is the only one of these physical and chemical properties which is at issue, a bag constructed solely of paper or of a laminate containing paper is used.   Paper is cheaper than any other flexible sheet material of equal strength.   When superiority in respect to imperviousness to gas or water vapor, to chemical inertness, to aging, or to grease-resistance is required, a search for the proper material usually leads into the metal foil and plastic film fields.   Descriptions of tests for measuring these properties abound in the literature.   Here we shall briefly outline essential steps as they are usually executed.

Bursting Strength (Mullen Burst Tester).—Increasing pressure of a rubber hydraulic bubble against the sample of sheet or film, clamped between two jaws having coincident circular openings, bursts the sample which had closed the circular opening.   Unit: p.s.i.

Tensile Strength and Elongation (Baldwin Static-Weighing Machine; Pendulum-Weighing Machine).—Each end of a sample strip 1 in. wide is clamped between a pair of jaws.   A load applied to one set of jaws, tending to stretch the sample, is increased gradually until the sample breaks in two.   Units: elongation: per cent; tensile: lb. per in. width.

Gas Transmission.—Sample of sheet or film, sealed across an opening in the wall of a vacuum chamber, transmits gas from outside to inside the chamber, causing the pressure in the chamber to increase.   Unit: cc. per 100 sq. in. per 24 hr.

Water Vapor Transmission.—Sample of sheet or film, sealed across the mouth of a cup containing a substance that absorbs water readily, transmits water vapor from atmosphere of 90 per cent RH, at 100°F. outside the cup, causing the desiccant to increase in weight. Unit: grams per 100 sq. in. per 24 hr.

Grease Resistance.—Sample of sheet or film of specified size (4 in. × 4 in.) in intimate surface contact with white paper, is treated on the other surface with the test reagent (grease or oil).   Unit: time (minutes or hours) required for first appearance of stain on the paper.

Aging.—Sample of packaged product is alternately exposed to different aging conditions, such as wet and dry heat at 160°F., extreme variations of temperature, extreme variations of relative humidity, various types of rays or extreme variations of free oxygen concentration. At proper intervals, the sample is examined for product deterioration, changes in weight and dimensions, dulling, crazing, warping and discoloration.

Laboratory test instruments for measuring other properties than those discussed above and the properties which they measure are listed as follows:

Instrument	Property
Tear tester (Elmendorf)	Tear resistance (gram per mil)
Folding endurance or stiffness tester (MIT)	Pliability or resistance to bending
Heat sealer	Temperature required to seal (°F.)
Size tester	Moisture absorptiveness (per cent increase weight)
Climatizer or testing cabinet	Holds controlled conditions of humidity and temperature
SPI tester	Flammability

Limitations of Tests

At best a test of aging is of questionable value as an aid in the selection of a packaging material for a food product unless it brings to light some defect such as delamination or a radical reduction in strength. To perform a true aging test, designed to tell whether or not a packaging material deteriorates with age, it would be necessary first to run the various tests of strength, resistance and transmission on the material, follow these with a conventional aging test, then repeat the complete series of tests of strength, resistance and transmission to find out whether or not the properties of the material have been changed. The results of a so-called aging test, as described in the preceding paragraph, often cannot, within themselves be intelligently interpreted.

Two other points of significance in the interpretation of property-measurements tests are: (1) residual air in a product when packed may have an important effect in bringing about deterioration of the product; and (2) the rates of transmission of odor and flavor are closely related to the rates of transmission of gas, water vapor and oil.

Light in the visible range is a quality deteriorating influence with some products for which flexible packages are used. A well-known example is ready-to-eat cured meat, in which the oxidation of myoglobin derivatives is accelerated by light, causing deterioration of color. A test to measure the rate of light transmission is not included, however,

TABLE 114

GENERAL CHARACTERISTICS OF PACKAGING FILMS[1]

| Film Material | Thickness, in. | Max. Width, in. | Yield-0.001 in. Thickness, sq. in./lb. | Clarity | Specific Gravity at 73°F. | Limit Conditions | | | | |
| | | | | | | Normal Performance | | | | Flammability, Temperature of Combustion, °F. |
						Max. Temp., °F.	Min. Temp., °F.	Sunlight	Aging[2]	
Cellophane-plain	0.0008–0.0016[6]	...	20,000[6]	Transparent[2] or colored	1.40–1.50[3]	300	...	No effect	...	155–216[2]
NC coated[4]	0.0009–0.0017	60	11,500–21,000	Transparent	1.40–1.50	300	About 0	No effect	...	Slow burning
Saran coated[4]	0.002–0.0014	46	19,500	Transparent	1.44	180	About 0	...	...	Same as newsprint
Polyethylene coated[4]	0.002 or more	60	11,800 (2 mil combination)	Transparent to translucent	1.20	180	...	Excellent	Good	Slow burning
Cellulose acetate	0.0005–0.010	40–60	21,000–22,000	Transparent or colored	1.28–1.31	150–220	Brittle at 0	Good	Excellent	Slow burning
Polyethylene Low density	0.0004–0.010	480	30,000	Transparent to translucent	0.910–0.925	200	−50	Fair to good	Excellent	Slow burning
Medium density	0.0004 or more	480	29,500	...	0.926–0.940	220	−60	Fair to good	...	Slow burning
High density	0.0004–0.010	60	29,000	...	0.941–0.965	250	−70	Fair to good	...	Slow burning
Polyester (Mylar Scotchpak, Videne)	0.00025–0.0075	50–55	20,000	Transparent or opaque	1.38–1.39	300	−80	Moderate	Excellent	Slow burning
Polypropylene	0.0005 or more	60	30,900–31,300	...	0.885–090	190–220	−60	Fair to excellent	...	Slow burning
Polystyrene (oriented)	0.00075–0.020	43–60	26,100	...	1.05–1.06	175–220	−60	Good to fair	...	Slow burning
Rubber hydrochloride (Pliofilm)	0.004–0.0025	60	25,000	Transparent to opaque	1.11	180–205	−20	Fair	Good in dark	Self extinguishing
Vinylidene Cryovac	0.0008–0.003	...	16,700	...	1.64	Softens 270	Depends on plasticizer	Excellent to good	Excellent below 76°	Self extinguishing
Saran	0.0005–0.010	40–54	16,000–23,000	Transparent to opaque or colored	1.20–1.68	150–200 (dry) 300 (wet)	−25 to −50	Excellent to good	Excellent below 76°	Self extinguishing
Vinyl chloride	0.001–0.010	54–84	20,000–23,000	Transparent to opaque or colored	1.20–1.45	150–200	Good depends on plasticizer	Good	Excellent	Self extinguishing
Nylon 6[5]	0.0005–0.01	60	24,000	Transparent or colored	1.12	400	−80	...	...	Self extinguishing

[1] All values by permission Modern Plastic Encyclopedia Issue for 1962, unless otherwise noted.
[2] By permission Modern Packaging Encyclopedia 1958. Copyright 1957 by Packaging Catalog Corp., 770 Lexington Ave., New York 21.
[3] Stone and Reinhart (1954).
[4] Test data assume coated side toward product.
[5] Miscellaneous sources.
[6] Miller (1959).

in the series of property-measurement tests usually employed with flexible packaging materials. Small degrees of difference in light transmitting capacity are not usually regarded with concern. As a rule, the only significant difference is between opaque material and material that transmits light.

Property-measurement tests of the above series are appropriate for use with most materials used for flexible packages. Exceptions include permeability tests on untreated paper and fabrics because these generally are highly permeable. Paper and fabric can be impregnated with substances which give them low permeability. Materials on which these tests are regularly used include aluminum foil, cellophane, cellulose acetate, polystyrene, polyvinyl chloride, rubber hydrochloride (Pliofilm), polyvinylidene chloride (Saran), polyethylene (as film and coating) polypropylene, polyvinyl alcohol (as film and coating), polyethylene terephthalate (Mylar, Videne, Scotchpak), nylon, polytetrafluoroethylene (Teflon), paper and fabric.

Peterson (1958, 1959) rendered a distinct service to packaging advancement by publishing an exposition, in nontechnical terms, of the principles underlying these tests; also of the principles underlying the establishment of an integrated system of test criteria embodying the use of a "competition quotient" in the design of packages.

Inventory of Properties

Properties of a film are modified by changing the caliper of the film, by applying a coating of a plastic or an adhesive material, or by laminating. A laminate of two films possesses, essentially, a combination of the properties of the individual films. Laminating techniques are employed to produce films that are capable of giving required protection to a product.

Typical values indicating the characteristics of various materials are given in Tables 114, 115 and 116. The information in these tables was compiled from many sources. Deserving special mention among these are "Modern Plastics Encyclopedia Issue 1962" (Plastics Catalog Corp.), which granted permission to reproduce portions of an elaborate tabulation, "Properties of Packaging Films," and an article from "Modern Plastics" (Anon. 1961).

Oxygen Permeability—Theory Versus Practice

Theories in regard to the effect of oxygen permeability of a package seem to be borne out in practice to only a limited extent. Results cannot be predicted solely on the basis of theory. For example, polyethylene has a high rate of gas transmission and cellulose acetate has

TABLE 115[1]

PERMEABILITY AND CHEMICAL PROPERTIES OF PACKAGING FILM

Film Material	Gas Transmission[2] cc./100 sq. in./24 hr. 72°F., 1 mil.			Water Vapor Transfer Gm./100 sq. in./24 hr. 76 cm. Mercury 100°F. 90% R.H., 1 mil.	Water Adsorption in 24 Hr. Immersion Test, %, 1 mil.
	Oxygen	Nitrogen	Carbon Dioxide		
Cellophane-plain	Low (dry); variable (moist)[3]			6.86–12.8[3]	44.7–114.8[3]
NC coated	Very low (dry); variable (moist)			1.4–2.7	45–115
Saran coated[4]	Very low			1.2	...
Polyethylene coated[4]		Low		1.2	
Cellulose Acetate	100–140	25–40	500–800	160	3.6–6.8
Polyethylene Low density	500	200	1350	1.4	0–0.8
Medium density	240[2]	...	500[2]	0.7	Nil
High Density	100–150	50–60	300–400	0.3	Nil
Polyester (Mylar) Scotchpak, Videne	5–10	0.50	7.30	1.0–3.0	0.5
Polypropylene	200–300	3–100	700–800	1.2	0.005 or less
Polystyrene (oriented)	200–300	40–100	500–1000	4.0–8.0	0.04–0.06
Rubber hydrochloride (Pliofilm)	38–3,250[2a]	...	288–13,500[2a]	0.5–15.0	5.0
Vinylidene Cryovac	0.1–0.2	0.025	0.30	1.0–1.4	Negligible
Saran	0.1–0.2	0.025	0.30	0.1–0.3	Negligible
Vinyl chloride	100 (est)	25–50 (est)	500 (est)	3.5–13.0[1]	Negligible
Nylon 6[5]	1.0	...	2.0	8.1	...

[1] All values by permission Modern Plastics Encyclopedia Issue for 1962, unless otherwise noted.
[2] Data courtesy Modern Plastics, 1961 all values unless otherwise noted.
[3] Stone and Reinhart (1954).
[4] Test data assume coated side toward product.

a medium rate, as does also cellophane when wet. It might be supposed, therefore, that foods that would benefit from the presence of free oxygen in the atmosphere surrounding them should be packaged in one of these films. Fresh vegetables, fruits and meats might be placed in this category. Upon trial, however, one learns that some fruits and vegetables appear to be affected as expected but others do not. Furthermore, fresh meat packaged in cellophane behaves colorwise for about 48 hr. as would be expected when the color pigments have access to free oxygen, but after that the color changes and is best if there is complete absence of oxygen. Reasons for these anomalies are still to be learned, but might to some extent lie in the fact that films have different transmission rates for different gases. The amount of void space within the package may also be an influencing factor.

Variations that exist in respect to transmission rates for different gases are indicated by values of the amounts of different gases at room temperature transmitted by ten different films 0.001 in. thick, given in

TABLE 115 (continued)

		Resistance To		
Acids	Alkalies	Greases and Oils	Organic Solvents	Water
Poor to strong acids[6]	Poor to strong alkalies[6]	Impermeable[6]	Insoluble	Moderate
Poor to strong acids	Poor to strong alkalies	Impermeable	Coating attached	Moderate
Excellent except H_2SO_4 & HNO_3	Good except ammonia	Impermeable	. . .	. . .
Excellent	Excellent	Like polyethylene	Like polyethylene	
Poor to strong acids	Poor to strong alkalies	Good	Soluble except in hydrocarbons	Good
Excellent	Excellent	May swell slightly on long immersion	Good except hydrocarbon and chlorinated solvents	Excellent
Excellent	Excellent	Good	Good	Excellent
Excellent	Excellent	Excellent	Good	Excellent
Good	Good	Excellent	Excellent	Excellent
Excellent	Excellent	Good	Good	Excellent
Good	Excellent	Good	Excellent to poor	Excellent
Good	Good	Excellent	Good except in cyclic hydrocarbons chlorinated sol-, vent	Excellent
Excellent	Good except ammonia	Excellent	Good to excellent	Excellent
Excellent except H_2SO_4 and HNO_3	Good except ammonia	Excellent	Good to excellent	Excellent
Good	Good	Moderate to good	Poor to good	Excellent
Poor	Excellent	Excellent	Excellent	Excellent

[5] Miller (1959).
[6] By permission Modern Packaging Encyclopedia Issue 1960. Copyright 1959. Packaging Catalog Corp., New York.
[a] Relative humidity, 0%.

Table 114, and by four films 0.001 in. thick and two films of other thicknesses, given in Table 117.

Important aspects of the strength and of the water- and gas-transmission of widely used flexible materials which are not revealed by the data of Tables 114 and 115 will be discussed under separate headings of these properties.

Water Vapor and Gas Transmission

The permeability of aluminum foil is due to pinholes. An indication of the relationship between gage of foil and the number of pinholes is given in Table 118.

The average values of WVTR shown in column 4 are data from determinations by the General Foods Southwick Method at 100°F. and 100 per cent relative humidity on every tenth sheet of those which yielded the data of columns 2 and 3.

The effect of thickness of Mylar polyester film upon WVTR was de-

TABLE 116

MECHANICAL PROPERTIES OF PACKAGING FILMS

Film Material	Tensile Strength,[2] 100 p.s.i.	Elonga- tion,[2] %	Tearing Strength,[2] g./mil.	Bursting Strength, 1 mil. thick, p.s.i.	Folding Endurance/ 1 mil. thick, no. of folds × 10[3]	Heat Sealing Range,[2] °F.
Cellophane-plain	104–186[3]	14–36[3]	275–426[3]	...	...	...
NC coated	70–150	10–50	2–10	55–65[1]	Over 15[5]	200–300
Saran coated	70–130	25–50	2–15	...	...	225–350
Polyethylene coated	50 and over[1]	15–25[1]	16–50[1]	40–50[5]	Good[5]	230–300[1]
Cellulose acetate	54–139[1]	25–45[1]	2–25[1]	50–85[3]	0.25–0.4[1]	350–450
Polyethylene						
Low density	13.5–25	200–800[1]	150–350	48[5]	Very high[5]	250–350
Medium density	20–35	150–650[1]	50–300	...	...	240–350
High density	24–61	150–650[1]	15–300	...	...	275–350
Polyester (Mylar Scotch-pak, Videne)	170–237	70–130	10–27[1]	45–50[3]	20[3]	275–400
Polypropylene	45–100	400–600	32–1750[1]	Very high[1]	...	325–400
Polystyrene (oriented)	80–120	3–20	20–30	23–60[1]	...	250–325
Rubber hydrochloride (Pliofilm)	35–50	200–800[1]	60–1600	Stretches[3]	10–1000[5]	250–350
Vinylidene						
Cryovac	60–120[1]	50–100[1]	15–20[1]	...	Over 500[5]	275–300
Saran	80–200	40–80	10–100[1]	20–40[3]	...	280–300
Vinyl chloride	30–110	5–250	30–1400[1]	25–40[5]	250[1]	200–350
Nylon 6[4]	138–170[4]	200[4]	50[4]	No burst[4]	...	400–450[4]

[1] Data by permission Modern Plastics Encyclopedia Issue for 1962.
[2] Data by permission Modern Plastics, 1961 all values unless otherwise noted.
[3] Stone and Reinhart (1954).
[4] Miller, (1959).
[5] By permission Modern Packaging Encyclopedia Issue 1960. Copyright 1959 Packaging Catalog Corp., New York.

TABLE 117

AMOUNTS OF DIFFERENT GASES TRANSFERRED IN 24 HRS. BY DIFFERENT FILMS AT ROOM TEMPERATURE

Cubic centimeters per 100 sq. in. of film at 15 lbs. pressure differential

Type of Film	Temp.— R.H. Variations	Nitro- gen	Oxygen	Carbon Dioxide	Air	Ethyl- ene	Ethyl- ene Oxide	Sulfur Dioxide
Cellophane (MSAT)[1,2]	...	32.0	43.0	111.0	35.0	...	...	...
Cellophane (MSAD)[5]	2% R.H.	...	6.30	37.04	...	...	...	...
	100% R.H.	...	205.4	346.8	...	...	...	...
Vinylidene[1] (Cryovac)	...	3.1	11.1	27.1	5.1	...	...	...
Cellulose Acetate[3]	25°C.	...	352.5	1912.0	...	549.2	19,500	18,510
(P-903)	0°C.	...	132.2	809.0	...	...	5,590	7,848
Cellulose Acetate[3]	25°C.	...	250.0	932.0	...	112.7	4,560	5,445
(P-912)	0°C.	...	112.7	421.0	...	...	...	...
Rubber Hydrochloride[4] (Pliofilm 100 FMI)	...	...	144.0	924.0	...	...	...	...
0.0005 in. Polyester[5] (Mylar)—	2% R.H.	...	18.67	24.65	...	...	...	...
0.0005 in. Polyester[5] (Mylar)—	100% R.H.	...	49.67	86.50	...	...	...	...
0.002 in. Polyethylene	2% R.H.	...	7.70	...	...	...	...	...
	100% R.H.	...	15.52	...	...	...	...	...

[1] Values by Cryovac Co., Food Processing 17, No. 8 (1956).
[2] With moist gas at high relative humidity.
[3] Values by Celanese Corp. on two types of film differing in flexibility and toughness (converted from investigator's values expressed in cc. per sq. meter per 24 hr. per cm. mercury pressures).
[4] Values by Goodyear Tire and Rubber Co.
[5] Values by Nagel and Wilkins (1957) converted from investigator's values expressed in grams per sq. meter per hr.

TABLE 118

TYPICAL VARIATION OF PINHOLES WITH GAGE OF ALUMINUM FOIL AND WATER
VAPOR TRANSMISSION OF FOIL[1]

100 sheets of foil, 12 in. square, were examined for each gage

Gage of Foil, (1 in.)	Number of Sheets with Pinholes	Number of Sheets with No Pinholes	Average WVTR, g./100 sq. in./24 hr.
0.00035	100	0	0.29
0.0005	100	0	0.12
0.0007	15	85	0.043[1, 2]
0.001	8	92	0.007[1, 2]

[1] Alcoa aluminum foil—its properties and uses (1953).
[2] Averages calculated by author from values for individual sheets given by Alcoa.

TABLE 119

WATER VAPOR TRANSMISSION OF ALUMINUM FOIL LAMINATES[1]

| | Thickness, in. | | WVTR g./100 sq. in./ 24 hr.; 100°F.; 100% R.H. | |
Material	Foil	Laminant	Flat	After Creasing[2]
Al. foil laminated to moistureproof Cellophane	0.00035	0.0009	0.00 0.01 0.01	. . . 0.03 0.01
Al. foil laminated to cellulose acetate	0.00035	0.0012	0.01 0.02	. . . 0.07
Al. foil laminated to rubber hydrochloride	0.00035	0.0008	0.01 0.01	0.01 . . .
Al. foil laminated to vinyl polymer	0.00035	0.0012	0.01 0.02	0.02 0.01
Al. foil laminated with wax to 30-lb. glassine	0.00035	. . .	0.00	0.04
Al. foil BEIS-O	0.00035	. . .	0.07	0.42
Al. foil laminated to moistureproof Cellophane	0.001	0.0009	0.00	0.00
Al. foil laminated to vinyl polymer	0.001	0.0012	0.00	C.00
Al. foil laminated with wax to 35-lb. glassine	0.001	. . .	0.00	0.02
Al. foil BEIS-O	0.001	. . .	0.00	0.40

[1] Alcoa aluminum foil—its properties and uses (1953). Each value is the average of measurements on 2 or 3 test pieces.
[2] "Creasing" means creased with 4 equidistant parallel folds and then with 4 more folds at right angles to the first.

TABLE 120

RESULTS OF STORAGE TESTS OF WRAPPED CHOCOLATE NUT CANDY BARS[1]

Description of Wrapper	Condition after 25 Days Storage at 85–90°F.		
	Weight Loss in Grams	Flavor Rating[2]	Appearance Rating[2]
Aluminum foil (0.001 in.) coated with heat-sealing lacquer and laminated on opposite side to acetate sheeting; lacquer coating next to chocolate. This wrapper was heat-sealed at seams and ends.	0.5	1	1
Aluminum foil (0.001 in.).	1.5	2	2
Aluminum foil (0.00045 in.) laminated to waxed glassine paper next to chocolate.	2.5	2	3
Waxed paper (0.0022 in.) separate inner wrap of aluminum foil (0.00045 in.) wax-laminated to glassine paper (0.0015 in.).	2.5	2	3
Aluminum foil (0.00045 in.) laminated to glassine paper (0.0015 in.) glassine next to chocolate.	2.5	3	3
Waxed paper (0.002 in.) separate inner wrap; glassine paper (0.0015 in.) over-wrap.	11.0	4	4

[1] Alcoa aluminum foil—its properties and uses (1953).
[2] In flavor and appearance, No. 1 is the highest and No. 4 the lowest rating.

termined by Nagel and Wilkins (1957). For films of 0.0005-, 0.001-, 0.002-, 0.005-in. thickness, respectively, the WVT rates in g./100 sq. in./24 hr. are 3.28, 1.70, 0.805 and 0.34 at 103°F. and at vapor pressure differential of 53 mm. mercury and are 0.31, 0.124, 0.046 and 0.0155 at 24°F. and vapor pressure differential of 2.2 mm. mercury. These values are converted from N. and W.'s values in grams/100 sq. M./hr.

It is illuminating to see how greatly the WVTR of even the thinnest aluminum foil is reduced by lamination with various film materials. This is shown by comparison of the WVTR values of Table 119 with those of Table 118.

Pertinent to the imperviousness to water vapor and gas are the subjects of weight loss, flavor loss, and changes in appearance of packaged products. Tables 120 and 121 give data resulting from tests of various packaging materials in respect to these properties as they affect the above mentioned quality characteristics of packaged candy bars.

The times required for five different odors to penetrate Mylar polyester of 0.001 in. thickness and MSAT cellophane of 0.0008 in. thickness to the point of olfactory perception are given in Table 122.

TABLE 121

STORAGE TIME REQUIRED FOR PERCEPTIBLE TASTE TO APPEAR IN WRAPPED SWEET
MILK CHOCOLATE BARS DUE TO ABSORPTION OF ODOR FROM OUTSIDE ATMOSPHERE[1]

| | Time to Taste | |
Description of Wrapper	Turpentine	Pepper-mint
Aluminum foil (0.007 in.) coated with heat-sealing lacquer and laminated one side to moistureproof cellophane; coated surface heat-sealed along side seam and ends.	20 days	19 days
Aluminum foil (0.0007 in.) coated with heat-sealing lacquer; wrapper heat-sealed along side.	6 days	7 days
Plastic bleached greaseproof paper $22^{1}/_{2}$-lb.; side seam and folds not sealed.	5 hr.	$3^{1}/_{2}$ hr.
Opaque greaseproof paper 30-lb., side seam and folds sealed.	5 hr.	$3^{1}/_{2}$ hr.
Control—no wrapper.	$^{1}/_{2}$ hr.	1 hr.

[1] Alcoa aluminum foil—its properties and uses (1953). Chocolate bars stored in glass desiccators, one containing cotton moistened with turpentine and the other containing peppermint candy.

TABLE 122

TIME REQUIRED FOR ODORS TO PENETRATE 1-MIL MYLAR POLYESTER AND 0.8-MIL
CELLOPHANE FILMS[1]

| | Time in Hours for First Olfactory Perception | |
Source of Odor	Mylar	300 MSAD Cellophane
Vanillin	141	20
Pinene	140	20
Methyl salicylate	116	24
Ethyl butyrate	20	0.5
Propylene diamine	92	1

[1] Nagel and Wilkins Reprinted with permission of *Food Technology* Vol. 11, 180–182. (1957).

The effects of variations in environmental conditions upon water vapor transmission rates through films of eight different types of construction are shown in Table 123.

In the test to which Table 123 refers, one-pound bags of eight different combinations of materials were subjected to three different types of water vapor transmission determinations, as follows: Set 1— the bags, each containing a bag of calcium chloride, were sealed and then stored at 100°F., 97 per cent relative humidity for 72 hr; Set 2—the bags, each containing one pound of ground coffee, were sealed and were subjected to treatment in a simulated shipping tester for 30 min.; Set 3—the bags, each containing one-pound of ground coffee, were sealed, then were stored at 100°F., 15 per cent relative humidity for 72 hr., then were subjected to specified treatment in a simulated shipping tester for 30 min. In all instances, the increase in weight of the

TABLE 123

WATER VAPOR TRANSMISSION RATES OF FLEXIBLE PACKAGES UNDER 3 SETS OF TEST CONDITIONS[1]

Material	WVTR (g./100 sq. in./24 hr.) for 3 Sets of Conditions		
	Set 1	Set 2	Set 3
MST Cello-wax-MST Cellophane	0.32	0.45	0.34
MST Cello-thermo-MST Cellophane	0.83	1.75	2.0
MSAT Cello-0.0015 in. polyethylene	0.77	0.71	0.79
MSAT Cello-0.0025 in. polyethylene	0.53	0.54	0.71
25-lb. paper-0.00035 in. aluminum foil	0.008	0.04	0.03
Duplexed MST Cellophane	0.36	0.48	1.2
Duplexed 450 K202 Cellophane	0.23	0.25	0.27
Single 450 K202 Cellophane	0.43	0.55	0.73

[1] Long (1957).

package contents during the treatment was determined and this was converted to water vapor transmission rate in gm./100 sq. in./24 hr.

Notes by the investigator relative to conditions that affected the results of these tests are as follows:

(1)   Film combination No. 1 maintained protection due to the wax barrier.

(2)   The structure or combination No. 2 was damaged in preparation of the lamination and was further damaged by shipping exposure.

(3)   In combinations Nos. 3 and 4, protection was provided by durable polyethylene components, which were essentially unchanged by the treatment received.

(4)   The protection by combination No. 5 was decreased considerably by the treatment received in the shipping tester but still remained good.

(5)   Low humidity exposure resulted in stiffening and embrittlement of combination No. 6; consequently a protection loss.

TABLE 124

RANCIDITY DEVELOPMENT IN PACKAGED FROZEN PORK CHOPS DURING STORAGE AT 5°F.[1]

Packaging Material	Storage Time to Beginning of Rancidity,[2] months
Vinylidene copolymer (Cryovac)	Over 14[3]
Cellophane (moistureproof)	3–4
Vinyl chloride-acetate copolymer and nitrile rubber base film	3–4
Rubber hydrochloride base film	2–3
Locker paper (wax controlled)	2–3

[1] Lowry and Nebesky (1953).
[2] Criterion for rancidity not given.
[3] End of test.

TABLE 125

PHYSICAL FAILURE OF PACKAGES OF SAUERKRAUT UNDER SIMULATED SHIPPING TEST[1]

	Per cent Failure During Exposure Period Indicated, min.						
Packaging Material	15	30	45	60	75	90	100
Cellophane × 0.0022 in. polyethylene[2]	10	30	30	40	50	..	100
Pliofilm × Pliofilm[2]	33	58	75	100	..	..	...
Cellophane × 0.0025 in. polyethylene[3]	..	..	..	67	..	67	...
Mylar × polyethylene[3]	..	..	..	17	..	32	...

[1] Long (1957).
[2] 10 test specimens in each series.
[3] 6 test specimens in each series.

TABLE 126

PHYSICAL FAILURE OF PACKAGES OF BEANS UNDER SIMULATED SHIPPING TEST[1]
RESULTS OF 12 TEST SPECIMENS IN EACH SERIES

	Per cent Failure of Packages Indicated During Exposure Period of 45 Min.	
Conditioning Treatment for 72 hr.	Cellophane No. 1	Cellophane No. 2
100°F., 15% relative humidity	25	0
77°F., 45% relative humidity	16	0
35°F.	16	16

[1] Long (1957).

(6) The coatings of combinations Nos. 7 and 8 were durable and protective.

One way of evaluating packaging materials for gas transmission is to determine the rate of development of rancidity in packaged products since rancidity development is a result of contact of the product with oxygen. The results of a test of frozen pork chops in several different packaging materials are given in Table 124.

Physical Strength

Before laboratory tests for physical strength of films can be properly interpreted from the standpoint of packaging efficiency, experimental evaluations of the packages in the form in which they leave the packaging plant must be made to determine how long they will hold up under handling conditions encountered during distribution.

Long (1957) published a report of a series of tests which yielded the data presented in Tables 125 and 126. In all tests, the packaged products were subjected to the treatment imposed by a simulated shipping tester. Table 125 refers to tests made with packages containing 1 lb. 11 oz. of sauerkraut and brine, conditioned at 40°F. The packages listed in the first two lines of Table 125 were machine-made from laminates of 0.0008 in. cellophane with 0.0022 in. polyethylene, and 0.0012 in. Pliofilm with 0.0012 in. Pliofilm. Those listed in the last two lines of Table 125 were machine-made from laminates of 0.0008 in. cellophane with 0.0025 in. polyethylene and 0.0005 in. Mylar with 0.003 in. polyethylene.

In the test to which Table 126 refers, two types of cellophane were compared for resistance to severe conditioning treatment. Each package contained one pound of beans.

Future of Flexible Packaging

"Polymer chemists in the United States and abroad are engaged in a vast effort to develop processes which will facilitate the creation of new products and reduce the cost of the present ones. They are exploring various polymerization methods, catalysts, continuous processes and conditions which will control reactions such as very high pressures, high and low temperatures, irradiation. Knowledge of the principles underlying the chemical properties is sufficiently advanced so that the chemists can introduce into a giant molecule, a monomer which will endow it with a high melting point or great resistance to solvents or high tensile strength, or some other desired quality.

"The products made so far can be considered only a foretaste of more spectacular ones to come. There are several frontiers inviting exploration. For example, the largest high polymers now in production have molecular weights in the neighborhood of 200,000. There is reason to believe that larger molecules would be much stronger. Consequently, several industrial laboratories are looking into the possibilities for producing 'super high polymers' with molecular weights in the millions. Another active frontier is the investigation of ways to raise the resistance of polymers to heat. The plastics, fibers, rubbers, and coatings now made break down at temperatures of 600°F. or less. But the prospects for making high polymers which will be able to withstand substantially higher temperatures look promising; they may be based on certain highly stable organic molecules, such as diphenyl oxide or diphenylmethylene, with additions of resistant elements, such as fluorine, boron or silicon."

This quotation from Mark (1959) lends great encouragement to the expectation that flexible packaging materials capable of meeting the many packaging requirements will be available at reasonable cost.

There may be no advantage from the standpoint of packaging food, to use films that will withstand temperatures above 600°F. This property may even be a disadvantage when one desires to heat-seal without the use of an adhesive. On the other hand, when the use of a thermoplastic or thermosetting adhesive is desirable, the capacity of a film to withstand high temperatures could be distinctly advantageous.

As examples of advances that are imminent may be cited the new films of nylon and the fluorine-containing compounds, including poly-tetrafluoroethylene (Teflon) and other fluorohalocarbon films. These films have numerous unique properties which appear to adapt them especially well for some packaging uses. As yet, however, either be-cause of economics or of questionable safety from a toxological stand-point, they have not attained a status of recognition as food packaging materials. Even when these obstacles, will have been overcome, it will still be necessary to determine by test the performance character-istics of these films for packaging specific products.

Radiation Effect on Flexible Containers

Bright prospects for the development in time of a wide variety of useful applications of ionizing radiation in the preservation of food products are responsible for a stimulation of interest in study of the effects of radiation upon flexible containers. Investigations include not only ionizing radiation but infrared and ultraviolet as well.

Radiation produces great changes in the physical characteristics of plastic films through changing the chemical structure of the films. Most of the chemical effects result in either crosslinking or scission of the molecules of the film. Crosslinking, by producing 3-dimensional orientation, results in increased strength and in elevation of the soften-ing point. Whether the latter is desirable or not depends upon the normal characteristics of the material and upon the purpose for which the film is to be used. Scission, through shortening the polymeric chains, results in a reduction in strength.

Polystyrene stands out among plastic packaging materials for its high resistance to radiation-induced change. Polyethylene, through crosslinkage, experiences substantial changes but most of them are re-garded as desirable for a material used to make containers. Intense ionizing radiation (about 20 million rad) increases the strength of polyethylene and makes it almost unmeltable.

Ultraviolet rays in the shortest wavelength range are reported to produce crosslinkage in both low-density and high-density polyethyl-ene. A tendency of the latter type to become brittle through expo-sure to a warm environment is eliminated by such radiation. Ioniz-ing radiations also promote grafting of foreign substances onto poly-ethylene chains, thus endowing the material with the properties of the foreign substances. For instance, polyethylene is made printable by grafting polyacrylamide onto it. In infrared radiation in the presence of oxygen, polyethylene is oxidized.

Gas, consisting largely of hydrogen but including some hydrocar-bons, is produced in polyethylene by the crosslinking process and by the formation of double bonds. These gases cause off-odors—one of the readily apparent effects of irradiation upon polyethylene. Aside from this effect the functional properties of polyethylene seem to suffer no substantial deterioration from ionizing radiation up to a dosage of 5.5 megarad,[1] which is regarded as the maximum that needs to be considered for food treatment.

Irradiation of Mylar polyester in a high neutron flux does not seem to produce gas in appreciable quantities; indicating that the effect on the Mylar molecule is one of scission rather than of crosslinking. The effects of ionizing radiation on the functional properties of polyethylene-coated Mylar are substantial, particularly in respect to sealing characteristics and elongation, as shown in Table 127.

TABLE 127

EFFECTS OF IONIZING RADIATION ON THE FUNCTIONAL PROPERTIES OF 0.0005 IN. THICK MYLAR COATED WITH 0.002 IN. THICK POLYETHYLENE[1]

Dose, megarad	Tensile Strength, lbs./in. width	Ultimate Elongation, per cent	WVTR 100°F. 90% R.H., g./100 sq. in./ 24 hr.	Strength of Irradiated Seal, lbs./in. width	Sealability of Irradiated Film, strength of seal, lbs./in. width
0	13.65	87.41	0.53	7.76	7.33
0.2	13.73	84.61	0.53	7.81	8.27
0.6	13.47	89.25	0.51	7.26	7.00
1.2	13.17	81.93	0.50	7.73	8.58
3.0	13.77	81.45	0.50	6.95	5.12
6.0	13.27	82.55	0.56	6.43	5.23

[1] Tripp and Crowley (1957).

Ionizing radiation of Pliofilm at food sterilization dosages is said not to change the permeability of the film to water vapor but does reduce its tensile strength and elongation and increase its sealing temperature.

When halogen-containing plastics, such as vinylidene (Saran), vinyl chloride and fluoroethylene (Teflon) are irradiated in a high neutron flux, halogen gases and halogen acids are liberated. The acids may cause deterioration of the film during storage. The resistance of Saran to tearing, for example, is seriously reduced by an irradiation dosage of 3.2 megarad.

High energy radiation of cellophane results in scission of the molecules and serious degradation of most of the properties of the film except grease-proofness. Similar effects occur in other cellulosic ma-

[1] Rad = radiation energy absorbed per unit mass; base unit = 100 ergs/gm.

TABLE 128

TENSILE STRENGTH (LBS./IN. WIDTH), INTERNAL TEARING RESISTANCE (G.), AND WATER VAPOR TRANSFER RATE (G./100 SQ. IN./24 HR.) OF IRRADIATED CELLULOSE MATERIALS[1]

| Dosage, megarad | 35-lb. Kraft Paper Coated With 18-lbs. per Ream of Polyethylene | | | 0.0013 in. MSAT 80 | | | | MSAT 87 WVTR | | MSAT 83 | MSAT 54 | MSB 3 | Bleached Glassine |
	Tensile Strength of Film	Internal Tearing Resistance	Tensile Strength of Irradiated Seal	WVTR Empty Package Irradiated	WVTR Water in Package Irradiated	Tensile strength	Internal Tearing Resistance	Empty Package Irradiated	Water In Package Irradiated	Internal Tearing Resistance	Internal Tearing Resistance	Tensile Strength	Tensile Strength
0	44.38	93	3.71	1.7	2.9	24.4	14	1.1	2.5	11	17	24.8	13.4
1.8	44.65	84	3.36			16.0	6			8	6	21.8	14.5
2.7													
3.2													
4.5	40.86		3.26		4.5			1.4	3.2				
6.4													
9.1	39.61		2.81	3.8	8.0			2.4	7.8				

[1] Tripp and Crowley (1957).

terials. Tripp and Crowley (1957) give the data presented in Table 128 to illustrate these effects.

The relative stabilities of seven plastic materials as compiled by Tripp and Crowley (1957), are given in Table 129.

FUNCTIONAL CLASSIFICATION OF PACKAGES

Paper bags were among the first flexible packages used in "grocery stores" to dispense commodities received in larger containers. Bags of paper, fabric and mesh are used for many commodities such as dried beans, cereals, flour, sugar, salt, and fruits and vegetables for which vapor and gas transmission are not objectionable. Problems associated with these containers deal with physical strength and/or protection of the contents from rodents and dust.

Bags and pouches of films and foils are used where factors including display of increased protection against moisture transmission, insects, etc., become important. A commonly accepted distinction between bags and pouches is based upon a definition of bags as formed from extruded tubular stock, sealed across the top and bottom, whereas pouches are formed from flat stock with seals either along all edges or along all but one edge.

Bags and pouches are used for similar purposes; functionally, there is little difference between them. However, some film materials are better for bags than others which may be weakened by folding. A film exhibiting more than average tendency to fail when folded is cellulose acetate. If folded containers of this film are allowed to remain stacked for a considerable period, film may be weakened along the fold line. Films which do not heat-seal well are better for bags than for pouches because bags are sealed only at the bottom and top.

TABLE 129

RELATIVE STABILITIES OF CHEMICAL GROUPINGS OF PLASTIC MATERIALS[1]

Representative Type Polymer	Dose Required to Cause 50% Loss of Tensile Strength, 10^9 rad	Predominant Effect
Polystyrene	>30	Crosslinking
Polyethylene	>10	Crosslinking
Polyvinyl butyral	0.6	Crosslinking
Polyvinyl chloride	4	Scission
Polyester, Dacron	4	Crosslinking
Polyvinylidene, Saran	1.0	Scission
Fluoroethylene, Teflon	0.07	Scission

[1] Tripp and Crowley (1957).

Ease and effectiveness of sealing are of utmost importance in the use of flexible packages. The necessity of applying an adhesive complicates the sealing operation and imposes the necessity of finding an adhesive which is proper for each particular application—sometimes a difficult task. Consequently, materials having sufficient thermoplasticity and a softening point within a convenient range of temperature to make heat-sealing possible have an advantage over films that do not have this property.

ALUMINUM FOIL

Advantages of aluminum foil as a packaging material are (1) large covering area per pound of material, (2) opacity and (3) almost absolute imperviousness to water vapor and gas in higher gages and good imperviousness in low gages.

In thickness of less than 0.0015 in., aluminum foil generally contains small perforations. The total area of such perforations increases as thickness of the foil decreases. The area of such perforations in 100 sq. in. of foil 0.0004-in. thick has been estimated at about 0.00004 sq. in. Because of these perforations, there is transmission of water vapor through foil.

Table 130 shows the covering areas of aluminum foil for thicknesses used in food packaging.

Some statements concerning significant properties of aluminum foil as a material for food containers are quoted from "Alcoa Aluminum Foil—Its Properties and Uses" (Anon. 1953).

TABLE 130

COVERING AREAS OF ALUMINUM FOIL[1]

Thickness, in.	Sq. In. Per Lb.	Thickness, in.	Sq. In. Per Lb.	Thickness, in.	Sq. In. Per Lb.
0.00025	41,000	0.00065	15,700	0.0015	6,800
0.0003	34,100	0.0007	14,600	0.002	5,100
0.00035	29,200	0.00075	13,670	0.0025	4,100
0.0004	25,600	0.0008	12,800	0.003	3,400
0.00045	22,700	0.00085	11,790	0.0035	2,930
0.0005	20,500	0.0009	11,390	0.004	2,550
0.00055	18,650	0.00095	10,760	0.0045	2,270
0.0006	17,000	0.001	10,250	0.005	2,050

[1] Alcoa aluminum foil—its properties and uses (1953).

"Aluminum foil is unaffected by sunlight, does not burn, and, being non-absorptive, does not exhibit dimensional change with variations in humidity. While intermittent contact with water generally has little or no effect, hygroscopic products packaged in thin foil may cause some reaction, particularly if the product contains salt or salt and an organic acid, as do cheese and mayonnaise. In general, food products such as candies, milk, unsalted meats, butter and oleomargarine, are not corrosive to aluminum. Aluminum foil is not commercially used with strong mineral acids, which may cause severe corrosion, but many weak organic acids, such as those found in many food products, have no appreciable effect. For the most part, mildly alkaline materials such as soaps and detergents necessitate protective measures to preserve the protective oxide film. Oils and greases, as a rule, have little or no action.

"The only safe rule with any new product is to make suitable tests. For contact with corrosive materials, protective coatings may be applied to the surface of aluminum foil.

"Mechanical properties of aluminum foil which are of interest include tensile strength, elongation and values for resistance to tearing and bursting. The tensile strength of annealed aluminum foil is about 8.5 lbs. per in. of width per mil of thickness. Tensile strength and values for resistance to tearing and bursting for strain-hardened foil are greater than the values for identical foil thicknesses in the annealed condition.

"While the tensile strength of aluminum foil is relatively high, advantage cannot always be taken of this strength in foil packages. Economic considerations may dictate the use of the thinner foils with reliance on lamination with other materials, such as plastic films and paper, for increased strength. The strength of these laminates depends upon the strength of component parts, but is generally less than the sum of the strengths of components.

"With constantly increasing interest in the storage of products at low temperatures, an important quality of aluminum foil is that it does not become brittle at low temperatures. In fact, aluminum increases in strength and ductility as the temperature is lowered, even down to $-320\,°F$."

CELLOPHANE

Originating as a brand name for a regenerated cellulose film, the term "Cellophane" seems to have assumed the status of a generic term for this type of material. Cellophane is of great interest in the field of flexible packages as a transparent, somewhat elastic, heat-resistant, water-and-oil-insoluble film. It is produced by precipitating viscose solution with ammonium salts. When dry, cellophane film is relatively gas-tight. When wet, however, it loses much of its imperviousness to gas. Either laminated with other materials or coated, Cellophane-containing films exhibit widely varying properties in this regard.

There are more than a hundred combinations of these types—all having Cellophane film as a base. Perhaps Cellophane's lowest-rated quality is that of flexibility. Lack of this property leads to comparatively easy breaking when used with dry products. On the other hand, relative stiffness facilitates handling of the film mechanically. Because of printability, Cellophane is often used in lamination with other plastic films. Cellophane-to-Cellophane is not heat-sealable but the film takes heat-sealable coatings readily, which permits sealing over a wide temperature range.

The Federal Food and Drug Administration has pronounced that those types of Cellophane that are now sold for use in food packaging to be "generally regarded as safe" for such use. This includes colored Cellophanes when the colors are nonmigratory.

Because of the hydrophilic property of Cellophane, the films should not be handled for use immediately after exposure for an extended period to conditions of low relative humidity. Likewise, after exposure to low temperature, it should not be handled for use until after it has been allowed to return to ordinary room temperature. Disregard of these precautions may result in cracking of the film.

CELLULOSE ACETATE

In respect to most properties pertinent to flexible packaging, cellulose acetate closely resembles Cellophane. In two respects, however, namely, gas and water vapor transfer, the two materials differ. Whereas Cellophane is better in water-vapor transfer resistance than in gas-transfer resistance, the reverse is true of cellulose acetate. The latter film however is moderately permeable to both water-vapor and gas. Because of its permeability to gas, it is well suited to the packaging of certain fresh vegetables and fruits. Were it not for its high transmission rate for water vapor, it would be a good film for fresh meat with 48-hr. shelf-life. Shrinkage and surface drying of meat preclude this application. Because of this permeability, acetate film fogs less readily than most other films under sudden temperature changes.

Cellulose acetate is sealed commercially with solvent adhesives. Acetate film is approved by the Federal Food and Drug Administration for packaging foods. Because of physical characteristics, it has wide use in laminates. With polyethylene, it is used in "skin"-packaging.

POLYSTYRENE

Polystyrene, a polymer of styrene, is not well-known in film form because its modulus of elasticity is within a range well-suited for films only at a comparatively high temperature (above 176°F). The material has recently attracted attention, however, because of its remarkable resistance to radiation-induced changes. It is three times as resistant as polyethylene, the next in order in this respect of plastics used in flexible packages.

Pliofilm is manufactured in a low plasticizer content, "N" grade, a medium plasticizer content, "P" grade, and a high plasticizer content grade designated "FF," "FM," "FM-1," "HP" or "SS." The rates of water vapor transmission and gas permeability, as well as the film strength vary directly as the amount of plasticizer in the film. The chemical properties are essentially independent of plasticizer content, as is also the water absorption property, which is negligible. For packages to be used at low temperatures, the heavily plasticized film is required. Pliofilm has Federal Food and Drug Administration approval for food packaging.

VINYLIDENE

Saran is a copolymer of polyvinylidene chloride and polyvinyl chloride. It is one of the best of the plastics for imperviousness to water vapor, gases, and odors. This property, together with shrinkability by simple means, provides possibilities for applications for which other films are less well suited. The form having the trade name "Cryovac" shrinks to the extent of 30 per cent when immersed in water at 200° to 205°F.

Because of these properties, vinylidene copolymer seems destined to become as interesting as polyethylene for flexible packaging. As cost decreases (the common experience with plastic films) its use will probably expand rapidly. Saran was first produced in 1946. Its development was an outgrowth of World War II, when a natural rubber shrinkable film, developed just before the war became unobtainable. In the manufacture of Cryovac film, extrusion is accomplished by means of a special screw-type device. A trapped gas bubble is employed to bring about the required orientation of molecules. Finely powdered vinylidene-vinyl copolymer, mixed with plasticizers, stabilizers, dyes, pigments and other agents, is fed into extruders, and is heated for the necessary time at accurately controlled temperature above the melting point. The syrupy extruded material passes through a circular die into cold water, thus producing a supercooled tube of amorphous material. By means of gas pressure, the tube is expanded to four times its supercooled diameter, causing the material to be stretched simultaneously in all directions, thus orienting the long chain molecules biaxially to give the film its quality of uniform shrinkability.

The contour-fit vacuum Cryovac package, which is obtained by sealing with a clip over a twisted column of film which constitutes the neck and mouth of the bag, combined with shrinking of the film, provides a protection for the packaged product which is of maximum effectiveness because voids within the package are at a minimum. This type of packaging is especially good for frozen products because elimination of voids precludes the formation of frost within packages. Cryovac film at present is used for either frozen or refrigerated foods, primarily poultry, meat, and fish products. Color is preserved in frozen meat by freezing at the moment of optimum color development. Prevention of dehydration, obviates "freezer burn."

The Cryovac system is used primarily with larger units because of cost. However, Saran film of lesser thickness is coming into use for small bags and pouches, usually as a constituent of laminations. It has, in some instances, replaced other films for candy and nuts owing to the fact that it does not become brittle; the soft, "fresh" feel appeals to consumers.

Saran film is highly resistant chemically and is varied in composition or given an appropriate coating to increase resistance to specific products. It takes printing and can be marked with a pen.

In heat-sealing, Saran tends to shrink away from the sealing bars, resulting normally in a reduction in thickness and a consequent weakening of the film along the edge of the seal. In practice this effect is minimized by intensifying the application of heat and using a very short heating period so as not to allow time for shrinkage to take place. This procedure is called impulse sealing. For heat-sealing Saran, heating bars are covered with Teflon to prevent the film from sticking to the bars.

Storage temperatures affect the properties of Saran. Bags stored a year at 95°F. lose about one-third of their shrink capacity; at 115°F. about one-half of their shrink capacity. At 40°F. there is no loss in shrink capacity. Stored below 40°F. Saran film loses pliability. The film is resistant to most solvents and has broad approval of the Federal Food and Drug Administration, provided that any adjunct to the film is of GRAS quality.

POLYESTER

The ester polymers are films of unusual strength and of light weight. They are of various compositions, depending upon the identities of the alcohols and acids from which they are formed. A popular type is polyethylene terephthalate, a polyester of ethylene glycol and terephthalic acid. "Mylar," first produced commercially in 1954, is a film of this type. It is a crystalline polymer with molecules oriented biaxially in planes parallel to the film surfaces.

"Mylar" is produced by the duPont Co., "Scotch-Pak" polyester film by Minnesota Mining and Manufacturing Co., and "Videne" polyester film by Goodyear Tire and Rubber Co.

Mylar's outstanding properties as a packaging material are great tensile strength, elasticity and stability over a wide range of temperatures ($-80°$ to $+300°F$.). Its tensile strength of 23,500 p.s.i. is one third as great as that of machine steel and more than 100 per cent greater than that of Cellophane or acetate film. Because of its great strength and its stability at low and high temperatures, polyester film is used in pouches for frozen as well as other types of food products which may be heated in boiling water before opening the package. For this application polyester is usually laminated with polyethylene. The film is used in most "heat in the pouch" packaging of foods.

Mylar film is produced in thickness from 0.00025 to 0.0075 in. The effectiveness of very thin film compensates in part for the higher cost of polyester resin. Notwithstanding the fact that there have been repeated reductions in the cost of polyester film, this film still is more expensive than polyethylene, cellophane, or cellulose acetate.

Polyester film is made heat-sealable by treatment with certain substances, one of which is benzyl alcohol. Sealing temperatures above $300°F$. are required, with a Teflon covering on sealing bars.

Polyester comes nearer than any other film used today to having the properties required of a film for packaging sterilized foods. It has strength and stability but still does not meet all requirements for imperviousness to water vapor and gas. Its orientation is destroyed by melting, but as its melting point is above $482°F$. this characteristic is of small importance from the standpoint of food packaging. Actually, stability at high temperatures is no longer necessarily a requirement for flexible packages for sterilized foods. With high-temperature, short-time sterilization processes and aseptic-filling and sealing systems coming into commercial use for low-acid foods, packages may not have to withstand temperatures even as high as $212°F$. unless the contents are to be heated in the package for serving. It is assumed that presterilization of the container will be possible without heat, for example, by irradiation.

Because of toughness, combined with clarity, attractive surface, and ability to take printing, polyester film has acquired a position as an over-wrap for certain food products, merely to "dress-up" packages, or to "handle" packaged specialties. Because of puncture resistance, the film is also used for packaging commodities with sharp extremities.

The superior strength, along with the low water vapor transmission and gas diffusion rates of polyester film make it the best film available today for vacuum packaging where physical abuse must be withstood.

Polyester film can be produced having properties that make it suitable for shrink packaging. The film is approved for foods by the Federal Food and Drug Administration for use at temperatures not exceeding 250°F. but uncoated film may be used in oven baking above 250°F.

POLYPROPYLENE

A very bright future in food packaging is widely predicted for polypropylene film. Its rate of growth in this area seems to depend upon the economic factor alone and the resolution of this handicap, which rests solely in the cost of raw material, appears to be well advanced. The film enjoys the advantage of having received early approval (1960) by the Federal Food and Drug Administration for use in packaging a variety of foods. This development will be accelerated if a prediction of some enthusiasts that polypropylene film of $1/2$ or $3/4$-mil thickness will compete with polyethylene film of twice that thickness proves to be valid.

Polypropylene film possesses a desirable combination of properties which gives it outstanding uniqueness of character. These properties include low density, low MVTR, good stiffness, dielectric properties, and resistance to stress cracking, high tensile strength and impact and heat resistance, extreme toughness and excellent resistance to chemicals. Heat sealing specifications are not unduly critical.

Skill in controlling polymerization is important in polypropylene film manufacture. Properties of the film, particularly toughness, depend upon the molecular weight and the molecular weight distribution of the material. Improvements in manufacturing techniques pertain not only to dimensional and strength characteristics of the film but also to clarity and permeability. Obtainable clarity is such as to make reverse printing attractive.

Biaxially oriented polypropylene film possesses excellent shrinkability and the Cryovac Division of W. R. Grace and Co. is adding this film under the designation Cryovac Y to its line of shrinkable films, consisting previously of Cryovac S (Saran) and Cryovac L (polyethylene). Shrinking temperature is higher for polypropylene than for most other readily-shrinkable film.

Food packaging with polypropylene up to now has been almost solely confined to bakery and confectionery products but manufacturers are anticipating a broadening scope of uses—particularly for the oriented film. The film may develop into a real competitor of polyester film for "heat-in-the-pouch" packaging. Only a few million pounds of the film were used in 1960. It is estimated that about 15 million pounds were used in 1961 and that by 1965, annual consumption will be between 50 and 150 million pounds.

VINYL

Vinyl films are produced with a wide variety of properties, depending upon (1) the method by which they are produced, (2) the combination of vinyl resins used in their formulation, and (3) the amount of plasticizer used in their formulation. The properties may thus be varied from stiff and glossy to soft and flexible.

The film may be formed by casting, by calendering, or by extrusion. The solvent casting method is especially well adapted for use when formulations of raw materials are varied. The variable composition of the films introduces complex problems in connection with Federal Food and Drug Administration approval for food use.

Vinyl resin has a sealing capacity which is superior in strength to that of other readily heat-sealing resins, such as polyethylene. The strenuous demands for strength in military packages requires, as a rule, that the seals be made with vinyl resin.

Straight polyvinylchloride film has unlimited approval of the Federal Food and Drug Administration. Films with modifiers must have special consideration.

PAPER

Paper and paperboard are made from wood pulp and from waste paper, with or without bleaching and with or without filler, coating or special treatment. The weight of paper is indicated in terms of pounds per 3,000 sq. ft. Three thousand square feet of No. 70 kraft weights 70 lbs. The term kraft (strong) is applied to unbleached heavy-duty paper used for wrapping and bags. It is the work horse of packaging and is used for protection and low cost packaging in large and small bags, with and without creping, multiwalling, etc.

Some paper products are intentionally produced with a high moisture absorbing capacity. Trays for meat, fish and poultry products absorb fluids which might otherwise impair the appearance of packaged products. Other papers are calendered, sized, coated or modified to render them less absorptive.

Glassine and greaseproof papers are made from long-fiber wood pulp, reduced by a long beating process to individual fibrillae which absorb water to become gelatinous. Translucent paper is formed containing a minimum of air and a maximum of residual moisture. By modifications in processes of preparing fibers and forming the paper, greaseproof and glassine papers are produced. Glassine may be coated with lacquer or wax to give a moisture barrier and make it heat sealable. Glassine is also coated with paraffin and other waxes and resins. Microcrystalline wax is used to improve flexibility and sealing.

An important factor is the use of microcrystalline wax to make papers more impervious to gas transmission after bending or folding. Glassine and greaseproof papers are used for liners, wraps and bags in packaging crackers, breakfast cereals, butter and margarine, candy bars, bread, doughnuts, cheese, dried fruit, potato chips, etc.

Vegetable parchment is made from unsized, bleached pulp paper by treatment in an acid bath which gives a gelatinous amyloid surface. When dried, this gives a water and oil-resisting paper which may be stronger wet than dry and which may even be boiled in water without disintegrating. It is used for wrapping butter and margarine and for various packaging operations where ability to take fine color printing and provide attractive appearance are involved.

Decorative papers are widely used for display packaging. They may be glazed on one or both surfaces by various processes for printing or special effects. Clay, casein, shellac and lacquers are used to coat paper to provide surfaces with special texture appearance, printing quality and sealing characteristics. Metallic surfaces are obtained by laminating with foil and also by applying aluminum, or bronze powders in a suitable vehicle.

Paperboard is made in a number of types including bending, chip or newsboard and may be coated with clay, casein, bleached or unbleached pulp, etc. Corrugated and solid kraft boards are used for forming shipping cases, dividers for glass containers, etc., which are discussed in Chapter 22. Folding carton boards are used for retail packages of frozen and dried foods, breakfast cereals, candies, meat products, fresh produce, etc., also for trays and in bundling or multipak holders of glass, metal or flexible containers. Polyethylene coated bending board is coming into increasing use for packaging certain foods. Laminates with foil are used for brown-and-serve rolls, and other heat-and-serve prepared foods.

Bags of kraft and sulfite papers are widely used, both singly and in combination with other papers, as well as in combination with plastic films. For greater protection of products against moisture, grease, etc., glassine greaseproof parchment, and waxed papers, laminated and unlaminated, are used.

Multiwall kraft paper bags, ranging from 1 to 200 lbs. in capacity but most commonly from 50 to 100 lbs. in capacity, are used for a variety of dry products including grain, seed, flour, milk, dehydrated meat scrap, pet foods, chemicals, etc.

Multiwall bags have 3 to 5 (or more) layers of papers, usually spot-adhered to one another, sometimes with a layer of asphalt between sheets of paper to provide resistance to the entrance of vermin and, to some degree, moisture. The conventional type of bag is made of smooth-surface paper, although a creped bag is attaining considerable popularity for dry milk, meat scrap and bulk frozen foods.

In multiwall creped paper bags, described by Greene (1943), every paper layer is creped. In assembling the bag, a rubber-type adhesive is spread lightly over creped surfaces so to give adherence between high points of contiguous surfaces. This permits slippage of surfaces over one another as layers of paper are stretched differently when the bag is in use. Adhesion recurs after slippage has taken place. An advantage of creped bags, as compared to noncreped bags, is elasticity. Another advantage is nonskid surface; they stack better than bags with calendered surfaces, because of minimum slide-angle. Smooth surface bags sometimes are treated with a special coating to improve stackability.

Probably 75 per cent of the 100-lb. bags used for dry milk are creped papers lined with polyethylene film to afford extra protection and to prevent sticking of products to crepe surfaces. Likewise lined with polyethylene film are 60-lb. bags used for prefrozen blueberries. The bag manufacturer claims that, through use of these bags, the cost of distributing blueberries has been reduced two cents per pound compared to shipping in rigid packages. Crepe paper-polyethylene bags are used as slip covers over bananas before harvesting to protect the fruit against minimum temperatures (below 50°F.) which interfere with normal ripening.

To provide improved protection against moisture and gas transmission and odor loss, multiwall sacks are also made of kraft-foil laminates. Aluminum foil 0.00035 in. thick, laminated to 40-lb. kraft and positioned between paper plies, is said to provide from 3 to 4 times as much moisture-vapor protection as 20-lb. polyethylene extruded on kraft. Further improved protection is provided by using polyethylene as the laminating adhesive between foil and kraft.

Most multiwall bags are closed by sewing, with or without bound-over tape. There are machines that position, open, fill, close and sew bags automatically and other machines that do part of these operations automatically. Sewing can be done by portable machines weighing from 10 to 15 lbs. each. A sewn closure is not sift-proof but there are special designs of "valve" closures which are said to permit less sifting than customary "sleeve" closures.

FABRIC

Fabric is rapidly disappearing as a packaging material for food. In comparison to performance characteristics provided by improved papers, plastics and foils, the properties of fabrics have little to recommend them, when relative cost is considered. The high tensile strength and tear resistance of fabrics do not generally give sufficient advantage to compensate for other advantages of competing materials.

ADDITIONAL PERFORMANCE CHARACTERISTICS

In-Package Desiccation

In the packing of dry or dehydrated products which require protection from moisture, a procedure known as "in-package desiccation" theoretically would provide protection (limited by the capacity of the

TABLE 131

RELATIVE PRICES OF FILMS[1] AS OF DECEMBER, 1961 (THICKNESS 0.001 IN.)

Film	Price/Lb., Approx.	Sq. In./Lb.	Cost/1,000 Sq. In., cents
Polypropylene (unoriented)	$0.71	30,900	2.3
Polyethylene			
Low density	0.48	30,100	1.6
Medium density	0.62	29,600	2.1
High density	0.61	29,000	2.1
Polystyrene (oriented)	0.61	25,400	2.4
Polyester	2.24	20,000	11.2
Cellophane			
(NC-coated)	0.63	19,500	3.2
(Saran-coated)	0.80	19,500	4.1
Cellulose acetate	0.75	22,000	3.4
Rubber hydrochloride	1.12	24,750	4.5
Saran	1.08	16,300	6.6
Vinyl chloride	0.73	21,500	3.4

[1]Anon. (1961).

TABLE 132

RELATIVE PRICES OF POLYESTER FILMS OF DIFFERENT THICKNESSES, 1957

Thickness, in.	Approx. Yield, sq. in. per lb.	Price		
		Per 1,000 Sq. In.		
		Actual, per sq. yd.	Approx.	Ratio (Basis: 0.0015 in. = 1)
0.0010	24,300	$0.29	$0.2238	0.966
0.0015	17,000	0.30	0.2315	1.00
0.0025	10,500	0.36	0.2778	1.19
0.0025	10,500	0.38	0.2932	1.27
0.0045	6,700	0.56	0.4321	1.87

desiccant) from water vapor penetration of the walls of flexible packages. Desiccants which react with water either chemically or by absorption may be sealed separately in small porous packages and placed in food packages. Porous stretchable paper is suitable for these packages. One of the best desiccants for this use is recalcined lime (calcium oxide).

Relative Costs of Films

We have previously stated that, of the films now having substantial use in packaging, polyethylene is cheapest and polyester most costly. Table 131 gives the relative costs of twelve major films. The cost of one-mil aluminum foil per square inch is about twice as much as that of vinyl chloride or cellulose acetate of the same thickness. Food-grade papers cost, on the average, about half as much per square inch as the above two one-mil films.

As a further illustration of the relationships existing among prices of films of different thicknesses and, by comparison with Table 131, of the relationship between prices of polyester film in 1957 and 1961, Table 132 shows figures published in 1957 by a manufacturer of that film.

Ratios between prices of films change frequently, principally because of reductions in price of costlier films.

Sealing Flexible Containers

The importance of a package seal is measured directly by the degree of protection needed of the package contents against changes in moisture content or against contact with oxygen. A container which is merely a wrapping with a sheet of material is usually sealed either with adhesive tape or, if the wrapping is of heat-sealable material, by touching the area to be sealed with a hot polished metal surface. The object is merely to make a neat closure. Where a seal which will protect the package contents from air or water vapor is required, a bag or a pouch is used which can be heat-sealed while being held either in the atmosphere at normal pressure or under vacuum.

Table 116 (p. 684) lists the sealing temperature for 15 films. Materials insufficiently thermoplastic to permit heat sealing may be made heat sealable by coating or laminating with heat sealable material provided a sufficient bond can be established between the two materials during the coating operation. Cellophane is made heat sealable by coating by roller, extrusion, or lamination with polyethylene.

Sealing machines are equipped with bars or rollers heated to temperatures controlled between 200° and 500°F. depending upon the material. Sealing rates with films from 0.001 in. to 0.0015 in. thick vary from 25 to 150 f.p.m.

The excellent heat-sealing characteristics of polyethylene make possible a method of sealing seams of empty packages at a rate as high as 500 f.p.m. A continuous strand of molten polyethylene resin is fed and pressed between two films to fuse them together. The method is said to be suitable not only for polyethylene film of practically any thickness but also for polyethylene-coated paper, polyethylene laminates and paper.

A seal for large polyethylene bags, being used for seeds, is made by gathering the film at the top and using a hot plate to fuse the polyethylene into a solid knob, which serves as a handle for the bag.

A nonheat method of sealing is used for shrinkable bags of either vinylidene copolymer (Cryovac) or polyethylene. In this procedure, the bag with its contents is vacuumized while being held at atmospheric pressure, as in the second method of heat-sealing described above. A double-turn twist is put into the neck of the bag, and a metal clip (usually aluminum) is compressed around the twisted portion of the neck. "Twist-ems" of various sorts of material, such as paper-covered or vinyl-coated wire, are used to seal nonvacuum packed bags of products which do not require complete protection from air.

In one system of vacuum-sealing, the entire package is placed in a vacuum chamber while the sealing operation is carried out. When the vacuum is released air pressure forces the film to conform to contours of the contents, subject to residual air. More complete removal of air results when a package is sealed by another system in which only the mouth of the package is enclosed within the vacuum chamber. The body of the package holding the product is subjected to atmospheric pressure which, when vacuum is drawn, compresses package walls against surfaces of the contents before the bag is sealed, by twisting and fusing the film to form a knob. Less air remains in the package than when the entire package is within the vacuum chamber at the time of sealing. This type of seal may also be used without drawing a vacuum.

Produce and Meat

The use of consumer packages of flexible type has had a phenomenally rapid growth. Meats and fresh fruits and vegetables have been involved in a large segment of this growth.

To illustrate a typical development, carrots formerly went to market tied in bunches with tops and leaves attached, iced in wooden crates. The tops lengthened the shelf-life of carrot roots. In 1951, one per cent of carrots with stems removed were shipped in transparent film bags. By 1956 the percentage of prepackaged carrots had increased to 75 per cent. This change took place despite a 20 per cent price increase for carrots packed in polyethylene bags (Stokes *et al.* 1957). Advantages of prepacked carrots enumerated by Hawes (1957) include:

The cost of handling prepackaged carrots at retail amounted to approximately two cents of every sales dollar, compared to more than 14 cents for bunched carrots. Waste and spoilage losses of prepackaged carrots were less than one per cent, compared with more than eight per cent. (There was less breakage of prepackaged roots in consumer handling and there was no loss in salability due to deterioration of the tops.) More than five cents of every dollar of sales of bunched carrots was earmarked for the cost of labor before reaching the retail outlet, compared to about one cent for prepackaged carrots.

In packaging carrots, polyethylene bags are sealed in normal atmosphere without vacuum either by the twist method or by heat. It is assumed that the permeability of polyethylene to oxygen, combined with its low transmission rate for water vapor is in some measure responsible for the excellent shelf-life. In the course of the development of the prepackaging procedure for carrots, both cellophane and rubber hydrochloride films were tried unsuccessfully.

Containers used for transporting prepackaged carrots to market include: (1) wire-bound crates holding 48 one-lb. bags each; (2) multiwall bags holding 48 one-lb. bags each; and (3) polyethylene bags holding 24 one-lb. bags each.

Other examples of the marketing of fresh produce in flexible packages were brought to successful culmination in 1960 by the Agricultural Marketing Service of the U. S. Department of Agriculture. One was the packaging of raw potatoes in ten-pound bags of either two-mil polyethylene film or 50-lb. wet strength kraft paper with mesh window. An account of this study was published by Chapagos and Hale (1960). The other was the packaging of grapes in two-pound cartons with windows of cellulose acetate, or folding paperboard trays overwrapped with either cellulose acetate or semimoisture proof Cellophane films. An account of this study was published by Hale and Stokes (1960). In both cases, the produce is packed at the point of production.

Cured Meats[2]

A cardinal principle applying to the packaging of cured meats for retail distribution is that oxygen and light complement each other in

---

[2] Much of this section is taken from Nebesky *et al.* (1961),

destroying the color of these products. Exposed to both air and light, the nitric oxide myoglobin or its derivatives, which are responsible for the red or pink color of these products, is oxidized to metmyoglobin, causing a degradation of color to brown within a few hours at 36°F. Exposure to air in the absence of light results in deterioration of color at a much lower rate than when light is present. When these products are vacuum packaged by a technic in which not quite all air is removed and are then exposed to light, there is progressive deterioration of color—apparently until all the oxygen in the package has been consumed—at such a rate as to produce a brown color in about two days. It is not known whether or not, in complete absence of free oxygen, light alone will result in loss of color in these products. Experimental results seem to indicate light is a more powerful influence than free oxygen. Samples sealed in air at atmospheric pressure, with as little air space as possible in the package, can be stored for several weeks in a blacked-out refrigerated cabinet and maintain an acceptable color. When held in the light, however, the color of these products is degraded at about the same rate as products vacuum-packed by a technic in which not quite all air is removed.

The shelf-life of these products, when they are exposed to light, depends largely on the vacuum-packing technic and upon how efficacious the packaging material is in preventing moisture loss and air access.

For cold cuts, current preference for packaging is either transparent film alone or in combination with another material, for example, metal. If packaging is done so as to protect the product effectively against oxygen and loss of moisture, the shelf-life (the period of good color) of ready-to-eat cured meat is longer than that of uncooked, cured, meat. When best packaging methods are used, therefore, the ready-to-eat products are packaged in the packing plant; then distributed to retail outlets. For cold cuts one packer uses a novel type of package, consisting of a sheet metal bottom to which is crimped, in a fashion similar to the rolling of a double seam of a can, a piece of transparent film which tightly encloses the produce resting on the metal bottom. Reliable information is that use of this package is growing. This fact could be a surprise to some inasmuch as polyethylene is the film material generally used for this package and polyethylene has high transfer rate for oxygen. The fact that this type of package has had some success in preserving good appearance in retail cold cuts seems to give added significance to the observation that a film which is highly pervious to oxygen, does not, when placed intimately in contact with the surface of meat, permit as great protection as would be expected from a consideration of film permeability.

The nature of such microbial spoilage in cold cuts also is influenced by the properties of the packaging film used.   Within a film package of low gas permeability, slime spoilage is the first to occur, whereas within a film package of gas permeability equal to that of wet MSAD-80 Cellophane, mold growth precedes the development of any other form of spoilage.   In packages of either type, the first spoilage appears in the same length of time,—about two weeks at 36°F.   Mold is visible in the unopened package, whereas, slime may not be detected until after opening.

Fresh Meat[3]

Fresh meats present more complex and interesting problems than cured meats.   The dealers' most serious problem in respect to quality deterioration of self-service fresh meat is appearance.   This is primarily a color problem which is aggravated by dehydration.   A packaging material for self-service fresh meat, besides being nontoxic and mechanically strong, must help to preserve the color.

For the first two days after packaging, a permeable type of package seems to be advantageous because, when air has access to meat through the package, oxygen tends to retard the loss of the red-pigmented oxymyoglobin on the surface of the meat.   For this reason, a film which is permeable to gas, such as Cellophane (when wet), Pliofilm, polyethylene or cellulose acetate, is usually preferred.

As in the case of carrots, film packaging of fresh meat was started with Cellophane;   unlike carrots, fresh meat has continued to be packaged largely in Cellophane.   The reason for this fact is generally said to lie in the transmission of oxygen by Cellophane in the wet state (as on meat).   Oxygen contributes to preservation of red color in meat.   Transmission of water vapor is retarded by coating the surface of the Cellophane film which is not in contact with the meat. While polyethylene, as a packaging material for fresh meat, performs in much the same manner as Cellophane (Ramsbottom 1959), the latter was in use for this purpose before polyethylene film came into volume production;   also, being stiffer, Cellophane is more easily handled as a wrapping material.   The lower cost and greater flexibility of polyethylene have not been sufficient to cause a substantial shift from Cellophane to polyethylene for fresh meat packaging.

Hypotheses based upon theories as they exist today pertaining to the relationship between characteristics of packaging materials and

---

[3] A portion of this section is taken from Ball (1960).

performance of those materials in prepackaging fresh meat hold only to a point. Performance provides the only reliable answer to questions regarding performance. Either the Cellophane wrapping on fresh meat ceases after a period of time to transmit oxygen in sufficient quantity to preserve the oxymyglobin (red color) in the meat or some condition develops within the meat which prevents oxygen from doing this. Meat generally loses its red color rapidly after 48 hr. in packages indicating that permeability of the film to oxygen gives only temporary benefit. This short period of color preservation after packaging precludes prepackaging in a central location for distribution to retail outlets. Phenomena involved are being investigated (Ball 1960–1961; Ball et al. 1957; Clauss et al. 1957; Dean and Ball 1958, 1960 A, B; Rikert et al. 1957 A, B, C; Rikert et al. 1958) in an effort to devise a system of prepackaging which would result in the preservation of desirable color for a longer period.

Manufacturers of Cellophane are attempting to increase the permeability of films to air and thus retard the loss of red color. Recent tests on one of the improved films, a modified nitrocellulose lacquer coated film, gave contradictory results.

Another nitrocellulose-coated film has been modified by the introduction of a bonding agent to improve the adherence of lacquer to the sheet. The purpose of this modification is to prevent early dislodgment of the lacquer which would leave the film vulnerable to absorption of moisture throughout, making it limp and stretchable. In this condition the film probably would be more pervious to oxygen than when the coating adhered to it, although the film would no longer be mechanically satisfactory as a packaging material.

The manufacturer of this bonding material does not claim that its use will prolong the retention of red color in the meat. If this happens, one must assume that it would occur because of a retardation of moisture loss from the meat.

Another Cellophane wrapper film is extrusion-coated with polyethylene. Some workers have reported unofficially that a film of this type extends the shelf-life by about two days, from the standpoint of preservation of fresh meat color.

The manufacturers of the polyethylene-coated Cellophane do not claim an extension of shelf-life in terms of days, but only indirectly in terms of a reduction of trouble and expense from rewrapping pieces of meat.

If the extension of red color preservation by the polyethylene-coated cellophane should, in practice, measure up to predictions, a color life of about four days would be attained under the usual temperature conditions in display cases and sectional centralized packaging would become feasible.   In other words, packaging in a central location from which the packages could be distributed to retail outlets within a radius of a few hundred miles would be possible.   There would still be a demand for further extension of color life of packaged fresh meat, so that packaging might be moved back to the slaughtering plant.

Frozen, Uncooked Meats

While inadequate packaging is not solely responsible for the lack of success in retail handling of frozen uncooked meats, it must accept a substantial part of the blame.   When all influencing factors are carefully weighed, it seems extremely likely that, if a transparent package and a method of packaging could be developed which would assure the presentation of an attractive appearance for a reasonable shelf-life (six months, for instance) and insure the retention of good flavor during the same period, the fortunes of frozen meat would be quickly reversed.

A satisfactory package must meet the following qualifications: (1) be transparent, (2) be impervious to air and water, (3) be completely sealable under vacuum, (4) contact all surfaces of the meat, (5) be mechanically capable of remaining impervious for the merchantable life of the meat, and (6) not be too costly.

The term "transparency" in this connection may be regarded in a qualified sense.   A material which has a slight cloud—not sufficient to materially impair the quality of the observed color of the meat—should be satisfactory.

A fairly heavy gage polyethylene-Cellophane laminate, a heavy gage polyethylene coated with polyvinyl alcohol, or Saran or Mylar of sufficiently heavy gage to give required durability, either laminated to a thin film of polyethylene or extrusion coated with polyethylene to give good sealing quality would give good promise of success.   These could be sealed under vacuum and, in the case of Saran, possibly shrunk after sealing to give better conformity to the surface contour of the meat.

It has been found that the flavor of frozen meat in laminates of polyethylene and either Cellophane or aluminum foil remains good longer than in polyethylene alone; also that, in straight polyethylene film, the degree of retention of good flavor varies directly with the thickness of the film.

Failure to exclude air from frozen meat in the package or failure to maintain close contact between the package surface and the meat surface is disastrous to color.

A venture that originated in 1960 in retail frozen meats was still in a trial phase in 1961 by a food chain in Florida. The meat without tray or backing board, was wrapped in the highly pervious Cryovac "Type L" film, heat sealed, and shrunk to form a "cling" package. After the slice of meat had been wrapped, the film at one end of the package was punctured. The wrapped slice was subjected to mechanical pressure by passing it, with the punctured end to the rear, between two heated sponge rollers, the upper one of which was weighted. After the air was forced out of the package through the perforation in the rear, the film was sealed and shrunken by the heat. Immediately following the rollers was a device which cooled the seal. Thus, the

FIG. 165. SHRINK-PACKAGED CUT HAM

film was made to cling closely to the surface of the meat. The package was then blast frozen at −20°F. Due to the cling of the film to the meat, freezerburn was prevented. The color of the frozen meat was good for from 4 to 5 weeks, while the meat was distributed from the packaging center to markets located from the east to the west coast of Florida. The novelty in this experiment lay in the use of a cling package of highly gas-permeable film, which had low water-vapor transmission and was flexible at very low temperature.

Shrink Packaging

Plastic materials that heat seal readily do not ordinarily possess the property of liberal shrinkage when subjected to hot water treatment.

Large bags of heat-sealable film of material, such as low density poly-ethylene, are sealed by putting a twist in the neck of the bag while it is under vacuum and applying heat to the twist, making a seal in the form of a knot.   The film is stretched over the product at the time of sealing under vacuum to produce an orientation of the molecules of the film; then the package of meat is submerged in a liquid at tempera-

FIG. 166. SHRINK-PACKAGED DRESSED TURKEY

ture 220° to 225°F.   The film will shrink slightly and conform in a measure to the contour of the meat.   This shrinkage effect is not, however, comparable to that obtained with vinylidene copolymer film. Furthermore, this application of polyethylene is not very practical in-asmuch as a high boiling point liquid must be used to accomplish the shrinking operation.

Polyethylene film is now available, which, because it has the ability to withstand excessive stretching in all directions and to maintain the stretched state, is able to shrink by from 50 to 70 per cent upon being heated to 180°F. The Cryovac Division of W. R. Grace and Co. markets this film as "Type L" film. The remarkable stretchability of this film is imparted to it by an ionizing radiation treatment by a two million volt generator, producing biaxial orientation of the molecules of the film.

DuPont, Inc. also markets a highly shrinkable "Alathon" polyethylene film, which may acquire its properties in a different manner than "Type L" film, since the specifications for using "Alathon" film call for a 300°F. shrink tunnel.

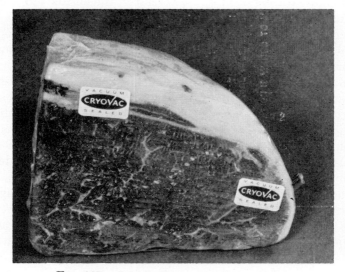

FIG. 167. SHRINK-PACKAGED ROAST BEEF

These films retain the comparatively high oxygen permeability and comparatively low water vapor permeability of the untreated polyethylene. "Type L" film is competitive in cost with Cellophane, but costs more than regular polyethylene.

Newest of the shrinkable films is oriented polypropylene, the properties of which were previously discussed.

Films of certain other materials, one of which is vinyl, possess better shrink properties than untreated polyethylene film but cost more than Cryovac L film.

Winter (1961) reported that the quality of shrink packed poultry is not influenced by the oxygen permeability of the packaging film. It is, however, greatly affected by the water-vapor permeability of the film. As is well known, both properties, namely, oxygen and water-vapor permeability, decidedly affect the color quality of meat cuts. Vinyl films have low water-vapor and variable oxygen transmission properties.

Winter (1961) found that vinyl and polyvinyl films, varying in oxygen permeability from less than, to more than ten times that of, vinylidene copolymer, had no effect upon the quality of shrink-packed fowls. The vinyl films, like polyethylene, polypropylene and polystyrene are given their shrink property by a biaxial orientation treatment. In the case of the films studied by Winter (1961) the treatment consisted of stretching the film while hot and maintaining it in stretched state during cooling. Thereafter, the shrink property is retained for a matter of months but gradually disappears.

Polyvinyl chloride film with "built-in" re-inforced microscopic perforations is offered commercially for shrink packaging of fruits and vegetables, which require a breathing film to maintain quality.

Shrink packaging of lettuce in highly permeable polystyrene film eliminates an exorbitant loss (about 30 per cent) which occurs in unwrapped lettuce before reaching the consumer because of waste of the wrapping leaves. After the lettuce has been trimmed and inspected, film wrapping, heat-sealing and shrinking are done by machines which are transported through the field. The package lettuce is delivered from the field already packed—12, 18 or 24 heads per carton. After being vacuum cooled, the product retains its crispness during a 7 to 10-day travel to market in iced cars.

All of the usual purposes of packaging are served by the practice of shrink packaging—one or two of them to an exceptionally high degree, particularly when the operation is applied to frozen fowls. While "freezerburn" is effectively avoided by prevention of dehydration, discoloration resembling that of "freezer burn" sometimes occurs on fowls because of the cuticle having been removed during dressing following a high temperature scald. Rapid freezing reduces the likelihood of such discoloration.

Fowls and primal cuts of red meat in plastic bags are usually packed in boxes or crates. Frozen turkeys, for example, are often packed six or eight in a crate.

A new application of shrink packaging has had some testing. Veal and lamb carcasses up to maximum weights of 120 and 55 lbs., respectively, half carcasses up to 65 lbs., and lamb saddles up to about 27 lbs. weight have been "shrink" packaged and hung by cable-grip hangers, for storage at refrigerator temperature. Advantages of the system are enumerated as follows: (1) in veal, the shrink which occurs in hide-covered carcasses is avoided; (2) the color of Cryovac packaged veal is said to be better than that of hide-covered carcasses (it is the much desired milky color); (3) in lamb, the reduction of shrink loss is even greater than in veal; and (4) the Cryovac packaged lamb is pink instead of reddish.

As a variation in procedure, lambs were packaged as they came from the killing floor when they were at temperatures of from 100° to 110°F. as well as after chilling by the usual procedure. The former did not become as firm as the lamb which was chilled before packaging but, in all other respects, the properties of the warm-packaged lamb were essentially the same as those of the other. The warm-packaged lamb seemed to retain more moisture but chilling of this lamb was retarded by the package. It may be possible to find means to accelerate the chilling of packaged lamb.

Following the introduction of veal and lamb carcass packaging during 1958-1959, a supermarket chain, in 1961, investigated bulk shrink packaging of primal beef cuts and also of lamb. Square cut chuck weighing from 50 to 60 lbs., trimmed round and rump weighing about 70 lbs., full loin weighing from 70 to 80 lbs., and entire hind quarter, trimmed, weighing from 125 to 140 lbs. were shrink packaged in Cryovac. This type of packaging, compared to the usual waxed paper and stockinet packaging was said to eliminate loss from otherwise necessary trimming, reduce the loss from shrinkage, and increase the shelf-life of the product.

DIMENSION DESIGNATION

In August, 1961, one manufacturer of films used for packaging announced that dimensions of rolls and sheets of its products are designated with the use of simplified numbers for fractions of an inch. The system being used is the same as that which is familiar to users of cans and glass jars, in which each sixteenth of an inch is designated by two digits which are the numerator of the fraction if that numerator is ten or greater, and is the numerator preceded by zero if the numerator is less than ten. For example, $12^3/_{16}$ in. and $12^{13}/_{16}$ in. are designated 12-03 and 12-13, respectively.

BIBLIOGRAPHY

ANON. 1953. Alcoa aluminum foil—its properties and uses. Aluminum Co. of America, Pittsburgh, Pa.

ANON. 1957. Speed shelf-life determinations. Food Processing *18*, No. 9, 98.

ANON. 1961. Polypropylene: What should film users look for? Modern Plastics *39*, No. 4, 87–91, 170–175.

ANON. 1962. Modern Plastics Encyclopedia Issue 1962. Modern Plastics, New York.

BALL, C. O.   1960–1961.   Here are facts on color changes in packaging of fresh meat cuts.   Natl. Provisioner *143*, No. 27, 10–12;   *144*, No. 1, 12–14.

BALL, C. O., CLAUSS, W. E., and STIER, E. F.   1957.   Factors affecting quality of prepackaged meat.   I.   Physical and organoleptic tests.   A. General introduction.   B.   Loss of weight and study of texture.   Food Technol. *11*, 277–283.

BALL, C. O., and OLSON, F. C. W.   1957.   Sterilization in Food Technology. McGraw-Hill Book Co., New York.

BRICKMAN, C. L.   1957.   Evaluating the packaging requirements of a product. Package Eng. *2*, No. 7, 19.

BRICKMAN, C. L.   1961.   Determining WVTR by new pouch method.   Part I. Development of method.   Package Eng. *6*, No. 12, 47–51.

CHAPAGOS, P. G., and HALE, P. W.   1960.   Prepackaging early California potatoes at point of production.   Marketing Research Rept. *401*.   Agr. Marketing Service, U. S. Dept. Agr., Washington, D. C.

CLAUSS, W. E., BALL, C. O., and STIER, E. F.   1957.   Factors affecting quality of prepackaged meat.   I.   Physical and organoleptic tests.   C.   Organoleptic and miscellaneous physical characteristics of product.   Food Technol. *11*, 363–373.

DEAN, R. W., and BALL, C. O.   1958.   Effects of package type, irradiation and treatment with aureomycin on redness of vacuum-packaged beef cuts.   J. Agr. Food Chem. *6*, 468–471.

DEAN, R. W., and BALL, C. O.   1960A.   Patterns of redness loss and regeneration in prepackaged beef.   Food Technol. *14*, 222–227.

DEAN, R. W., and BALL, C. O., 1960B.   Analysis of the myoglobin fractions on the surfaces of beef cuts.   Food Technol. *14*, 271–286.

GREENE, E. B.   1943.   Bag composite material and method of making.   U. S. Pat. 2,314,816.   March 30.

HALE, P. W., and STOKES, D. R.   1960.   Prepackaging California grapes at shipping point.   Marketing Research Rept. *410*, Agr. Marketing Service, U. S. Dept. Agr., Washington, D. C.

HAWES, R. L.   1957.   Marketing Research Rept. *185*, 32, Agr. Marketing Service, U. S. Dept. Agr., Washington, D. C.

LONG, F. E.   1957.   Durability performance of flexible packages.   Package Eng. *2*, No. 10, 31–34, 68.

LOWRY, R. D., and NEBESKY, E. A.   1953.   Cryovac packaged foods.   A paper presented at 124th Meeting of the Am. Chem. Soc., (Sept.).

MARK, H. F.   1959.   Giant molecules.   Sci. Am. *197*, No. 3, 80–89.

MILLER, B. M.   1959.   Nylon 6, now a packaging film.   Package Eng. *4*, No. 3, 62–64, 78.

NAGEL, H., and WILKINS, J. P.   1957.   Properties and food applications of a new packaging film.   Food Technol. *11*, 180–182.

NEBESKY, E. A., and BALL, C. O.   1961.   Packaging of processed meats in flexible plastic films—an analysis.   Natl. Provisioner *144*, No. 4, 16–17.

OLSON, R. L.   1960.   Objective tests for frozen food quality.   Conference on frozen food quality.   Agr. Research Service, U. S. Dept. Agr., Albany, Calif., Nov. 4–5.

OSTER, G.   1958.   Polyethylene.   Sci. Am. *197*, No. 3, 139.

PETERSON, M. S.   1958.   Looking at physical principles that explain packaging tests.   Package Eng. *3*, No. 4, 36–51.

PETERSON, M. S.   1959.   A "CQ" for evaluating containers.   Package Eng. *4*, No. 3, 52–59.

RAMSBOTTOM, J. M.   1959.   Packaging meats for self-service.   Proceedings of the 20th Annual Packaging Forum of the Packaging Institute, Inc.   Abstracted in Paper, Film, and Foil Converter, Feb.

RIKERT, J. A., BALL, C. O., and STIER, E. F. 1957A. Factors affecting quality of prepackaged meat. II. Color studies. A. Effect of package characteristics upon color of product. Food Technol. *11*, 520–525.

RIKERT, J. A., BRESSLER, L., BALL, C. O., and STIER, E. F. 1957B. Factors affecting quality of prepackaged meat. II. Color studies. B. Effects of storage time, storage temperature, antioxidants, bacteria, light, freezing and fat upon color of product. Food Technol. *11*, 567–573.

RIKERT, J. A., BRESSLER, L., BALL, C. O., and STIER, E. F. 1957C. Factors affecting quality of prepackaged meat. II. Color studies. C. Effects of air and oxygen under different pressures upon color of product. Food Technol. *11*, 625–632.

RIKERT, J. A., BALL, C. O., and STIER, E. F. 1958. Factors affecting quality of prepackaged meat. II. Color studies. D. Effects of nitrogen and carbon dioxide under different pressures upon color of product. Food Technol. *12*, 17–23.

RUBINATE, F. J. 1961. Flexible packages for heat processed foods. Proc. Thirteenth Research Conference, 107–111, Am. Meat Institute Foundation, 110–11.

STONE, M. C., and REINHART, F. W. 1954. Properties of plastic films. Modern Plastics *31*, No. 10, 203–208.

STOKES, D. R., and BARRY, G. 1957. Development of carrot prepackaging. Marketing Res. Rept. *185*. Agr. Marketing Service, U. S. Dept. Agr., Washington, D. C.

TRIPP, G. E., and CROWLEY, J. P. 1957. Effect of radiation energy on flexible containers. Activities Report, Research and Development Associates Food and Container Institute *9*, 112–122.

VAN ARSDEL, W. B., and GUADAGNI, D. G. 1959. Time-temperature tolerance of frozen food. XV. Method of using temperature histories to estimate changes in frozen food quality. Food Technol. *13*, 14–19.

WINTER, J. D. 1961. Vinyl film packaging for frozen turkeys. Package Eng. *6*, No. 1, 52–59.

SUPPLEMENTAL NOTE ON PUBLIC HEALTH CRITERIA

The safety of films used in packaging foods is subject to Food and Drug regulations. In a personal communication, referring to safety criteria for flexible packaging materials, Gilbert (1966) stated: "If the material is not volatile, it should be present in a simulated extract at not more than 0.5 mg./sq. in. of packaging material. More work is needed to define the degree to which this standard can be raised.

"If the material is volatile, generally little or no danger is present when the additive produces a characteristic change in the odor and/or taste of the packaged food at levels appreciably below the threshold for chronic toxicity. For most of the volatile residues in packaging materials, the problem of sales acceptance is usually more acute than that of safety.

"It appears reasonable to expect that the establishment of federal standards based upon known toxicology and extractability, combined with the assurance of good manufacturing practice under proper quality control tests, should provide an adequate set of safety criteria for flexible packaging materials for food use."

INDEX